Theories of the Mind

THEORIES
OF THE MIND

Edited by Jordan M. Scher

New York: The Free Press

London: Collier Macmillan Limited

To Jan, Jo, & Jill—
that they may one day understand.

PREFACE

> *All men by nature*
> *desire to know.*—ARISTOTLE

Mind—man's sole superiority over other forms of life—functioned over the ages with an inborn proclivity to master the earth without self-conscious knowledge of what made this now uncontested command possible. Awareness of mind, from the dim premonition of the head-hunter that the skull held something especially potent and his simple logical conclusion that to devour it was to profit in power, has been transmuted into a perhaps equally absurd attempt of the modern mind to grasp itself and, if not to consume, at least to control.

The evolution of thought about mind followed as a long shadow the evolution of the mind itself. If mind is still enlarging and sharpening, even at an imperceptible rate, its understanding of itself must always be a matter of lessening a gap. Like the mythical hoop snake, it can probably never completely encompass itself. Yet the impossible constantly challenges that community of minds that represents increasing development in the direction of humanness.

Thus, this book is compiled with the awareness that it is still a direction we seek, not yet a goal. Yet even so elementary a beginning is long overdue. The almost universal fear that the physical scientists have overreached man's ability to control himself is reflected in the plea of the poets and philosophers for self-understanding. Some have gone so far as to demand that the physicists cease their exploration of space until the morals of mankind move beyond murder and suicide. It is a vain

plea. The seething, restless mind of man, despite individual failures, cannot be paralyzed into inactivity out of fear of what he may find. And,
although ethical standards that claim to enable man to live in peaceable
progress exist in profusion, the means of convincing people to adopt
unanimously any one set of them remains elusive. Force of arms, special
pleading, threats of doom, appeals to historical inevitability, even the
example of comparative success, have not, except for limited times and
in limited areas, bent the willful mind of man into sufficiently coopera-
tive behavior. Yet we yearn for the intellectual flowering that is both
result and cause of peace and plenty.

There is nothing for it but to begin the slow, hard spadework of
weeding out the jungle growth of noxious superstitions, bizarre notions,
and passionately defended positions extrapolated from individual desires and to start from scratch. To do this, the scientific method of careful observation, close reasoning, and statistical manipulation claims
first place as having a long record of success in other fields. Accordingly,
the first section of the book is given over to the physiological aspects
of the brain, nervous system, and endocrine glands and the laboratory
behavior of animals and men. Until very recently, functional maps of
the brain have been so crude, compared with medical knowledge of the
rest of the body, that progress now appears to be making enormous leaps.
The factual approach of geneticist John Ranier, the report by E. R. John
of his experiments in electrical stimulation of various areas of the cortex,
and the work of Harold Himwich on the specific effects of drugs are
particularly illuminating. The fifteen-year study of affective states of
malfunctioning humans by physiological methods—many of them new—
by Charles Shagass suggests the usefulness of this approach when
combined with observations of behavior.

Physiological investigation of sensory behavior and simple reflexive
reactions continues to yield results. James Taylor and Joseph Wolpe
have adapted these older techniques to a new set of problems with
provocative results. Laboratory studies of animal behavior have moved
well beyond Pavlov with the work of Howard Liddell on sheep and
goats, particularly their young. He is convinced that "the very process
of conditioning is traumatizing," supporting his contention with the
cheering tale of the experimental dog Nick. Nick rebelled against his
reward biscuits so violently that, even after he was excused from further laboratory work because of psychotic behavior, he continued to
vent his fury on the laboratory food by barking at it and—the ultimate
insult—urinating on it.

The study of nonlaboratory animals reacting to the stimuli of their
natural habitat is coming to the fore in the newly important speciality of
ethology. Jules Masserman's "Ethology, Comparative Biodynamics, and

Psychoanalytic Research" is illustrated with a wealth of material that can no longer be ignored by the tradition-minded. Departure from cliché thinking follows also from the work of A. Bradford Judd and Milton Greenblatt, who scotch the heretofore happy illusion that synapses jump together with each new piece of information. "New synaptic associations are not formed as a result of function," they have found. One hopes that this information will trickle down to the educational psychologists, who still envision the facts of the multiplication table as discrete operations in which 3×7 closes one synapse and 7×3 closes another.

The truer view of the complexity of brain functioning both inspires and intimidates. The historical overview with which Percival Bailey opens the book cannot beget a complacency with our present advance. Our sophomoric certainty of even the few things we thought we knew grows, as we read, into an awed respect for the distance yet to be traveled. We are not even certain that, should the chemistry and physics of the brain become completely clear, we would have a competent guide to the healthy functioning of the individual and mass mind. The dreaded manipulation of the mind for political purposes or for gentle healing of the mentally ill appears less immediately possible as Ralph Gerard explains how behavior habits are as deeply ingrained as language.

John Ciardi, the poet, has summed up elsewhere problem-solving thinking as both useful and admirable: "Let us by all means be exact where exactness is possible. There still remains an order of mind that can lead to knowledge of the inexact. It is that order of mind that must engage the question, 'What is man?'" Part Two, then, engages that order of mind which, as Ross Ashby points out in his essay on cybernetics, the scientist does not deny, but prefers to ignore as not susceptible of solution within the rigor of his limited methodology.

Mind as participation, mind as more than brain (Eugen Kahn), mind as creative love (Charles Hartshorne), mind as a sense of integration (Donald Glad), mind as entity (Peter Bertocci), mind as more than a mechanical model (Errol Harris), mind as idealism (C. A. Campbell), mind as transaction (Hadley Cantril)—these are the inexact but nevertheless real aspects of mind that defy ignoring. Harold Kelman, in analyzing language behavior, makes clear the difference between a thing and a process, a semantic distinction not available to the primitive mind but essential to the modern if we are to leave behind futile debates as to the location of mind. Like "speed," mind exists as motion, action, participation, not in addition to the matter of the brain and body but as a function of it.

For the pure scientist, if he is dubious of philosophers as fuzzy-minded manufacturers of unworkable systems, perhaps the best place to start is with the essay of Anatol Rapoport, a clear, readable, serious attempt to define terms and discuss their dimensions in ways acceptable to scientist and philosopher alike. For the nonscientist who cannot "think of my kids as particles of energy caught into atoms made up into molecules of organic goo" (to quote Ciardi again) and yet is concerned about the inner urgencies, frustrations, longings, triumphs, defeats, and cross-motives of mankind, we recommend the essay of Henry Veatch upholding intentionality and referring good-naturedly to the everyday world.

Irving Good's essay on the mind-body problem subtitled "Could an Android Feel Pain?" will pull the sophisticated addict of English humor irresistibly into the tumbling stream of controversy that enlivens the pages of this book with fact, logic, debate, conclusion, corollary, speculation, and probably some as yet unidentified forms of communication, intentional or inadvertent.

And yet, when all this has been said, mind remains largely an enigmatic elephant of unknown dimensions and uncoordinated aspects. A description of the view from the rear, or of a single atypical patch, is no less valuable than a mighty guess at the whole. Views through a microscope or a telescope add bit by bit to our working map, which must contain minutiae as well as massive outlines. Our third section, then, which has been subtitled "Of Elephants & Men," is concerned with comparative methodologies. The oft-despised introspection, for example, is far from the mere maundering of individual minds. Peter McKellar presents a reasoned, factual, and convincing discussion of how introspection—sometimes under other names—has been and is used in research in educational, military, clinical, and industrial milieus. Irving Rock examines a new aspect of memory from the Gestaltist's vantage, and Gustav Bergmann smooths out some of the Watsonian excesses, while paying respects to a redoubtable pioneer. The documentary method of the sociologist takes an original turn as Harold Garfinkel twits the advisory type of counseling. His human interest material reads as easily as floating downstream and yet convinces the one who thinks he knows the answers that he isn't up to date on the questions.

The mathematician of statistical man (Edward Barankin) and the mathematician of industrial man (J. B. Chassan) are both represented; the hypnotist (Milton Kline) is here, and the partisans of paranormal communication (W. M. S. and Claire Russell). If the whole appears a potpourri, we have an accurate reflection of the state of our present knowledge about mind. The miscellany may mystify when it is thus spread out—a confused jumble of nuts, bolts, cogwheels, and cinchpins —yet somehow each represents a part of the necessary knowledge of what makes the mind tick. In applying the soothing oil that makes it run smoothly, the psychiatrist who visualizes the enmeshment is best prepared.

The call for an interdisciplinary approach, like campaign oratory, seldom results in action. It sends the audience home happy, agreed, at least in principle, that cooperation would be fruitful. This book does not escape the inevitable—but with a difference. Clifford Geertz, the anthropologist, applies his special learning to the subject of mind; and the result, "The Growth of Culture and the Evolution of Mind," brings a good many of the pieces together, and lo! they fit.

The banquet has been set before you, the blessing said. May each find food to his fancy and the excitement of discovering that a taste of something new and different adds zest, enjoyment, and nutrition to his mental diet.

A few words of thanks to those who have helped in the editing and preparation. To Adah Maurer, who has done a lion's share unstintingly; to Mary Ann Smajo, who organized so well the voluminous correspondence, and to my wife, Carlotta, who helped with details; and to many others—my sincere gratitude.

JORDAN M. SCHER, M.D.

October, 1962

CONTRIBUTORS

W. ROSS ASHBY, M.D., D.P.M.
Director, The Burden Neurological Institute
Bristol, England

PERCIVAL BAILEY, M.D.
Director of Research
Illinois State Psychiatric Institute,
Chicago

EDWARD W. BARANKIN
Professor of Statistics
University of California, Berkeley

GUSTAV BERGMANN
Professor of Philosophy and Psychology
State University of Iowa

PETER A. BERTOCCI
Borden Parker Bowne Professor of Philosophy
Boston University

C. A. CAMPBELL
Emeritus Professor of Logic
University of Glasgow

HADLEY CANTRIL
President
The Institute for International Social Research
Princeton, N.J.

J. B. CHASSAN
Research Statistician
Hoffman-LaRoche
Nutley, N.J.

HERBERT FEIGL
Professor of Philosophy
Director, Minnesota Center for Philosophy of Science
University of Minnesota

HAROLD GARFINKEL
USPHS Senior Research Fellow
The Neuropsychiatric Institute
Associate Professor of Sociology
Department of Anthropology and Sociology
University of California, Los Angeles

CLIFFORD GEERTZ
Associate Professor of Anthropology
University of Chicago

RALPH W. GERARD, M.D.
Director of Laboratories
Mental Health Research Institute
University of Michigan

DONALD D. GLAD
Director, Department of Psychology
Greater Kansas City Mental Health Foundation

IRVING JOHN GOOD
Deputy Chief Scientific Officer
Admiralty Research Laboratory
Teddington, Middlesex, England

MILTON GREENBLATT, M.D.
Assistant Superintendent and Chief of Research
Massachusetts Mental Health Center
Assistant Clinical Professor of Psychiatry
Harvard Medical School

ERROL E. HARRIS
Professor of Philosophy
University of Kansas

CHARLES HARTSHORNE
Professor of Philosophy
Emory University

HAROLD E. HIMWICH, M.D.
Director, Thudicum Psychiatric Laboratory
Galesburg State Research Laboratory
Galesburg, Ill.

E. ROY JOHN
Professor of Psychology
Director, Center for Brain Research
University of Rochester

A. BRADFORD JUDD, M.D.
USPHS Fellow
James Jackson Putnam Children's Center
Roxbury, Mass.

EUGEN KAHN, M.D.
Professor of Psychiatry
Baylor University College of Medicine

HAROLD KELMAN, M.D.
Dean, American Institute of Psychoanalysis
Editor, *American Journal of Psychoanalysis*
New York

MILTON V. KLINE
Director, Institute for Research in Hypnosis
Research Consultant
Grasslands Hospital
Valhalla, N.Y.

HOWARD LIDDELL, M.D.
Professor of Psychobiology
Director of the Behavior Farm Laboratory
Cornell University

PETER McKELLAR
Senior Lecturer in Psychology
University of Sheffield
Sheffield, England

JULES H. MASSERMAN, M.D.
Professor of Neurology and Psychiatry
Northwestern University

JOHN D. RAINER, M.D.
Associate Research Scientist (Medical Genetics)
New York State Psychiatric Institute
Assistant Clinical Professor of Psychiatry
Columbia University

ANATOL RAPOPORT
Mental Health Research Institute
University of Michigan

IRVIN ROCK
Professor of Psychology
Yeshiva University

CLAIRE and W. M. S. RUSSELL
Department of Zoology and Comparative Anatomy
University College
London, England

JORDAN M. SCHER, M.D.
Assistant Professor, Department of Neurology and Psychiatry
Northwestern University
Editor, *Journal of Existential Psychiatry*
Director, Chicago Psychiatric Foundation and
        Chicago Ontoanalytic Institute

CHARLES SHAGASS, M.D.
Professor of Psychiatry
State University College of Medicine and Psychopathic Hospital
State University of Iowa

JAMES G. TAYLOR
Senior Lecturer in Psychology
University of Capetown
Capetown, South Africa

HENRY B. VEATCH
Professor of Philosophy
Indiana University

JOSEPH WOLPE, M.D.
Professor of Neurology and Psychiatry
University of Virginia School of Medicine

CONTENTS

xvii

PART TWO: Mind as Participation
Definitions: Humane, Psychiatric, & Cybernetic

PART THREE: **Mind as Method**
Of Elephants & Men

Mind as Brain

———

Basic Considerations of

Physiology, Biochemistry, & Behavior

Cortex and Mind

Deep, deep, and still deep and deeper must we go, if we would find out the heart of a man.—HERMAN MELVILLE

In 1665 Niels Steenson[51] (Nicolaus Steno) gave a talk on the brain at the home of Melchisedech Thévenot, a wealthy patron of science in Paris, in the course of which he said: "I am nevertheless very much convinced that they, who seek for solid knowledge, will find nothing satisfactory in all that has been written about the Brain, but it is very certain that it is the principal Organ of the Soul, and the Instrument by which it works very wonderful Effects." Nor do we find any satisfaction today if we try to study the brain only as the organ of the soul that is impalpable and immeasurable. From this point of view we can arrive only at the conclusion of the psychoanalyst that the study of the nervous system adds nothing to our understanding of the behavior of human beings.

Our conclusion becomes quite different, however, if we look at the brain from the standpoint of the theory of evolution, which demands that mental operations be derived from ordinary physical principles by progressive steps.[31] From this point of view the nervous system may be considered as a mechanism for the transmission of signals that

An address given at the opening of the Institute for Psychosomatic and Psychiatric Training at the Michael Reese Hospital and Medical Center, Chicago. Reprinted, with slight alterations, by permission of the author and of Roy R. Grinker, M.D., director of the Institute.

arise in the peripheral sense organs, are transmitted by the sensory nerves as pulses of electrical potential to the central nervous system, and there are variously integrated and then reflected over the motor nerves to result in our behavior.[21] Their integration in the spinal cord is relatively simple and invariable; that in the cerebral cortex is fluctuant and relatively unpredictable.[41] The handling of signals in the brain has never been understandable by analogy with such inflexible machines as telephone systems, juke boxes, or harpsichords;[35] and this has been a chief stumbling block to understanding it as a machine. But, since the invention of the thermionic valve, it has been possible to construct machines that have many of the properties heretofore believed to be peculiar to the brain. Such machines seek goals, learn, forget, foresee and avoid dilemmas, and, in other ways, comport themselves like living beings.

It has been shown that the cerebral cortex, under certain circumstances, acts like a computing machine, such as is used for radar control of antiaircraft guns, responding to misalignment by giving a neural response calculated to reduce the misalignment, thus correcting its error by the process known as "negative feedback."[16] Such mechanisms have long been known to physiologists and psychologists; only the name "feedback," borrowed from engineering, is new.[48] It means only the joining of a receptor and an effector in such a way that the receptor not only can stimulate the effector but also can be stimulated by it. Together with the external world the cerebral cortex forms such a dynamic system, which tends to reach a stable equilibrium and improves its stability against disturbance.[2] Its structure is entirely compatible with such an analogy, because of its vast areas of random neural nets and self–re-exciting chains[32] between input and output.

For a long time our ideas concerning the structure of the cerebral cortex were confused by the erroneous hypothesis that it consists of a mosaic of organs,[11] doubtless because of the persistent influence of Franz Joseph Gall. In accordance with this hypothesis the anatomist's task was to locate and delimit areas of special structure, since a difference in structure implies a difference in function.[26] The physiologist could then investigate the functions of the organs so identified. This method of approach was clearly stated by Meynert from his study of the striate area and was encouraged by the discovery of the large cells in the precentral gyrus by Betz; the striate area was shown to be concerned with vision, and the Betz-cell area with motion of the skeletal muscles. And so the search was on for other areas of specific structure and function. The search resulted in the discovery of two other regions whose structure approached that of the striate area in that they tended to be formed of small cells, so that Economo called them "koniocortices,"[18] which have been shown to be the regions where the auditory and somesthetic impulses, respectively, arrive at the cortex. The greater part of the cortex, however, was found to have a six-layered structure so similar that students of cytoarchitectonics have been unable to come to any consensus as to its important subdivisions. Nevertheless, elaborate maps have been made and extensively used by physiologists who forgot that, if a difference in structure means a difference in function, the converse may also be true and areas of essentially identical structure have the same function, insofar as that function depends on the intrinsic structure.[8]

Since the cortex is a communication machine, its functioning must also be determined in large part by its extrinsic connections. These connections are now known in considerable detail, and they make it clear that the isocortex may best be understood by considering it as one machine for handling signals.[10] The inputs for visual, somesthetic, and auditory signals are known, as we have just remarked, and the main output also. We are not surprised that both have relatively fixed mosaic patterns of organization, nor that the structure of the input differs from that of the output. But what of the vast remainder of the isocortex, which has a practically uniform structure? It consists, so far as we now know, of myriads of nerve nets,[34] primordially random, capable of being connected together in an infinity of ways under the impact of experience so that its patterns are dynamic and fluctuating. As Hughlings Jackson pointed out long ago,[26] it is necessary that we begin with an unorganized and readily modifiable cortex, otherwise we could not make adjustments to new circumstances. How the definitive connections are made during development we do not know, but Ashby[3] has proven that it is possible for a machine, provided it is furnished with a sufficient number of step-functions. The cortex has a sufficiently vast number,[23] since it is composed of neurons each of which either discharges or does not in accordance with the well-known all-or-none law, automatically changing its connections until it reaches a successful combination.

The greater part of the cortex, then, composed of neuronal nets arranged somewhat at random at first, completes its structural organization some time after birth and modifies its functional organization constantly by the interaction of new experience with old experience retained in the form of memories. In order for the cortex continually to alter its organization in this way, it is necessary that its equilibrium be dynamic, a multitude of parts being free to interact with one another after the manner of feedbacks. There is abundant evidence, since the initial demonstration of Hans Berger, of the dynamic nature of the cortex, and Grey Walter[53] has shown that it is possible, by altering the feedback relationships, to cause serious perturbations of its functioning, even epileptic attacks.

However random may be the horizontal organization of the cortex, we must not forget that it has a very definite vertical organization in six layers. The significance of this arrangement is not known, but Craik[15] supposed that it might imply a scanning mechanism, and this scanning was related by Grey Walter[52] to the alpha rhythm. Pitts and McCulloch[46] have shown how such a mechanism might enable the cortex to recognize universals, such as chord regardless of pitch, or shape regardless of size. This ability is the so-called suprasensuous reason—the power to indicate universals and relate them one to another.

Most of these hypotheses need a great deal of experimental work in support, but they already point the way to the understanding of many matters heretofore thought to be outside the realm of scientific investigation, such as curiosity, foresight, or free will.

Many years ago Hughlings Jackson[26] maintained that the highest level of nervous activity—the mind—had two aspects, intellect and emotion, and that these activities went on in the cortical areas of generalized structure, then called the "associational" areas. He maintained further that the greater part of mentation went on in the form of visual images. Certainly, visual images play a large role in many forms of thought, but a great deal of it goes on in the form of internalized conversation, as George H. Mead[38] has so conclusively demonstrated. This sort of internalized activity, whether visual, auditory, or other, is the characteristic activity of large areas of the cerebral cortex, and all the evidence we have at present indicates that it goes on predominantly in the areas of generalized structure. Now machines have recently been built that behave in a strangely similar manner. A good example is Ashby's homeostat,[5] which, by internal self-induced action and interaction, adapts to a disturbance by rearranging its own wiring so as to reach a new state in equilibrium with the new conditions. This is essentially the process of thought. By means of this process tentative solutions are compared with memories of previous solutions and of their results, and a new combination is reached in relation to the new conditions. This is perhaps the most distinctive property of the human cortex.[23]

During all this process of internal activity the output is blocked; the ultimate result is normally an external activity of the machine directed toward its environment. This external activity has for its purpose to alter or abolish the conditions that disturbed the state of equilibrium in the dynamic system. For this purpose much energy may be necessary, the source, the nature, and the necessity of which are imperfectly understood.[24] The quarter of a kilogram-calorie[36] per minute furnished by the oxidation of glucose in the brain is undoubtedly sufficient for the transmission of signals, since communication machines need only small amounts of energy for such activity; but the brain is a living organism and needs other materials for its trophic processes. The greatest students of abnormal psychology have found it necessary to postulate sources of energy for the apparatus of the mind; Janet[30] based a whole system of psychology on the fluctuation and economical administration of this energy, and Freud[22] looked forward to the possibility of influencing its amount and distribution by chemical means. If we understand the vague sense in which they used the word "energy" as something necessary for the healthy functioning of the cortical neurons, we must agree with them.

Cannon[12] has extensively investigated the mechanisms utilized by the body to mobilize energy. Whenever the external action follows almost immediately upon the disturbance that aroused it, these mechanisms operate smoothly, but, when the external action is blocked and not utilized, energy accumulates in the organism and perturbations are produced of which we become aware as emotions. The common man has long recognized that one way out of this situation is to "blow off steam" like a steam engine, in ways not adapted to the goal of removing the initiating disturbance, such as weeping, ranting and raving, aimless activity, trembling, and sweating. It is common parlance to say that these relief activities are caused by the emotions. This ignores the fact that an emotion is itself a derivative phenomenon and causes nothing, being aroused by the disturbance to which it is necessary to adapt. This disturbance is the cause of all the activity that goes on in the dynamic system, the internal travail (thought) as well as the derivative phenomena (emotion) and finally the external activity (behavior).

If we look at the cerebral cortex in this way, as a machine, the apparent conflict between psychogenesis and somatogenesis begins to evaporate. A machine may function badly because it was constructed from inferior materials, because of water in the gasoline, because of rusting from being left out in the weather, because of long hard usage, or merely from overloading. Of course, an inferior machine will break down sooner from overloading, but even the best machine has its limits. In the same way a nervous system may function badly because of hereditary or congenital defect, because of improper food supply, because of being soaked in alcohol, because of constant wear from interminable conflict, or because of a single overwhelming crisis.

It is futile to talk of the effect of the mind on the body. "Thought" is a name we give to the functioning of our thinking machine (cortex) just as "flight" is a name we give to the functioning of flying machines (airplanes). The plane is worn out *during* flight, but not *by* flight; it is worn out by friction of the air, of the crankshafts, by buffeting from wind and weather. Our cerebral cortex is worn out also by the buffeting of the environment, both internal and external, that gives rise to thought and, if too severe, causes it to knock or chatter in its functioning, which we call "the mind."

It follows that there are many ways to remedy the malfunction. It is not possible to remove a defective part of our cerebral cortex and replace it with a better part in any particular machine; but we may, by proper genetic procedures, by better maternal care, or by prevention of disease during development, see to it that future human machines function better and are built of better materials. And we can see to it that the defective machines are not set to tasks beyond their strength. We can see to it that our human machines are given the proper fuels and lubricants, that they are properly cared for, and that damaging intoxicants or poisons are eliminated. They may even function better for certain limited tasks if parts are removed, as by lobotomy, thus removing harmful reverberating chains.[32] We may remove them from environments where heavy tasks are too often set them. We may find them other tasks better fitted to their capacity. By means of drugs we may reduce the sensitivity of certain receptors on which the functioning depends or increase certain resistors which will change the flow of power within the machine.

You may agree with all this and yet say that this does not explain those things which are peculiar to the human machine—purpose, adaptability, foresight. On the crude analogy to an automobile, an airplane, or a telephone exchange—even an automatic one—much will remain obscure, and it would be presumptuous to say everything is now understood. Yet machines have been built that follow goals, explore, learn. By analogy with these new machines that learn, correct their errors, break down if their feedbacks are maladjusted, we begin to see more deeply into these formerly mysterious matters; and, the deeper we penetrate, the more the fog begins to dissipate, and it becomes ever clearer that the concepts that we gather under the term "mental" are only names given to various aspects of the functioning of the cerebral cortex. It has often been said that we think with our entire body, but it can be readily demonstrated that mental processes go on with negligible disturbance in the absence of all parts of the body below the fifth cervical segment and after most of it is lost above that level except for the brain stem and cortex. The maximal disturbances of the mind result from destruction of the cerebral cortex; the mind is essentially its functioning.

It is even conceivable that it might be possible to build a machine that would have insight, or could be given insight, into its own malfunctioning and take certain measures to correct it. Perhaps this will have to wait until our insight into our own difficulties is less rudimentary. Even so, the machine would have to find ways that avoid the necessity to replace a defective part, just as we are unable to replace cortical neurons destroyed by toxins or senile decay; no psychotherapist can do it for us, and God will not. But the machine can be built to recognize obstacles and avoid them instead of wearing itself out against them. And the mechanic can, by increasing the gain, make it see obstacles that it previously did not recognize. In the same way the psychotherapist can aid our human machine to see an obstacle to our functioning that we may or may not be able to avoid. Mere awareness of a difficulty does not, in spite of the assertions of the analysts and others, guarantee its avoidance and the proper functioning of the machine.

The cerebral cortex is, therefore, a machine—a machine for handling signals. That does not mean that it is only a machine; neither is it all of the brain. Hughlings Jackson used the word "consciousness" as synonymous with mentation, but we know from the work of Janet, Freud, and others[25] that processes go on while we are asleep or under the influence of an anesthetic that, when we are aware of them, we call thought. Identification of consciousness with the mind leads to much confusion; and the resolution of the difficulty is usually purely verbal, for example, the substitution of the term "extraconscious" for "subconscious."[13] The distinction of consciousness from the mind leads to its being chased out of the cortex and down through the basal ganglia,[17] the hypothalamus,[45] and the midbrain[6] into the bulb.[20]

The soul also has been chased about in the brain. It has been said that the human being is more than a machine because he suffers and is conscious that he suffers. Then a dog must also be more than a machine. Certainly the antivivisectionists believe that dogs suffer and are conscious that they suffer; I know no valid reason to believe otherwise. Do they then have souls? And has a patient whose frontal lobes have been detached and is no longer conscious of suffering lost his soul? Buddha said he taught suffering and the relief of suffering. The surgeons have found a much more effective remedy than Buddha's eightfold path—or than a psychoanalysis that brings repressed conflicts clearly into consciousness and may increase as well as relieve suffering.

Perhaps the relief of suffering is not a valid goal for a physician.[47] Christianity teaches that only through suffering can one know God and save one's soul. Nevertheless, surgeons are industriously constructing stereotaxic instruments which will enable them to strike more shrewdly at the soul in its very inner citadel.[50] But these matters are best left to the theologians and jurists, who, I am sure, will soon be obliged to pronounce upon the legitimacy of these destructive interventions on the brain. Whatever we may think of such concepts as mind, personality, and soul, there is no doubt whatever that mutilating operations on the brain alter aspects of human behavior that have been long called by these names. And it does not help our understanding to create a pseudoscientific terminology for such concepts and call them the "Superego," the "Ego," and the "Id."[7] The ego is a resultant of the two forces personified as the superego and the id, hence not in the same category. Similarly, the mind and the body are concepts of different categories and cannot be discussed as two similar persons or forces acting on each other. It is impossible to separate thought from matter that thinks.[42] The word "mind" is a verbal symbol that we use to refer to activity of the cerebral cortex. Mental processes are fragments of the complex conduct of the individual;[39] thought is only a detail and a form of human actions.[29] Only in this sense is it permissible to say that mental activity influences the general behavior of the organism, since the response of the cortex will depend on the pattern of its activation at the moment of arrival of a train of impulses. Fragments of this activity may fail to be integrated with the rest, because they arise in an abnormal manner from infection or intoxication and disrupt the personality so seriously as to result in chronic deliria.[14]

In thermionic machines, to which we have likened the cortex, the goals sought are set by the maker—an airplane, for example, in the case of an antiaircraft gun. In the case of our human machine the goals were set by God, who created man in His own image, by the insertion of goal-setting mechanisms that make us seek food for self-preservation and the female of the species for self-propagation. These goal-setting mechanisms are very complicated, including hormonal chemical factors as well as nervous ones. The nervous factors lie mainly in older parts of the brain nearer the central canal in the brain stem, the paleothalamus, and the allocortex. The activity of these parts of the nervous system is likely to bring us into conflict with other machines seeking similar goals. These then become essential parts of the environmental disturbance that arouses the behavior of any particular organism. The various methods for controlling and utilizing these interpersonal factors constitute a large part of educational and social theory and practice. It is necessary to make the organism seek other intermediate goals—the acquisition of money, the planting of crops—as necessary factors in reaching a final state of equilibrium. One means of doing this has been extensively investigated by Pavlov[44] and his school and is known as "conditioning." This process goes on in the cerebral cortex, to be more specific in the isocortex, and is fostered in the home, schools, and churches. The insertion of these derivative intermediate goals delays the reaching of a state of equilibrium in the organism, even until a new world after death, as the result of which a permanent state of unrest is produced accompanied by various symptoms of malfunction in the machine. These have to be treated, as before indicated, by the physician or the priest.

As civilization becomes more complicated and attainment of ultimate goals becomes more delayed, the mechanisms within the isocortex, built up largely by social conditioning, since on them depends the smooth functioning of society, need strengthening as against the more individualistic mechanisms seeking the ultimate goals immediately and directly. Even such a fundamental social goal as charity (mutual sympathy and aid) needs constant reinforcement.[9] This is accomplished largely by words. Words, like other symbols, are information, giving rise in the afferent nerves to trains of signals on which the functioning of the cortex depends. Once the cortex has been conditioned to respond to a symbol, as it would to the actual situation to which the symbol refers, the latter becomes a potent factor in the dynamic system, either for good or for evil, for peace or for war.[1]

Words that state that the all-powerful Maker of mankind, who can preserve us even after death, approves of the intermediate goals but disapproves of a fundamental one (such as sexual congress) can be used to block the output of our nervous machine with all the attendant disorders resulting from malfunction. Since God made man in His own image, including the goal-seeking mechanisms that the cortex must control, it was found necessary to adopt, from Zoroaster by way of Mani,[40] a lesser god—a demon known as Satan—to account for these persistent urges that impede the working of the cortical machine. To those who insist on monotheism, Satan must be held to be merely another aspect of the Deity and, if we wish to follow the mystics,[43] so also is man. It does not clarify matters to rename them the superego, the id, and the ego.

When looked at from this point of view, the mind-body problem evaporates. Not so that of consciousness. We do not know that any machine built by man has ever been aware of its behavior, even though it be theoretically possible.[54] Although we know that consciousness is closely bound to the nervous mechanisms of the brain stem, no analogy exists in man-made machines that gives a hint toward its understanding. This fact should not deter us from our search. Hope is not necessary to enterprise or success to perseverance. At any rate, we gain nothing by thinking in terms of a paradise before which stands a mythological censor with flaming sword to keep Janet's traumatic reminiscences submerged in a subconscious hell. Whether thinking in terms of reverberating neuronal chains will prove more fruitful remains to be seen. Recent formulations sound again very much like the conceptions expressed long ago by Janet[27] in his study of subconscious fixed ideas, but stated, this time, not in anthropomorphic theological terms but in the jargon of modern engineering. In some way, by free association, hypnosis, or otherwise, we must gain access to harmful engrams so as to remove them by reconditioning, or else destroy them by shock therapy or lobotomy without trying to bring them into consciousness.

Having transformed the mind-body problem into the mind-cortex problem and solved it to our own satisfaction, if to no one else's, we are left with a consciousness-brains stem problem. This is the same old problem from a metaphysical standpoint if, indeed, it be a problem at all. My old teacher—Pierre Janet—used to say that the essential error of the metaphysician was to believe that he had a problem.[28] However that may be, the matter will continue to be discussed.[49] Perhaps we could do no better than to end with a statement made by Paul Flechsig[19] concerning the relationship of brain and soul in an address at his inauguration as rector of the University of Leipzig. "So long as medical thought remains scientific, and strives to go beyond the immediate practical necessities, outstanding physicians of all civilized nations endeavor to view the arena where the sentient soul labors and where the thinking and mind constructs a picture of the world."

REFERENCES

1. Ackerly, S., "Prefrontal lobes and social development," *Yale J. Biol. & Med.*, 1950, 22:471-82.
2. Ashby, W. R., "Adaptiveness and equilibrium," *J. Ment. Sci.*, 1940, 86:478-83.
3. ———, "Dynamics of the cerebral cortex: The behavioral properties of systems in equilibrium," *Am. J. Psychol.*, 1946, 59:682-86.
4. ———, "Design for a brain," *Electronic Engineering*, 1948, 20:379-83.
5. ———, "The cerebral mechanism of intelligent action," Chapter VI in *Perspectives in Neuropsychiatry* (D. Richter, ed.), Lewis, London, 1950, pp. 79-95.
6. Bailey, P., *Intracranial Tumors*, Thomas, Springfield, Ill., 1933, 475 pp.
7. ———, "Alterations of behavior produced in cats by lesions in the brainstem," *J. Nerv. & Ment. Dis.*, 1948, 107:336-39.
8. ———, "Considérations sur l'organisation et les fonctions du cortex cérébral," *Rev. Neurol.*, 1950, 82:1-20.
9. Baruk, H. *Psychiatrie morale, expérimentale individuelle et sociale. Haines et réactions de culpabilité*, 2ème édition, Presses Univ., Paris, 1950, 298 pp.
10. Bonin, G. von, *Essay on the Cerebral Cortex*, Thomas, Springfield, Ill., 1950, 150 pp.
11. Brodmann, K., *Vergleichende Lokalisationslehre der Grosshirnrinde*, Barth, Leipzig, 1925, 324 pp.
12. Cannon, W. B., *Bodily Changes in Pain, Hunger, Fear and Rage. An account of recent researches into the function of emotional excitement*, Appleton, New York, 1929, 404 pp.
13. ———, *The Way of an Investigator*, Norton, New York, 1945, 229 pp.

14. Clérambault, G. de, *Oeuvre psychiatrique*, 2 vols. Presses Univ., Paris, 1942.
15. Craik, K. J. W., *The Nature of Explanation*, Cambridge Univ. Press, London, 1943, 123 pp.
16. ———, "Theory of the human operator in control systems. II. Man as an element in a control system," *Brit. J. Psychol.*, Gen. Sect., 1948, 38:142-48.
17. Dandy W., "The location of the conscious center in the brain—the corpus striatum," *Bull. Johns Hopkins Hosp.*, 1946, 79:34-58.
18. Economo, C. von, *The Cytoarchitectonics of the Human Cerebral Cortex*, Oxford Univ. Press, London, 1929, 186 pp.
19. Flechsig, P., *Gehirn und Seele*, Veit, Leipzig, 1896, 112 pp.
20. Foerster, O., *Uber die Bedeutung und Reichweite des Lokalisationsprinzips im Nervensystems*. Verhandl. d. Deutsch. Gesellsch, f. innere Med. (Hirnstamm und Psyche, p. 208), Bergmann, Munich, 1934, pp. 117-211.
21. Forbes, A., "The interpretation of spinal reflexes in terms of present knowledge of nerve conduction," *Physiol. Rev.*, 1922, 2:361-414.
22. Freud, S., *An Outline of Psychoanalysis*, Norton, New York, 1949, 127 pp.
23. Herrick, C. J., *Brains of Rats and Men*, Univ. of Chicago Press, Chicago, 1926, 382 pp.
24. Himwich, H. E., *Brain Metabolism and Cerebral Disorders*, Williams & Wilkins, Baltimore, 1951, 451 pp.
25. Holmes, O. W., "Mechanism in Thought and Morals," Chapter VIII in *Pages from an Old Volume of Life*, Houghton Mifflin, Boston, 1871.
26. Jackson, J. H., *Selected Writings*, Hodder and Stoughton, London, 2 vols., 1931-32.
27. Janet, P., *Les névroses et les idées fixes*, Alcan, Paris, 2 vols., 1898.
28. ———, *La pensée intérieure et ses troubles*, Chahine, Paris, 1926, 451 pp.
29. ———, *L'évolution de la mémoire et de la notion du temps*, Maloine, Paris, 1928, 624 pp.
30. ———, *La force et la faiblesse psychologiques*, Maloine, Paris, 1932, 326 pp.
31. Koehler, W., *The Place of Value in a World of Facts*, Liveright, New York, 1938, 395 pp.
32. Kubie, L., "Theoretical application to some neurological problems of properties of excitation waves which move in closed circuits," *Brain*, 1930, 53:166-77.
33. Lashley, K. S., "The problem of cerebral organization in vision," *Biol. Symposia*, 1942, VII:301-22.
34. Lorente de Nó, R., "Facilitation of motoneurones," *Am. J. Physiol.*, 1935, 113:505-23.
35. McCulloch, W. S., "Modes of functional organization of the cerebral cortex," *Fed. Proc.*, 1947, 6:448-52.
36. ———, "The brain as a computing machine," *Electronic Engineering*, 1949, 68:492-97.
37. ———, "Physiological processes underlying psychoneuroses," *Proc. Roy. Acad. Med.*: Sect. Psychiatr., 1949, 42:71-80.
38. Mead, G. H., *Mind, Self and Society*, Univ. of Chicago Press, Chicago, 1934, 401 pp.
39. ———, "The philosophy of the act," Chapter XXI in *The Process of Mind*, Univ. of Chicago Press, Chicago, 1938, pp. 357-442.
40. Melamed, S. M., *Spinoza and Buddha*, Univ. of Chicago Press, Chicago, 1933, 391 pp.
41. Meyer, A., "Critical Review of the Data and General Methods and Deductions of Modern Neurology," *Collected Papers*, 1950, I: 77-148.

42. Nersoyan, T., *A Christian Approach to Communism,* Muller, London, 1943, 103 pp.
43. Nicholson, R. A., *The Mystics of Islam,* Bell and Sons, London, 1914, 178 pp.
44. Pavlov, I. P., *Conditioned Reflexes and Psychiatry,* Intern. Publ., New York, 1928, 199 pp.
45. Penfield, W. G., "The Cerebral Cortex and Consciousness," Williams and Wilkins, Baltimore, *Harvey Lectures,* 1936-37, 32:35-69.
46. Pitts, W., and McCulloch, W. S., "How we know universals: The perception of auditory and visual forms," *Bull. Math. Biophysics,* 1943, 9:127-47.
47. Prick, J. J. G., "La leucotomie est-elle moralement permise du point de vue de ses suites post-opératoires?" *Folia, psych., neurol. et neurochir. Néerlandica.,* 1949, 52:391-400.
48. Rosenbleuth, A., Wiener, N., and Bigelow, J., "Behavior, purpose and teleology," *Phil. Sci.,* 1943, 10:18-24.
49. Ryle, G., *The Concept of Mind,* Hutchinson, London, 1949, 334 pp.
50. Spiegel, E. A., Wycis, H. T., Marks, M., and Lee, A. J., "A stereotaxic apparatus for operations on the human brain," *Science,* 1947, 106:349-50.
51. Steno, Nicolaus, *A Dissertation on the Anatomy of the Brain,* Busck, Copenhagen, 1950, 50 pp.
52. Walter, W. G., "Features in the electrophysiology of mental mechanisms," in *Perspectives in Neuropsychiatry,* Lewis, London, 1950, pp. 67-78.
53. ———, "The functions of electrical rhythms in the brain," *J. Ment. Sci.,* 1950, 96:1-31.
54. Weinberg, M., "Mechanism in neurosis," *American Scientist,* 1951, 39:74-99.

JULES H. MASSERMAN

Ethology, Comparative

Biodynamics, and Psychoanalytic Research

In its first and still most important sense, research in psychoanalysis is pre-eminently *clinical*. In effect, every encounter of every analyst with every patient (and less self-consciously, with everyone else) can be made the occasion for a searching reappraisal of the dyadic interplay of motivations, semantics, and symbolisms between two people transacting their business in an implicitly intricate cultural and transference milieu. Unfortunately, this necessarily difficult scrutiny of the endless flow of multivectorial data may grow so wearisome that some analysts are easily tempted to revert to the classical practices of Procrustes, the Attic tyrant whose way of dealing with any stranger consisted in cutting, stretching, or otherwise mutilating him to fit a preformed bed. As you will recall, Procrustes himself was eventually slain by the Greek hero, Theseus, who then formed an Aegean League that welcomed all free-thinking and amicable city-states into an enlightened confederation. It may be noted in this historical context that the Academy of Psychoanalysis, too, is dedicated to the elimination of arbitrary and destructive constrictions and to the amicable, creative union of free-thinking people.

Portions of this paper are reproduced, by permission of the author and the publisher, from Jules H. Masserman (ed.), *Science and Psychoanalysis,* Vol. III, Grune & Stratton, Inc., New York, 1959.

Read in part at the semiannual meeting of the Academy of Psychoanalysis, New York, Dec. 6, 1958.

But our Academy has a more recent and direct precedent in its own field: Freud's equally non-Procrustean dedication in his earlier years to adaptive and discerning clinical observations from which he derived a succession of concepts and insights of great heuristic if not determinative value to the behavioral sciences. Moreover, Freud's orginially fluid formulations set up various other predominantly advantageous scientific cycles, in that they stimulated workers in related branches of the behavioral sciences to review their own data, postulates, and systems and then to offer to psychoanalysis valuable confirmations of, or amendments to, specific aspects of analytic theory and practice. In this manner, psychoanalysis has had beneficial interchanges with anthropology, sociology, history, linguistics, political science, philosophy, and even theology; more lately, public relations practices and advertising techniques have apparently been added to the list. But despite Freud's own biologic and medical orientations and a recently overwhelming flood of somewhat speculative "psychosomatic" literature, only a relatively few workers (e.g., L. von Bertalanffy, D. Levy, D. Rioch, S. Rado, and R. Grinker, *et al.*) have remained deeply interested in what psychoanalysis can contribute to, or receive from, the more basic sciences of morphology and physiology, with special reference to the evolving higher neural functions and their correlations with the individual and social complexities of human conduct. Since our psychoanalytic literature is relatively limited in this field, permit me to devote my initial discussion to a survey of biologic data relevant to various psychoanalytic problems of fundamental import. Let us pose just a few such questions:

What relationship do the "instinctive" or "innate" or "unconditioned" behavior patterns of animals have to the concepts of pre-experiential or "libidinal" drives and potentialities in man?

Can the order of the appearance of such patterns in young animals be correlated in any way with the postulated stages of "psychosexual maturation" in the child and adolescent? And are these phases related to the differential phylogenetic and ontogenetic development of the nervous system?

Is there determinative or presumptive evidence for the postulate of "primal aggression" or of a "death instinct"? Or may the battles over territoriality, dominance and sexual possession in both animals and man be as readily formulated by Kropotkin's, Simpson's, or Huxley's concepts of a universal seeking for individual participation in an evolving social order? If so, is the ostensibly self-punitive or self-destructive behavior also observed in animals based on deviant individual experiences without primal atavistic resonances? Or is the relatively rare occurrence of mass intraspecies warfare (e.g., in some varieties of ants, as described by Schnierla) more in accord with Freud's gloomy concepts of man's fate?

Relevant to this, of what epistemologic significance are animal studies of modes of communication, of courting customs and sexual patterns, and of group behavior, or studies on the experimental inductions of patterns of "masochism," of diffuse "aggression," and of "animal neuroses"? Can the phenomena of the latter be characterized by clinical terms such as phobias, inhibitions, compulsions, regressions, symptom formations, and "social maladaptations"?

What bearings do the ethologic concepts of "trigger-stimuli" and "social releasers" have in the early channelizations of fixations of reaction patterns in the human infant? In view of the relative impersonality of such early automatic responses, is every subsequent relationship in the human primarily a reiteration, or at best, a "transference" displacement or elaboration of previous attachments and repulsions?

And, perhaps most germane of all to our interests as clinicians, can a study of the methods that may or may not be effective in relieving these symptoms in any way contribute to the understanding of clinical psychotherapy? Indeed, how readily, in contrast to lower animals, may humans be reorientated an redirected by analytic or other techniques so that they may attain a greater versatility and adaptability in human relations?

Those of us who follow Freud in a broad scientific tradition must wish to adduce evidence from every available source that might help us answer such questions and understand all we can about all behavior, including our own. I propose to survey such evidence—though of course my review must be partial and barely indicative—under two major headings: first, *ethologic*, i.e., "naturalistic"; and, second, *comparative biodynamics*, i.e., animal experimental. Then, perhaps, we can proceed to correlates of clinical research and practice.

Psychoanalysis and Ethology

Basic Concepts

It seems as though nearly everyone is now familiar with some of the key concepts of ethology: e.g., *instinct, social releaser, imprinting,* etc. *Instinct,* a term approved after considerable debate by the International Ethologic Congress, has as its operational referent any mode of behavior governed by hereditary patterns of function in the central nervous system and therefore characterized, in Lorenz' words by *spontaneity, rigidity,* and *modifiability through learning.*[1] A *social releaser* is an external object or situation that, however fragmentary in itself, is interpreted by the organism as a completed *Gestalt* and thereby furnishes an "objective" or external goal to instinctive behavior. As an example, if a red-spotted ball is exhibited above the horizontal to a Siamese fighting fish, the total situation is apparently interpreted by the fish as an encroachment on its territory and the ball is attacked as a rival (Tinbergen); so also, the shadow of a toy airplane which, moving ahead, may look vaguely like the silhouette of a flying hawk will make new born chicks run for cover, whereas moving in the other direction it apparently has the appearance of a harmless swan and is therefore ignored. *Imprinting* is a permanent modification of behavior by a *social releaser;* e.g., Lorenz observed that if he himself squatted and quacked a few times before a brood of newly hatched ducklings, they would thenceforth follow him and ignore the mother duck whose "normal" priority was thus usurped. The importance of *imprinting at optimum early periods* was highlighted by Riesen, who observed that if baby chimpanzees are blindfolded for six months after birth, they are apparently kept from taking advantage of that phase of cortical development best suited for the acquisition of visual perceptions; consequently, when the blindfold is removed, they can no longer "learn to see" or to recognize objects and may even make themselves physically amaurotic by staring wide-eyed and uncomprehendingly at the sun.

It is immediately apparent that such ethologic observations may be highly relevant to corresponding concepts of instinct or "libido," the

1. Compare with K. M. Colby's less clearly operational definition of an instinct as a "force" devoid of any Freudian "direction" of "aim" but consisting simply of "neutral cathexis energy." Norbert Wiener (1950) furnishes a healthy connective to such concepts in the following words:

"One of the most abused terms in biology and psychology is that of energy. In its Aristotelian connotation, it signifies the potential of action, and is not really physical, but rather a metaphysical term. Under these conditions there is perhaps some jusification for using it for the tendency of an animal to follow a certain tropism or for the mind to seek a certain goal. However, it is impossible in this day and age to use the term without a strong suggestion of its physical use, and this suggestion seems to be actually intended by many of those who employ it in the science of life. In physics, energy is a quantity which represents one of the constants of integration of a certain system of ordinary differential equations, etc. . . . In the employment of the word by Freud and by certain schools of physiologists, neither justification (for the use of the term energy) is present; or at the very most, no one has proved it so. There was a plethora of materialistic biological writing at the end of the last century in which the language of physics was bandied around in a very unphysical way. The same sort of quantity was now termed an energy and now a force regardless of the fact that the laws of transformation of force are widely different from those of energy. . . . It is in the line of this scientific journalese that one finds the words 'force' and 'energy' interchangeably applied to whatever it is that drives the moth into the light and the flatworm away from it. However, the moth is not pulled by the light nor is the flatworm pushed away from it. They are steered—the one toward the light and the other away. In this steering process, all the energy which the animal possesses in any true physical sense is ultimately converted into heat. . . ."

permanent effects of early infantile experience, or Bowlby's contention that if a child does not experience warm maternal care in the first years of life he can never appreciate or seek friendly relationship with anyone thereafter and thereby becomes "autistic" and "schizophrenic." But since parallel lines of thinking in ethology and analytic dynamics may never meet, the following paragraphs will attempt to build bridges between them at important points, with draw spans as necessary to permit incidental traffic to pass.

"Protoplasmic" Learning

We cannot here go into the current controversies among Geller, Jensen, and A. F. Mirsky, *et al.*, on whether or not unicellular organisms can be "conditioned" to feeding and avoidance responses, but it seems certain that learning can occur in the most primitive neural organization.* As but one example, Bharucha-Reid noted that earthworms simply left in a maze showed a greater facility in learning a subsequently imposed route than those newly introduced; so also, Zymnarski and others found little difficulty in training cockroaches, perhaps the most ancient of living insects to reverse their "instinctive" escape and other patterns. May, then, not only self-maintenance and reproduction but also *an innate capacity to retain learning* be said to be the three essential characteristics of all life? In this connection, H. S. Jennings observed that the members of a colony, or *clone,* of protozoa growing from the conjugation of a single pair divide asexually for several months and then become sexual, the *community* thus achieving a development from infancy to sexual maturity that earlier generations of individuals cannot attain. It would be interesting to see who would first dare to compare this with Spencer's concept of social "superorganisms" or Toynbee's parallel of the birth, growth, vigor, and decline of nations.

Neural Correlations of "Instincts" and Experience

Sauer, in an article entitled "Celestial Navigation in Birds," thus eloquently puts the case for "pure instinct."

When fall cames, the little garden warbler, weighing barely three quarters of an ounce, sets off one night on an unbelievable journey. All alone, never in the collective security of a flock, it wings its solitary way south-westward over Germany, France and Spain and then swings south to its distant goal in southern Africa. It flies on unerringly, covering a hundred miles or more in a single night, never once stopping in its course, certain of its goal. In the spring it takes off again and northward retraces its path to its nesting place in a

---

* More recently, J. McConnelli *planaria* acquire the conditional concepts of their cannibalized cousins.

German or Scandinavian thicket—there to give birth to a new generation of little warblers which will grow up, without being taught, with the self-same capacity to follow the same route across continents and oceans by the map of the stars.

Sauer could also demonstrate that his warblers navigated "instinctively" by the seasonal azimuths and declensions of the sun and the stars; however, no two warblers ever took exactly the same compass course in either spring or autumn; i.e., the behavior of his birds could not be proved to be totally independent of their post-natal experiences.

But are learned patterns merely modifications of "instincts" or "drive reductions," supposedly also referrable to circumscribed neural centers? Certainly, minor CNS injury or altered general metabolism affect behavior profoundly. As Neal Miller points out in his critique of Skinnerian theory, hypothalamic lesions (or stomach distention) diminish hunger, whereas electrostimulation of the septal region increases it; so also, stimulation of the medial forebrain bundle in rats always causes ejaculation. Do then such part-functions really indicate "centers of libido" to be further engrammed by experience? Not always; for example, Delgado and Roberts in Miller's laboratory at Yale have confirmed our findings that stimulation of the hypothalamus—a region previously supposed to be the center of emotional mimetics—cannot be conditioned at all to external experience.[2] Conversely, we have also shown that dorsomedial thalamic operations modify the expressions of rage and that amygdaloidectomies profoundly affect sexual behavior, *but the effects of these ablations depend specifically on the animal's previous experience;* i.e., they are contingent on each animal's level of maturity and individual history.

So also, satisfaction or reduction of a drive as fundamental as hunger is certainly changed in tempo and form (1) by external circumstances which modify total inner neural sets and (2) by what may be termed an "orgiastic" summation within the central nervous system itself. As to *environmental influences,* it has been observed that hens will eat almost twice as much from large or replenished mounds of grain as from small heaps, more from a soft as compared with a hard surface, and more when other hens are present; i.e., "The same subjective state in animals as well as men can be the basis of widely different forms of behavior according to external circumstances." (Katz, p. 169.) Experimentally, rats will work far less ardently for food if it is tinctured with quinine, if the lid to the food box is weighted, or if they merely

2. Recently, Nakao at Kyushu University reported success in conditioning hypothalamic stimulation to a buzzer, but his experimental technique was more likely to produce total affective learning.

anticipate the recurrence of a deterrant electroshock. For that matter, penguins deprived of eggs may attempt to hatch rounded pieces of ice (Levick) demonstrating how far awry in external expression even the relatively simple "brooding instinct" may go.[3] As to *inner CNS summations,* modifications, and reversals, Miller noted that rats will press bars to stimulate electrodes inserted in the median forebrain bundle, and then promptly rotate a wheel to turn the stimulus off: i.e., the same nerve centers would then be said to mediate both "pleasant" and "unpleasant" drive potentials. David Rioch, too, has concluded: "The feelings of 'euphoria' and 'dysphoria' are apparently related to adequacy of CNS functioning in the interaction of the organism with the environment, rather than to activity in any localized area." Indeed, in view of the complex neural bases, environmental sensitivities, and infinitely varied expressions of all behavior, can one really postulate any simple roots called "instincts"? And, if drive, adaptation, and retained learning become thus indistinguishable, what becomes of our artificial and quasi-mythological distinctions between "conscious"[4] and "unconscious," or, for that matter, among "id," "ego," and "superego"?

Innate Learning

It must be noted that, subtly but inescapably, such considerations reopen the whole question of the hereditary transmission of learning. In 1928, Pavlov asserted unequivocally that rats taught to run a maze in his laboratory gave birth to rat pups that learned the same maze with progressive ease; i.e., 300 lessons in the first generation as compared with only 10 lessons in the fourth. According to Razran, Pavlov himself later questioned these experimental results, but never denied his attraction to Lamarckism, and thus lent himself to eager identification in communist ideology with pseudoscientific party stalwarts such as Michurin and Lysenko. But such thinking is not necessarily hemmed behind an Iron Curtain; in an article bravely entitled "Influence of Pre-natal Maternal Anxiety on Emotionality in Young Rats," W. R. Thompson of Canada describes how he shocked pregnant mother rates in a Skinner cage and observed that their young were later deficient in foodseeking,

---

3. Herring gulls will desert their own small unspectacular eggs to sit on a large blue black-spotted china one—termed by Lorenz "a cover-girl egg-saggeration of attractive releasers."

4. Tolman (Chapter 22) writes: "And if psychology would only be content with the lower animals, and preferably with rats, and not try to mess around with human beings, this whole question of consciousness and of idea may well have been omitted. But human beings insist on being included in any psychological purview. And they insist that they are conscious and do have ideas—however improbable this latter may often appear . . . (p. 205). It is in the moment of changing behavior, in the moments of learning, the consciousness will appear."

in spontaneous activity, and in learning to manipulate the shock-lever. These effects could, of course, have been due merely to a metabolically impaired milieu in the troubled mother's uterine environment, but they highlight Stieglitz' maxim that organisms age—and in a sense "learn"— far more in the uterus than they do after birth. Primitive adaptations that occur so early that they may change hereditary predispositions other than through selective survival have also been noted by Béach; e.g., a certain female moth will always lay her eggs on hackberry leaves, but if her young are raised on apple leaves, some of them will lay on apple leaves. The perennial question, then, is again raised: Can our experiences, despite what we were taught in our strict Darwinian class-rooms, really in any way affect the innate predilections of our children?

The Value of Movement

Ethologic observations challenge another cherished shibboleth in some fields of psychiatry; namely, the prejudice against "acting out" as a form of learning or of solutions of inner dilemmas. Eckhard Hess has observed, for example, that at an optimum time of 13 to 16 hours after hatching, wild mallard ducklings can be imprinted to follow a decoy *only if they are permitted to waddle after it;* Hess therefore concluded that "the strength of the imprinting appeared to be dependent not on the duration of the imprinting period but on the effort exerted by the duckling"—i.e., the youngster learned by doing. Nikolaas Tinbergen, in his classic observations, noted that a male stickleback fish threatened by a dummy rival so near the border of his territory that he is placed in obvious conflict as to whether to fight or run must either divert his energies into the absurdly inappropriate busy-ness of building a nest, or else almost literally perish in a paretic impasse. In our human education we have learned to teach scientific principles through learned skills,[5] in general adult life we pay lip service to the adage "a sound mind in a healthy active body" (the Greek *sanitas* stood for indissoluable physical and psychic health), and in geriatrics we deplore physical in-activity as quickly leading to total senescence. And yet, in some forms of psychotherapy, we forbid "acting out," pretend that life problems can be solved by supine conversation between two people respectively immobil-ized by chair and couch, and hope that somehow behavior will be improved without necessarily concomitant re-explorations, relearnings, and new achievements in, quite literally, the *act-uality* of living.

5. Mittleman has recently re-emphasized the importance of the "motor urge" in exploratory expansions during early childhood; he advocates free skeletal motility and cautions against adverse reactions to restraint as respectively favorable or neuro-tigenic determinants of life-time personality patterns.

Adverse Early Experiences

Equally significant are observations as to the adverse effects of induced extremes of early experience in animals. Innumerable studies can be cited, but a particularly striking pair may be here adduced. Thompson and Melzock report that, if puppies are raised with the best of metabolic care but in almost complete isolation, they grow into adults subject to periods of glazed staring, apparently illusory startles, fears, and rages, and peculiar attacks of epileptoid whirling. In a contrasting study, Thompson and Heron report that excessively protected and petted pups grow into insecure, helpless, overdependent, and jealously demanding dogs—a not uncommon development in species other than canine. Liddell observed that kids separated from the mother ewe for only a two-hour period the first day after birth developed persistent difficulties in maternal and herd relationships and such severe neurotic and psychosomatic handicaps that all died within six months. Others less severely traumatized in infancy survived, but bore kids whom they in turn neglected and so perpetuated a "neurotic family history."[6]

Regression

Relevant to such studies are the universal dynamics of the *fixation* of an activity designed to satisfy an intercurrent need, or the *regression* under stress to patterns of behavior previously found to be satisfying. In relation to fixation, David Levy noted that pups adequately fed by tube or dropper, but thus kept from a normal suckling experience, persisted for years in nuzzling tassles, fingers, or other teat-substitutes; as to regression, the same author observed that a fully grown police dog which, as a puppy, had been indulgently nursed and pampered after breaking its leg, began limping again in full adulthood whenever its master played with a child or another dog, but frisked in four-footed glee when its security seemed restored.

The Modes of Communication

Nor do animals lack other intra- and interspecies communication; on the contrary, there seems to be an unbroken line from the relatively simple chemical or contact-signaling motions of infusoria to the complex communicative kinesics—of which the vocal chords are only the audible part—in man. As described by Morris, the female swordtail understands and responds very well to the courtship swimming patterns of the

6. P. Seitz has also observed that rat pups raised in large litters became subject to various later handicaps in adaptation and hoarded food more strenuously than those from smaller and better tended litters.

male.[7] As to effective social propagandizing, few human speeches are as compelling as the hour-long dance, interpreted by von Fritsch and Lindauer, of a few scout bees who finally convince 50,000 hive-mates that it is time to leave their brethren in an overcrowded nest and swarm to a new one.[8] In birds, kinesic and auditory forms of communication are more obviously present. Morris has written an exhaustive report, the dry language of which can hardly conceal the versatility with which birds, by altering the arrangement of their body feathers, can signify the subtlest changes of mood in agreeable, thwarting, or "neurosis-engendering" situations. On the vocal side may be cited an article by Frings and Jumber, who first recorded on tape the cry of distress and warning emitted by a starling held upside down and shaken, then amplified the sound to 30 decibels through the loud speaker of a mobile sound truck and in three nights were able to frighten away an estimated 10,000 to 12,000 starlings which had infested Millheim, Pennsylvania. Equally interesting was the fact that, possibly because of an odor left by the frightened starlings, few came to replace them.

Monkeys and apes are, of course, exceedingly responsive to both kinesic and auditory communication,[9] and more sensitively dependent on

7. Or, as the ethologist Ogden Nash phrased it for another species:

"Consider the happy jumping flea
You cannot tell what sex it be
A she-flea looks just like a he
But he can tell, and so can she."

8. Parenthetically, Lindauer reports that he once observed "a swarm that was unable to make up its mind. The choice had narrowed to two sites and the partisans [two delegations of bees that had returned to the nest after searching for new sites] kept up their competitive dance for 14 days with neither side giving in. Then they stopped and the groups proceeded to commit mass suicide. They built a new hive on the nearest available bush, and froze to death the following winter."

9. Zuckerman (page 263) writes as follows about baboons in the London Zoo: "Many characteristic vocal sounds are associated with specific social activities of baboons . . . rhythmical lip, tongue and jaw movements . . . usually accompany friendly advances between two animals. In more direct sex activity this sound may give way to a rhythmical series of deep grunts similar to those with which the animals greet the sun. These grunts are commonly made in all states of well-being. One grunting baboon seems to stimulate several others. Another characteristic cry of the baboon is the high-pitched screech of a young animal or a female, made either in a situation of obvious danger, or in sets, which to the human observer do not appear to contain any cause for fear. This cry usually attracts neighboring dominant baboons [who rush to protect the supplicant]. Sometimes adult males make a similar cry, but it is not so high-pitched and accompanies states of rage occasioned either by the attack of a more dominant animal, or by its own impotent attempts to attack a fellow. By attracting other animals, it may begin a new fight. This cry is altogether different from the far-carrying, deep-throated barks heard in the wild when the members of a troop of baboons are scattered, or when a possible enemy, for instance a man, is observed approaching. This cry, which in the wild probably effects the reunion of a scattered troop is only rarely made in captivity. I once heard a female barking this deep call after the death and removal of her baby. It is always heard

individual training. For example, I. A. Mirsky observed that a monkey trained to depress a switch that prevented electroshock to itself would also do so when it observed a cagemate being shocked; again, a young rhesus in our laboratory would fetishically fondle a rubber glove with which it had been nursed whenever it thought another monkey was being mistreated. Kathy Hayes taught a baby chimp to say and mean "cup," to understand many nouns (e.g., "foot," "mamma") and verbs (e.g., "give," "kiss") and to obey—though with obvious surprise—an irrational command combining these (e.g., "kiss your foot") the first time it was uttered. I leave it to etholinguists, pet owners, and fond mothers to judge how eloquently expressive the mews, whines, growls, barks, and chatterings of squirrels, chipmunks, cats, dogs, monkeys, and preverbal human babies can be, and how well they can "mind" when they want to.

Tool Using and Art

The contention has often been advanced that animals differ from man in two major respects: (1) that they do not project, modify, or enhance their power through tools, and (2) that they lack, or are not interested in, esthetic creativity. But ethologists can reply that the first of these shibboleths simply distinguishes those who refuse to believe that sand spiders use pebbles to tamp their tunnels, that Geospizas pick cactus spines with which to dig out their insect prey from the bark of trees, that monkeys can open cage locks with keys, and work for differently colored "coins" with which to secure grapes from vending machines (the "value" of the token in terms of the number of grapes it can secure determining the effort and ingenuity the monkey will put forth to earn it), or that chimpanzees can assemble complex levers and drive electric cars. A most interesting variant in the construction of a trap device is the modernized Iron Maiden technique used by the Arizona roadrunner: as described by Dobie, this bird builds a corral of cactus leaves or prickly cholla joints around a sleeping rattlesnake, which then either starves to death or dies of multiple puncture wounds in attempting to leave its prison of daggers. In organisms with more highly potentiated nervous systems, exploration of the physical universe, presumably wih a view to its control and manipulation—i.e., an urge to research—may take precedence over all other motivations. Thus, in an article aptly entitled "Curiosity in Monkeys," Butler reviews the observations by Harlow, Yerkes, and others to the effect that monkeys and

---

when bodies are removed from the Hill [a free-roaming space] to a new cage and is then raised by many animals. For several weeks after the females were removed from the Hill to a new cage two hundred yards away they continued to call in this way and to be answered by the males whom they had left behind."

apes—particularly young ones—would leave food and other rewards to indulge in exploration and "play activities" that consisted essentially in the development of increasing knowledge about, and control of, the physical milieu.

Parallel to such pragmatic and research pursuits are animal aspirations to art. In the field of architecture and domestic decoration only one of numerous examples need be cited. The bower birds of Australia and New Guinea, as reported by A. J. Marshall, build elaborately designed landscapes, tunnels, and maypoles out of sticks, pebbles, seashells, or other materials, paint them with berry juice or charcoal mixed with saliva, and decorate them with flowers in a manner that inspired the painter Sibol to co-artistic tribute.

Courting, Contrectation, and Sexuality

On these intriguing topics I can do no better than repeat a trenchant paragraph from Burton's book on *Animal Courtship* (page 14):

For humans, as for animals, symbolism and ceremony play a very large part. Moreover, both these things do, on occasion, look so very much alike in both the human and the animal spheres. There are in both the giving of gifts, the exhibitionism, the dressing-up, the bowing and curtsying, the communal interest in the proceedings, the rivalries, jealousies, antagonisms, in fact the whole gamut; and all so very much according to tradition and custom (or, as we say for animal courtship, so stereotyped). If man has devised all these things for himself independently of what has been going on in the rest of the living world for a thousand million years or more, then the coincidence is most remarkable.

Further trenchant passages from ethologic writers relevant to our present interests may be quoted:

Aggression. (Burton, page 150) "If a male stickleback in full breeding condition is imprisoned within a glass tube held horizontally, it will not display aggressively to a rival. As soon as the tube is held vertically, however, he will display violently. . . . A corresponding situation is seen in the case of a human being, who finds it very difficult to be aggressive sitting down. And is not our first impulse, in calming someone who is becoming aggressive, to induce him to sit down? (Page 63) This is not to say that wild animals do not throw their whole being into their aggressive displays and sometimes go beyond the bounds of common animal decency, especially where two contestants are equally matched in prowess and determination; but really bloody fights are rare. (Page 75) Fundamentally, the loyalty has been primarily to the territory and only secondarily to the mate. The parallel is clear in business affairs. Wars are fought over territory; social revolutions arise from land-hungry masses; more marital difficulties spring from having to share space . . . than from any other single cause." In discussing in ethologic terms the transition from aggression to friendship, Lorenz writes:

In a very great part of higher animals, particularly of vertebrates, two individuals of the same species will fight when meeting fortuitously or being confronted experimentally. The high survival value of this intraspecific fighting (spacing out of territory, defense of offspring, selection of the fittest, etc.) has long been securely established by ecologists. For species in which common parental care necessitates the staying-together of two individuals after copulation, and particularly in truly social species, it was necessary to evolve mechanisms which prevent the fighting between certain individuals, without, however, otherwise impeding the important functions of intraspecific contention. The development of appeasing ceremonies ensued. The most important of these are those evolved by the ritualization of so-called re-directed activities, in which aggression primarily released by and directed at the mate or social partner, is side-tracked and directed at the hostile neighbor, or, in some cases, at a purely "symbolic" substitute object. In cases in which higher ritualization has set in, these behavior mechanisms, for example, the "triumph-ceremony" of geese, have obtained a high degree of autonomy and form a supremely strong bond between the individuals taking part in it.

Friendship. (Burton, page 243) "A wounded elephant has several times been seen surrounded by the rest of the herd, who keep it upright and by the pressure of their bodies carry it to safety in the jungle. . . ." Otters, too, will rescue a wounded comrade. Antelopes place sentinels for the herd, who remain on watch until relieved (Katz, page 205). Loveridge frequently observed a male baboon in flight returning in the face of danger in its natural habitat to rescue a wounded fellow, or a female remaining behind to protect a dead colony-mate's body.[10] In cross-species friendships there are records of harmonious companionships between a domestic dog and a vixen, a domestic bitch and a dog fox . . . permanent and without any attempt at mating. Other more bizarre friendships are those between a goose and a goat, a goat and a llama, a cat and ducklings. . . . Badgers, fox, and rabbits, having grown up together, have a mutual tolerance (Burton, page 253).

Wooing. (Burton, page 50).

A hen robin has been known to take a crumb from an observer's hand, fly with it to the cock, place it at his feet, open her mouth and quiver her wings [like a fledgling] until he picks it up and gives it to her. To stand on

---

10. In contrast, baboons *kept in captivity* may act more like men in concentration camps, attack the weak, the ill, and the aged, manhandle the female after sexual satiation, and otherwise act in a manner that would appear cruel and destructive to a human observer. However, these animals do not seem to recognize the death of their own kind (Zuckerman).

a saucer of food and to look to her mate to wait on her may be automatic behavior. If so, then a good deal of human behavior, which we fondly imagine to be the result of free-will must also be automatic. [Page 122.] The male empid spider [who is sometimes eaten by the female] is credited with a cunning trick for avoiding such an end. His wooing is preceded by a hunt to catch a fly . . . which he enshrouds in fine silk threads [and presents to the female]. While she is unraveling the [victim] . . . mating takes place. But a male empid will sometimes take a small piece of a tick, a petal . . . or any small object, enshroud it and present it to the female. Unpacking the parcel keeps her busy long enough for him to avoid the possible fatal results of this approach. [Page 115.] The premating behavior of animals high and low [brings] us as near to a rule as is possible in biology: that the male may do the courting but the female has the whip hand . . .

Parenthetically, O. Heinroth also noted that a dominant gander may interfere in the public mating of couples in his pond, and observed "To be scandalized by the sexual acts of others is often observed in the animal world." Lorenz, despite his fears of being labeled "anthropomorphic," once commented: "This is not jealousy, it is pure Puritanism."

Uxorial Relations.   (Burton, page 56.)

Male starlings often carry flowers into their nesting hole when the female is incubating. A herring gull will take a shell or a sea-pink to his brooding mate. But as the species approaches man, the uxorial patterns seem to change in accordance with the description given by Yerkes for chimpanzees: "The behavior of each mate [with regard to feeding and other privileges] seems to change in correlation with their sexual relationships, and the female comes to claim as if it were her right what previously she had allowed the male to take, while he as if in recognition of, or in exchange for, sexual accommodation during the mating period, defers to her and unprotestingly permits her to control the food-getting situation.

Conversely, a chimpanzee separated from its mate may refuse to eat (Kohler).

Parental Conditioning.   Such observations, of course, bring up the further important question of what ethology can contribute to the clarification of child-parent relationships. To begin with, J. P. Scott calls our attention to the fact that in animals as highly developed as canines, no conditioning can occur until the eyes and ears open at three weeks (after which pups can be weaned without leaving the Levy sucking effect)—and that perhaps of all dogs only the cocker spaniel is "born socialized." In comparing his data with those on humans, Scott insists that, contrary to the concepts of the Kleinian school, no conditioning of the human infant can occur until six weeks after birth—an observation in accord with Rene Spitz' finding that babies do not really differentiate faces until fully six months old. And yet very early fixations of affection can occur at considerably lower evolutionary (though perhaps comparatively older ontologic) levels; for example, Leonore Brandt explains how an orphaned baby Diana monkey became exceedingly attached to her human foster-mother, fed her cherished bananas, and pushed her out of feared open spaces into the protection of presumably safe trees. This is reminiscent of Lorenz' pet jackdaw who, after adopting Dr. Lorenz, insisted on feeding him mashed-meal worms through the ear canal—or the raven who warned him of the approach of an avian enemy with ravenesque swoops and tail-flips while uttering its own German name in deference to the language preference of its adopted Viennese communicant.

Experimental and Comparative Biodynamics

But the question may still be raised: since man alone is capable of "higher symbolism" and "culture," is he not therefore yet the only creature subject to the disruptive semantic and social aberrations known as neuroses and psychoses? Such questions are asked sufficiently frequently and sincerely to deserve extended consideration (cf. my *Behavior and Neurosis* and related writings).

Here a further analogy may be helpful. It is obvious that a man can live long and fairly happily knowing very little about the structure and function of his central nervous system; however, should he wish to become a neurologist, this technical information would become essential. In his first explorations of the field it might then appear to him that the human CNS is far too intricate to be profitably compared with, say, the simple neuraxis of an Amphioxus, and that therefore he had best confine his studies to human neuroanatomy, physiology, and "clinical" problems. And yet as his knowledge broadened and deepened he would begin to appreciate that an antithetical position might be nearer the truth: namely, that he could not really understand the fundamental structure and function of the human CNS without studying that of the Amphioxus, since only then would he comprehend the basic organization (or "plan") common to all vertebrates in the evolutionary scale, including that of man. So also, the psychiatrist and psychoanalyst cannot analyze human conduct merely by studying wild and semidomesticated animals or, for that matter, mice in mazes, cats in cages, or monkeys in pharmacologic hazes. Nevertheless, with proper criteria and controls, such studies can lead to the discovery of fundamental biodynamic principles underlying all behavior, and thus furnish us with as many valuable leads to behavioral science and psychotherapy as does comparative neurophysiology to neurologic theory and practice. For further validation and

elaboration of this statement the reader is again referred to my more
detailed writings (cf. bibliography); here we can do little more than
state that from such comparative-integrative approaches to behavioral
functions the following four clinically relevant principles of biodynamics
may be derived:

Principle I: Motivation. All behavior is motivated by physiologic
needs: survival, procreation as indicated above, and probably also esthetic creativity in various configurations of contingency and urgency.

Principle II: Adaptation. Every organism reacts not to an absolute "reality," but to its own interpretations of its milieu in terms of
its uniquely developed capacities and experiences.

Principle III: Displacement. Whenever goal-directed activities are
blocked by external obstacles, the organism tries either (1) different
methods to reach the same goal or, (2) other partially or wholly sub-
stitutable objectives. As a corollary, it is manifest that the optimal
milieu must be sufficiently challenging to maintain vitality and creativity, but not so frustrating as to cause excessively deviant conduct.

Principle IV: Conflict. However, when two or more urgent motivations are in sufficiently serious opposition so that the adaptive patterns
attendant to each become mutually exclusive, the organism experiences
a mounting internal tension ("anxiety") while its somatic and motor
behavior become persistently ambivalent, ineffectively substitutive and
poorly adaptive (i.e., "neurotic"), and/or progressively disorganized, regressive, and bizarrely symbolic ("psychotic").

To most psychiatrists these principles will appear immediately relevant to clinical experience—though, perhaps, no more so than other
systems of thought. Let us now review various animal experimental
and other data that give them more fundamental significance.[11]

Species

Any animal can, of course, be used for the study of living behavior.
French, Jennings, and Loeb used amoebae for basic observations of vital
patterns of adaptation; as noted, Szymanski employed cockroaches to
demonstrate primitive modifications of behavior through individual experience; Pavlov and Gantt studied more elaborate forms of learning in
dogs; and Liddell studied pigs and sheep for essentially the same purposes. Similarly, Yerkes and more recently Lashley and his co-workers
have confided themselves to man's embarrassingly close relatives, the
great apes, again with highly significant results. The author and his associates chose cats, dogs, and monkeys because they are relatively easily

---

11. The material in this section is adapted from Chapter 25 of my *Practice of
Dynamic Psychiatry* by permission of W. B. Saunders Co.

obtained and kept, yet are instructively comparable to man in the complexity of many of their "normal" behavioral capacities and, as we shall see, in their reactions to stress and conflict.

Motivations
(PRINCIPLE I)

As expressed in the first biodynamic principle, any physiologic need can be evoked to actuate experimentally observable behavior: thirst, physical escape from constriction or discomfort, sexual drives, the urge of a lactating mother animal to feed her young, etc. These and other conations of greater or less complexity were all tested in appropriate experiments; in practice, however, we generally utilized the "hunger" drive because, though feeding behavior is itself a relatively complex expression of direct and indirect metabolic needs, it has the advantages of being easily induced, rapidly renewed, and fractionally analyzable. Parenthetically, and partially in accord with "libido" theory, it could be demonstrated that nutritive needs had deep motivational interrelationship with patterns of gregariousness, dominance behavior, and sexuality.

Experimental Design. This was essentially simple: an animal was placed in a glass-enclosed compartment for easy observation and photography, and trained to develop various "normal" response and manipulative patterns to obtain specific rewards. In parallel experiments, two or more animals were placed simultaneously in such situations to elicit their interactions of "cooperation" or "hostility." Each animal was then made to contend with various obstacles and frustrations, and, finally, conflicts of motivation were induced in order to study their etiologic and phenomenologic relationship to maladaptive and aberrant conduct. In special series of experiments these techniques were elaborated to include the effects of various drugs and of local stimulations or lesions of the central nervous system on "normal" or "neurotic" behavior. Finally, a large variety of procedures, both theoretically and empirically selected, were tested for their influence in exacerbating or ameliorating these pattterns of conduct. To promote objectivity or analysis and for permanence of record, tables of data, instrumental tracings, motion picture films,[12] and independent reports of important behavioral observations were secured in all experiments.

"Normal" Learning and Adaptation. In a typical experiment a dog, a cat, or monkey that had been deprived of food from 12 to 24 hours was taught first to open a food box in response to a sensory signal and then to circumvent various barriers and manipulate various electrical switches

12. Cf. films listed under references.

or other contrivances to secure its own signals and food rewards. In such preliminary studies it was found that animals could form quite complex "symbolic" associations when appropriately motivated; for instance, cats and monkeys could be taught to count (i.e., press a series of switches in a required order a definite number of times), diffierentiate between "signs" (e.g., German script readings *"fressen"* or *"nicht fressen"*), distinguish single or combined odors, etc.; for that matter, the animals often anticipated the experimenter's intentions and prepared for what he was going to do by interpreting correctly subtle clues in his behavior of which he himself had not been aware. If the animal's perceptive, mnemonic, integrative, and reactive (i.e., "intellectual") capacities were exceeded during this training period, it became recalcitrant and resistant to further learning; instead, it would not infrequently resort to aimless play, sporadic attempts to escape, or episodic diffuse destructiveness. Certain experiments indicated that these characteristics may persist in young animals which had been subjected to an overly intensive regime of training and had thereby suffered permanent impairment of their adaptive responses—a pedagogic tragedy exemplified by the stultified genius of William Sidis, and still neglected by some teachers of our young. Nearly all of our experiments, on the other hand, conformed to Principle I in that no learning took place in the absence of relevant motivation; e.g., an animal that was not hungry would pay only passing notice to the food cup, whereas one trained to manipulate the signals, barriers, and switches would cease to be directly interested in these paraphernalia for receiving food as soon as its hunger was satiated. Conversely, if the training remained in accord with the animal's needs and well within its capacities and temperament, it readily entered into the experimental situation, learned avidly and effectively, continued to be generally friendly to the experimenter (except, in our experience, in the case of Vervet, Cynamologus, or adult Mangabey monkeys) and was, on the whole, an active, contented, and thereby "well-adjusted" animal.

Symbolization and the Semantics of "Masochism"
(PRINCIPLE II)

It will be recalled that the second biodynamic principle states that each organism interprets and evaluates its milieu in terms of its own needs, capacities, and experiences. This was particularly well illustrated by experiments in which the animal's responses, though they seemed paradoxical to a casual observer, could nevertheless be accounted for by just such a premise. For example, monkeys who ordinarily like bananas could be made to show avoidance reactions by having even the odor of the fruit associated with some unpleasant occurrence. Conversely, cats taught to depress an electric switch which gave them a mild electric shock signaling the availability of food could be made so eager to administer increasingly severe electric shocks to themselves even when the original reward was suspended that their behavior would almost invariably be called "masochistic" by observers unacquainted with their histories. This, of course, again raises the question as to whether many clinical patterns usually interpreted as masochistic are not essentially "self-punitive," but instead rooted in expectations of previously available rewards through temporarily strenuous or painful behavior.

External Frustration and Adaptive Substitutions
(PRINCIPLE III)

If an animal which had become accustomed to obtain food by manipulating electrical switches, running mazes, and responding to sensory signals was subsequently kept from securing its reward by some mechanical obstruction (an impassable barrier, a nonoperative switch, etc.), its first reactions would be to expend more effort to overcome that obstacle. For example, the animal would push against the barrier, energetically work or actually jump upon the switch in attempts to close its circuit, try to pry open the locked food box, or use other methods of forcing a way toward its original goal. If these methods became particularly intensive (i.e., the animal would use its teeth or claws as the only tools at its command) its efforts would, of course, appear to become "destructive" or "hostile" in that the animal would seem to be "attacking" its environment, yet such behavior remained on the continuum of adaptive initiative and needed no new rubric of "aggressivity" to account for its dynamics or economics. A further instance of this is the fact that, when such reactions did not succeed in their turn, the animal did not proceed to annihilate the switch or food box even when it had the capacity to do so; instead, it shifted to substitutive actions or goals (principles II and III). Each species would then adapt in its characteristic way; most cats and monkeys would go about pressing other objects in lieu of the experimental switches or try to open containers other than the food-box, whereas dogs would generally attempt by barks and gestures to appeal to the experimenter to manipulate the recalcitrant gadgets. If none of these substitutive patterns proved effective in its turn, the animals temporarily relinquished striving for the food and instead sought other satisfactions, such as drinking excessive quantities of water, attempting to reach a sexual partner or playing with various objects, including their own bodies. However, most of these substitutive activities, including various displacements into diffusely exploratory or regressive behavior, disappeared rapidly whenever the external obstacles were removed and the animal once again found that normally adaptive patterns were effective. There was, then, no actual "extinction" of learned "conditional" responses in the Pavlovian sense; instead, in greater accord with analytic theory, such responses were merely held in abeyance ("repressed") when intercurrent experience showed they were temporarily ineffective. Consistent with this, they reappeared promptly ("return of the repressed") when the opportunity once again offered.

Inter-animal ("Social") Adaptations.   DOMINANCE AND AGGRESSION: Only two of the many experiments in animal interrelationships can be cited here to demonstrate their relevance to the first three biodynamic principles. When two animals, each of which had been trained to open a food box in response to the same signal, were placed together and the feeding signal given to both of them, competition for the single reward was necessarily engendered. In nearly all cases the rivalry resulted in one of the animals becoming "dominant" in securing the reward whereas the other became "submissive"—i.e., it adapted to its partner as an irremovable obstacle and thereafter occupied itself in other pursuits until the "dominant" animal ceased to pre-empt the food. Such hierarchies could be set up in groups of four or more animals, and the members of such groups, after a period of exploratory jockeying, would range themselves in a set order of precedence in feeding without resource to mutually aggressive behavior. Indeed, close observation of such interactions indicated that the submissive animals treated those above them as more or less impervious barriers and adapted accordingly. This raises the interesting question as to whether organism A ever reacts to or even recognizes organism B except as B facilitates or blocks the current or anticipated satisfaction of A. If the interactions are unilaterally or bilaterally satisfying the relationship may then be termed "love" and lead to various forms of symbiosis; in the case of mutual interference, the reciprocal attitudes may range from aversion to defensive or eliminative aggression.

COLLABORATION AND PARASITISM: Another intriguing paradigm of human relationships appeared in a separate series of experiments in which animals were individually trained to work an electric switch that flashed a signal light and deposited a single pellet of food in the food box. Two of the animals were then placed together in the experimental apparatus with a transparent barrier between the switch and food box so arranged that the animal which assayed to work the switch was itself barred from feeding, whereas the food reward became readily available to its partner. Obviously, many patterns of animal interaction were possible under such circumstances, but the following occurred most typically: after some initial random activity and individual readjustment, both animals would discover that "cooperation" was the only way in which either would get fed, so that for a time the animals alternated in working the food switch for each other. This arrangement broke down when one of the animals began to linger near the food box in order to gulp every available pellet; under such circumstances its partner, deprived of all reward, likewise refused to work the switch. The inevitable result was that each animal, in a joint caricature of a sitdown strike, remained. stubbornly inactive on its own side of the barrier while both starved. Eventually, one of the animals—usually the one that had previously shown the most initiative—would make another discovery: if it worked the switch six or eight times in rapid succession and *then* hurried to the food box, it could salvage the last two or three pellets before its partner, who had waited at the box, had eaten them all. From this a unique relationship evolved: one of the pair remained a "parasite" who lived off the "worker's" toil, whereas the worker remained seemingly content to supply food for both. Finally, an even more satisfactory solution was achieved by two of the workers in this series who, in the feline world, would rank as mechanical geniuses. In what seemed to be a flash of inspiration they so wedged the switch into a corner of the cage that it operated the automatic feeder continuously and thus provided a plenitude of pellets for both animals without further effort from either—a technological solution in the modern mode of a previously disruptive socioeconomic problem.

Effects of Adaptational Conflict
(PRINCIPLE IV)

Previous to our investigations Pavlov, Shenger-Krestovnikova, Gantt, and others had induced conflicts of adaptation by the traditional method of making the signals for positive or negative "conditioned reflexes" approach too closely to each other: i.e., a circle meant food but an almost circular ellipse meant none, or nearly synchronous metronome beats signaled opposite events. Under such circumstances the animal, in Pavlov's words, could no longer differentiate between "positive" and "negative" stimuli and, therefore, became "experimentally neurotic." In accordance with a broader biodynamic approach, we found that direct conflicts of motivation were not only technically easier to arrange, but induced behavior that could justifiably be called more generally, intensely and persistently neurotic. These conflicts could be set up by opposing motivations of approximately equal strength; e.g., poising a hungry lactating (or oestrual) female between food and an importunate litter (or male) in such a manner that one attraction neatly balanced and excluded the other. Or even more simply, conflicts could be induced between "goal-directed" conations such as hunger, thirst, or sex on the one hand, as opposed to "aversive" ones, e.g., inertia, or fear of falling or injury.[13] In the latter instances a typical experiment would run as follows:

Technique of Neurotigenesis. A cat, dog, or monkey which had been long accustomed to securing its food by, say, pressing a series of switches in a definite order and obtaining appropriate signals that food was available in the food box, would one day, when opening the box to receive the reward, be subjected to a traumatically deterrent stimulus. The latter need not be made somatically damaging; it could take the form of any "unpleasant" physical sensation such as a harmless condenser shock or an equally benign but startling air blast across the food box. Even more effective in the case of monkeys was a completely "psychologic" trauma such as the sudden appearance of the head of a toy snake through an aperture in the box in lieu of, or accompanying, the expected food reward. This last phenomenon was of such great semantic interest that we made it an object of special study and found that, whereas animated toys or even live frogs and lizards would rarely produce aversive effects, the artificial snake was highly traumatic even to laboratory-born monkeys which could have had no contact with snakes of any kind previously, yet nevertheless seemed to have an innate fear of anything that resembled them.

Development of Neuroses. In any case, the net effects in all animals were parallel, although the intenstiy of the neurotigenic conflict induced and the severity of its consequences naturally varied with the urgency of the opposing motivations, the possibility of escape, the availability of partial solutions of the dilemma and of previously learned skills to effect them, and many other factors.[14] In general, however, the following series of events could be observed:

13. That severe anxieties, paralyzing ambivalences, futile compulsivities, and even deep depressions can be set up by conflicting *positive* motivations (e.g., toward mutually exclusive jobs or spouses) as well as "negative" ones (a difficult choice between alternative methods of escape from danger) is a clinical phenomenon of special significance, since it supports the importance of *conflict* rather than fear alone in the etiology of neurotic behavior.

14. Pechtel and I (1956) evaluated our data in this regard as follows: "A differential analysis of observations on 142 cats and 43 monkeys during the last twelve years indicates that animals which adapted well to general laboratory routine, which learned efficiently, and which explored various substitutive maneuvers in initial efforts to resolve conflictful situations, subsequently showed longer continued resistance to severe stress and resumed effective behavior more readily under therapy. Younger animals were more susceptible to the induction of neurosis than were older ones. There were definite species differences: *i.e.*, spider monkeys and mangabeys were more vulnerable to conflict than were vervets and rhesus. Other factors which expedited neurotigenesis [included] repetition of the traumatic experiences at unexpectedly long intervals, minimal opportunities to escape from traumata, representational re-enforcement (e.g., rubber snake with grille shock added) and a diminution of adaptive capacities produced by cerebral lesions."

First the animal, after a preliminary startle, acted as if to deny the unwonted experience; it would work the switches once more, secure the signals and again open the food box, though now with some hesitation and a subtly changed mode of manipulation. The usual procedure was then to permit the animal to feed again, but after it had consumed several pellets it was once more subjected to the "traumatic" stimulus. Following a number of such conflictful experiences (two to seven in cats or dogs, generally more in monkeys) the animal began to develop the following patterns of aberration, so closely akin to those seen clinically that the term "experimental neurosis" could with considerable validity be applied:

Pervasive anxiety was indicated by a low threshold of startle with persistent hyperirritability, muscular tension, crouched body postures, mydriasis, and other measurable physiologic indices such as hidrosis, irregularly accelerated pulse rate, raised blood pressure, and increased coagulability of the blood.

Psychosomatic symptomatology: In addition to these bodily changes many animals (though, with respect to individual "psychodynamic" as opposed to species "specificity," we could never precisely predict which and when) showed recurrent asthmatic breathing, genitourinary dysfunctions, and various gastrointestinal disturbances such as persistent anorexia, flatulence, or diarrhea of so severe a degree that food would pass through almost undigested in less than an hour.

Defensive reactions were likewise protean and took the form of inhibitions of feeding even outside the experimental apparatus to the point of self-starvation and serious cachexia; phobic aversions first to stimuli directly associated with the traumatic experiences such as signals (especially odors), switches, constricted spaces, etc., and then spreading to other situations; muscular tics of the face and body; stereotyped motor compulsion such as ritualized turning to right or left; epileptiform seizures and, in some cases, cataleptic rigidity with partial flexibilitas cerea.

Sexual deviations became evident in markedly diminished heterosexual interest, accentuated homosexual activity, and, especially in the case of monkeys, greatly increased direct and vicarious masturbation. One vervet monkey, for several months after being made experimentally neurotic, spent most of his waking hours in autofellatio while completely ignoring a receptive female cage-mate.

Disturbances of the sensorium were obviously more difficult to deduce, but some neurotic animals were exceedingly sensitive to even minor changes in their surroundings, whereas others showed recurrent episodes of disorientation and confusion. Some monkeys appeared to act out wishfully vivid imagery: although they refused food readily available to their food box, they could be observed to pick nonexistent pellets off various surfaces of the cage or from the air and chew and swallow these fantasied tidbits with apparent relish.

Alterations in social conduct generally took the form of inertia and withdrawal from competition, with consequent loss of position in the group hierarchy. Significantly, overt hostility toward group-mates appeared only in neurotic animals which had been accustomed to dominance, but had then become neurotically inhibited from achieving direct oral, erotic, or other satisfactions. Under such circumstances, they turned upon more successful rivals with a displaced fury energetically wielded through tooth and claw. Regressive behavior was manifested by staid, relatively independent adult dogs or cats which, after being made neurotic, resumed many of their previously recorded puppyish or kittenish characteristics. Spider monkeys also tended to become more passively dependent and receptive of the experimenter's ministrations, but other species showed no such proclivities.

Factors That Accentuated Neurotic Symptomatology. Experimentally, these were precisely those that also exacerbated the basic conflict or prevented escape from it: i.e., increase of either hunger or fear, or forced transgression of the phobic, compulsive, or regressive defenses described above. Under such circumstances anxiety mounted to panic, inhibitions became paralyzing, and psychosomatic disturbances grew serious enough to threaten the life of the animal.

Procedures That Ameliorated Experimental Neuroses

It would be inaccurate, of course, to state that the choice of methods selected for investigation was not influenced by the experimenter's psychiatric and psychoanalytic training, since certain preferences, consciously or not, undoubtedly remained operant. Nevertheless, a large number of techniques of "therapy" were investigated as objectively as possible, of which the following with brief mention of their possible clinical parallels, were found most effective:

1. Satiation of One of the Conflictful Needs. If, for instance, a neurotic animal with marked inhibitions of spontaneous feeding and corresponding aversions to symbolic associations were tube-fed, its neurotic symptomatology was temporarily relieved, only to recur when the necessity and the fear of spontaneous feeding returned simultaneously.

To cite a single clinical comparison: forced intercourse may relieve repressed sexual desire temporarily, but does not usually dispel symbolically elaborated sexual conflicts and may, indeed, exacerbate them.

2. Prolonged Rest Away from the Neurotigenic Situation, in a sense, dulled the other horn of the dilemma by removing the animal from the original environs of fear, although it is significant that this form of relief was minimal in monkeys in whom, as in the case of man, neurotic reactions quickly became generalized. Moreover, animals which were returned to the laboratory even after a year of relatively peaceful sojourn elsewhere soon redeveloped their neurotic patterns, even though the original traumata were not repeated.

Clinically, "rest cures" and vacations away from disturbing situations may alleviate acute symptoms, but do not alter the underlying conflicts that originally led to the disruptive tensions. So also, soldiers with "combat neuroses" may feel relieved when removed from immediate danger, but unless the impasse between self-preservation vs. military duty is more basically resolved, a return to the front almost inevitably spells the reappearance of neurotic reactions.

3. Forced Solution. When hunger was maximal (from one to three days of starvation), food was made particularly attractive and openly available, and since no escape from the temptation was possible, some neurotic animals broke through their feeding or other inhibitions, began eating spontaneously, and showed gradual relief from the various symptoms originally engendered by the hunger-fear conflict. On the other hand, animals with less readaptive capacity ("ego-span" in analytic terminology), when placed in similar situations calculated to shatter the motivational impasse, reacted instead with an exacerbation of phobias, furors, and destructive aggressivity, or even retreat into a quasi-cataleptic stupor.

Thus also, actively directing patients paralyzed by indecision and anxiety into some course of action is occasionally necessary and effective, but may likewise present the danger of further bewilderment, panic, or psychotic reactions.

4. Re-exploration and Spontaneous Solution. Animals which had been trained merely to respond to a food signal given by the experimenter and which were then subjected to a counterpoised fear of feeding remained neurotic indefinitely since, without the help of the experimenter, they had no way of re-exploring the traumatic situation. Markedly different, however, was the case of animals that had been taught to manipulate various devices that actuated the signals and feeding, since in this way they could exert at least partial control over their environment. This stood them in crucial stead even after they were made neurotic inasmuch as, though for a time they feared almost every aspect of the apparatus, as their hunger increased they would gradually make hesitant but spontaneous attempts to re-explore the operation of the switches, signals, and food boxes and grew bolder and more successful as food began to reappear. If the fear-engendering experiences were prematurely repeated, their effects were even more traumatizing, but if each animal's efforts were again rewarded with food as in its preneurotic experiences it eventually became, to all appearances, as confident and effective in its behavior as ever.

This, perhaps, is a paradigm of how most conflicts are solved in most instances—i.e., by spontaneous re-exploration of the problem situation leading to the immensely reassuring discovery that something previously feared either does not recur, or may be mastered if it does. Pertinent also is the necessity all of us feel for acquiring a large variety of techniques to control our environment, not only for normal living but also as a means of trial re-entry after retreat or flight. Explicitly, we invoke this principle in preparing our children for a wide variety of contingencies; pragmatically, we employ "occupational therapy" or "job training" in our correctional institutions and hospitals to give our patients the skills, whether major or minor, which they can later utilize to meet social challenges in the world outside. Implicitly also, as we shall see, a comparable process is at work in psychoanalysis as the analysand, in a protective, permissive situation, re-explores his conflictful and deeply repressed interpersonal desires and fantasies both verbally and, through the *transference* (v.i.) relationship, finds himself not punished or rejected as he had unconsciously feared he might be and thus, gaining confidence and aplomb, retransfers his relationships and transactions to people and things in the real world about him.

5. "Transference" Therapy. This leads to the question: but what about animals that had been trained to respond only to external signals and had not been taught manipulative or social skills; or if so taught, were later rendered too inhibited to use them? In such cases, it was found possible to alleviate the neurotic behavior through the more direct influence of the experimenter, who could assume the role of a reorientative trainer or "therapist." Dynamically speaking, this influence itself was derived from the circumstance that the animal had been raised in a provident, kindly manner either in the laboratory by the experimenter himself, or elsewhere by someone who also liked animals. Indeed, if the latter were not the case, when the animal came to the laboratory the first requirement was to dispel its mistrust of human beings and cultivate its confidence; i.e., convert an initial "negative transference" into a "positive" one. Significantly, some experimenters[15] were not able to secure this favorable relationship in normal animals, and were correspondingly unsuccessful in helping neurotic ones. Whenever possible, all experimenters dissociated themselves (though such dissociation was rarely complete in the case of the highly perceptive monkeys) from the animal's traumatizing experience by having the latter administered either by remote control or by an automatic electrical governor on the apparatus.

15. Particularly one in my laboratory who had himself been raised in an Oriental country where cats and dogs were kept as guards or as scavengers, sometimes eaten, but almost never liked or respected.

If, then, the animal's expectancy with regard to the experimenter, based on its previous experience with him or his surrogates, was predominantly favorable ("positive transference") the latter could utilize this influence "therapeutically." Thus, even the most "neurotic" animal, huddled in cataleptic rigidity in a dark corner, might be led by gentle petting and coaxing to take food from the hand. Once this initial receptivity was established, the animal might be induced to eat from the floor of the apparatus if the experimenter remained near the cage; later, it sufficed that the experimenter was merely in the room. At any stage of this retraining the premature repetition even of a faint feeding signal would re-precipitate the conflict and disrupt the animal's recovery, perhaps irrevocably. However, if the experimenter exercised gentleness and patience and did not at any time exceed the gradually regained tolerances and capacities of the animal, he could eventually induce it in successive stages to open the food box, again begin to respond to signals and manipulate switches, and eventually to reassert its former skills and patterns of self-sustenance. The retraining could then be continued to include acceptance of previously traumatic stimuli, so that at the end of the process the animals would welcome even an airblast or electric shock (though not the toy snake) as itself a harbinger of food or other reward, and avidly work switches that actuated these previously feared stimuli. After such patterns were in their turn reestablished, the experimenter could complete the therapeutic process by gradually withdrawing from the situation as the animal reasserted its self-sufficiency, until finally his ministrations or presence were in no way necessary.

To claim sweeping identities between the mechanics of these experiments and the almost incomparably more complex dynamics of clinical psychotherapy would be committing the grievous scientific error of oversimplification. And yet certain clinical parallels need not be overlooked. The psychotherapist, too, is preconceived as a helpful parent surrogate, else his help would not be sought at all. Endowed by the patient with anticipatory confidence (though often this is explicitly denied), the skilled psychiatrist gently but effectively approaches the patient in his neurotic retreat, fills his needs personally insofar as practicable, permits him to re-explore, retest and re-evaluate experiential symbols and their disruptive conflicts first in the protected therapeutic situation, then gradually—and never faster than the patient's anxiety permits—in the outside world, and finally fosters and redirects his personal relationships onto persons and activities that can play a favorable and permanent role in the patient's future. This done, the therapist may relinquish his Virgilian role of guide and mentor as the patient takes his place once more in the world and no longer needs the psychiatrist personally except, perhaps, as another friend among a new-found many. Words, of course, are facile but deceptive instruments of communication, and abbreviations of statement should not contain abrogation of fact; nevertheless, perhaps it will be seen that, in a field more plagued by overobfuscation than by oversimplification, these comparisons and parallelisms are more than merely rhetorical.

6. "Social" Therapy. In some animals, the success of a sixth method dubbed, debatably but conveniently, "social" therapy or "therapy by example" indicated that one factor in the process of so-called "transference" therapy was the relatively impersonal one of making the solution of a motivational or adaptational impasse seem easier or at least possible. In this procedure, the neurotic animal was simply placed with a well-trained normal one and permitted to watch the latter work the switches, secure the signals, and feed unharmed. After from one to several days of such observation, about half the neurotic animals would begin to approach the food box, cower less at the signals, tentatively try the switches, and finally "emulate" the normal animal in resuming effective feeding patterns. Once the conflict was thus resolved its other neurotic expressions were also in large part—but never completely—mitigated, and the animal, aside from minor residuals such as slight furtiveness, restlessness, or tension appeared to be recovered.

Though the method was simple and certainly took the least effort on the part of the experimenter, it seems most difficult to formulate theoretically, especially since the convenient fiction of a postulated "inter-animal relationship" or "identification" might be dispelled if a properly furred, scented, and activated automaton would play the role of the normal animal in "answering" the signals, revealing the tempting presence of food by opening the box and otherwise changing the neurotic animal's external and internal milieu. Perhaps, as implied previously, this is the solipsistic nidus of all "interpersonal" relationships and "influences." But whatever the dynamics, we utilize such influences empirically in our clinical work. Again, to cite but one example, we place a neurotic child in a foster home or a special school in the hope that our young patient may be favorably influenced by the "example" of normal children being duly rewarded for patterns of behavior we wish our patient, too, to acquire.

7. Drug Therapy. Heretofore we have dealt exclusively with "psychologic" techniques of mitigating conflicts and ameliorating neurotic conduct, leaving as yet unexplored the use of drugs, electroshock, neurosurgery, and other methods. The question then arises: Can these, too, be brought within the purview of a comprehensive, integrative, and yet essentially dynamic approach to total behavior and to the rationale of treating its deviations? Biodynamically speaking, the supposed hiatus

between the "psychological" and "organic" approaches implied by the above question is seen to be illusory if one remembers that the behavior of an organism can be defined in no other way than its total organic functioning, and that this in turn depends first on its physiologic status as influenced by a multiplicity of structural and chemical factors (Principle I) and, second, on the changes in the configuration of these factors wrought by the "milieu" *as the organism perceives and reacts to its environment* (Principles II, III, and IV). A priori, then, since physiochemical factors are the very basis of all function, alterations in the former can and should be employed effectively in influencing behavior— a trite statement, were we not inclined to dismiss as trite anything tiresomely true enough to be disconcerting. The point at issue may be clarified by the following experimental demonstrations.

As has been mentioned, we had found that many drugs employed clinically as adjuncts to psychiatric therapy (e.g., ethyl alcohol, the bromides, many of the barbiturates, and some of the opiates) had one biodynamic action in common: they dulled perception, prevented the formation of elaborate associations, and partially disorganized complex behavior patterns already formed by previous (especially recent) experiences. For instance, a dog or cat under the influence of these drugs would not react as violently to traumatic stimuli and would consequently be protected to a demonstrable degree from developing a neurosis in an experimentally controlled (but to it, a "real life") conflict-engendering situation. Thus, an animal long trained to open a food box on a conditional signal would, when drugged, do so less efficiently— but neither would the same animal be as much disturbed by an air-blast or electric shock concurrently administered, nor would it show seriously disruptive manifestations of conflict thereafter.[16] Moreover, even severely neurotic animals, after being given these drugs, would apparently dissociate their recently acquired fears from their previously long-established feeding patterns, temporarily "forget" their inhibitions, phobias, defensive compulsions, and regressions and begin, however slowly or ineffectively, to work simple switch patterns to secure their food as they had done in their preneurotic state. This effect was particularly marked with alcohol; under the influence of this drug, a neurotic animal would change when even a little drunk from a huddled, tense, frightened creature into a seemingly carefree one, which, though ataxic and inefficient, would amble about the apparatus working switches, flashing signals, securing its food, and eating it with relish. An unexpected (though, it must be confessed, delightfully significant) development in such experiments was that more than half of the neurotic animals,

16. Conger has confirmed this in rats.

after being initially forced to take alcohol, experienced an apparently welcome amelioration of their neurosis and thereafter began to ingest food or drink containing alcohol to the point of self-intoxication. Moreover, this artificially induced avidity for the drug diminished markedly when the animals' neuroses were mitigated, partially by their own re-explorations while intoxicated, or more effectively by the other techniques of therapy outlined above. Throughout all such experiments, however, it was noted that *the effects of alcohol and all other manipulations and medications depended not only on their specific nature, intensity, and timing, but also on complex combinations of factors comprising the genetic, physical, and metabolic constitution of the animal, its unique experiences, its material and social transactions during and subsequent to the procedure in question, and configurations of many other relevant influences, including the beliefs and interpretations of the observer.*

The possible clinical significance of these pharmacobiodynamic observations cannot here be discussed in detail; it may be recalled, however, that mankind nearly always and everywhere has concocted and consumed various nepenthics (e.g., volatile ethers and alcohols and drugs allied to mesca), marihuana, and the opiates to guard or release him from real and fantasied threats of disappointment or injury. And we prescribe sedative (sitting) or hypnotic (sleeping) drugs in measured doses to our patients to dull their perceptions, blunt their fears, and give them temporary but welcome surcease from anxiety until we can reach and ameliorate their underlying conflict—a therapeutic procedure the pharmacologic aspects of which are at times inextricable from concurrent parental-ministrative, group-participant, or other magical connotations. Unfortunately, because of such added attractions and wider opportunities, human neurotics are much more likely than their animal cousins[17] to take such drugs to the point of addiction.

8. Electroshock. Animals subjected to cerebral electroshocks corresponding in frequency and intensity with those used in clinical therapy showed a disintegration of recently acquired inhibitions, phobias, compulsions, or other neurotic deviations and the re-emergence of earlier, simpler, more normally effective patterns. As in ancillary drug therapy, the animal's adaptations could then be further improved by environmentally guided solutions, "transference" training and other corrective

17. Nevertheless, Schultz, quoted by Katz (p. 22), observed that a certain species of ant "keeps beetles, whose secretions they like to the point of intoxication in which they may damage their nests and give their larvae to the beetles to eat, though at other times they will fight to the death for the same larvae." The highly protected strains of yeast kept in the vats of our breweries and distilleries lend their products to a more highly developed technology of production, sale, and consumption—but the effects on human behavior are not altogether different.

procedures. However, all electroshocked animals—even those subjected to the comparatively mild undirectional Leduc current—showed a permanently impaired capacity for complex learning even when no detectable histopathologic changes in the brain had been produced.

9. Neurosurgery. Obviously, any cerebral operation will (a) produce a transient general disorganization of response patterns which, like the effects of electroshock on recently acquired neurotic deviations, may be temporarily salutory and (b) result in a circumscribed hiatus in the organism's response capacities. Although neurosurgical studies in either animals and humans are difficult to interpret[18] our work has indicated that lesions in the ventromedial thalami or amygdalae—and less so in the cingulate gyri—may disintegrate experimentally induced neurotic patterns and overbalance the corresponding organic loss in adaptive skills by a sufficiently wise margin so that, from the standpoint of survival and apparent contentment, the animal is undoubtedly benefited. However, although there are many qualifications, one may outweigh the others in basic significance: again, *that the effects of apparently indentical lesions in different animals vary with the preceding experiences of each.* For example: lesions in the dorsomedial nucleus of the thalamus in normal cats impaired their acquired skills and relearning ability but rendered them relatively passive and friendly; in contrast, identical lesions in cats which had previously been made experimentally neurotic produced similar effects on learned behavior, but released unmistakable patterns of hostility and overt aggression. So also, kittens or young monkeys subjected to bilateral amygdaloid lesions were relieved of previously acquired neurotic patterns to a far lesser extent and remained much more disorganized and diffusely erotic and "unrealistic" in their behavior than was the case with adult animals.

---

18. Pechtel and I (1956) summarized the precautions and comprehensiveness of approach desirable in neurophysiologic experiments as follows: "Studies such as these must contend . . . with many . . . unknowns which can at best be only partially dealt with. Among these are (1) the unique genetic and experiential background of each animal; (2) its subtly but necessarily different handling . . . by different experimenters, no matter how purportedly constant the procedure; (3) the impossibility of absolutely objective observation, grading, or reporting of complex behavior patterns; and (4) the surgical impracticality, in view of variability in blood supply, projection pathways, and other anatomic features, of producing exactly delimited cerebral lesions. Finally, from the standpoint of comparative neurophysiology, the troublesome question remains as to whether homologous lesions in animals can inform us accurately about functions in the human central nervous system, in which such marked encephalization and other shifts of function have occurred. Nevertheless, these studies have once again helped to substantiate an important clinical maxim: that the permanent effects of a cerebral lesions depend perhaps less on its site or even extent than on the personality of the patient, his significant pretraumatic or preoperative experiences, and the physical and psychiatric care given him during the crucial period of rehabilitation."

Here, then, was further evidence that the effects even of discrete physical traumata can be understood or treated *only with reference to the "engrammed" functional effects left in the central nervous system by the previous experiences of the organism.*

Translated clinically, each person behaves differently from every other because (a) he was differently constituted at birth and (b) because he has had different experiences: ergo: (1) he will react uniquely to any given cerebral lesions and (2) he will need rehabilitative therapy specially tailored to fit his frame and modes of action, hide his defects, and best utilize his remaining capacities for optimal adaptation. Moreover, in human imagery, the experience of an operation or of induced convulsions or comas may have the added symbolic significance of disruptive psychologic cataclysms, of expiations of unconscious guilt, of mystical survival, and of final rebirth under the welcoming aegis of a kindly and seemingly omnipotent therapist.

This section, then, has presented a highly condensed account of various studies of experimental biodynamics conducted in our laboratory during the past two decades. Fortunately, many observations by others in widely different fields are in accord with our own findings. To cite only a few representative reports:

As long ago as 1931, Hillwold observed that hens frightened by a guinea pig at food-taking time became excited, avoided the "haunted" spot because of the "fear complex" and had to be fed elsewhere after five days to prevent death from starvation.

B. Rensch taught elephants to distinguish 100 different patterns of dots on cards that signified whether they would or would not be fed; when, however, a card pattern was equivocal and induced uncertainty and thereby conflict, the elephants attacked it and became generally dour and recalcitrant in their behavior. So also, ordinarily gentle Wendy, Yerkes' favorite chimpanzee, would turn her rage on Yerkes whenever the problems he or his colony set for her would become too difficult. She would then become sullen and refractory for long periods and preoccupied with symbolically substitutive acts. Commented Yerkes: "Sometimes it seemed as if the subject were trying to save face or deceive itself by ignoring something which is potentially dangerous, as, for example, the temptation to interfer with a companion by trying to take food out of turn."

J. Brady observed that if monkeys were required to press a lever every twenty seconds for six hours to prevent shock (i.e., became what Brady calls "executive monkeys"), they died in twenty-three days of massive duodenal hemorrhages; in contrast, control monkeys, who were actually shocked but who had no lever available and were therefore in no conflict about pressing it, showed no ill effects from their experience.

Jacobsen and Skaarup repeated our experiments in cats and reported that they could induce neuroses so predictably that they used numerous animals in the comparative titration of tranquilizing drugs. Seitz and Hoff, Shenker, and Schneider have also confirmed our results.

Bykov and his associates in Russia condition the movements and functions of inner organs to external physical and, more significantly, social stimuli. Scull reports an extension of this work as follows:

> One experiment involving the production of hypertension in primates is an amusing example of the ingeniousness of research done in Russia with use of an extension of Pavlovian technique. A male and a female ape are mated. Subsequently, the male is removed to an adjacent cage and a younger, more virile male is put in with the female. The first male is obliged to look on as his former mate enjoys the affections of the interloper. The "emotional" strain on the deprived male produces hypertension.[19]

Finally, Richter observed that wild Norway rats handicapped by having their whiskers clipped and then stressed by being made to swim in glass jars under circumstances that made the conflict seem "hopeless" died rapid "vagus deaths"; in contrast, Richter noted that "after elimination of the hopelessness, the rats do not die." Here then, is an instance in which stress of conflict can lead, in psychological terms—and with definitely secondary physiologic resonance—to the ultimate psychosomatic disruption: death itself.

Etho-Anthropologic Significance

The preceding and countless other observations form the background for the increasing frequency of statements like the following from eminent biologists:

> For that which befalleth the sons of men befalleth beasts . . . as one dieth so dieth the other; yes, they have all one breath, so that a man hath no preeminence above a beast.
>
> —*Ecclesiastes* II, 19

19. "A second experiment with primates involves mother and offspring. The mother is dressed in a blanket every time the child is placed with her for feeding. Soon the offspring associates 'mothering' with the blanket and not the mother and is thus literally weaned away from the mother and 'weaned to' the blanket." Curtis and Jean Pechtel in our laboratory have studied such fetishism in young rhesus in great detail: e.g., the permanent values attached to toys and other objects cherished in infancy and early childhood.

No absolute structural line of demarcation can be drawn between the animal world and ourselves; and I may add . . . that the attempt to draw a psychical distinction is equally futile, and that even the highest faculties of feeling and of intellect begin to germinate in lower forms of life.

—T. H. HUXLEY, *Man's Place in Nature*

Whatever may have been his views at the start of his career, a biologist comes to realize after years of close study that there is no fundamental difference between himself or the rest of mankind and the living world as a whole, plant or animal.

—M. BURTON, page 22

Comparisons between *Homo sapiens* and other animals are legitimate contributions to comparative psychology, and comparisons between two or more non-human species are equally admissible. Like any other responsible scientist, the Comparative Psychologist is concerned with the understanding of his own species and with its welfare; but his primary aim is the exposition of general laws of behavior regardless of their immediate applicability to the problems of human existence.

—F. A. BEACH, "The Snark Was a Boojum"

Most of us would by now be inclined to agree, and be no longer troubled by yet another shibboleth: that of "anthropomorphism." It can instead be asked: What attitude, "datum," perception, inference, conclusion—or, for that matter, wish or hope—is *not* anthropomorphic? Is there a more redundant word in any language or technical jargon—including, as Max Planck has pointed out, the formulas of physics? Or, if we contend that there must be an order *beyond* man, do we not also "inform" that order and influence it, as Heisenberg insists, by the very act of our observation? In the present connection, let us quote another slyly discerning metaphysician. Comments Bertrand Russell in his *Outline of Philosophy*:

All animals that have been carefully observed have behaved so as to confirm the philosophy in which the observer believed before his observation began. Nay, more, they have all displayed the national characteristics of the observer. Animals studied by Americans rush about frantically with an incredible display of hustle and pep, and at last achieve the deserved result by chance. Animals observed by Germans sit still and think and at last evolve the solution out of their inner consciousness.

Let us, then, speak freely among ourselves as human beings in human language about human perceptions and human thought. There are no other media available to us—and we need no other for human understanding and action.

Clinical Research in Psychoanalysis

With this biologic background, we may now review briefly various research studies within the field of clinical "psychoanalysis proper." Unfortunately, an early deterrant to anyone who may wish to conduct a survey of the literature will be a growing sense of bewilderment as to the wide variations in the definition of key terms, including what is meant by the basic term "psychoanalysis proper." As A. Stern puts it: *quot capita, tal sensus;* i.e., people calling themselves psychoanalysts seem to have little more operational agreement in their referential concepts or methods than, for instance, a thousand other men all of whom happen to have been named Paul. Or else, to use a parallel from Epictetus, psychoanalytic theory and practice seem to be "like a fair of buying and selling where everybody [prices and] seeks only what is useful to his business." That this is far from an idle analogy may be confirmed by the following paragraph from my *Practice of Dynamic Psychiatry*, 1955, page 422:

What is Psychoanalysis? In 1947, the American Psychoanalytic Association appointed a Committee on the Evaluation of Psychoanalytic Therapy. This group for a time tried earnestly to discharge its functions, but met "resistance" to its attempts to gather data on the actual results of analytic therapy. The committee therefore changed its field of investigation to a study of psychoanalytic treatment practices. Again it found that analysts "resented direct enquiries or even simple questionnaires"; therefore "workshops" were organized in which local groups met to evolve an acceptable definition of their specialty. Unfortunately, to quote the final official report by J. G. N. Cushing on this four-year project (*Bulletin of the Am. Psychoanalyst A.*, 1952, 8:44), this endeavor, too, "met with hostility. . . . Only occasional groups could cooperate . . . [because] (1) There is tremendous variance of opinion concerning the criterion for psychoanalysis, and (2) There is considerable difference between what the practitioner of psychoanalysis says he does, and what he really practices once he has been pinned down to direct answers." The committee, with commendable objectivity, concluded that: "1. It has been impossible to find any definition of psychoanalysis that is acceptable to even a large group of members of the American Psychoanalytic Association. 2. This study has shown that a very strong resistance exists among the members of the American Psychoanalytic Association to any investigation of the problem even on the basis of their own definition. . . 3. The insistence upon a uniform, rigidly circumscribed procedure in training of candidates may be indicative of a defense against the training analysts' own doubts and uncertainties." Further data as to the suspicion, rancor and innuendo which such research can evoke among training analysts may be found in a report by C. H. Katz of the Conference on Problems of Psychoanalytic Training, American Psychoanalytic Association, July 24, 1952.

Ernest Jones in his attempts to explain such breakdowns of communications and rapport had written only two years previously:

> The analyst makes himself as inaccessible as possible, and surrounds his personality with a cloud of mystery . . . [and] a lengthy, involved and circuitous form of fiction. Distressing . . . is the *attitude of disinclination toward the acceptance of new knowledge* . . . [since] anyone who already knows it naturally cannot be taught anything new.

In a further extension of such self-examinations, R. Waelder in his 1954 presidential address to the Philadelphia Psychoanalytic Association, pointed out that since "psychoanalysis is not yet really proved or widely accepted" its practitioners tend to seek mutual support and security in Psychoanalytic Associations—which, however, "like churches, may cease to serve their original purpose and become ends in themselves."

Previous Reviews

In 1953, the Hixon Lectures given with the sponsorship of the California Institute of Technology were published under the title *Psychoanalysis as Science*. This volume contained over 200 references from which Ernest Hilgard had assembled a section on "Experimental Approaches," L. Kubie one on "Problems and Techniques of . . . Validation," and E. Pumpian-Mindlin one on "Relation to the Biological and Social Sciences." Hilgard's correlations of comparative psychologic and clinical data are so rich and searching (parenthetically, he is quite kind to my own contributions) that they can hardly be summarized here, but some of his conclusions are worth quoting directly:

> If experiments supporting psychoanalytic interpretations are any good, they ought to *advance* our understanding, not merely *confirm* or *deny* the theories that someone has stated. . . . So many of the experiments give merely trivial illustrations of what psychoanalysts have demonstrated to their own satisfaction in clinical work. Such illustrations may be useful as propaganda, or in giving psychoanalysis a fair hearing, but they do not really do much for science unless there is some fertility in them [page 43]. Psychoanalysts seem to prefer defending an accepted theory to an impartial examination of evidence, and they move too quickly to a complete and final explanation of events. . . . Anyone who tries to give an honest appraisal of psychoanalysis as a science must be ready to admit that as it is stated it is mostly very bad science, that the bulk of the articles in its journals cannot be defended as research publications at all. Having said this, I am prepared to reassert that there is much to be learned from these writings. The task of making a science of the observations and relationships may, however, fall to others than the psychoanalysts themselves [page 44]. [But if] psychoanalysts are themselves to make a science of their knowledge, they must be prepared to follow some of the standard rules of science.

Unfortunately, much of the rest of *Psychoanalysis as Science* runs almost precisely counter to Hilgard's dicta, in that it does little more than mix psychoanalytic concepts of various vintages (some of which cannot really be combined without precipitating indigestible residues) and then pours them over otherwise unpalatable clinical facts in attempts to make the resulting word salad seem more appetizing at least to analysts. The sections on "Validation" and on "Inter-disciplinary Studies," despite the scholarship and manifest erudition of both Kubie and Pumpian-Mindlin, are worth reading only because they furnish a continuous reminder in reverse of Godel's mathematically demonstrable caution that even the most careful scientists are limited by the fact that no science can really "validate" itself through its own "data," concepts and quasi-logical elaborations of its indigenous jargon. It is refreshing that in a later (1957) publication, Pumpian-Mindlin himself recognized these strictures as particularly applicable to psychoanalytic rationale, and therefore took a more wholesomely relativistic view of the processes of therapy.

Other literature on psychoanalytic investigations since 1953 may be marshaled under the following headings: "Research for Meanings," "Research of Methods," and "Research of Results." Let us now briefly explore each of these categories.

Research for Meanings

Articles under this heading range in value from Brady's peculiar perversion of the usual connotations of "normal" ("[In training analysands] the need to be normal is not always recognized as a neurotic symptom") to Szasz' reformulations of psychoanalytic instinct theory as exemplified in the following quotation:

In an attempt to explain the nature of life processes, the principle of entropy (the second law of thermodynamics), valid for closed systems only, was extended to include organic systems. Since, however, life can occur only in open systems, the principle of entropy is not applicable under these conditions. . . . There is but one primary instinct, a life instinct . . . the results of frustrations of the life instinct (and its derivatives) bridge the gap between biological principles and psychoanalysis.

However, Stanley Cobb adds this caution.

There is no excuse, however, for loose thinkers to confuse the different theoretical and operational levels, and talk of such impossibilities as the effects of alcohol on the superego! The ego and superego are useful psychological concepts with which to explain interpersonal relations. But that is all they are. And concepts are not vulnerable to drugs!

In the same vein, Bieber traced the various phases in the emergence of the "libido theory" in psychoanalysis and pointed out that (a) libido could no longer be meaningfully equated simply with sexual desire in various forms, (b) that its supposed source in the sexual organs (v. Freud's postulate of "distended seminal vesicles . . . and paths to the cerebral cortex") was physiologically untenable, (c) that its postulated displacement onto "external ego objects" in the form of "oral, anal and genital cathexes" was an excursion into semantic absurdities, (d) that all human behavior (e.g., chorea, epilepsy) was not necessarily "purposive," and that (e) the postulate of a death instinct was a particularly futile attempt to hold together a crumbling theoretic system. Bieber concluded:

> Freud evolved an instinctual theory of human motivation and behavior in relation to his conviction that sexual development and organization and sexual disturbances were the fundamental factors in neuroses and in personality development. He conceived of instincts as "Unlust" tensions which operated the psychic apparatus. The somatic operations were conceived of as a continuous excitatory process taking place predominantly in the erotogenic organs. Freud's somatic operational concept had no basis in physiology or in biology, even though it referred to existing organs such as the mouth and genitals.
>
> He connected his fanciful construct about real organs to a completely fictitious psychic apparatus giving the entire structure an appearance of reality. The psychic apparatus operated along principles derived from the mechanical physics of fixed systems. These physical principles and their language were transferred to the discipline of psychology for which there was little relevancy of application. A complex somatico-physico-psychological structure was elaborated in the Libido Theory which confused and obscured Freud's brilliant clinical observations and separated psychoanalysis from the other sciences.

Ruesch reformulated another important psychoanalytic concept—that of *transference,* in a manner similar to that employed in previous sections of this review:

> The foremost obstacles . . . in psychiatry is the obsolete . . . assumption of discontinuities in functioning, a theoretical position which precludes operational approaches and measurements. The formulation of transference in terms of communicative exchange between two people verbal, or more basically, non-verbal avoids these shortcomings and attempts to explain transference as a general feature of human behavior.

Symbolism. Linn, in tracing the developmental analogic aspects of the body image as indicated in analytic symbolism, pointed out that the primal face region is still neurologically dominant in two-point discrimination, and that the hand (often thought of as the principle organ of "Ego reality-manipulation") is ontologically merely a tentacle-like extension of the facial sensoral and oral functions. Under the rubric of further symbolic elaboration of inner engrams may also be placed Charles Fischer's tachistoscopic studies of the incorporation of subliminal visual images into dreams and fantasies through which they are invested with unconscious meanings unique to the individual.

Dynamics and Personality Development. Other important leads to a reconsideration of psychoanalytic concepts of personality development have been implicit in many studies of the child and adolescent, only a typical few of which can here be cited. Piaget, for example, recorded demonstrations of how a child quickly generalizes experiences into value-systems: e.g., if a baby pulls a string that makes toys rattle, that baby may conclude that a "pull" makes everything happen for the best. Lapouse and Monk reported that even fairly severe deviations of bed-wetting, cleared spontaneously, if not introgenically by unwise "psychotherapy"—a finding which led Leo Kanner to observe:

The high annoyance threshold of many fond . . . parents keeps away from clinics . . . a multitude of early breath-holders, nail-biters, nose-pickers and casual masturbators who, largely because of this kind of parental attitude, develop into reasonably happy and well-adjusted adults.

As a thought-provoking addendum, O'Neal and Robins reported that:

Patients *referred to a child guidance clinic 30 years ago*[20] were found to have a high rate of psychiatric disease as adults as compared with a matched group of normal controls. They differed little from the normal controls in their rate of neurotic reactions but presented many cases of sociopathic personalities, psychotic reactions, and alcoholism. . . . While children with neurotic problems came from families of better socio-economic background than children with anti-social problems and delinquency, class background was not found to account for the greater proportion of psychiatrically well as adults among the subjects who had had neurotic problems in childhood. . . . While patients had a higher rate of broken homes than controls, broken homes were not found to be related to the continuance of psychiatric problems into adult life.

Various other studies have emphasized cultural considerations not always given due weight in classical psychoanalytic accounts of the "post-Oedipal" development of the child. As but one example Linden points out that the mushrooming phenomena of teen-age delinquency may be highly correlated to the permissive overglorification of "youth-

20. Italics mine.

ful freedoms" and the rejection of patriarchal veneration and control in our Western culture.

As another example of a re-examination of the data on which early psychoanalytic formulations were based, we may cite Macalpine and Hunter's careful rescrutiny of the famed Schreber case. These authors concluded that the "latent homosexuality" discerned in Schreber by Freud was merely an offshoot of his then current allegiance to Fliess' peculiar concepts of numerology and "universal bisexuality," and that, in any case, homosexuality has no really demonstrable relationship to Schreber's or anyone else's paranoia.

Research of Methods

Perhaps fortunately, this section may be made relatively brief, not because there is any dearth of material to review (if all reports of analytic "interpretation" and treatment were to be regarded as research studies, the number of relevant articles in the past half-decade would exceed 3000), but because these articles range among "parameters" (to use a current neologism) that place almost every conceivable technique within the boundaries of psychoanalysis. Under the aegis of this term, S. Margolin can recommend literally infantilizing the patient, L. Stone can advocate the median of occasionally making him sit up and take notice of current realities, J. Scher can invoke Jung and Rank by insisting that near-extremes of authoritarianism are often therapeutically beneficial, and some psychoanalysts (e.g., May, Fleisch, Kelman, *et al.*) can follow many of their European and Oriental colleagues in combining analytic therapy with heady doses of transcendental and even mystical experience. Within these and many other sectors of transaction, including sound and motion picture recordings, multiple judges, etc. (cf. Strupp; Bellak; Cohen; Alexander; Bateson, Birdwhistle, Brosin, *et al.*), can apparently demonstrate that almost any procedure can and does influence the behavior of the patient, though usually as to the how and why the deponent either sayeth not or else differs with nearly every other deponent testifying to comparable data.

As but one example of how sensitive the patients' reactions to even ostensibly innocuous transactions in "the analytic situation" can be, Greenspoon has recently shown that when subjects are instructed to "say all the words you can think of," the interposition of "Mm-hmm" by the experimenter following a particular class of responses, such as plural nouns, significantly increases the production of these responses over successive periods, without the subjects being aware of the contingency between their behavior and that of the experimenter. While "unconscious" learning without awareness is not new in the psychological literature, the effect of an innocuous phrase, as a very active reinforcer may be of particular interest to advocates of Rogerian "non-directive-ness" or of psychoanalytic "non-participation."

In view of such protean developments in the rationale, data, and practice of psychotherapy, it is hardly any wonder that many more analysts are following the example of Pumpian-Mindlin previously referred to in recognizing the dynamic continua that link all therapeutic procedures and therefore modifying monothetic conceptions of therapy in favor of holistic understandings of, and dealings with, the total indi-vidual in his environment.

Research of Results

This reorientation has recently been reinforced by the fact that whenever studies of the actual long-term effects of either "psycho-analytically oriented therapy" or "classical psychoanalysis" itself have been conducted with proper thoroughly and objectivity, the findings have been, to say the least, somewhat disconcerting. As an example, we may cite Levitt's series of unusually well-controlled follow-up compari-sons of untreated children with those treated by analytically oriented methods for various behavior problems. Levitt's findings were as follows:

Roughly the same percentages were found for the respective [treated and] control groups. A crude analysis indicates that time is a factor in improvement in the follow-up studies; the rate of improvement with time is negatively accelerating. . . . The results of the present study fail to support the view that [analytically oriented] psychotherapy with "neurotic" children is effective.

After extending these studies, Levitt concluded:

A recent survey of thirty-seven investigations of the efficacy of psycho-therapy with children, indicates that absence of difference between treated children and defector controls is widespread. It is significant that almost all of the 8,000 child patients involved in the survey were treated at clinics.

It may, of course, be properly contended that most of the clinical therapists involved in Levitt's study were relatively young and insuf-ficiently trained in proper psychoanalytic techniques. Let us, then, turn to the 1958 report of an official body y-clept "The Central Fact-Gathering Committee" (the adjectives may well modify *fact*) of the American Psychoanalytic Association itself. The preface of this report contains perhaps its most remarkable feature: namely, the recommenda-tions of the committee that "none of this material be published [since] controversial publicity on such material cannot be of benefit in any way." However, since there is a codicil to the effect "that all will agree [to] limit discussions of this material to those professionally qualified to recognize the serious limitations"—a qualification this audience certainly meets—and since there is and should be no secrecy or copyright on scientific research presumably in the public interest—we shall proceed to examine the essential contents of this intriguing document.

The introduction engages our attention with another interesting statement; to wit:

Starting modestly and testing a procedure that ensured professional secrecy [i.e., questionnaire forms mailed to analysts], it was hoped that increasingly valid, meaningful data might be accumulated. However, the long-recognized difficulties—diagnosis, nomenclature and measure of effectiveness—all have led to increasing resistance and a resultant falling-off in the number of completed questionnaires. Scarcely any reports are now being received.

With this commendable recognition of the inverse relationship between the data and their clinical significance, the report proceeds to analyze the replies to 10,000 "initial" questionnaires about patients under psychoanalysis, and 3000 "final" questionnaires as to the therapeutic results being obtained. We may summarize the committee's findings as follows:

A. *Statistics of current psychoanalytic treatment*
  1. Males under therapy, 48 per cent; females, 52 per cent.
  2. Whites, 99 per cent (compared with 11 per cent nonwhites in the United States).
  3. Median age range, 26–35.
  4. Sixty per cent were college graduates (vs. 6 per cent in the general population).
  5. Median annual income of analytic patients was $11,000–$15,000; in contrast, nearly all poorer patients were given "psychotherapy."
  6. One-sixth had had previous analyses, and five-sixths of these had changed analysts.
  7. Only about 54 per cent of patients were listed as being "in analysis"; the rest were designated as "in psychotherapy."
  8. Only 5 per cent of the patients were being treated in a hospital or clinic.
  9. Most analytic patients were seen four times a week; but a few (7 per cent) were interviewed only once or twice weekly, and 2 per cent six or more times.
  10–11. The "initial diagnoses" were "in agreement" with psychological tests in 75 per cent of the cases [but] the diagnostic listings are presented with full appreciation of and emphasis on the inadequacy, invalidity, uncertainty, and probably insignificance."

B. *Results of psychoanalytic treatment*

1. Only about half the cases were reported as having achieved a "complete analysis," with an average duration of 3–4 years; the rest presumably either broke off themselves or were discharged as "unanalyzable." It was thought likely—but not demonstrated—that about half of those who discontinued analysis were "improved."

2. Even with regard to patients recorded as being completely analyzed, a summation of 70 per cent of the returns on a final questionnaire indicated the following remaining concerns on the part of the analysts:

	Per cent
(a) Doubt of diagnosis	28
(b) Suspicion of underlying psychosis	25
(c) Previous analysis	18
(d) "Standard" (or classical) analysis	90

3. In projecting such experiences, 45 per cent of the analysts questioned on prognosis expect no cure in any of the following conditions: "neuroses, character disorders, schizophrenia, schizoid personality and homosexuality." Of those that expect "some cure . . ." the proportion which anticipated favorable results was:

	Per cent
(a) Anxiety, conversions, and phobic reactions	50
(b) Dissociation, obsessional and depressive reactions	33
(c) Schizophrenia	10
(d) Homosexuality	20

In view of the serious reservations as to the validity or significance of (a) the differential diagnostic categories used by analysts, (b) their criteria of improvement or cure, and (c) the possible bias on incompleteness of the results reported, this report of the Central Fact-finding Committee brings us back to the central fact that we must indeed reexamine the data, theories, and practices of our specialty in the revealing light of broader and more scientific orientations.

Beyond the Above: The Ur-Defenses of Man

And yet all these ethologic, experimental, psychoanalytic, and philosophic considerations will not move those among us who prefer to regard man in his self-appointed position as a demigod—possibly because this would relieve "classical" psychoanalysts in particular of any need to study or apply any discipline other than a somewhat peculiar form of demi-theology,[21] replete with mythologic figures of Narcissus, Eros, Oedipus, and Thanatos and Homeric accounts of their intrapsychic struggles. Curiously, even this position, too, is of some heuristic value, since it must be admitted that human behavior is indeed vastly (though not incomparably) more versatile and elaborately transactive than that of other animals, and that its complexities arise mainly out of three fundamental assumptions deeply implicit in the behavior only of human beings. These articles of faith, axioms of conduct, or, as I have called them, the Ur-defenses of man, can be marshaled into the following trilogy: first, a covert belief in various forms of personal invulnerability and immortality; second, a wishful trust in intraspecies loyalty and mutual service; third, confident claims of knowledge about and authority over transcendent forces, powers, and beings arrogantly conceived and equipped and commissioned to serve man's needs everywhere.

So sacrosanct are these Ur-defenses that merely listing them seems as sacriligious to some contemporary men[22] as pronouncing the secret name of Yahveh was to a biblical Israelite. Indeed, throughout the ages man has presumed himself to be an immortal, quasi-divine being differing from all the rest of creation[23] as expressed in cherished doctrines of his

21. Allen Wheelis, in an article entitled "The vocational hazards of psychoanalysis" points out that among the greatest of these is the defensive isolation of the analyst in his magical self-convictions: "A living science is more concerned with probing its unknowns that in praising its knowns, and he who cannot live with some fundamental uncertainties is not an investigator but a pilgrim."

22. In all the recent psychoanalytic literature only S. Novey seems to have arrived, a bit later chronologically but probably quite independently, at fairly similar formulations. These quotations from Novey are particularly apropos:

"I have [postulated] certain delusions which present, as it were, a necessary operation, based on what we describe as faith, which are essential if man is to function as a mature being . . . at the 'genital' level. It would seem that the heretofore sharp delineation between the . . . neurotic and psychotic has been too rigid and that we have been prone to overlook or describe as dysfunction certain synthetic operations within the mature person which I perceive as constructive delusions." (In *J. Psychoanal. A. 36*:88.)

"Man's capacity to delude himself . . . is essential to his very existence, however mature he may be. . . . Psychoanalysis cannot and must not do more than alter a malfunctioning personal myth [so] as to allow it this myth to operate. . . ." (*Ibid., 36*:90.)

23. First, life itself was held to be super-"natural" and therefore inaccessible to earthly inquiry: for example, long after Friedrich Wohler derived urea from ammonium acetate in 1828 many chemists refused to abandon Berzelius' dictum that no compound essential to "vital" processes could ever be synthesized—an attitude still reflected in our reluctance to accept Stanley's demonstration that a crystallizable protein like the tobacco virus is "really alive." So also any modern physician wishing to know, for instance, whether a patient was pregnant would test this by observing the specific effects of her hormones on the ovaries of a frog—thus admitting, with no loss of gallantry, that she and *Rana pipiens* are endocrine sisters under the skin. Nevertheless, both patient and physician might continue to contend that they are

special human creation, the indestructability of his "soul," and a geo-centric universe in which man is served by seducible and subversible deities. But what is more germane to our present concern is the subtler influence of these cherished articles of faith on the behavioral sciences. As Susanne Langer points out, all doctrines (e.g., Zen Buddhism, classical Freudian metapsychology, *daseinsanalyse,* or various other assertions as to the special nature of man) differ from all sciences in that the former are designed not to expand or correlate man's consensual knowledge of reality but to provide him with supposedly impervious systems of wish-fully assumed "facts" and pseudological derivations dogmatically en-sconced as exclusive and eternal truths. As psychiatrists, we admit the necessity of such forms of security and comfort; however, as scientists, we may also seek to clarify the intriguing issues involved. And yet, the essence of therapy may derive from a more subtle and profound insight: that, contrary to our former presumptions of analytic omniscience, we need not aim to abolish man's ever-precious delusions, for that would be both cruel and impossible. Instead—and only when necessary for his own and society's welfare—we must help him gently to find happier beliefs and more creative applications of them. Indeed, the wise psychia-trist and psychoanalyst eventually learns—along with the devoted teacher and the good minister—that the best therapist is he who helps troubled men rebuilt, largely on their own terms, their faiths in themselves, in their fellow men, and in their wishfully conceived "scientific," philosophic and theologic systems.

REFERENCES

Alee, W. C., *Cooperation among Animals,* Henry Schuman, New York, 1951.

Ashby, W. R., *Design for a Brain,* Wiley, New York, 1952.

Beach, F. A., "The Snark was a Boojum," *Am. Psychologist,* 1950, 5:115.

Bellak, L., "An experimental exploration of the psychoanalytic process," *Psychoanal. Quart.,* 1956, 25:385-414.

Bertalanffy, L. von, "An essay on the relativity of categories," *Phil. Sci.,* 1955, 22:243.

Bharucha-Reid, R. P., "Latent learning in earthworms," *Science,* 1956, 123:222.

Bieber, I., "A critique of the libido-theory," *Am. J. Psychoan.,* 1958, 18:52.

Bonner, J. T., *Cells and Societies,* Princeton Univ. Press, Princeton, 1955.

Brady, J. V., "Ulcers in 'executive' monkeys," *Scient. Amer.,* 1958, 199:95.

Brady, Morris, quoted by Calder, K. T., *J. Am. Psychoanal. A.,* 1958, 6:552.

Brandt, Leonore, "Operation Diana," *Child-Family Digest,* 1956, 15:19.

Brunswick, E., *Perception and the Representative Design of Psychological Experi-ments,* Univ. of California Press, Berkeley, 1956.

---

so uniquely possessed of "communication," "creativity," "values," "altruism," etc., that any evolutionary approach to "higher" human conduct is heuristically repre-hensible.

Burton, M., *Animal Courtship*, F. A. Praeger, New York, 1954.

Butler, R. A., "Curiosity in monkeys," *Sci. Amer.*, 1954, 190:70.

Cannon, W. B., *The Way of an Investigator*, Norton, New York, 1945.

Cobb, S., "Instincts," *Am. J. Psychiat.*, 1955, 112:149.

Delgado, M. R., Rosvold, H. E., and Looney, E., "Evoking conditioned fear by electrical stimulation of subcortical structures in the monkey brain," *J. Comp. & Physiol. Psychol.*, 1956, 49:373.

Dobie, J. R., "The roadrunner in fact and folklore," *Arizona Highways*, 1948, 34 (May).

Ducasse, C. J., *A Philosophical Scrutiny of Religion*, Ronald Press, New York, 1952.

Einstein, A., and Infeld, L., *The Evolution of Physics*, Simon & Schuster, New York, 1938.

Feigl, H., "Existential hypotheses," *Phil. Sci.*, 1950, 17:35.

Fischer, C., "Studies of induced dream symbols," *Proc. Am. Psychoanal. Soc.*, May, 1957.

Frings, H., and Jumber, J., "Preliminary studies on the use of a specific sound to repel starlings," *Science*, 1954, 119:318.

Fromm-Reichmann, Frieda, and Moreno, J. (eds.), *Progress in Psychotherapy*, Grune and Stratton, New York, 1956.

Gantt, W. H., *The Origin and Development of Behavior Disorders in Dogs*, Psychosomatic Monogr., New York, 1942.

Green, H., "Perverted appetites," *Physiol. Rev.*, 1925, 5:1.

Greenspoon, J., *Am. J. Psychol.*, 1955, 68:409.

Heinroth, Oscar, *Beiträge zur Biologie*, Int. Ornith. Kongs., 5, 1910.

Hellwold, H. "Untersuchungen über Triebstarken bei Tieren," *Ztach. Psychol.*, 1931, 123:38.

Hess, Eckhard, "Imprinting in animals," *Sci. Amer.*, 1958, 198:81.

Hoebel, E. A., *The Law of Primitive Man*, Harvard University Press, Cambridge, 1954.

Huxley, T. H., *Man's Place in Nature*. Thomas, Ltd., London, 1898.

Isakower, O., "A contribution to the pathopsychology of phenomena associated with falling asleep," *Int. J. Psc.*, 1938, 19:38.

Jacobsen, E., and Skaarup, Y., "Experimental induction of conflict-behavior in cats: its use in pharmacological investigations," *Acta pharmacol. et toxicol.*, 1955, 11:117.

Jennings, H. S., *The Biologic Basis of Human Nature*, Norton, New York, 1930.

Jones, E., *The God Complex. Essays in Applied Psychoanalysis*, Hogarth Press, London, 1951, 2:244.

Katz, D., *Animals and Man*, Longmans Green and Co., New York, 1937.

King, J. A., "Parameters relevant to determining the effect of early experiences upon the adult behavior of animals," *Psychol. Bull.*, 1958, 5:46.

Lapouse, R., and Monk, M., *Medical News* (August), 1958.

Levik, G. M., *Antarctic Penguins*, Trench Trubner, London, 1914.

Levitt, E. E., "The results of psychotherapy with children," *J. Consult Psychol.*, 1957, 21:109.

———, Beiser, Helen, and Robertson, R. E., "A follow-up evaluation of cases treated at a community child guidance clinic," personal comm., 1958.

Levy, D., "The relation of animal psychology to psychiatry," in *Medicine and Science*, I. Galdston, ed., Internation. Univ. Press, New York, 1954.

Liddell, H. S., "Discussion of Konrad Lorenz," *Proc. Center Post-Grad. Training*, New York, October 23, 1958.

Lindauer, M., "House hunt," *Sci. Amer.*, 1958, 196:70.

Linden, M. E., "Relationship between social attitudes toward aging and the delinquencies of youth," *Am. J. Psychiat.*, 1957, 114:444-448.

Linn, L., "Some developmental aspects of the body image," *Int. J. Psychoanal.*, 1955, 36:36.

Loveridge, A., "Notes on East African Mammals," *J. E. Afr. N.H. Soc.*, 16, 1938 and 17, 1939.

Macalpine, Ida, and Hunter, R. A., Tr. *of Memoirs of My Nervous Illness*, by Donald Paul Schreiber, Robert Bentley, Cambridge, 1955.

Margolin, S. G., "On some principles of therapy," *Am. J. Psychiat.*, 1958, 114:1087.

Marshall, A. J., "Bower birds," *Sci. Amer.*, 1956, 194:48.

Masserman, J. H., "Psychobiologic dynamisms in behavior," *Psychiatry*, 1942, 5:341.

———, *Behavior and Neurosis*, Univ. of Chicago Press, Chicago, 1943.

———, "Civilian morale and the professional worker," *J. Am. Diet. A.*, 1943, 19:91.

———, "The psychodynamisms of propaganda and morale," *Dis. Nerv. System*, 1943, 5:101.

———, "Wartime industrial psychiatry," *Ment. Health Bull.*, 1943, 21:1.

———, "Experimental neuroses and psychotherapy," *Arch. Neurol. & Psychiat.*, 1943, 49:53.

———, "The contribution of psychoanalysis to the civilian defense program," *Psychoanalyt. Rev.*, 1944, 31:34.

———, "Dynamic psychology and wartime communication and morale," *Dis. Nerv. System*, 1944, 5:101.

———, "Language, behavior and dynamic psychiatry," *Internat. J. Psychoanal.*, 1944, 25:1.

———, "Neurosis and alcohol," *Am. J. Psychiat.*, 1944, 101:389.

———, "Principles of biodynamics," *Tr. New York Acad. Sci.*, 1944, 61-71.

———, "Report of the Committee on animal experimentation 1943-44," *Psychosom. Med.*, 1945, 7:46.

———, "Psychiatry, mental hygiene and daily living," *Ment. Hyg.*, 1945, 29:650.

———, *Principles of Dynamic Psychiatry*, Saunders, Philadelphia, 1946.

———, "Una contribucion experimental al problema de la neurosis," *Rev. argent. de neurol. y psiquiat.*, 1946, 11:3.

———, "Problems of the neuroses: an experimental approach," *Cincinnati J. Med.*, 1946, 27:73.

———, "A note on the dynamics of suicide," *Dis. Nerv. System*, 1947, 8:324.

———, "Tension in modern living," *N.U. Rev. Stand*, 1947, 9:6.

———, "Mental hygiene in a world crisis," *Dis. Nerv. System*, 1948, 9:210.

———, "How to relax," *N.U. Rev. Stand*, 1948, 10:22.

———, "Psychological medicine and world affairs," in Harris, G. (ed.), *Modern Trends in Psychological Medicine*, Hoeber, New York, 1948.

———, "A biodynamic psychoanalytic approach to the problems of feeling and emotion," in Reymert, M. L. (ed.), *Feelings and Emotions*, International Symposium, 2nd, Mooseheart, Ill., 1948; 1st ed. McGraw-Hill, New York, 1950.

———, "Mental hygiene; half-century mark, part 2," *Today's Health*, 1950, 28:40.

———, "New experimental approaches to psychiatric problems," *Sci. Amer.*, March, 1950.

———, "Experimental neuroses," *Sci. Amer.*, 1950, 182:38-43.

———, Arieff, A. J., Klehr, H., and Pechtel, C., "Effects of direct interrupted shock on experimental neuroses," *J. Nerv. & Ment. Dis.*, 1950, 112:384-392.

———, "Some current concepts of sexual behavior," *Psychiatry*, 1951, 14:67-72.

———, "Experimental approaches to psychoanalytic concepts," *Samiksa*, 1952, 6:4.

———, "Music as a tool of delightful delusion," *Music Therapy*, pp. 3-14, 1953.

Masserman, J. H., "Psycho-analysis and biodynamics—an integration," *Internat. J. Psychoanal.*, 1953, 34:3-29.

————, "Music and the child in society," *Music Therapy*, pp. 183-187, 1952; also in *Am. J. Psychother.*, 1954, 8:63-67.

————, "An integration of group therapeutic techniques," *Dept. of Med. & Surg. Inf. Bull. Psychiat. & Neurol. Serv.*, VA (February), 1954.

————, "The conceptual dynamics of person, religion and self," *Psychoanalyt. Rev.*, 1954, 41:303.

————, "Proceedings," *Music Therapy*, pp. 5-7, 1954.

————, "Moreno's 'Transference, counter-transference and tele.,'" *Group Psychother.*, 1954, 7:309.

————, "Moreno's interpersonal therapy," *Group Psychother.*, 1955, 8:62.

————, "Emotional reactions to death and suicide," in Liebman, S. (ed.), *Stress Situations*, Lippincott, Philadelphia, 1955.

————, "Sociologic and psychologic correlates of music therapy," *Music Therapy*, 1955.

————, "Fundamentals of psychotherapy, with special reference to respiratory diseases," in Sparer, P. (ed.), *Personality, Stress and Tuberculosis*, Int. Univ. Press, New York, 1956.

————, "Psychiatry in Latin America, part I," *Northwestern Univ. Quart. Bull.*, 1956, 30:270.

————, "Biodynamic therapy in the aging," *Imprensa Medica*, 1957, 21:275.

————, "Experimental psychopharmacology and behavioral relativity," *Res. Assoc. Nerv. & Ment. Dis.*, 1957.

————, Levitt, M., McAvoy, T., Kling, A., and Pechtel, C. T., "The cingulates and behavior," *J. Nerv. & Ment. Dis.*, 1958, 126:148.

————, and Balken, E. R., "The clinical application of phantasy studies," *J. Psychol.*, 1938, 8:81.

————, and Balken, E. R., "The psychoanalytic and psychiatric significance of phantasy," *Psychoanalyt. Rev.*, 1939, 26:343. *Ibid.*, 1939, 26:535.

————, and Balken, E. R., "The language of phantasy," *J. Psychol.*, 1940, 10:75.

————, and Carmichael, H. T., "Diagnosis and prognosis in psychiatry," *J. Ment. Sci.*, 1938, 84:893.

————, Hecker, A. O., Pessin, J., and Booth, B. E., "Philosophy and methodology in the training of 500 psychiatric residents," *Am. J. Psychiat.*, 1949, 106:362.

————, and Jacques, M. G., "Effects of cerebral electroshock on experimental neuroses in cats," *Am. J. Psychiat.*, 1947, 104:92.

————, and Jacques, M. G., "Experimental masochism," *Arch. Neurol. & Psychiat.*, 1948, 60:402.

————, and Jacques, M. G., "Do lie detectors lie?" *The Nation*, 1952, 174:368-9.

————, and Pechtel, C. T., "Neuroses in monkeys: a preliminary report of experimental observations," *Ann. New York Acad. Sci.*, 1953, 56:253-265.

————, and Pechtel, C. T., "Conflict engendered neurotic and psychotic behavior in monkeys," *J. Nerv. & Ment. Dis.*, 1953, 118:408-409.

————, and Pechtel, C. T., "The osmatic responses of normal and neurotic monkeys," *Ann. New York Acad. Sci.*, 1954, 58:256-260.

————, and Pechtel, C. T., "Differential effects of cerebral lesions on susceptibility of animals to induction and relief of experimental neuroses," *Army Medical Service Research Progress Report*, 1st quarter, p. 433, 1954.

————, and Pechtel, C. T., "How brain lesions affect normal and neurotic behavior," *Am. J. Psychiat.*, 1956, 112:865-872.

————, and Pechtel, C. T., "Normal and neurotic olfactory behavior in monkeys," *Tr. Soc. Biol. Soc.,* 1956, 11:30.

————, and Pechtel, C. T., "Neurophysiologic and pharmacologic influences on experimental neuroses," *Am. J. Psychiat.,* 1956, 113:510.

————, and Pechtel, C. T., "An experimental investigation of factors influencing drug action," *Psychiatric Research Reports* 4, Am. Psychiat. A., 1956.

————, and Pechtel, C. T., Symposium: "The role of drug therapies in current and future psychiatric practice," *Psychiatric Research Reports* 4, Am. Psychiat. A., 1956.

————, Pechtel, C. T., and Cain, J., "Creation de nevroses experimentales chez le chat par un traumatisme psychologique," *Soc. de Biol.,* 1954, 118:2041.

————, Pechtel, C. T., and Gross, Z., "Abnormalities of behavior," *Ann. Rev. Psychol.,* 1954, 5:263-280.

————, Pechtel, C., and Schreiner, L., "The role of olfaction in normal and neurotic behavior in animals: A preliminary report," *Psychosom. Med.,* 1953, 15:396-404.

————, and Rubinfine, D. L., "Counting behavior in cats," *J. General Psychol.,* 1944, 30:87.

————, Schreiner, L., Rioch, D. McK., and Pechtel, C., "Behavioral changes following thalamic injury in cats," *J. Neurophysiol.,* 1953, 16:234-246.

————, and Siever, P. W., "Dominance, neurosis and aggression," *Psychosom. Med.,* 1944, 6:7.

————, Schreiner, L., Pechtel, C., and Levitt, M., "Differential effects of lesions of the mediodorsal nuclei of the thalamus on normal and neurotic behavior in the cats," *Nerv. & Ment. Dis.,* 1955, 121:26.

Miller, N. E., "Experiments in motivation," *Science,* 1957, 126:1276.

Mirsky, I. A., and Katz, M. S., "Avoidance 'conditioning' in paramecia," *Science,* 1958, 127:1498.

————, Miller, R. E., and Murphy, J. V., "The communication of affect in rhesus monkeys," *J. Am. Psychoanal. Ass.,* 1958, 6:433.

Mittelman, B., "Psychodynamics of mobility," *Int. J. Psychoanal.,* 1958, 39:1.

Montagu, M. F., "Man—and human nature," *Am. J. Psychiat.,* 1955, 112:401.

Morris, D., "The courtship dance of the swordtail," *Aquarest.,* March, 1955.

Morris, D., "The feather posture of birds and the problem of the origin of social signals," *Behavior,* 1956, 9:6.

Nakao, H., "Emotional behavior produced by hypothalamic stimulation," *Am. J. Physiol.,* 1958, 194:411.

Novey, S., "The concept of the genital character," *Int. J. Psychoanal.,* 1955, 36:90.

————, "Some philosophical speculations about the concept of the genital character," *Int. J. Psychoanal.,* 1955, 36:88.

Olds, J., "Self-stimulation of the brain," *Science,* 1958, 127:315.

O'Neal, Patricia, and Robins, L. N., "The relation of childhood behavior to adult psychiatric status," *Am. J. Psychiat.,* 1958, 114:961.

Oppenheimer, R., "Analogy in science," *Amer. Psychol.,* 1956, 11:127.

Pavlov, I. P., *Lectures on Conditioned Reflexes,* International Publishers, New York, 1928, p. 242.

Piaget, J., "The child in modern physics," *Sci. Amer.,* 1957, 196:46.

Pumpian-Mindlin, E., "Changing concepts of therapy in a Veterans Administration mental hygiene clinic," *Am. J. Psychiat.,* 1957, 113:1095-1099.

———— (ed.), *Psychoanalysis as Science,* Stanford University Press, Stanford, Calif., 1953.

Razran, G., Pavlov, I. P., and Lemarck, *Science,* 1958, 128:758.

Rensch, B., "The intelligence of elephants," *Sci. Amer.*, 1957, 196:44.

Richter, Curt P., "On the phenomenon of sudden death in animals and man," *Psychosom. Med.*, 1957, 19:191-198.

Riese, W., "An outline of history of ideas in psychotherapy," *Bull. Hist. Med.*, 1951, 25:442-456.

Rioch, D. McK., "Certain aspects of 'conscious' phenomena and their neural correlates," *Am. J. Psychiat.*, 1955, 111:810.

Rosvold, H. E., "The effects of electroconvulsive shocks on gestation and maternal behavior," I. *J. Compar. Physiol. Psychol.*, 1949, 42:118; II., 1949, 42:207.

Ruesch, J., "Transference reformulated," *Acta. Psychother.* (Schweiz) Supp., 1955, 3:596.

———, "Communication difficulties among psychiatrists," *Am. J. Psychother.*, 1956, 10:432.

Russell, B., *An Outline of Philosophy*, Allen and Unwin, London, 1927.

Sauer, E. G. F., "Celestial navigation in birds," *Sci. Amer.*, 1958, 199:42.

Scher, J. M., "The structured ward," *Am. J. Orthopsych.*, 1958, 28:291.

Scott, J. P., *The Process of Socialization in Higher Animals*, Milbank Fund Publ., New York, 1953, p. 82.

Scull, C., Nance, M., and Rolls, G. F., "Research in the Soviet Union," *JAMA*, 1958, 167:2120.

Seitz, P. F. D., "The effects of infantile experiences upon adult behavior in animal subjects: I. Effects of litter size during infancy upon adult behavior in the rat," *Am. J. Psychiat.*, 1954, 110:916.

Sibol, J., "The strangest birds in the world," *Life*, March 25, 1957, p. 88.

Stern, A., "Science and the philosopher," *Am. Sci.*, 1956, 44:281.

Stone, L., "Brief psychotherapy," *Psychoanal. Quart.*, 1951, 20:215.

Strupp, H. H., "The psychotherapist's contribution to the treatment process," *Behavioral Science*, 1958, 3:34-67.

Szasz, T. S., "On the psychoanalytic theory of instincts," *Psychoanal. Quart.*, 1952, 21:25.

Szymanski, J. S., "Modification of the innate behavior of cockroaches," *J. An. Behav.*, 1912, 2:81.

Thompson, W. R., "Influence of prenatal maternal anxiety on emotionality in young rats," *Science*, 1957, 125:698.

———, and Heron, W., *Canad. J. Psychol.*, 1954, 8:17.

———, and Melzock, R., " 'Whirling' behavior in dogs as related to early experience," *Science*, 1956, 123:939.

Tolman, E. C., *Purposive Behavior in Animals and Men*, Century, New York, 1932.

Vexhall, J. von, *Umwelt and Innenwelt der Tiere*, Springer, Berlin, 1920.

Wailder, R., "The function and the pitfalls of psychoanalytic societies," *Bull. Philadelphia Assoc. Psychoanal.*, 1955, 5:1.

Whorf, B. L., *Language, Thought and Reality*, M.I.T. Press, Cambridge, 1956.

Wiener, N., "Some maxims for biologists and psychologists," *Dialectica*, 1950, 4:3.

Weinstock, H. I., "Summary and final report of the central fact-gathering committee," Amer. Psychoanal. Assoc., January 5, 1958.

Wheelis, Allen, "The vocational hazards of psycho-analysis," *Internat. J. Psycho-Analysis*, 1956, 37:171-184.

Yerkes, R. M., *Chimpanzees, a Laboratory Colony*, Yale Univ. Press, New Haven, 1943.

Zuckerman, S., *The Social Life of Monkeys and Apes*, Kegan, Paul, Trench, Trubner and Co., London, 1932.

J O H N   D.   R A I N E R

The Concept of Mind

in the Framework of Genetics

Scientific psychology is part of physics, or the study of nature; it is the record of how animals act. Literary psychology is the art of imagining how they feel and think.—GEORGE SANTAYANA

A definition of mind, like a definition of life, is as elusive as a butterfly in a meadow. No one scientific discipline can wield the net with sufficient dexterity. The eclectic nature of the present panel in itself points up this tantalizing state of affairs. Nevertheless, those of us who work at "the proper study of man" do well to take time out and satisfy our need to reflect on some of the broader concepts implicit in our own particular endeavors.

When it comes to an examination of mind, we find ourselves up against a special problem, over and above the paucity of tools. The very act of introspection is often a suspect procedure. Yet it is the source of more data than some may care to admit. Since it is plain that one's predispositions and biography affect one's choice of method and scene of investigation, an intimate personal portrait may come of expressing oneself on these larger concerns. By the same token, a brief autobiographical glimpse, which is usually gratuitous in a scientific work, may be useful here as a preamble to such an enterprise as this one.

To begin with, I turned from early studies in the pure manipulative thought of mathematics to the field of philosophy and presently managed to convince myself, at least in the metaphysical sense, of such fundamentals as the existence of me and the world, the orderliness of matter and hence of experience, and the emergence of ethical and aesthetic values. My growing interest in natural science, focused on a concern with the human organism, led me to the study of medicine.

As it became clear that the whole phenomenon of man could neither be delineated at the anatomy table nor by physiological demonstrations, I chose to specialize in psychiatry in order to have an opportunity to learn about human feelings and behavior through clinical investigation. In pursuing this course, I took an interest in genetics because it seemed an expanding and potentially unifying science. By combining physiological and psychological procedures in modern psychiatry, this particular discipline makes it possible to view man comprehensively in a temporal framework.

A psychiatrist, of course, deals with something called *mind* while practicing at one and the same time the science and the art alluded to in the quotation at the head of this essay (Santayana, 1923, p. 252). It is true that psychiatric thought and research have long been hampered by the tendency to separate two aspects of the human being—the physiodynamic from the psychodynamic, the body from the mind.

In philosophy this kind of division goes back to Descartes and even Plato. Save for the early Greek naturalists or such isolated thinkers as Spinoza and Santayana, and those working close to the practical sciences, it has permeated thought up to the very present.

In the history of psychiatry this dichotomizing trend has stemmed to a large extent from the uneven rate at which different techniques and unifying principles came to the fore. At one time or another and in different places, certain approaches were more highly developed and offered more sophisticated theories and methods than others. In modern times, for example, neuropathology, bacteriology, and psychology have each in turn predominated in capturing the attention of leaders in psychiatry.

There were efforts to synthesize the various schools, such as the psychobiology of Adolf Meyer. From the investigative point of view, however, these attempts were premature since the state of knowledge in the various disciplines was not sufficiently advanced. It was only very recently that refinements were made not only in the physiological sciences but also in the technique of observing and interpreting reported introspective data. Thus, it became possible to examine the concept of mind within the framework of biological psychiatry.

As a working definition, mind may be considered a highly developed neurological apparatus with which an animal interprets his inner and outer environmental stimuli. Attaining consciousness, mind initiates and carries through action or the delayed type of action called thought.

Thought may either be readily open to awareness, or for some reason be confined to the "non-reporting" level (Rado, 1949) where its content and motivational significance may only be inferred from evidence gathered by special investigative (psychoanalytic) techniques. In any event, mind, whether at the reporting or extrapolated level, is the functioning of a complex and highly integrated organization of biological material.

As such, mind falls within the province of genetics. Indeed, so potent is the guiding influence of the organized molecules which make up chromosomal material in the development of both the individual and the human race that we find the discipline of genetics fast becoming the cornerstone of the biological sciences, or better still the cement that holds them together and gives them structure.

When it comes to the individual, a comprehensive view of the organism in a temporal framework must begin with the fertilized ovum and the potentialities it contains, including the primordia of what we later call mind. Subsequent growth and development are determined by the interaction of changing nuclear, cytoplasmic, enzymatic, and anatomic forces as they become manifested in neural, hormonal, and total behavioral responses.

Just as the organism gains in complexity as it develops from its zygotic beginning, so methods of studying it become highly specialized of necessity and may sometimes seem far apart. Viewed phylogenetically, man is a product of biological evolution representing a complex form of matter which is able to adapt and create. Ontogenetically, he is a developing anatomical, structural, chemical organism. From the standpoints of ecology, demography, and sociology, he is a member of a human society in a complex natural and social world. Naturalistically, he is a biographical entity observed by his contemporaries and successors. Poetically, he may be thought of as a stream of subjective experience, conscious or unconscious. No one of these approaches can claim a monopoly on concern with the human mind. Seen in different perspectives by the various disciplines concerned with man, mind is only in part defined by each of them.

From any point of view mind is never a static phenomenon. It is a living function which comes about as we know it at a certain level of organization of the phylogenetic tree as well as of the developing individual. Because genetics is the science of ordered and directed biological change in time, it affords useful insights about mind.

Modern genetics has come a long way from its Mendelian phase during which, like Newtonian physics, it made accurate observations and coined explanatory descriptive labels for hypothetical entities. Today the emphasis is on cytological and biochemical analysis of the intracellular constituents whose powerful and regulated activity affects all human functioning, healthy and diseased.

Not the least important corollary to this new focus is that it places the study of mind squarely in the central unifying concept of biology—that of evolution. Mind has arisen via evolution as part of the adaptation of animal and man to his environment. This environment includes not only the inorganic, nonsentient physical universe but also, and with increasing importance, the organic world, the animal world, the human social world.

The developing type of mind of the species as well as the individual mind may both be visualized as the product of the interaction between chromosomally determined equipment and the world at various levels of organization. In the process of evolution the development of effective mental functions (adaptive and creative) has required on the one hand an ordered world yielding a set of ordered experiences,[1] and on the other a balanced set of neurological response and control mechanisms. Similarly, in each individual, soundness of mind depends not only upon a favorable set of life influences but also, as emphasized here, upon a balanced genetic endowment.

Organic evolution begins with the origin of life. At least once in the history of the earth and undoubtedly many times in the history of the universe, self-catalyzing reactions in a primordial chemical soup with appropriate energy sources have led to self-duplicating chemical systems of a graduated order of complexity. Helping to form each other's environment, these primitive molecules selectively filled the niches on the earth's changing crust. Marginally suited organisms were subsequently replaced, while sense organs, nervous system, complex adaptive behavior, and goal-directed activity made their successive appearances, but just as gradually over evolutionary periods of time as in the ontogenetic development of each infant.

In this frame of reference a number of knotty problems have arisen regarding the emergence of mind, thought, or consciousness. William James (1890, p. 146) points out,

In a general theory of evolution the inorganic comes first, then the lowest forms of animal and vegetable life, then forms of life that possess mentality, and finally those like ourselves that possess it in a high degree. As

1. "Intelligence amid chaos would have had no survival value" (Sherrington, 1951).

long as we keep to the consideration of purely outward facts, even the most complicated facts of biology, our task as evolutionist is comparatively easy. We are dealing all the time with matter and its aggregations and separations; and although our treatment must perforce be hypothetical, this does not prevent it from being *continuous*.

The point which as evolutionists we are bound to hold fast to is that all the new forms of being that make their appearance are really nothing more than results of the redistribution of the original and unchanging materials. The self-same atoms which, chaotically dispersed, made the nebula, now, jammed and temporarily caught in peculiar positions, form our brains; and the "evolution" of the brains, if understood, would be simply the account of how the atoms came to be so caught and jammed. In this story no new *natures*, no factors not present at the beginning are introduced at any later stage.

Considering consciousness as an *inward* fact, James posits a mind-stuff present in even the simplest matter.

In a similar vein Sherrington (1951, p. 251) writes,

Mind as attaching to any unicellular life would seem to me to be unrecognizable to observation; but I would not feel that permits me to affirm it is not there. Indeed, I would think that since mind appears in the developing soma that amounts to showing that it is potential in the ovum (and sperm) from which the soma sprang. The appearance of recognizable mind in the soma would then be not a creation *de novo* but a development of mind from unrecognizable into recognizable. While accepting duality we remember that Nature in instance after instance dealing with this duality treats it as a unity.

Again, in the synoptic view of Teilhard de Chardin (1959), mind and thought are seen as the preordained goals of evolution, and implicit from the start.

Needing to reckon with the existence of thought, particularly conscious thought available by introspection, scientists have apparently found it hard to avoid dualistic or vitalistic viewpoints in considering the evolution of mind. Perhaps the only satisfying descriptions at present are analogies. Be that as it may, even if we admit gaps in our knowledge of the evolutionary process (not in the process itself!), we may still derive two working principles from a biological approach:

1. Mind is organized at the most complex levels of integration of matter.

2. There are genetic mechanisms whereby this organization is transmitted from two parents to their offspring.

With genetics having to do with mind, it is fortunate that the tools and concepts of this science are continually being sharpened and extended. Two main periods may be distinguished in the development of modern genetics, the first, as previously mentioned, largely descriptive and static, the second more explanatory and dynamic. Stemming from Gregor Mendel's crucial garden pea experiments in 1865, the early era provided the first description of populations in terms of the frequency and distribution of types on a genetic basis. These findings, when coupled with the idea of natural selection, account for the various statistical phenomena of evolution (Fisher, 1958).

Later, the more intimate study of gene action came to hold greater appeal for geneticists who regarded the statistical or "hyperatomistic" viewpoint in human genetics as too static, requiring too many additional entities (such as modifier genes) to explain the complexity of genetic adaptation.

As far back as the discovery of the chromosomes by Fleming and Waldeyer in the 1880's, a broader physiological conception of genetic phenomena became possible. The emphasis was placed on an understanding of variations in the effective functioning of the human organism (including mind) in terms of gene action and developmental systems. By studying the phenomena of cytoplasmic interaction, embryonic regulation, and integration, modern genetics extended its field of action beyond its classical boundaries.

The insight provided by biochemical and cytological findings makes it possible for genetic theory to include within its scope the processes of normal development. Although it may still be true that "mutants which affect general features like growth, fertility, sterility and viability, frequently cannot be isolated and localized like the standard mutants of elementary Mendelism" (Goldschmidt, 1955, p. 132), the study of gene action in the fullest sense is the key to the analysis of behavior.

To be sure, unusual behavior must always be viewed "as an extremely complex and continuous chain of events in the individual's adaptive history, rather than the automatic expression of a fixed congenital error in metabolism" (Kallmann, 1958, p. 10). As stated by Fuller (1960, p. 51), in discussing animal investigation, one studies "not so much the inheritance of emotional characters as the effects of the genotype upon the developmental history of emotional behavior. . . . Strain differences are merely a starting point for detailed studies of behavioral development, and as sources of biochemical, anatomical and physiological variations, which can be correlated with behavior."

The process begins anew each time two gametes unite to form a fertilized ovum or zygote. We have covered considerable ground in learning about the cellular chemistry responsible for the formation of these gametes and for the guided process of growth and development. In the Mendelian era, proceeding from the premise that single characters (or traits) behaved as if determined by paired particles in the germ plasm (later called genes or alleles), a study of the results of various types of mating confirmed the expected statistical ratios for both phenotypes and genotypes in the next generation, the results differing according to the dominance or recessiveness of the gene in question.

Today genes are considered to be constituent parts of the set of darkly staining threads in the cell nucleus called chromosomes. An organism's range of potentialities, in specific as well as general life processes, is implicit in the structure of that one cell with which it starts. The individual genes, their arrangement in chromosomes, the entire chromosome complement, very likely the cytoplasm, and the whole procession of surrounding and interacting environments, beginning in the mammal with the intrauterine, are all potent factors in the temporal process of growth and development, maturity, and senescence. In neither animal nor man is behavior, or its subjective aspect which is mind, exempt from this biologic fact.

The gene, as defined above, has been identified primarily with deoxyribonucleic acid (DNA), a substance that in all higher forms of life is both necessary and sufficient for the transmission of genetic information. For example, one strain of bacteria can be transformed into another by placing it in a medium consisting of the other's specific DNA. In the phenomenon known as transduction, this transformation is probably mediated by the entrance of a virus-like particle which substitutes its DNA for that of the host.

There are now well-substantiated models and analytical techniques describing the structure and composition of DNA. This genetic substance, made up of polynucleotide chains, is currently conceived of as a bound double helix in which the coded information is related to the sequence of its purine and pyrimidine bases. In cell duplication the helix splits, each half then synthesizing a copy of its mate to re-create the original double strand.

Through fractionation of cellular DNA it has been possible to show that the substance found in any given type of cell is a mixture of molecules that are present in a specific characteristic proportion (Bendich, Pahl, and Beiser, 1956). Thus, the chemist has come close to isolating the units of hereditary transmission that had previously been resolved by cross-breeding techniques.

The developmental potential contained in the fertilized ovum is determined not only by its individual genes but by other aspects of the cell. Just as one person functions as part of a group, so the genes are parts of chromosomes which in turn are members of a species-specific complement with respect to their size, shape, and number. Disarrangements in the structure of one or more of these chromosomes or irregularities in their number will have as profound an effect on the developing organism as mutations in individual genes.

Studied for a long time in plants and lower organisms, these effects have recently been demonstrated in man by means of newly developed techniques for staining, identifying, and counting human chromosomes. Various types of sexual maldevelopment are associated with an extra sex chromosome in a male (Klinefelter's syndrome), an extra sex chromosome in a female ("super" female), and a missing sex chromosome (Turner's syndrome). In mongolism, a syndrome affecting the entire bodily and intellectual development, there is found an extra autosomal chromosome resulting from an asymmetrical division at the time of the ovum's formation. Although no single gene mutations seem to be involved, this disarrangement in the chromosome complement results in a profoundly deviant but viable developmental pattern. The net genetic effect depends upon the quantitative and structural organization of all the genes at the chromosomal level.

As the lifelong interactional process begins, the first "environment" of this nucleus with its structured gene-chromosome pattern is represented by the cytoplasm of the original cell, derived mainly from the mother. The early interaction of this first cytoplasm with the nuclear substances in influencing the choice of developmental pathways available to the zygote has been investigated only in the case of one-celled organisms. The key process is protein synthesis. Nutrient material, provided prenatally and immediately postnatally by the mother and then by increasingly independent activity of the individual in a natural and social world, is converted via gene-directed metabolic pathways into specific protein and other biochemical substances.

With the help of particular enzymes (themselves protein in nature and formed as described here), the message encoded in the chromosomal DNA is passed via ribonucleic acid (RNA) to the cytoplasm. There each gene pattern determines the sequence of amino acids which form a particular protein, and possibly their configuration as well. By means of high-energy bonds, the protein is fully synthesized into one of the building blocks of the various interconnected systems making up the organism.

The basic problem in embryology, as yet unsolved, is the mechanism of differentiation into various tissues during ontogenesis. Generally speaking, every cell in the body has a set of chromosomes identical in appearance and with the same number (or occasionally an exact multiple of this number). However, from the earliest embryonic growth, it is a fact that cell lines become differentiated and specialized.

Under what conditions and at what stage nuclei lose their omnipotentiality and what has happened to the nucleic acids representing the genes which are inactive are still matters of conjecture. Chromatographic analysis of fractionated DNA of various tissues reveals characteristic differences in profile, suggesting that the effective genetic material has indeed come to vary. Further study of cells grown in tissue culture may reveal more about chemical or morphological differences in their nuclei.

On a more complex level of integration there are the organs and organ systems and, in particular, the nervous system. While leaving a detailed account of modern experimental neurophysiology to other contributors, we may bear in mind that in this field and the allied one of neurochemistry, such factors as brain enzyme concentrations as related to behavior, and variations in conditioning and electroencephalographic patterns have been successfully studied in accordance with the genetic approach. For example, evidence of correlation has been found between acetylcholine concentration in the brain and the variable propensity of the rat for maze-solving techniques (Krech, Rosenzweig, Bennett, and Krueckel, 1954); glutamic acid metabolism has been implicated in convulsive seizure-prone strains of mice (Ginsburg, 1954), and human conditionability has been shown to be related to introversion-extraversion score (Franks, 1956).

A step removed from these investigations is the behavioristic description of the entire organism in experimental or natural settings. Much work has been done in studying the hereditary aspects of sexual, maternal, aggressive, feeding, and exploratory activity in laboratory animals, extending from genetic selection for phototaxic and geotropic behavior in fruit flies (Hirsch, 1958) to more complex behavior in mammals. It is clear from these studies that only interaction between the subjects with their inborn propensities, other animals (e.g., parents), and the experimenters can account for the variations in behavior that are found, a fact known to Pavlov.

Within the framework of the naturalist, a newly developed science has become prominent, known as "ethology." This science studies "innate behavior," defined as behavior characteristic of the species which develops in apparent independence of the environment and represents an organized pattern of adaptive activity. Such behavior is also termed "instinctive," an instinct being defined as a hierarchically organized nervous mechanism which is susceptible to certain priming, releasing, and directing impulses of internal as well as external origin and which responds to those impulses by coordinated movements that contribute to the maintenance of the individual and the species.

To be sure, there is a controversy between those using the concepts of ethology and those who consider the nervous system and behavior of an animal, its "mind" if you will, as more moldable in its particulars by the environment through the learning process. Learning is seen by these investigators as a modification of action resulting from the development of stimuli equivalents or expanded arousal properties, a process of sensory integration. Learning is analyzed on different levels—prelearning (adaptation, fatigue), classical conditioning (contiguity), insightful learning (integration of noncontiguous experience), and the special case in which language is involved.

The ethologist, for his part, defines learning somewhat differently—as a central nervous system process causing more or less lasting changes in the innate behavioral mechanism under the influence of the outer world. He implies that, in addition to the "innate" mechanisms, animals are born with the predisposition to "learn" special things. Evidently the focus is on the postulated innate behavioral mechanism which is a complex organization in the central nervous system that defies further analysis.

It may be that genetics can play a role in reconciling these viewpoints. Although an "*organized pattern* of adaptive activity" may not be conceivable, except as a result of interaction with the surroundings, a pattern which even on the chromosomal level defines the organism's part in this interaction does make sense. Identical twins are very similar within a very wide range of environmental differences. Both in animals and man, this problem requires investigation by chemists, biologists, and psychologists.

On the psychological level, the study of learning and the acquisition of action patterns as a result of the interaction of an inherited nervous system (or its chromosomal or embryonic precursors) with cytoplasmic, intrauterine, nutritional, and social environments calls for the utmost objectivity and improved techniques.

Some specific and urgent problems of psychiatry may be examined in this light. In terms related to the process of learning, it is necessary to explore the nature of unconditioned reflexes in man and the earliest period during which they are evident. If nervous tissue is characterized by its universal ability to learn (in the sense of integrating sensory impressions), adaptation and maladaptation, which depend equally upon the predictability (suitability, "rationality") of the environment and on the proper functioning of the organism's equipment, still have to be defined.

The introspective approach to these problems in modern psychiatry is typified by psychoanalysis. This discipline, with its particular methods, undertakes to contribute to the study of development and adaptation, both as a research tool and in the treatment of maladaptation. Of course, in psychoanalysis the problems of innate or instinctive versus acquired or learned behavior appear in a new guise. Freud variously defined instinct as the measure of the demand made upon the mind in consequence of its connection with the body, or a borderline concept between the mental and the physical. While this concept has been criticized as nonoperational, it may be useful in separating the source, aim, and object of human drives. Having their source in the temporary states of tissue disequilibrium which occur during metabolic and other life processes, such drives may aim at achieving a homeostatic condition. In pursuing this aim, the individual comes to choose those methods which depend on the history of his relations with other persons ("objects") who have been important in helping him. Typical action patterns develop as the drives are directed toward such persons and adapted to the super-structure of social relationships.

As part of this process, there arise feelings of pleasure and pain and their more complex emotional derivatives. These affective states, so significant in human affairs and not adequately dealt with on other levels of inquiry, are particularly amenable to psychoanalytic investigation. However, their accurate study will require help from chemistry and anatomy, genetics, biology, and the sociological sciences.

In all of these questions psychodynamics may be considered part of a total integrated picture of human biology. If attention is paid to both genotypic and phenotypic levels, the understanding of motivation and emotional control depends on genetic, physiological, and psychological insights.

This view extends a horizon of psychoanalytic thought which appeared with Freud and his contemporaries and is becoming increasingly valuable, especially in studies of the infant and child in the family setting, and in psychosomatic research. Such an integrated approach affords an opportunity to recognize fundamental genetic differences among individuals and to correlate them with prenatal and postnatal developmental interaction. Freud (1913, p. 122) expressed it in the following way, "We divide the causes of neurotic disease into those which the individual himself brings with him into life, and those which life brings to him—that is to say, into constitutional and accidental."

Similar thoughts were expressed by Jones (1930a, p. 133; 1930b, p. 160), who wrote,

Ever since Mendel's work it has been evident that in estimating the relation of heredity to environment in respect to any character, we have first to ascertain the component units in that character; in other words, what actually constitutes an individual gene. . . . By means of psychoanalysis one is enabled to dissect and isolate mental processes to an extent not previously possible, and this must evidently bring us nearer to the primary elements, to the mental genes in terms of which genetic investigations can alone be carried out . . . the next study to be applied would be one in the field of heredity.

These statements, of course, referred to the relative strength of instinctual fixations and erogenous zones. However, Freud (1937, p. 343) anticipated current trends by characterizing primary ego differences as follows, "We have no reason to dispute the existence and importance of primary congenital variations in the ego. A single fact is decisive, namely, that every individual selects only *certain* of the possible defensive mechanisms and invariably employs those which he has selected."

In line with these observations, psychodynamic concepts embody the premise that man is selective with respect to important aspects of his life experiences and for this reason can be thought of as helping to create his own environment. Therefore, it is apparent that the complexities of aberrant development and behavior, as delineated with increasing skill by psychodynamic research, will be fully understood only if the genetic dimension is considered an integral part of the over-all frame of reference.

In the field of infant and child psychiatry, many workers have now come to regard intrinsic differences among children as equipotent with maternal attitudes in determining lifelong behavior patterns. These differences have been found in sleep habits, feeding, and sensory responses (Escalona, Leitch, et al., 1952), general activity level (Fries and Woolf, 1953), motor behavior (Mittelmann, 1954), and specific reaction patterns (Thomas and Chess, 1957).

Likewise, in the field of psychosomatic medicine, the causative role played by psychodynamic factors can be determined only with the help of (a) comparative morbidity risk figures based on statistically representative and clinically homogeneous samples and (b) adequate information about underlying metabolic processes and their variations.

For example, blood pepsinogen level has been studied as a measure of gastric activity and secretion (Mirsky, 1960). Functional differences among infants in this area may first cause correspondingly different feeding responses, then modify personality development, and end up in vulnerability to peptic ulcer. Other measures of autonomic function (Lacey, Bateman, and Van Lehn, 1953) have demonstrated many individual variations in systematic and idiosyncratic patterns of response.

While dealing with the human being in terms of his intellectual, emotional, and behavioral qualities is the province of the psychological and psychiatric specialist, he is forced to enlist the services of the sociologist, social anthropologist, and human demographer in order to round out a temporal view of man in which mind is seen in its genetic context.

As a rule, the smallest social unit studied is the family, and the first transactions of the newborn child are with his mother. Here the formulations of ethology (mother's face as a releasing mechanism) and psychoanalysis (mother as provider of food to satisfy the infant's basic needs) furnish a framework in which the earliest development of mind and its mechanism may be conceived.

On one score there is little doubt. The newborn infant is already as much of an individual "mentally" as he is physiognomically. The groundwork for future interaction, present in the germ plasm and already molded in intrauterine life, exists at birth and is ready to respond *and be responded to* by the mother. All recent studies on motherhood make explicit what mothers the world over have always known—that babies are different and that they require different treatment.

The studies on peptic ulcer referred to previously illustrate this fact in the case of a special kind of intense feeding craving. It has also been shown that if nonidentical twins come to be treated differently, it is because of their personality differences rather than simply because they do not look alike. Beyond doubt improvements in describing personality dimensions in infants will enhance the developmental study of behavior, even before more is known about the general and special properties of mind.

While collaboration between the disciplines of psychodynamics and psychogenetics is certain to provide better insight into normal and extreme variations in human behavior, it may still not fully account for the dynamics and variable stratifications of human populations. Yet the changing composition of these groups and their various modes of interaction with physical and social surroundings depend to a great extent on determining genetic principles. Such basic influences as assortative mating, the effects of population size, and the phenomena of mutation and selection are the major causes of generation to generation changes in what would otherwise be constant genetic composition. Behavioral differences play a major role in initiating these processes in two ways—they help to determine patterns of mating and reproduction and they are effective in the process of natural selection, both in creating the environment and adapting to it.

In the first instance, within the framework of a rapidly expanding radius of contacts, mate choice and marital fertility depend greatly on differences between cultures and between individuals which are behavioral in nature. Analogous to isolating mechanisms in other forms, they serve to perpetuate phenotype diversification.

Secondly, the products of the human mind at the same time constitute a technological and cultural environment which creates new selection pressures in the evolution of man. The use of tools, for example, appears to have preceded "biological changes in the hand, brain, and face" (Washburn, 1959), while adaptation to climate by the use of clothes may have been effective in reducing body hair (Muller, 1959). So whether by way of assortative and selective mating patterns or by ecological adaptation, human mind and behavior have influenced the course of human evolution.

One major dimension of mental functioning that has not explicitly been discussed may be mentioned here in passing with a brevity disproportionate to its human importance—namely, that concerned with moral and ethical values and goals. In psychoanalytic terms, we have dealt mainly with the ego functions—learning, adaptation, integration—and not with that section of the mental apparatus which Freud called the superego—conscience, control, value-judgment, and identification with an ideal. In an essay by Hartmann (1960) psychoanalysis was described as a specialty that recognizes the superego as part of the "mind" and explores its genesis and development. It was denied, however, that this discipline advocates a particular philosophy of life or code of morals, these being determined variously on personal, social, or religious grounds. While recognizing the importance of a consistent set of moral values for the individual, Hartmann doubted that psychology alone can fulfill the need.

Whether the study of biological evolution can by itself provide a code of ethics is equally uncertain. As with most world views, various perfidious schemes have historically been proposed or carried out in its name. On the other hand, responsible individuals have either found in Nature the prototype for altruistic behavior (Allee, 1938), or they have argued that Nature's amorality makes it all the more essential for man to gird himself with moral convictions and to assume ethical responsibilities (Huxley, 1897; Pearl, 1946). Their source notwithstanding, one of these responsibilities would clearly be for man—in whom "for the first time a product of evolution perceives that process" (Sherrington, 1951, p. 278)—to make the most of his increasing scientific knowledge for the betterment of all mankind.

Further evolutionary development of the human organism that would yield a more effectively controlled, more perceptive, and more intelligent mental apparatus would seem to depend primarily on avoiding the dysgenic effects of war, overpopulation, negative selection, and ionizing radiation. Conscious and conscientious measures might then be taken whereby the human mind can achieve its potentialities. To think and act in this area with full knowledge of the consequences, man must fall back on some knowledge of genetics, if only in the interest of human survival, the prerequisite for all his future biological, intellectual, and social development.

The human mind, representing the mediator between the genetic constitution of the species on one side and the natural and man-created worlds on the other, is the product of both. Individually and collectively, the mind links these two aspects of life in a continuous stream of interaction.

REFERENCES

Allee, W. C., *The Social Life of Animals,* W. W. Norton, New York, 1938.
Bendich, A., Pahl, H. B., and Beiser, S. M., "Chromatographic fractionation of deoxyribonucleic acid with special emphasis on the transforming factor of *pneumococcus,*" *Cold Spring Harbor Symposia on Quantitative Biology,* 1956, 21:31-48.

Escalona, S., Leitch, M., *et al.*, "Early phases of personality development: A non-normative study of infant behavior," *Monogr. Soc. Res. Child Developm.*, 1952, Vol. 17.

Fisher, R. A., *The Genetical Theory of Natural Selection*, Dover, New York, 1958.

Franks, C. M., "Conditioning and personality. A study of normal and neurotic subjects," *J. Abn. & Soc. Psych.*, 1956, 52:143-150.

Freud, S., "The predisposition to obsessional neurosis, a contribution to the problem of the option of neurosis (1913)," in *Collected Papers, Vol. II*, Hogarth, London, 1924.

———, "Analysis terminable and interminable (1937)," in *Collected Papers, Vol. V*, Hogarth, London, 1950.

Fries, M., and Woolf, P., "Some hypotheses on the role of the congenital activity type in personality development," *Psychoan. Study of the Child*, 1953, 8:48-62.

Fuller, J. L., "Behavior genetics," *Ann. Rev. Psych.*, 1960, 11:41-70.

Ginsburg, B. E., "Genetics and the physiology of the nervous system," in Hooker, D., and Hare, C. (eds.), *Genetics and the Inheritance of Integrated Neurological and Psychiatric Patterns*, Williams and Wilkins, Baltimore, 1954.

Goldschmidt, R. B., *Theoretical Genetics*, Univ. of Calif. Press, Berkeley, 1955.

Hartmann, H., *Psychoanalysis and Moral Values*, Intern. Univ. Press, New York, 1960.

Hirsch, J., "Recent developments in behavior genetics and differential psychology," *Dis. Nerv. Syst., Monogr. Suppl.*, 1958, 19:17-24.

Huxley, T. H., *Evolution and Ethics*, Appleton, New York, 1897.

James, W., *Principles of Psychology*, Henry Holt, New York, 1890.

Jones, E., "Mental heredity" (1930), in *Essays in Applied Psychoanalysis, Vol. 1*, Hogarth, London, 1951a.

———, "Psychoanalysis and biology," *ibid.*, 1951b.

Kallmann, F. J., "An appraisal of psychogenetic twin data," *Dis. Nerv. Syst., Monogr. Suppl.*, 1958, 19:9-15.

Krech, D., Rosenzweig, M. R., Bennett, E. L., and Krueckel, B., "Enzyme concentrations in the brain and adjustive behavior patterns," *Science*, 1954, 120:994-996.

Lacey, J. I., Bateman, D. E., and Van Lehn, R., "Autonomic response specificity: an experimental study," *Psychosomat. Med.*, 1953, 15:8-21.

Mirsky, I. A., "Physiologic, psychologic and social determinants of psychosomatic disorders," *Dis. Nerv. Syst., Mongr. Suppl.*, 1960, 21:50-56.

Mittelmann, B., "Motility in infants, children, and adults: patterning and psychodynamics," *Psychoan. Study of the Child*, 1954, 9:142-177.

Muller, H. J., "The guidance of human evolution," *Perspectives in Biol. & Med.*, 1959, 3:1-43.

Pearl, R., *Man the Animal*, Principia Press, Bloomington, Indiana, 1946.

Rado, S., "Mind, unconscious mind, and brain," *Psychosom. Med.*, 1949, 15:165-168.

Santayana, G., *Skepticism and Animal Faith*, Scribner, New York, 1923.

Sherrington, C., *Man on His Nature*, 2nd ed., University Press, Cambridge, 1951.

Thomas, A., and Chess, S., "An approach to the study of sources of individual differences in child behavior," *J. Clin. Exp. Psychopath.*, 1957, 18:347-357.

Teilhard de Chardin, P., *The Phenomenon of Man*, Harper, New York, 1959.

Washburn, S. L., "Speculations on the interrelations of the history of tools and biological evolution," in Spuhler, J. N. (ed.), *The Evolution of Man's Capacity for Culture*, Wayne State Univ. Press, Detroit, 1959.

E. ROY JOHN

Some Speculations on

the Psychophysiology of Mind

The problem of mind has not been a matter of urgent concern to the contemporary biological scientist. Issues of mind-body dualism have largely been resolved by the expedient of focusing on functional mechanisms amenable to experimental analysis with present tools, and ignoring the existence of more subjective phenomena. Now that the present amount of data about neural processes has been accumulated, perhaps we may ask whether some real problem domains have not been overlong neglected.

People, including scientists, are likely to perceive problems in terms of their own experience. As biological scientists, we have more and more become preoccupied with understanding that aspect of our experience

The author owes much to the constructive criticisms of this paper which have been made by Ross Adey, Kao-Liang Chow, Robert W. Doty, Endré Grastyán, Victor Hall, Frank Morrell, and Carlo Terzuolo.

In the process of preparing this paper the author has become aware of a large amount of speculative writing previously unknown to him. Some of these early works present formulations similar to aspects of the present paper. The author is not sufficiently scholarly to be able to identify the initial proponents of various ideas expressed herein. Suffice it to say that many of these ideas have been stated earlier and better. What may be unique here is that the author, from the vantage point of a broader body of experimentation than his predecessors, has ordered the ideas in a different fashion. The notes are old, but the song is new.

The preparation of this paper has been aided by Grants MY-2811 and MY-2972 from the USPHS.

related to the observation of particular waveforms on cathode-ray tubes or ink-writers, the scattering or absorption of electrons by matter as represented on photographic emulsions, the rates of chemical reactions, or the performance of conditioned responses. As we have gathered these various measures from nervous systems, we have tended more and more to perceive problems in terms of these measures, and to lose sight of problems posed by our own immediate personal experiences. The salient aspect of our experience is that *we experience*. To paraphrase our famous speculative predecessor: We think; therefore, a problem exists.

Recently, terms like consciousness, pleasure, attention, and meaning have started to reappear in the literature of brain research. So, too, have altercations about the propriety of these terms. The appearance of such concerns heralds the refocusing of our attention on the neurophysiology of mind. As this shift occurs, there will be a building of new tools and a sharpening of old ones. Perhaps the most striking feature of mind is the property of *awareness*, particularly self-awareness. We have not yet devised a measure to tell us whether or not an organism is aware, unless it volunteers the assertion verbally. Unfortunately, those organisms for which the bulk of our tools have been fashioned do not talk. The fact that an electrical potential occurs, or that a behavioral response is emitted, does not provide this information. Devices exist in profusion which can make selective and appropriate behavioral responses and which generate potentials. Potentials can be measured in computers and in planaria, and both can be taught adaptive responses. I do not know if either may be aware.

The newborn human infant does not have awareness, in the sense which I wish to use the word. As stimuli impinge on it, gross and global effects ensue. Not until a period of experience has accumulated does appreciable differentiation of response emerge. Global reactivity to sensation evolves toward differentiated perception as the organism acquires experience. Awareness, the intrinsic property of mind, is the totality of momentary exogenous and endogenous sensation, ordered and colored by affect and evaluation unique to, and characteristic of, the experiencing organism. The meaning of stimuli and the needs of the organism, as well as the stimuli themselves, modify awareness. Awareness would seem to be a resultant arising from an interaction between afferent stimulation and the residual effects of past stimulation, and highly dependent upon the over-all state of the nervous system.

This paper will attempt to generate a model for such interaction from a number of hypotheses which are suggested by a body of research findings. While the model provides for the interactions which seem prerequisites for awareness, it offers no insight into how these processes result in the subjective experience of awareness.

The basic outline of the process of awareness which has been proposed above is presented in Figure 1.

Abundant recent contributions by neurophysiologists and psychologists have elucidated some basic outlines of neural mechanisms related to processes of attention and motivation. The outstanding and renowned researches of Magoun, Lindsley, Hernández-Peón, Galambos, Sharpless and Jasper, Fuster, Hess, Olds, and Grastyán, and others cannot be reviewed here in detail. Suffice it to say that a picture has emerged of the central nervous system as a structure with dynamic control over afferent input, which includes two antagonistic subsystems, one related to the mediation of pleasurable experiences and one related to the mediation of painful experiences. While this grossly oversimplified picture does an injustice to the volume of painstakingly acquired knowledge about mechanisms related to attention and motivation, our purpose here is

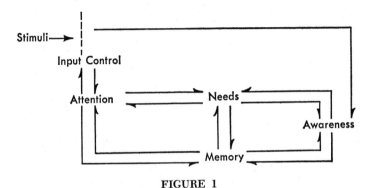

FIGURE 1
Conceptualization of processes basic to awareness.

merely to point out that, in the attempt to formulate a description of the interaction processes hypothetically involved in the phenomenon of awareness, a major stumbling block arises from our lack of knowledge about how the effects of past experience are retained in the central nervous system in more or less permanent form.

Our first concern in this paper, therefore, is to propose a model for some physiological mechanisms which may underly the learning process. The model is based upon a number of phenomena which seem to illustrate a fundamental property of the central nervous system; namely, that under certain circumstances more or less temporary functional relationships can be established between two central regions such that stimulation of one of these regions acquires the capacity to evoke activity in the second region.

Probably the earliest description of this phenomenon was reported in 1884 by Brown-Séquard, who wrote:

Chez des chiens et des lapins, . . .; j'ai excité énergiquement l'écorce cérébrale, à l'aide de deux appareils Dubois-Reymond, les excitateurs de l'un d'eux
étant appliqués au maximum d'intensité sur la partie occipitale de l'écorce
cérébrale, ceux de l'autre, à un moindre dégré de puissance, étant appliqués
sur la zone motrice. Deux effets importants ont été observés un grand nombre
de fois: le premier est que, pendant la passage des courants, qui a été continué
environ vingt secondes, il y a eu dans le tronc et les quatre membres des
mouvements plus énergiques que ceux que je produisais lorsque les courants
des deux piles étaient appliqués sur la zone motrice seulement; le second est
qu' après le passage des courants dans les deux parties *la zone dite non motrice
est devenue motrice.* En la galvanisant faiblement (à 12 ou 13 centimètres,
avec un appareil Dubois-Reymond animé par un pile peu forte), j'ai vu et
revu, à chaque excitation, des mouvements tout à fait semblables à ceux qui
suivent l'application d'un courant de même intensité sur la zone motrice. Cette
partie (circonvolutions occipitales et sphénoidales, surtout les premières) devi-
ent donc tout aussi motrice que la partie de l'écorce, que l'on considère comme
le siège des centres moteurs des membres. J'ajoute que la face, le cou, la queue
se meuvent aussi dans ces circonstances par une excitation galvanique peu
forte des l'écorce cérébrale occipitale. Ces expériences réussissent plus souvent
chez le chien que chez le lapin.[8]

In 1897, Wedensky[72] reported a similar finding. If in a dog under light
narcosis, shortly after electrical stimulation of the motor point for the
extensors of the forepaw (center *A*), stimulation is applied to the motor
cortex region of the flexors of the forepaw (center *B*), it is possible to
observe a paradoxical effect; the result of stimulation of center *B* is as if
center *A* had been stimulated, and extension of the forepaw occurs.

In 1905, in a startlingly elegant series of experiments in which chroni-
cally implanted electrodes were used to study the effects of cortical
stimulation in unrestrained dogs, Baer[2] confirmed and extended the
earlier findings of Brown-Séquard. The conclusions to which Baer came,
as well as his methods, merit more careful consideration than they
have received:

Nachdem ich hiermit die Zusammenstellung meiner Untersuchungen been-
det habe, erübrigt es noch zum Schlusse eine allgemeine Deutung der gewon-
nenen Ergebnisse anzuschliessen.

Das Auffälligste sämtlicher Ergebnisse war, dass es gelang, eine der
"unerregbaren" Zone zugehörige Gehirnstelle dadurch erregbar zu machen,
dass man auf eine zweite an und für sich erregbare Stelle gleichzeitig oder
kurz vorher einen kurzen Dauerstrom einwirken Liess. . . . Denn auf Grund
der obenerwähnten Beobachtung, dass von allen Teilen der Gehirnoberfläche
alle willkürlichen Muskeln in Erregung versetzt werden können, mussen wir
wohl die Vermutung hegen, dass alle Teile der Gehirnoberfläche durch eine
ausgedehnte netzförmige Verbindung untereinander in Beziehung stehen.

These and other reports indicate that, for some time after stimulation of a region of the central nervous system, a physical state may exist such that other input to this region, presumably as a result of diffuse irradiation from some more directly stimulated location in the extensively interconnected network that is the brain, although it normally would be ineffective, now results in the discharge of that region. Such functional relationships might either be due to previously subthreshold influences of the second region upon the first becoming suprathreshold because of enhancement resulting from the prior stimulation of the first region or might indicate the formation of new "temporary connections" where such influences were previously absent. (An alternative possibility, which seems to the author to be functionally equivalent, although anatomically different, might be pointed out. Stimulation of the first region may exert a sustained but subthreshold effect on some other region, so as to raise its excitability. Input from the second region, previously ineffective, may now cause the discharge of that third region.)

In 1929, Zal'manson[77] showed that such an altered functional state can be produced by strychninization. After establishing a conditioned defensive reflex of the left rear paw to the beat of a metronome, he placed strychnine on the motor cortical representation of the right forepaw. Subsequently, presentation of the metronome beat that was the conditioned stimulus was found to elicit vigorous flexion of the right forepaw, rather than the left rear paw. These results show that a local increase in state of excitability can be chemically induced. More significantly, they indicate that an excitable region so produced may in a sense dominate the hierarchy of responses of the animal, so that afferent input which has normally been processed in a particular fashion, learned or nonlearned, now has a different consequence.

Ukhtomski, in 1926,[69] assigned to the central state assumed to underly these phenomena the term *dominant focus*. Ukhtomski characterized the condition of excitation in dominance by four aspects: (1) relatively heightened excitability of a neural center, (2) temporal stability of the local nervous excitation, (3) capacity of the center to summate excitation from the stream of indifferent afferent impulses, and (4) excitation inertia, i.e., the capacity of the mechanism to retain excitation once established and to be able to continue when the original stimulation has disappeared.

The dominant focus can be considered as an aggregate of neurons sharing a sustained state of altered excitability. The excitability of a population of neurons in a region would normally tend to be randomly distributed. An afferent input to the region would be expected to cause a diffusely distributed response throughout the region. The percentage of responding cells in any unit volume would be that fraction of the total population which was in a nonrefractory state of excitability and for which the input was supraliminal. The establishment of a dominant focus in an area of this region would make more uniform the excitability of neurons in that area. An adequate afferent input to the region would now cause a diffusely distributed response throughout the region, as before, but in the area of the dominant focus a massive synchronized response would occur which involved a high percentage of the neurons in that area. Such an organized nonrandom discharge from the area of the dominant focus might well be expected to dominate the pattern of efferent outflow from the otherwise randomly organized region. *These consequences would seem to follow whether the effect of the dominant focus were excitatory or inhibitory.* However, it would seem that inhibitory influences might exert a relatively *more* pronounced effect, since neurons could escape from excitatory influences by discharging and entering the refractory phase.

Some indication exists for possible mechanisms to mediate such an altered excitability of neural regions following stimulation. It would be expected, from the work of Hodgkin and Huxley,[22] and it has been demonstrated by the work of Cicardo and Torino[10] and others, that a stimulated region in the central nervous system will release potassium into its environment. John, Tschirgi, and Wenzel[35] have reported evidence suggesting long-lasting effects of small local increases in central potassium. In addition, MacIntosh and Oborin have reported[49] evidence for the central release of acetylcholine in an amount proportional to the electrical activity of cortical tissue. Since, in appropriate concentration, these substances can have an excitatory effect, either one, or possibly both, may play a role in maintaining a state of residual hyperexcitability in a local region after stimulation.

Tschirgi[68] has suggested that the ionic environment of neurons may be controlled locally in response to neuronal activity within a small region, by virtue of localized changes in blood-brain barrier permeability brought about by the action of acetylcholine released as a consequence of the initial response. Thus the threshold of a neural aggregate might be partly determined by the admission or exclusion of certain ionic species to the region.

In a recent paper,[25] Hughes uses the term "post-tetanic potentiation," not in its original sense as an increased postsynaptic discharge elicited homosynaptically because of increased presynaptic action, but in a broader sense to refer to a long-lasting increased responsiveness following repetitive stimulation. He reviews the evidence for such increased responsiveness, not only from neuromuscular preparations, but in sympathetic ganglia, spinal cord, subcortical nuclei, and the visual, auditory, and olfactory systems, and concludes that post-tetanic potentiation is a generalized phenomenon found at all levels of the nervous system, consisting of postexcitatory increases in responsiveness which may last for minutes or even hours, and which may be mediated by changes in the extraneuronal concentration of potassium and/or acetylcholine.

It seems reasonable to suggest that the phenomena of functional transformation, described earlier, attributed by Ukhtomski to the establishment of a dominant focus, may be manifestations of locally induced postexcitatory facilitation analogous to post-tetanic potentiation, or an equivalent phenomenon.

A Physiological Model for Simple Conditioned Responses

The model to be proposed is based upon some fundamental hypotheses about dominant foci and systems of dominant foci as related to the mode of organization of functional neural systems.

1. A *dominant focus* is a neural aggregate which shares a sustained excitability state, such that the probability that an adequate afferent input to the aggregate will cause synchronized discharge is high.

2. When a number of central nervous system neurons are active repeatedly during the same period of time, they become organized into a system that is characterized by a tendency for its constituent neurons to discharge as a group.

3. By the *strength* of the group discharge tendency is meant the probability that, if any member of the group discharges, the other members of the group will discharge. The strength of the group discharge tendency is a function, among other variables, of the frequency with which such associated discharge has occurred in the past, and the time since such discharge.

4. If a particular temporal pattern has characterized the discharge of the group of neurons during their repeated association, it will characterize the mode of discharge of the system.

5. The various neural aggregates in which activity has been associated during the establishment of a system constitute a *set* of reciprocally interlocked dominant foci. These foci and the relationships between them constitute a representation of the configuration of central excitations which have been so associated. Such a system of interrelated dominant foci will subsequently be referred to as a *representational system.**

---

* While reciprocity of the interaction is suggested, this reciprocity need not be symmetrical, particularly when the associated discharges did not occur simultaneously in two particular foci. Assume that if a definite dominant focus is established in an area due to associated discharge of a group of neurons, afferent activity propagated into the region has an increased probability of achieving markedly nonrandom discharge from the focal area. The more recent the previous associated discharge which activated the focus, the higher the probability of subsequent nonrandom discharge which might be expected. Thus, activity propagating through a network from some

6. By *significant level of activation* is meant the discharge of some critical proportion of the set of neural aggregates in a representational system. When the configuration of afferent input into the system causes a significant level of activation, the interrelationships of the responding aggregates with the set of interlocked foci which compose the representational system cause the associated discharge of the entire representational system with its characteristic temporal pattern.

A number of recent experiments are relevant to various aspects of these hypotheses. This paper will be confined to the presentation of salient examples of such experiments, and does not purport to be a comprehensive review.

Some characteristics of an electrically established dominant focus have been investigated recently by Rusinov.[62] This worker placed an electrode on a region of motor cortex in the conscious rabbit which, if cathodally stimulated, gave forelimb flexion. An *anodal* current, from 5 to 8 microamperes, was applied through this electrode.* While this current flow was maintained, some strong sensory stimulus, such as a touch, a sound, or a light, was presented repeatedly. After a number

---

region A, where associated discharge of an aggregate occurred earlier in time, might occasion markedly nonrandom discharge of some region B organized into a dominant focus by a more recent strong input from another origin. Conversely, the activity propagating through the network from the discharge of this strong focus B, established later in time than A, will subsequently enter the region A. While some cells in region A may well be responsive to this input originating at B, discharge in region A is likely to be more random than at B because more time has elapsed since the focus was established, excitability of neurons in the region is more likely to have deviated from the common state, and thus the strength of the group discharge tendency is lower.

Thus, although the interaction is hypothesized to be reciprocal, the action of later events on earlier is expected to be markedly attenuated relative to the effects of earlier events on later.

* Ostensibly, the consequence of an anodal polarization should be to raise threshold of the subjacent cortex. A slight inhibitory influence of this sort would serve to diminish variations in excitability within the region. One would expect a somewhat raised threshold and more massive response to characterize the region. It is possible, however, that the distribution of current flow with these particular current parameters is such that although thresholds may be raised in superficial regions of the cortex (axodendritic synapses), thresholds are actually lowered in deeper regions (axosomatic synapses) or even at the terminal ramifications of axons projecting from these cortical cells to subcortical structures. This suggestion seems compatible with the conclusions of Bishop and O'Leary.[4] The effect may occur at the unknown location of some "virtual cathode."

Note that essentially the same effect which Rusinov[62] achieved by imposing an anodal polarization on a region of motor cortex was also achieved by Zal'manson[77] by placing strychnine on a region of motor cortex. Bishop and O'Leary[4] compared the effects of cortical strychninization and anodal polarization and concluded that strychnine acted much like surface-positive polarization. Their results indicated that anodal polarization raises the threshold, increases duration of discharge, and decreases the absolutely refractory period. It is of interest that they observed that surface-positive currents induced paroxysmal discharge at much lower current values than surface-of such presentations, the occurrence of the sensory stimulus elicited forelimb flexion. If the anodal current were then discontinued, presentation of the same sensory stimulus continued to elicit forelimb flexion for about half an hour and was then no longer effective. However, recent data suggest that during the period when the "conditioned stimulus" was effective, the presentation of novel stimuli might occasionally also elicit flexion, indicating that the phenomenon might be a sort of sensitization.[52] Further experiments are necessary to determine whether this phenomenon can be established in a differential fashion.* Yet, whether differentiated or generalized, this phenomenon represents a basic example of the formation of "temporary functional connections."

It was also found that if foreleg flexion were conditioned to some particular stimulus and the conditioned response then extinguished, establishment of a dominant focus at the forelimb region in motor cortex "disinhibited" the extinguished response, and facilitated the action of the conditioned stimulus. In subsequent work, Rusinov[63] found that establishment of a dominant focus in an animal conditioned to make a

---

negative currents. They concluded that *any* slowly developing biological potential should be looked upon as a factor influencing the excitability of neurons upon which it acts.

Arduini[1] observed that surface-negative potential shifts, accompanied by EEG arousal, occurred in cortex after reticular formation stimulation, after midline thalamic nuclei stimulation, and after sensory stimulation. Low concentrations of strychnine applied to cortex strongly augmented the amplitude of such potential shifts, as did surface-positive (anodal) polarization of cortex. Similar findings have been reported by Brookhart *et al.*[7]

Jung[38] reported changes in the reactivity of cells in visual cortex during stimulation of the mesencephalic reticular formation and the nonspecific intralaminar thalamic nuclei. Such stimulation was accompanied by a surface-negative cortical wave, resembling a polarization of the cortex. During such stimulation of the nonspecific system, the number of neurons of the visual cortex responding to retinal afferents increased. His evidence indicated that convergence and complex interactions of specific and nonspecific impulses occur on the neurons of the visual cortex. The discharge patterns of cortical neurons influenced and modified the effects of the nonspecific inflow, and vice versa. These interactions can be such as to facilitate or to inhibit cortical neurons.

Evidence is cited by Purpura[60] that stimulation of midline brain stem reticular regions can cause late prolonged surface-positive responses in certain cortical regions, with a marked facilitation of dendritic synapses during this positivity. It seems possible that surface-positive polarization, with a subsequent enhancement of surface-negative effects (i.e., axodendritic discharges) of subcortical stimuli, may occur in a number of different ways. It appears that the surface-positive polarization which seems to facilitate the establishment of a dominant focus enhances the surface-negative effects of stimulation of nonspecific structures. The consequences of such local enhancement of nonspecific components may be to facilitate locally the convergence and interaction of specific and nonspecific impulses such that corticofugal discharge occurs most readily from a surface-positive polarized region when specific systems are stimulated.

* Since this article was written, differentiation to auditory and visual stimuli has been demonstrated by Morrell.[52a] Therefore, the dominant focus phenomenon cannot be dismissed as "sensitization" but must be considered as a model of neural learning.

response involving other central nervous system regions than the site of the dominant focus resulted in the suppression of the previously established conditioned reflex when the conditioned stimulus was presented. Apparently, establishment of a dominant focus is not compatible with performance of a previously established conditioned response. This suggests that the activity propagated in the central nervous system by the presentation of the conditioned stimulus, instead of being directed into the pathways established during the conditioning process, is directed into pathways determined by the directly imposed dominant focus. Implicit in this interpretation is the inference that a *representational* system, built during conditioning, normally routes the activity propagated in the central nervous system by the conditioned stimulus.

Some evidence that the characteristic configuration of excitability necessary to establish a dominant focus can arise from processes related to the responses of neural tissue to stimuli, as well as from externally imposed and sustained anodal polarization, is afforded by the work of Roytbak.[61] This worker observed that tetanization of a cortical region A was followed by a period of slow hypersynchronous activity of varying frequency. Stimulation of other cortical regions B was found to have no pronounced effect on region A previous to tetanization. If, however, as the tetanizing stimulation of region A stopped, cortical regions B were stimulated at some specific frequency F, the subsequent hypersynchrony of region A displayed the frequency F. This phenomenon was observed for many different cortical regions. Thus, the state of a cortical region after a tetanizing stimulation appears to be such that many other regions of cortex can control its pattern of discharge, although normally such control is not apparent. The functional similarities between sustained anodal polarization and the aftereffects of tetanizing stimulation are of interest, and raise questions as to possible mediating mechanisms which may be common to both phenomena.

Chow (personal communication) has recently investigated the effects of tetanization and of polarization on the responsiveness of a region, A, on a slab of isolated cortex, to electrical stimulation delivered to a distant point, B, on the same slab. Not only did the response of region A to stimulation at point B alter following tetanization or polarization, but also, if stimulation at point B were changed to frequency 2 following a period of stimulation at frequency 1, *region A continued to respond at frequency 1*. A similar observation has been reported for the Mauthner's cell of telecast by Shelanski (personal communication). Finally, Morell[52a] has studied the effect of surface anodal polarization on the response of visual cortex units to flicker. Anodal polarization facilitated bursts of response from the unit at the frequency of the flicker. More important, if the driving were continued for several minutes and a single flash of light would elicit a series of burst responses *at the original flicker frequency*. These various findings provide clear illustrations of the capacity of a dominant focus to retain a representation of an imposed temporal pattern of stimulation for a relatively long period of time.

The work of Giurgea and Doty[18] provides what seems to be a demonstration that central electrical stimulation of a less drastic sort than tetanization or DC polarization can also create the conditions required for the establishment of dominant foci and associated representational systems. These workers paired brief electrical stimulation of a region of motor cortex, A, which produced some definite motor response, R, with electrical stimulation of some other region, B, of cortex. After a number of such paired stimuli, presentation of the electrical stimulus to region B elicited response R. According to these workers, a minimum of three minutes must intervene between trials. Failure of previous attempts to accomplish such direct "central conditioning"[46] is probably to be attributed to insufficiently long intervals between paired presentations.

Feedback from the performance of R itself probably is not involved in the establishment of this "central conditioning" since it has been shown not to be an essential component of more conventional procedures.[3] It is noteworthy that no reinforcement is involved in the establishment of the centrally conditioned reflex. Although the two procedures differ in the parameters of electrical stimulation, the salient difference between the procedure of Roytbak and the procedure of Giurgea and Doty appears to be that in the former procedure an electrical response is the index of "connection formation" while a motor response is used in the latter procedure. The similarities between the procedures are sufficient to suggest that they share a common mediating mechanism, and that brief intermittent stimulation of the motor cortex serves to establish a dominant focus.

Indication that the pathways established during this procedure are not transcortical was obtained. If region A (motor) is located on one hemisphere and region B on the other, transection of the corpus callosum after establishment of the "conditioned response" did not abolish the response, nor did transection before stimulation prevent establishment of the response. This suggests that the cortical activity is reflected subcortically and that the link which is built during congruent periods of cortical activity may be between the respective subcortical projections, possibly in the thalamus.

It seems reasonable to suggest that the work of Doty, Rutledge, and Larsen[14] can be interpreted as evidence that representational systems can be established in a somewhat more physiological fashion, but still analogous to the work of Giurgea and Doty. The essential difference between the procedure used by Giurgea and Doty and that of Doty, Rutledge, and Larsen is that the motor response in the latter experiments was elicited by shock to the foot instead of to the motor cortex. The "conditioned stimulus" was still direct electrical stimulation of cortex, paired with shock to the foot. After a number of such pairings, the electrical stimulation of cortex evoked leg flexion, although prior to the conditioning procedure this had not occurred. Neural activity in the motor system associated with the leg flexion caused by shock has apparently established a dominant focus.

Loucks[48] had previously reported use of cortical stimulation through an implanted coil as a conditioned stimulus. His results were ambiguous because of the possibility of concomitant vibratory stimulation. In later work,[47] however, he successfully used direct central stimulation as a conditioned stimulus.

The basically physiological quality of the system built during the procedure of Doty, *et al.*, seems to be demonstrated by the fact that if such a conditioned response is established to direct electrical stimulation of a sensory region of cortex, subsequent acquisition of the same conditioned response to stimulation of the peripheral sense organs of the same modality is greatly facilitated.[13] Similar saving of trials can be observed with the opposite sequence of learning. (Comparable results have been reported by Neff and his co-workers,[54] see below.) Thus it appears that the representational system elaborated during conditioning to a direct central stimulus is a normally functional system, in that a physiologically natural stimulus can apparently gain functional access to it. This conclusion would seem to justify interpretation of the various manipulations of this preparation described below as providing information about the organization of representational systems during more conventional conditioning procedures.

When a flexion conditioned response has been established to a conditioned stimulus consisting of direct electrical stimulation of some cortical region A, transfer of this conditioned response to stimulation of other cortical regions can be established with substantial saving of trials. This suggests that the representational system established during the initial training mediates, to some extent, the conditioned response elicited by stimulation of other areas. Apparently cortical region A is not an essential part of this system, because ablation of region A does not severely impede transfer. Circumsection of the cortex around the site of stimulation does not abolish the established conditioned response. Transection of the corpus callosum leaves unaffected performance of a conditioned response established to a conditioned stimulus delivered to one hemisphere and an unconditioned stimulus delivered to the other hemisphere. These findings suggest that transcortical transmission is not essential in the mediation of the response, as would also be indicated by such data as those of Sperry.[66] However, undercutting the site of cortical stimulation abolishes the conditioned response, indicating corticofugal pathways play an essential role. These conclusions correspond to those reported by Loucks.[47] It is interesting that continued training enables the conditioned response to be re-established to electrical stimulation of an undercut cortical region, indicating that transcortical transmission can contribute to mediation of the conditioned response under certain conditions.

It would seem, therefore, that during conditioning to a direct central stimulus, a representational system is established in which the cortical sites of the conditioned and unconditioned stimuli become functionally connected via a subcortical path. The failure of ablation of the cortical site of the conditioned stimulus to impede transfer indicates that activity resulting from the stimulation of other cortical regions gains access to this representational system via subcortical regions.

Experiments investigating the phenomenon of cortical conditioning, conducted by Morrell and Jasper,[53] Yoshii, et al.,[75] and others, may provide information related to temporal patterns of discharge in representational systems. In this paradigm, a steady tone is presented for several seconds and then paired for an additional 10 to 15 seconds with a low-frequency flickering light. After a number of such paired presentations separated by random intervals of time, upon the onset of the steady tone and before the onset of flicker, a repetitive response at the frequency of the flicker appears in the visual cortex. The writer and his co-workers,[31] and Yoshii and Hockaday,[73] have observed that, if the paired stimuli are presented at *regular* intervals, e.g., every 30 seconds, and then occasionally both are withheld, a frequency specific repetitive response will often be observed in the visual cortex. This would seem to provide clear evidence that the repeated regular experience with flicker has organized a representational system which can, under the appropriate conditions, reproduce the temporal pattern of electrical activity in certain structures which typically accompanied the events which established the system.

In this view, then, during cortical conditioning a representational system may be established which has the capacity of producing a fluctuation in the potentials recorded from visual cortex, corresponding to the activity induced by flicker, which established a dominant focus there. The tone, occurring while this system is being built, activates structures which become part of the system. Subsequently, activation of these structures by the presentation of tone causes activation of the representational system and a consequent frequency-specific repetitive response appears in the visual cortical region which, since it has been repeatedly active as the system was built, is functionally integrated into that system.

It is of great interest that, according to Yoshii, et al.,[75,76] frequency-specific repetitive response appears in subcortical structures, including the mesencephalic reticular formation and the intralaminar nuclei, before it appears in visual cortex. Further, Yoshii and Hockaday[73] have reported preliminary evidence suggesting that cortical conditioning is blocked in animals with lesions of the center median. Thus, the intralaminar nuclei of the thalamus, the so-called nuclei of origin of the recruiting response (Morison and Dempsey[51]), may occupy an essential position in the function of the representational system built during this procedure.

The various experimental results which have been described would seem to comprise a set of examples of basically the same phenomenon. In each of these instances, some stimulus S_1 which has repeatedly been associated with some other stimulus S_2 ultimately seems to acquire the property of simulating the action of S_2. The examples which have been provided illustrate a process of "functional connection formation," resulting in what might be considered the establishment of functional equivalence with respect to some aspect of the action of two stimuli. If we call S_1 the conditioned stimulus and S_2 the unconditioned stimulus, we make explicit the already obvious similarity between these various procedures and classical conditioning. Classical conditioning can be considered as a process whereby S_1 becomes equivalent to S_2 with respect to the eliciting of the unconditioned response, which we thereafter call the conditioned response.*

The common features of the procedures that have been described are illustrated in the summarizing Figure 2.

The steps in formation of such functional stimulus equivalence would appear to be approximately as follows: The effect of the unconditioned stimulus, S_2, is to establish a dominant focus in the corresponding cortical region. Initially, the consequence of this dominant focus may be considered as essentially a sensitization of the region such that it can be induced to massive discharge by any adequate afferent input. Repeated association of this discharge with a particular input results in formation of a representational system which somehow stabilizes the dominant focus so that its susceptibility to that particular input persists. Simultaneously, however, the specificity of control of the discharge from this region increases. This may be due partially to a decrease in sensitization as the representational system becomes established and partially to the diminution of response[20, 33, 65] to nonrelevant stimuli occurring concurrently with the conditioning experience.

Ultimately, presentation of the conditioned stimulus causes activa-

---

* No attempt will be made herein to discuss the possible mechanisms of formation of an instrumental response. The author, however, believes that the establishment of a stimulus-controlled instrumental response might be analyzed in an essentially similar fashion.

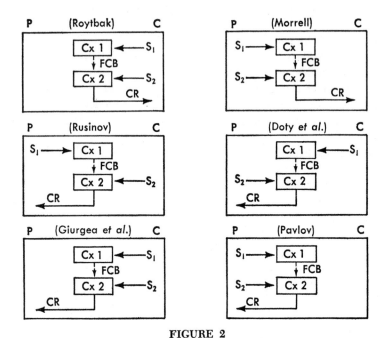

FIGURE 2

Stimulus substitution paradigms: P = peripheral, C = central, FCB = functional connection built, CR = conditioned response, Cx = cortex.

tion of the cortical region of the conditioned stimulus, with consequent activation of the thalamic projections from that region. This excitation is then propagated (perhaps at the thalamic level, perhaps via the reticular formation) to the thalamic structures which project to the cortical region of the unconditioned stimulus. The consequent thalamocortical activation of the region of the unconditioned stimulus evokes the unconditioned response, now, however, called a conditioned response. The conditioned stimulus, thus, becomes a "releaser" for a pattern of response.

A Proposed Physiological Model for Discriminative Learning

The hypothetical mechanism that has been described would seem adequate as a preliminary formulation of the possible mechanisms of connection formation and hence of stimulus substitution. Such mechanisms are the essential ingredient for a description of simple classical or stimulus-controlled instrumental conditioning, wherein the response will occur if the stimulus is perceived. A mechanism of this sort, however, is inadequate to explain performance of differential responses requiring discrimination between stimuli. This is particularly true of discriminations between stimuli which cannot be based on instantaneous stimulus characteristics. A tone or a chord cannot serve to identify a symphony. A flash of light of specified intensity and duration occurring ten times a second cannot be distinguished from an identical flash occurring six times a second on the basis of the number and distribution of retinal elements excited per flash. Discrimination between sequential series of stimuli comprised of nonunique components would seem to necessitate internalization of the time series of events and comparison with representations of the temporal pattern of previously experienced sequences of stimuli in order to achieve identification.* A model for this process is proposed herein.

When an animal experiences stimuli in a learning situation, some configuration of activity of the viscera, endocrine system, hypothalamus, reticular formation, and rhinencephalon reflect what we might call the affective and vegetative state of the organism. A basic dichotomy seems to exist between appetitive configurations and aversive configurations. The afferent stimuli themselves are transmitted centrally along two essentially distinct pathways, one of which is the appropriate specific sensory pathway, the other of which is the ascending reticular system.

We postulate that a *general representational system* is built as a consequence of repeated experiences of this sort, which might be called the "memory trace" or "engram" of that experience. This system lies in structures which do not belong to any specific sensory system. Into this general representational system become associated those regions of the reticular formation, the intralaminar and association nuclei of the thalamus, the hypothalamus and the rhinencephalon which are in a sustained state of activity during the stimulus or which are activated by the stimulus. At the same time, a *specific representational system* becomes established between structures in the specific sensory system which are activated by the stimulus. As these two representational systems are elaborated, a set of associational links is established whereby activity in the two systems interacts. *Such interaction may be inhibitory or facilitatory.*

A mature animal has, in nonspecific structures, a large number of established general representational systems. The nonspecific systems of the animal are not a globally acting reticulum, but seem made up of a set of "specifically sensitive" subsystems, reciprocally antagonistic, with equated global effects but different patterns of inhibition and excitation. The relative levels of activation of these various systems at any

---

* This problem is closely related to the problem of serial order in behavior, discussed so lucidly by Lashley.[41]

time are affected by the state of the animal. Those general systems which largely include the regions of reticular formation, hypothalamus, and rhinencephalon which reflect the present state will tend to dominate those general systems which do not include such representation of the "drive level" of the moment. Thus, the relative activation of the various general representational systems will vary during time as the condition of the organism changes.

When a stimulus impinges on the organism, it is propagated centrally along the appropriate specific sensory system. This propagation is accompanied by activation of the specific representational system in accordance with the constraints imposed on that system by the possible presence of modulating inflows along links with the momentarily dominant general representational system. The activity pattern in the specific sensory system and the constituent specific representational system tends to be stimulus-bound; that is, the characteristics of this pattern are largely determined by the characteristics of the stimulus, although they can be modulated as a consequence of interaction with the general representational system most dominant at the moment.

Simultaneously, the stimulus, probably via collaterals to lateral regions of the reticular formation,[6] has activated certain regions in the brain stem. That general representational system, in nonspecific structures, which maximally includes the regions in reticular formation activated by the total stimulus complex, including interoceptive as well as exteroceptive stimuli, plus those regions in hypothalamus and rhinencephalon which reflect the present "mood and motivation" of the animal, will become fully activated in all its constituent parts. The activity pattern in this general representational system, while arising as a consequence of the afferent stimulus, need not be determined by that stimulus. Rather, it represents the configuration *most compatible* from past experience with the combination of effects of that stimulus in the presence of a given prior internal state. Thus, the characteristics of the pattern evoked by the stimulus in the nonspecific structures comprising the extent of the general representational system are "stimulus in the context of state"–determined.

Finally, we postulate that if a sufficient correspondence exists between the activity in the general and in the specific representational systems, there must be a significant departure from randomness in the activity of some central nervous system region serving essentially as a coincidence detector. As a result of the corticofugal outflow of activity from such a discharging coincidence detector, the configuration of dominant foci shifts so that a pattern of motor system discharge is initiated which corresponds to that pattern previously most often associated with such coincidence. On the other hand, if such coincidence does not exist, no shift of foci occurs and no particular motor discharge ensues.*

The characteristics of the mechanism here proposed for gaining access to information stored in "memory" seem to differ in an essential way from the processes usually considered necessary. Most theorists, for example, Pitts and McCulloch[58] and Walter,[71] have suggested that the stores of information in memory, registered in some unstipulated code, are "scanned" until a counterpart of the incoming information is found. In view of the vast amount of information presumably stored in an adult central nervous system and the remarkable speed of access to memory, a "parallel" rather than "serial" scan has been suggested by some.

Note that in the present scheme no "scan" of memory occurs. Memory, rather than consisting of a set of registers in which information lies passively with location of the relevant items based on random search, is considered to be a dynamic process.† As the state of the animal and

---

* A possible mechanism for such an influence of the corticofugal discharge may be envisaged as analogous to one described by Hugelin and Bonvallet. These workers, investigating a facilitation of motor discharge originating from cortex as a consequence of reticular formation stimulation,[24] concluded that the cortical excitation which resulted from action of the ascending reticular activating system produced a secondary corticofugal inhibitory discharge which controlled the motor facilitation. They proposed[23] a reticulo-cortico-reticular circuit such that the ascending reticular activating system causes the discharge of a diffuse interneuronal cortical ensemble. This inhibitory corticofugal discharge arrests the reticular activation, controlling the motor facilitation. This permits differentiation of motor excitability as a function of the configuration of activity in cortex and recticular formation.

† The writer does not mean to imply, by stressing the dynamic aspects of memory activation, that memory has no static structure. Numerous experiments have clearly demonstrated that information is not centrally retained by a regenerative electrical pattern. There appears to be a relatively short-term process coupled to a long-persistent process. The former is probably regenerative in nature, the latter not. It is assumed that a physicochemical configuration is established within aggregates of nerve cells such that their electrical activity is subsequently altered in a characteristic fashion.

Isotope experiments on the turnover of substances in brain, not within the province of this paper to review, show clearly that the molecular framework of brain is in rapid flux. No static molecular species has been found; all which have been observed are in rapid and continuous breakdown and synthesis. If we assume that the phenomenon of memory must be based on a physicochemical structure, we cannot account for the stability of memory by invoking a static property for the molecular basis of memory. Therefore, it would seem necessary to postulate, as did von Foerster,[70] that the molecules of which memory is built are such as to be rebuilt in the same form as they possessed before breaking down. This apparently necessary postulate, of a dynamically retained structure, directs one's attention to such molecular species as the ribonucleic acids (RNA). A number of considerations suggest that more attention might profitably be directed at this possibility.

Brattgård[5] has shown that RNA synthesis in ganglion cells is proportional to luminous flux, indicating some fashion by which excitation of nerve cells is coupled to RNA synthesis. Hydén[27] has suggested the possibility that altered ionic environments (which might ensue from the breakdown of membrane impermeability and

the configuration of his environment alter, there ensues a continual fluctuation in the levels of excitation of the numerous general representational systems which have been established by experience. Those general
systems that most subsume nonspecific regions which reflect the present
state of the animal and his environment are most excitable, those which
only slightly involve presently active regions are less excitable. As a
consequence, memory patterns are ordered in accordance with their
relevance to the present configuration of the relevant central nervous
system parameters. The organism need not scan a vast number of equally
probable patterns in order to identify an input. Rather, the most probable pattern, in terms of over-all resemblance to the present animal-
environment complex, will be the one with easiest access, i.e., lowest
threshold for nonrandom levels of discharge, and the remainder of
memory will be hierarchically ordered in terms of relevance at the
moment.

Thus, a stimulus complex activating the specific representational
system will impinge on an animal in which the most relevant general
representational system, best reflecting the internal state of the organism
and the exteroceptive stimulus complex, is already being selected.

Clearly, in order for such a process to occur, there must exist a mechanism for comparison of the patterns of activity in the general and
specific representational systems. One possible mechanism suggests itself.
The model which we have outlined can be conceptualized as one in
which "reality" is primarily represented in the specific sensory cortex
and its afferent pathways. "Memory" is generated subcortically in nonspecific structures. The diffuse thalamic projection system would seem
to be a ready-made mechanism for displaying the dominant pattern of
the memory over large regions of cortex. We might propose that the
dominant pattern activated in reticular formation by a stimulus, reflecting the tonic influences of the moment from structures reporting the
state of the organism, is propagated upward to the intralaminar nuclei

---

subsequent massive movements of sodium and potassium, as shown by Hodgkin and
Huxley [22] and others) might cause an alteration in the exchange between RNA molecules and free amino acid residues in the environment, so as to cause a particularly
ordered sequence of amino acids to be organized on the RNA molecule. Subsequent
interactions between RNA molecules so organized and ionic species involved in the
polarization of nerve cell membranes might provide a basis for "time-binding" of the
effects of prior neuron discharge. Whatever the mechanism involved, Kreps [40] has
reported an increase in RNA turnover in auditory cortex of dog after establishment
of a conditioned response to an auditory stimulus. Preliminary experiments [36] in our
laboratory, initiated as a consequence of the foregoing considerations, have shown
that intraventricular injection of ribonuclease causes temporary deficits of as long
as four days in the performance of certain discriminative responses. To date, the
appropriate control experiments to indicate whether this effect is due to the action
of ribonuclease on central RNA or to other consequences of ribonuclease injection
have not been performed.

of the thalamus, thence to the association nuclei, and thence to association areas of the cortex. From the association areas, this pattern might project to the specific sensory areas of cortex via axodendritic synapses. Information arriving along the classical sensory pathways would activate axosomatic synapses. Proper phasing of axosomatic and axodendritic impulses impinging on a cortical neuron might drastically alter the probability of consequent efferent discharge from the cortex. That such interactions actually can occur is shown by the work of Jung.[38]

Chang[9] has discussed the possible functional contributions of axosomatic synapses (pericorpuscular) and axodendritic synapses (paradendritic) of the cortex to elaboration of conditioned responses, concluding: "The importance of the thalamoreticular system in the formation of conditioned reactions is that these subcortical structures are the source of subliminal excitation for the cortical dendrites. The final integrating function is affected, not by the reticular formation alone, but by the cerebral cortex." He considers paradendritic synapses as mechanisms for modulating the state of excitability of cortical neurons, and pericorpuscular synapses as mechanisms to evoke activity. Jasper[28] has described differences in the effects on cortical neurons of impulses arriving there from stimulation of specific and nonspecific thalamic nuclei, and has discussed the possibility of such a modulatory function of the nonspecific projection system.[30]

Alternative sites for the postulated interaction between patterns of activity of specific and nonspecific origin exist at other cortical and subcortical levels. Whatever the location of this interaction, its most crucial feature is that a marked nonrandomness of activity arises in the coincidence detector when congruence occurs between the two sources of input.

When the postulated congruence occurs between the two representational systems, the dominant pattern of activity arising in the nonspecific systems sensitive to the over-all state of the organism and reflecting past experiences is the same in essential aspects as the pattern of activity in the specific systems which reflect the present configuration of the environment. With this congruence, "memory" and "reality" become identical, and the current input is identified. This would appear, on logical grounds, the achievement of a crucial step in the process of analyzing sensory input to achieve adaptive differentiated response.

Once a configuration of sensory input were "identified" by such a sufficient congruence with the representation of past experience, response might occur by a mechanism analogous to that described for classical conditioned reflexes earlier in this paper. Corticothalamic or corticoreticular projections from the cortical area in which congruence became established might result in activation of those response system patterns which were previously associated in their activity with the establishment of that general representational system which was dominant at the moment of congruence.

One version of the proposed model is diagramed in Figure 3.

Psychological data and theory, particularly the learning theories of Estes[15] and Hull,[26] might be hoped to describe the rate of organization of a general representational system and the precision with which coincidence between general and specific representational systems must be achieved in order for properly discriminated response to occur. The author has, at this juncture, no explanation to offer for the apparent stabilization of a general representational system by reinforcement, whether positive or negative, other than the view suggested by Konorski,[39] nor for the varying effectiveness of different schedules of reinforcement. Konorski suggests that reinforcement produces a rapid rate of change of activity in certain centers and that this rapid rate of change exerts a "stamping-in" effect.

A detailed examination of the compatibility of the proposed model with behavioral data is beyond the scope of this paper. Incompatibilities undoubtedly exist in profusion. A number of encouraging compatibilities do, however, come to mind, and the writer finds the model a conceptually useful tool. Generalization gradients, for example, become an index of the extent to which other stimuli cause significantly nonrandom activity

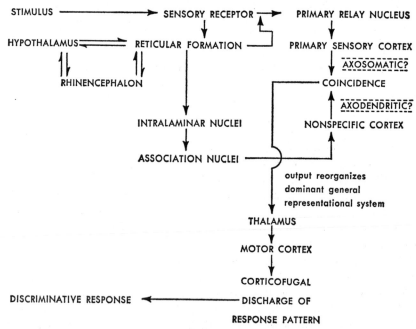

FIGURE 3

Proposed mechanism for differential response.

in the coincidence detection system. Hallucinations, fixations, and delusions become undue activity of a particular general representational system.

The bewildering failure of workers like Lashley to demonstrate localization of an engram for visual patterns might become more understandable, if spatial arrays of stimuli upon the retina were coded as a transform to a temporal sequence in many visual system fibers and transmitted to the entire sensory cortex. Spatial relations may not be isomorphically preserved as a topological array on the visual cortex. They may be transformed to temporal sequences projected, with different latencies but invariant time series of events, to many regions of the sensory cortex.[12] Retinocortical correspondence would still exist, but as a temporal-spatial transform, not as a spatial array. The cortical mantle need not be a screen onto which pictures are flashed to be watched by a popcorn-munching homunculus. So long as sensory cortex remained to respond to this temporal sequence of input from the peripheral receptors, it would be affected by the temporal pattern projected from the dominant general representational system, coincidence detection could occur, and corticofugal discharge could ensue. If the nonrandomness of such discharge were sufficient to affect the nonspecific regions from which the general representational system discharge originated, the activity therein could be reorganized, accomplishing "recognition," and redirected to cause motor response appropriate to the peripheral stimulus.

Some Experimental Support for the Model

There appear to be three salient features to the model which has been proposed: (1) The general representational system built by experience can retain the configuration of experienced stimulation; (2) the general representational system is extensive in its anatomical distribution; and (3) congruence between the temporal patterns of activity in specific and nonspecific systems is crucial for the performance of discriminations between stimuli. A body of experimental findings seems relevant to these aspects of the model. While these findings certainly do not constitute confirmation of the model, they appear sufficiently compatible with it to be presented as supporting evidence. These data are not presented as exhaustive documentation, but rather as an indication that the preceding material is not mere speculation with no foundation in fact.

1. Retention of Stimulus Configurations by Representational Systems

a. "Assimilation of the Rhythm" and Its Functional Significance. Livanov and Polyakov,[4] Yoshii, *et al.,*[73-76] Liberson, *et al.,*[43] John and Killam,[32, 33] and others have observed that during conditioning of various behavioral responses to a conditioned stimulus consisting of a light flickering at a given frequency, *patterns of central electrical activity similar to those initiated by the conditioned stimulus may be observed during intertrial intervals, in the absence of the conditioned stimulus.* Using a trace avoidance conditioning technique in dogs, Stern, Ulett, and Sines[67] have shown that during the delay period there is a significant increase in electrical activity at the frequency of the conditioned stimulus, as measured with a frequency analyzer. Although specificity of frequency of the assimilated rhythm has been demonstrated in one set of researches using a wave analyzer, there seems to be little justification for the expectation of *precise* frequency representation. Not until frequency discrimination training has been carried out does one see behavioral evidence of appreciable perceptual specificity. Normally, rather broad generalization gradients exist, and might be expected to correlate with variations in the frequency of central representation of the experience.

Modification of the resting electroencephalogram, in the absence of the conditioned stimulus, in a fashion which reflects the frequency of the conditioned stimulus, has been reported in cat, dog, rabbit, and rat. These observations of what Livanov termed "assimilation of the rhythm" seem to indicate that the representational system which is established during experience has patterns of discharge which preserve certain temporal characteristics of the stimulus.

The functional relevance of such assimilated rhythms is suggested by several pieces of evidence. Livanov and Korolkova[44] established a conditioned defensive reflex in rabbits to a flickering light. Subsequent weak stimulation of the motor cortex with an electrical stimulus caused performance of the conditioned response. The latency period of the motor response was minimal when the frequency of the electrical stimulus coincided with the flicker frequency used during conditioning. These workers also showed that rhythmic electrical stimulation of the visual cortex, to which 10 seconds later was added stimulation of the motor cortex at the same frequency, resulted in the appearance of a conditioned motor response to subsequent stimulation with flickering light at the same frequency, without any electrical stimulation.

Essentially parallel results have been reported by Neff, Nieder, and Oesterreich.[54] These workers conditioned cats to perform avoidance responses to a series of 100-per-second clicks presented over a loudspeaker. Subsequent central electrical stimulation of auditory regions at the same frequency produced immediate performance of the conditioned avoidance response. The converse procedure, conditioning to electrical stimulation of auditory pathways and testing with clicks at the same frequency, also yielded positive results.

Liberson and his co-workers[43] conditioned rats to respond to a flickering light. Pairing of the flicker with unilateral hippocampal stimulation at the same frequency, previously ineffective, led to performance of the conditioned response to subsequent frequency specific stimulation of the hippocampus alone. At this stage, stimulation of the contralateral hippocampus alone, at the flicker frequency, had no behavioral consequence. Brief *bilateral* hippocampal stimulation at the flicker frequency resulted in performance of the conditioned response to subsequent stimulation of the previously ineffective contralateral hippocampus alone.

Apparently related phenomena have been observed by John, Killam, Wenzel, and Mass.[34] Cats conditioned to perform an avoidance response to a steady visual stimulus showed moderate transfer of training in subsequent conditioning to a steady tone. Cats trained in the reverse order showed essentially no transfer to the second task. An average of about 400 trials was required to establish the conditioned avoidance response to criterion to the first conditioned stimulus, in both groups of animals. Other cats, conditioned using either a pulsed sound or a pulsed light as the first conditioned stimulus, required about the same number of trials to reach criterion. These animals, however, showed essentially *complete* transfer of training in one to ten trials in subsequent conditioning with light or sound *pulsed at the same frequency as the first conditioned stimulus.* In one animal, conditioned first to 10-per-second flicker and second to 10-per-second clicks, it was observed that following the transfer of training, which required four trials, the auditory stimulus evoked potentials in visual structures resembling those which were evoked by the visual conditioned stimulus.[33] These data suggest that, in contrast to the situation when steady stimuli were used, the second *pulsatile* stimulus has ready access to the general representational system established during prior conditioning with another stimulus pulsed at the same frequency, even though the two stimuli are of different sensory modalities. The fact that marked transfer occurred from flicker training to subsequent click training, and vice versa, indicated the probable independence of this phenomenon from processes unique to a particular sensory modality, and suggested mediation of nonspecific structures in the representation of the temporal pattern of stimulation common to the two stimuli.

An interesting piece of evidence, further supporting the assertion that representational systems can retain the temporal configuration of stimuli, was recently provided by Podsossenaia.[59] The foot of a rabbit was stimulated with electric shocks occurring twelve times per second. Following systematic variation in shock intensity, it was observed that subsequently a defensive reflex of the limb occurred on the presentation of previously indifferent sensory stimuli. These continuous stimuli elicited foot contractions occurring twelve times per second.

These various data seem compatible with the postulate that a representational system is built during conditioning that reflects certain attributes of the stimulus configuration. Stimulation of portions of this representational system by electrical stimuli with the appropriate attributes results in the activation of the entire system and performance of the conditioned response. Stimuli of other modalities but proper representational attributes (i.e., flicker instead of click, click instead of flicker, electrical pulses instead of flicker or clicks, flicker or clicks instead of electrical pulses) seem to gain functional access to the previously structured representational system with remarkable facility. These observations, in conjunction with observations of "assimilation of the rhythm" during conditioning with intermittent stimuli, and the phenomena observed in cortical conditioning[53] and cyclic cortical conditioning[31, 73] cited earlier, indicate that, at least for intermittent conditioned stimuli, the representational system that is established must reflect the temporal configuration of stimulation.

b. Selective Suppression or Facilitation of Response. A further line of evidence arises from work by Hernández-Peón and his collaborators[20] demonstrating the habituation of arousal to repeated stimuli. Sharpless and Jasper,[65] studying this phenomenon further, have shown that when arousal is habituated to a specific stimulus, presentation of other stimuli of the same modality indicates that arousal can still be elicited. That is, the habituation of arousal to a repeated stimulus of a particular modality is specific to that stimulus. Galambos, studying the reappearance of the habituated response after pairing the stimulus with various consequences to the animal, has demonstrated that the *reversal* of habituation can also be differential.

Recently, John and Killam[33] reported the diminution of response in a situation slightly different from that used in the studies of habituation. In the familiarization procedure, as we call it, an animal is repeatedly exposed for 15-second periods to a flickering light, with random intervals averaging one minute intervening between successive presentations. Twenty such periods of flicker occur in a session; one session occurs every twenty-four hours. Therefore, long intervals of time are interposed between rather short sessions of exposure to the stimulus, to which no consequences are attached. Under these circumstances, a gradual but rather uniform diminution of frequency-specific potentials can be observed in many places in the brain. In more recent studies,[32] we have observed that this diminution of frequency-specific potentials, or *labeled potentials,* is differential. If an animal has been exposed repeatedly to frequency 1 such that diminution of response to that frequency has occurred, presentation of light flickering at frequency 2 evokes potentials of amplitude comparable to those obtained before any familiarization has taken place. The change in response brought about by the familiarization experience is differential, diminution being more marked with respect to the frequently experienced stimulus than to the novel stimulus. These various data suggest that during repeated experience a stipulation of the stimulus which had had no consequence was somehow elaborated, and that representation, once established, served as the reference for differential suppression or inhibition of input with comparable characteristics.

Thus, various lines of evidence indicate that repeated experience with a particular temporal sequence of stimulation organizes in the brain a system which can discharge with the same temporal pattern. The involvement of nonspecific regions of the brain in this phenomenon might here be recalled.[73, 76] Further evidence that a system can be organized in the brain during conditioning, which is capable of reproducing and in that sense representing a temporal pattern of stimulation, was described recently by John and Killam.[33] When cats were trained to perform an avoidance response to a 10-per-second flickering light, we observed that the fully trained animals characteristically displayed a 20-per-second response to the conditioned stimulus in the visual cortex, double the stimulus frequency. Such an animal, immediately after reaching criterion, was presented with a 6.8-per-second flicker in a test for generalization. During the first few presentations of the new stimulus, performance of the conditioned avoidance response occurred. Inspection of the electrographic recordings showed that the discharge of the visual cortex was clearly at 20 per second rather than at 6.8 per second. We have repeatedly obtained similar results in more recent work, involving the use of other flicker frequencies.

Unpublished studies recently conducted in our laboratories by Marc Weiss, utilizing an average response computer, indicate that during behavioral generalization of an avoidance response to a new flicker frequency, average response waveforms computed from visual cortex and the reticular formation contain a strong component at the flicker frequency used during training. At the same time, this component is not present in the response of the lateral geniculate body and a number of other structures, which simply reflect the actual peripheral flicker frequency.

Thus, it appears that when a new stimulus is presented to an animal which resembles a stimulus which has been repeatedly experienced in a conditioning procedure, mechanisms may exist which are capable of altering the electrical response to the new stimulus in such a fashion as to achieve correspondence with the electrical response to the familiar stimulus. Such correspondence is accompanied by performance of the conditioned response which has been established to the familiar stimulus.

One might interpret this as suggesting that a system has been built, during the conditioning procedure, which has the capacity of discharging with a temporal pattern of electrical activity characteristic of the responses evoked by the conditioned stimulus. Presentation of a new stimulus which is somewhat similar to the conditioned stimulus, in the same environmental context as that in which the conditioned stimulus has repeatedly been experienced, causes an activation of the general representational system, which can facilitate discharge of the specific sensory afferent pathways in a fashion which corresponds to the pattern of activity of the general representational system rather than to the pattern of stimulation of the peripheral receptors. Conversely, it seems possible for differential suppression of response to occur, suggesting an inhibitory interaction between the two systems.

2. Extensive Nature of the General Representational System

Segundo and his co-workers[64] have recently shown that the effects of reticular formation stimulation can be elicited as conditioned responses to exteroceptive stimuli. Rusinov[59] has reported data indicating that conditioned hypothalamic responses can be established following imposition of a hypothalamic dominant focus. These and other findings[32, 33, 43, 73-75] are compatible with the suggestion that during conditioning, regions in nonspecific structures, within which general representational systems are postulated to be established, can become differentially susceptible to the conditioned stimuli.

The work of Delgado, et al.,[11] and of Grastyán, et al.,[18] further support the assertion that the general representational system which is built during conditioning can involve extensive regions. These workers have found, in animals conditioned to perform approach and avoidance responses to different stimuli, that it is possible to elicit a coordinated differential performance of one or the other response by direct electrical stimulation of a number of rhinencephalic and mesencephalic regions.

The work of Gavlichek[17] provides electrographic evidence that aspects of the experimental environment can acquire signal significance during conditioning, serving to activate response systems established to conditioned stimuli which have been presented in that environment. Similarly, it has been reported that animals repeatedly exposed to a specific frequency of flickering light in an experimental room show spontaneous electrocortical activity at that frequency, in the absence of flicker, upon being brought into the room.[74] Such findings, together with numerous behavioral examples of "secondary reinforcement," might be interpreted as indicating that stimulation of a region which was part of a general representational system established during conditioning can cause activation of the complete representational system, thereby producing a well-integrated and complex sequence of behavior.

Although the data indicate that representational systems mediating a conditioned response can be established without drive reduction or "reinforcement," motivational components can be included in these representational systems. The work of Nielson and his collaborators[55] provides evidence which suggests that a neural region related to motivation can be incorporated into a representational system by conditioning. They report that when a region, initially not negatively reinforcing for self-stimulation, is directly stimulated to provide the conditioned stimulus for an avoidance response, subsequent evaluation of that region using the self-stimulation procedure shows it to be negatively reinforcing. Thus, the "motivational" aspects of central stimulation of certain regions seem to be susceptible to change with experience.

Grastyán and his co-workers[19] have provided evidence that, in the mesencephalon, approach responses and avoidance responses seem to be differentially mediated by two separate systems roughly lying side by side. A similar distinction may exist for dorsal versus ventral hippocampal regions. It would seem reasonable to expect that during approach conditioning, certain hypothalamic areas, including the so-called trophotropic areas of Hess,[21] would be active to a greater extent than the so-called ergotropic areas. During avoidance conditioning one would expect approximately the opposite configuration of activity. One might expect, therefore, a differential incorporation of these areas, among others, into the respective representational systems established during these various conditioning procedures or by life experiences related to approach toward or avoidance of certain stimuli. Activation of such systems might account for an approach or avoidance tendency following the stimulus which caused such activation. These considerations seem relevant to the interpretation of results obtained by Olds[56] and others in "self-stimulation" experiments. Further, it seems possible that the combination of neural events ensuing from proprioceptive and other feedback from an instrumental response simultaneous with such direct electrical stimulation is such as to create a dominant focus in the regions mediating the instrumental response, so that they become incorporated into a simultaneously activated representational system.

3. Congruence of Temporal Patterns in Specific and General Representational Systems

In more recent experiments,[32] we have observed a number of phenomena which appear relevant to the role of interactions between the specific and general representational systems during discriminative responses.

Initially, a cat was conditioned to perform a lever-pressing response for milk, on a 1:1 reinforcement ratio. After steady lever-pressing rates were established, presentation of flicker stimuli (10 per second) evoked sporadic and small labeled responses in both specific and nonspecific structures, as illustrated in the upper portion of Figure 4.

Next, the cat was trained to press the lever only during the presence of the 10-per-second flicker. Responses in the absence of flicker were not reinforced. After the lever-pressing response was brought under flicker stimulus control, frequency-specific (labeled) responses to flicker which were stable and of higher amplitude than previously appeared in both specific and nonspecific structures. These responses are illustrated in the lower portion of Figure 4.

Next, differential training was instituted. Lever responses were reinforced during presentation of 10-per-second flicker (S^a) but not during

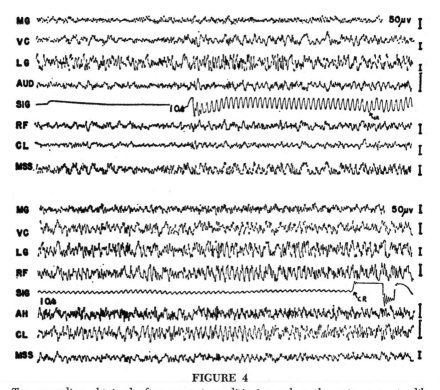

FIGURE 4

Top, recording obtained after operant conditioning, when the cats were steadily pressing the lever, on introduction of the 10-per-second flicker. Arrow denotes lever press. *Bottom,* recordings obtained after the lever-pressing response was brought under control of the 10-per-second flicker as the discriminative stimulus (S^D). Arrow denotes lever press. (MG, medical geniculate body; VC, visual cortex; LG, lateral geniculate body; AUD, auditory cortex; SIG, record of conditioned stimulus and conditioned response; RF, fornix; CL, centralis lateralis; MSS, medial suprasylvian gyrus; AH, ventral hippocampus).

absence of flicker or during presentation of 6-per-second flicker (S^Δ). As training proceeded, stable and large amplitude labeled responses were evoked by both the S^d and the S^Δ. However, these responses tended to appear differentially in some structures. For example, labeled responses were observed more markedly in posterior (dorsal) hippocampus during presentation of S^Δ than during S^d, while anterior (ventral) hippocampus tended to respond more markedly to S^d than to S^Δ.

As the animals learned the discrimination, they committed an appreciable number of errors. It was by contrasting correct performance with errors that the most interesting features of the data were made evident.

When the lever-pressing response was performed correctly, during the S^d, stable and marked 10-per-second labeled response was observed in the visual system, fornix, *N. centralis lateralis,* and ventral hippocampus. A typical configuration of electrical activity during correct response to S^d is illustrated in the upper portion of Figure 5.

On occasion, *errors of omission* occurred. The animal, although long fluid-deprived, failed to press the lever during presentation of the 10-per-second S^d. During such errors of omission, a marked 5-to-6-second rhythm could be observed in various structures, including the fornix and

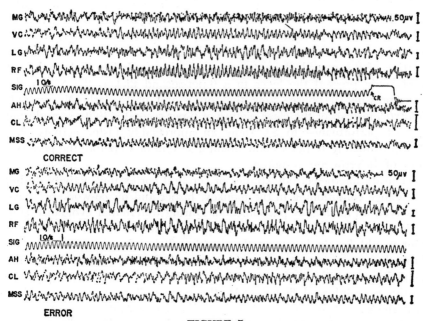

FIGURE 5

Records obtained during differential conditioning. In this and subsequent figures, leads labeled as in Figure 4. *Top,* correct response to 10-per-second flicker. Arrow denotes lever press. *Bottom,* Error of omission to 10-per-second flicker.

N. centralis lateralis, and sometimes in visual cortex, with occasional 10-per-second waves superimposed upon the slower rhythm. An example of labeled response configuration during such response failure is presented in the lower portion of Figure 5.

During errors of omission, the dorsal hippocampus characteristically displayed marked slow 5-to-6-per-second activity. If the S^d presentation were continued, the following was frequently observed: The 5-to-6-second waves abruptly disappeared from dorsal hippocampus, giving way to a fast activity with no slow hypersynchrony. As this happened, the activity in *N. centralis lateralis* came into better correspondence with that in the fornix. The 10-per-second activity in the fornix became quite marked, and the slow amplitude modulation disappeared from visual cortex. As visual cortex, *N. centralis lateralis* and the fornix came into correspondence, displaying labeled responses at the frequency of the S^d, an abrupt change in waveform took place in the three structures so that the previously rounded 10-per-second waves became spike-like at the same frequency, and within 1 or 2 seconds appropriate conditioned response occurred. This sequence of events was observed on many occasions, and characterized the activity recorded during errors of omission.

In Figure 6, we see the electric activity recorded from the same animal looking at a 6-per-second flicker. The upper portion of the record shows us the *correct* response to a 6-per-second flicker; that is, the cat does *not* press the lever. Notice that the fornix and *N. centralis lateralis* show a clear 6-per-second discharge. In contrast, the lower portion of the record illustrates an *error of commission,* that is, the cat mistakenly pressed the lever to a 6-per-second flicker, the S^Δ for the lever-pressing response. Now the fornix and particularly *N. centralis lateralis,* instead of the clear picture of 6-per-second activity seen during correct performance to S^Δ, show an appreciably faster activity that is approximately 10 per second, about a second or so before the performance of the erroneous response.

During microelectrode studies of cerebral cortex unit activity during avoidance conditioning in the monkey, Jasper and his co-workers[29] have observed an analogous phenomenon. During differential avoidance conditioning to two different flicker frequencies, it was found that a single unit would fire in bursts at the positive flicker frequency and be inhibited during presentation of the other flicker frequency. When the animal made an error of commission, performing the avoidance response to the nonreinforced flicker (S^Δ), the same unit response occurred as with the S^d.

As our experiments proceeded, the animal was conditioned to perform a conditioned avoidance response on the presentation of the 6-per-second flicker, which had previously served as the S^Δ for the lever-

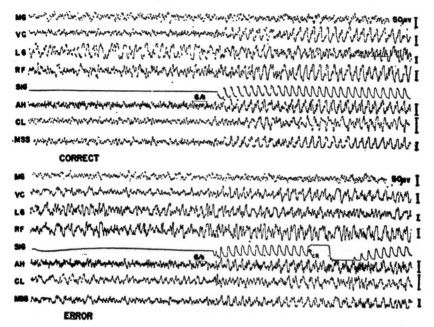

FIGURE 6

Record obtained during differential conditioning. *Top,* correct response to 6-per-second flicker. *Bottom,* error of commission to 6-per-second flicker. Arrow denotes lever press.

pressing response. Simultaneously, however, performance of the lever-pressing response was maintained to the 10-per-second flicker.

At this stage an additional interesting phenomenon was observed. On the presentation of the 10-per-second flicker for the conditioned approach response (lever pressing), the labeled responses which were characteristically evoked in the fornix, *N. centralis lateralis,* and dorsal hippocampus were at a frequency approximately 5 to 6 per second. In visual cortex and ventral hippocampus, a stable and clear 10-per-second labeled response was observed, with the cortical response sometimes modulated in amplitude in correspondence with the fornix potentials. After 2 to 3 seconds, a 10-per-second labeled response tended to appear in fornix superimposed upon the slower waves. Gradually, this faster activity came to dominate the pattern of potentials in the fornix and then again gave way to the slower activity. This configuration of activity is illustrated in Figure 7. Sometimes such oscillation of the dominant frequency persisted throughout the period of stimulus presentation and no lever pressing occurred. Almost invariably, if the lever-pressing response occurred, it took place during a period of 10-per-second activity

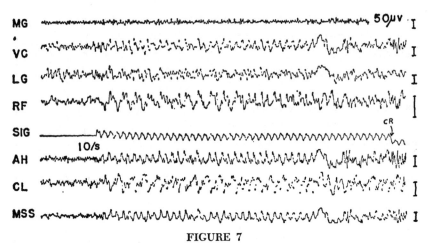

FIGURE 7

Records obtained during lever press to 10-per-second flicker after avoidance conditioning to the 6-per-second flicker. Arrow indicates lever press.

in the fornix and *N. centralis lateralis,* and was preceded by the change in waveform in those structures and in the visual cortex that was previously described.

A number of manipulations were performed at this stage which provide further insight into the nature of the labeled responses in the fornix and *N. centralis lateralis.* If the animal were satiated with milk *ad libitum* so that it evinced no interest in drinking further and would not press the lever during the 10-per-second flicker, presentation of the 10-per-second signal for lever pressing was accompanied by a predominantly 6-per-second labeled response in the fornix and *N. centralis lateralis.* Sometimes the 10-per-second labeled response in visual cortex was markedly modulated by this slow activity in the nonspecific structures and on occasion, when such a configuration was observed, the animal performed the conditioned *avoidance* response.

If, instead of being satiated with milk, the animal received reserpine and performance of the conditioned avoidance response was consequently abolished,[33, 37] presentation of the 10-per-second flicker evoked large and stable labeled responses at a 10-per-second frequency in *N. centralis lateralis* and in the fornix with no sign of the previously inevitable 6 per second. This response configuration is illustrated in Figure 8. Administration of amphetamine in an amount sufficient to counteract the reserpine-induced blockade of the conditioned avoidance response resulted in a reappearance of the 6-per-second labeled responses in the fornix and *N. centralis lateralis* on the presentation of the 10-per-second flicker.

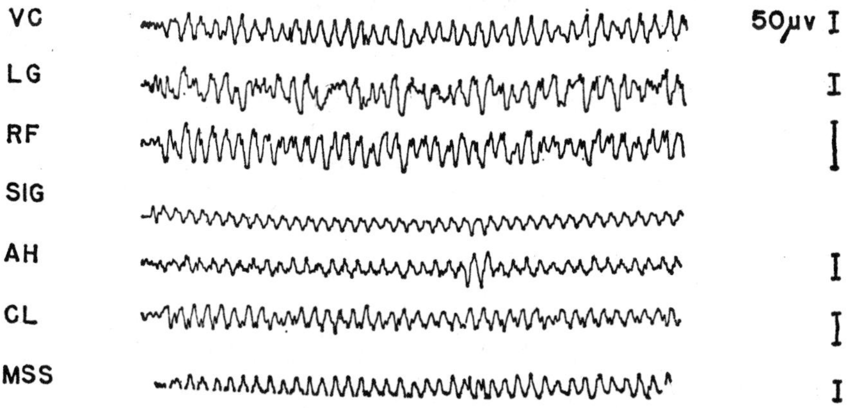

VC ~~~~~~~~~~~~~~~~~~~~~~~~~~~ 50μv I

LG ~~~~~~~~~~~~~~~~~~~~~~~~~~~ I

RF ~~~~~~~~~~~~~~~~~~~~~~~~~~~ I

SIG ~~~~~~~~~~~~~~~~~~~~~~~~~~~

AH ~~~~~~~~~~~~~~~~~~~~~~~~~~~ I

CL ~~~~~~~~~~~~~~~~~~~~~~~~~~~ I

MSS ~~~~~~~~~~~~~~~~~~~~~~~~~~~ I

FIGURE 8

Records obtained on presentation of the 10-per-second flicker after performance of the conditioned avoidance response to the 6-per-second flicker was blocked by injection of reserpine (100 micrograms per kilogram).

The illustrations of these various phenomena included herein were all obtained from the same animal. The events which have been described were observed with greatest clarity in that animal. However, data from three additional animals, while not as clear or consistent as the above, were in essential agreement with this picture.[32] Potentials at both S^d and S^Δ frequencies were repeatedly observed also in the reticular formation in these animals. It would appear that during the acquisition of two different conditioned responses to two flicker stimuli of different frequency, two distinct general representational systems were established in nonspecific subcortical structures. Differential modification of the drive level for the two conditioned responses by satiation with milk or by the administration of drugs seemed to alter the relative ease of activation of these two systems. Amplitude modulation of labeled responses in visual cortex in a fashion corresponding to the dominant response pattern in nonspecific structures suggests that the probability of cortical discharge to afferent input along the specific sensory pathways may be phasically varied as a function of the pattern of reticular activation of nonspecific structures.

The observation of high correlations in activity pattern between N. *centralis lateralis* and the fornix, in the absence of high-voltage hypersynchrony in the dorsal hippocampus, suggests that the interaction of rhinencephalic activity with that of the primary sensory cortex may be achieved at least partially via an outflow through the intralaminar pathways of the diffuse projection system, in a fashion which can be modulated by the levels of reticular formation activity. This rhinencephalic-reticular interaction, perhaps at the level of the intralaminar nuclei, would provide a way in which the effectiveness of activated general representational systems might be modified so as to reflect the overall "emotional state." It seems clear that the dominant general representational system at a particular moment need not necessarily correspond to that system which was established during previous presentations of the stimuli impinging on the peripheral receptors at that moment. The dominant general representational system need not be "stimulus bound," but may vary in a manner dependent on the state of motivation of the organism and on its past experiences.

The repeated observation of appropriate performance of conditioned responses at a time when the activity of these postulated general representational systems and their anterior projection comes into approximate correspondence with the activity in the specific representational system suggests more than a fortuitous basis for this phenomenon. In the proposed model, when such correspondence occurs between the two systems, the dominant pattern of activity arising in nonspecific systems, responsive to peripheral stimulation but also sensitive to the over-all state of the organism in the context of previous experiences, becomes quite similar to the pattern of activity in the specific sensory systems, reflecting primarily the present stimulus configuration impinging on the organism from its environment. As this correspondence increases, "memory" and "reality" come into congruence. This would appear, on logical grounds, to constitute a crucial step in the process of analyzing sensory input to achieve differentiated adaptive response.

The change in waveform often observed when such correspondence is established between the two systems may indicate an increase in the nonrandomness of corticofugal discharge. The precision with which congruence between the two systems needs to be established, that is, the critical level of nonrandomness in the activity of the coincidence detector, depends on the "level of confidence" required by the system controlling motor response. This level of confidence probably varies appreciably with the amount of past experience and the state of the organism. When acceptable nonrandomness of activity in the coincidence detector was achieved as general and specific system activity became similar, "triggering" of the appropriate response system might occur in a fashion analogous to that proposed for simple stimulus substitution response earlier in this paper: sufficiently nonrandom corticofugal discharge to the region of the reticular formation which was dominant at the time that congruence was achieved might alter the pattern of discharge of the general representational system, activating a modulated discharge of the motor response system.

Summary and Conclusion

Many years ago, Lashley[42] said: "The facts of cerebral physiology are so varied, so diverse, as to suggest that for some of them each theory is true, for all of them every theory is false." Whether the various explanations proposed herein are true or false cannot easily be evaluated. Time and effort will be required to test these formulations and to clarify the ways in which they must be revised. Of more immediate significance is the cohesiveness of the data that have been presented, and the compatibility of these data with the proposed theory. The theory *might* be right; that is, whether or not the postulated mechanisms do in reality generate adaptive behavior, such mechanisms could. A computer, were it to be programed in accordance with the functional constraints which have been described, could probably be conditioned to produce differentiated adaptive responses. Yet the scheme which has been propounded affords no explicit process which generates awareness.

One of the processes that has been assigned a crucial role in this model, the achievement of a congruence between specific and nonspecific system activity, has been suggested by Morison[50] as related to awareness:

> For the moment let us assume then that the reticular sensory system is the most primitive sensory system and that it makes central connections in midbrain and diencephalon with other reticular areas which can store traces, engrams or what not as a result of past experience. Coincidence or congruence between an incoming pattern of impulses and a "filing card" of past experience results in a sense of awareness or consciousness. The more rapidly conducting classical sensory system may be thought of as a more recent arrangement for projection of precisely refined sensory pictures on cortex and lateral thalamus. Under normal conditions these may be "looked at" by, let us say, the centrencephalic system in order to add precision to the more generalized awareness aroused by the reticular sensory system. When all these elements are working nicely together the organism is in a position for nice adjustment to external reality.

In a number of recent well-known symposia, a great variety of orientations toward the phenomenon of consiousness and awareness have been elaborated. These have ranged from the proposition that awareness was an integrative process of the whole brain to the suggestion that awareness arose from the convergence of information upon a reticular neuron. In a scintillating paper, Fessard[16] has reviewed the alternative formulations for the mediation of consciousness. He defines *experienced integration* as "the integration itself, the relationship of one functioning part to another, which is mind and which causes the phenomenon of consciousness." He concludes that it is the concept of patterns of excitatory states which stands out of these formulations and raises the question: What makes a pattern "conscious" of its own patterning?

The very paucity of neurophysiological data relevant to this problem seems to necessitate speculation and exploration, rather than to constrain it. The richness and texture of subjective experience constitutes eloquent refutation of the suggestion that awareness resides in "one ultimate pontifical neuron." Yet it must have a locus, albeit an extensive one, because "the flickering pattern on the enchanted loom" is woven with a constant thread. Perhaps that constant thread consists of the fact that the same aggregate of cells constitutes the loom. Awareness would seem a more likely property of the aggregate than of the components.

Since, as Morison recognized, the achievement of coincidence between nonspecific and specific system patterns offers a peculiar advantage for adjustment of the organism to external reality, perhaps this process can be used to provide a conceptual entry to the problem. Awareness may be a property arising from the process of "corticoreticular resonance." Such resonance may arise between cortical regions, achieving nonrandom levels of corticofugal discharge from the interaction of afferent influx from specific and nonspecific origins, and the reticular and thalamic reticular regions, which were active at the time of the cortical discharge, serving as dominant foci. As different patterns of excitation arise in the reticular formation and modulate cortical responsiveness, and as different corticofugal influences impinge upon it, at varying levels of nonrandomness, the state of the aggregate shifts constantly. Such "resonances" are configurations of relationships between aggregates of neurons. Awareness may be the concomitant of the effect on the aggregate of its own configuration of activity.

For awareness to consist of an integrated representation of the state of an aggregate of neurons demands sensing devices which are multineuronal, which are themselves aggregates. The most parsimonious representation of the state of such an aggregate might be the aggregate itself. Such a view might seem to be incompatible with our present knowledge of neural activity. Yet, perhaps mechanisms exist which are responsive to the state of an aggregate. A system such as the reticular core, composed largely of closely arrayed neurons with very short axons, in which the voltage gradients from action potentials may exert a relatively less pronounced effect and graded slow potentials might be of primary significance, might have peculiar characteristics. The interactions of electrical and chemical fields might here provide a medium for informational transactions of a radically different sort. Perhaps the activity of a region in such an aggregate is markedly affected by factors such as the extent of nonrandomness of activity in other domains of the system.

Using the tools which we have fashioned thus far, we have learned much about the activity of neurons. Much of this knowledge is relevant to problems basic to an understanding of subjective experience, a fraction of which has been reviewed in this paper. While I believe that subjective experience arises from the activity of neurons, I feel that the properties of neurons on which we have hitherto focused are unlikely to provide the basis for mediation of awareness, which seems most likely to be a property of relationships between neural aggregates. The properties of neural aggregates as distinct from properties of neurons are still to be clarified. Of crucial importance in the elucidation of such properties seems to be detailed analysis of the language in which information is coded and stored in the brain. Memory and subjective awareness seem constantly to abut on one another, and if we could specify the coding system, we might stipulate the necessary functional characteristics of the "read-out" or decoding systems which are at the core of experienced integration.

Penfield said it well:[57] "How it may be that ganglionic activity is transformed into thinking and how it is that thought is converted into the neuronal activity of conscious voluntary action we have no knowledge. Here is the fundamental problem. Here physiology and psychology come face to face."

REFERENCES

1. Arduini, A., "Enduring potential changes evoked in the cerebral cortex by stimulation of brain stem reticular formation and thalamus," in *Reticular Formation of the Brain*, Little, Brown and Co., Toronto, 1958.

2. Baer, A., "Uber gleichzeitige electrische Reizung zweier Grosshirnstellen am ungehemmten Hunde," *Pflügers Arch. f.d. ges. Physiologie*, 1905, 106:523-567.

3. Beck, E. C., and Doty, R. W., "Conditioned flexion reflexes acquired during combined catalepsy and de-afferentation," *J. Comp. Physiol. Psych.*, 1957, 50:211-216.

4. Bishop, G. H., and O'Leary, J. L., "The effects of polarizing currents on cell potentials and their significance in the interpretation of central nervous system activity," *EEG Clin. Neurophysiol.*, 1950, 2:401-416.

5. Brattgård, S. O., "The importance of adequate stimulation for the chemical composition of retinal ganglion cells during early postnatal development," *Acta Radiologica*, 1952, Suppl. 96, 1-80.

6. Brodal, A., *The Recticular Formation of the Brain Stem. Anatomical Aspects and Functional Correlations*, Oliver and Boyd, London, 1957.

7. Brookhart, J. M., Arduini, A., Mancia, M., and Moruzzi, G., "Thalamocortical relations as revealed by induced slow potential changes," *J. Neurophysiol.*, 1958, 21:499-525.

8. Brown-Séquard, C. E., "Existence de l'excitabilité motrice et de l'excitabilité inhibitoire dans les regions occipitales et sphénoïdales de l'écorce cérébrale," *Compt. rend. et memoires de la société de biologie,* 1884 (8e Serie, Pt. I), 36:301-303.

9. Chang, H. T., quoted by Gershuni, G. V., in "International colloquium on the electroencephalography of higher nervous activity," *Sechenov Physiological Journal of the USSR,* 1959, 45:189-199.

10. Cicardo, V. H., and Torino, A., "Release of potassium by the brain of the dog during electrical stimulation," *Science,* 1942, 95:625; Colfer, H. F., and Essex, H. E., "Distribution of total electrolytes, K, and Na in the cerebral cortex in relation to experimental convulsions," *Am. J. Physiol.,* 1947, 150: 27.

11. Delgado, J. M. R., Rosvold, H. E., and Looney, E., "Evoking conditioned fear by electrical stimulation of subcortical structures in the monkey brain," *J. Comp. Physiol. Psych.,* 1956, 49:373-380.

12. Doty, R. W., "Potentials evoked in cat cerebral cortex by diffuse and by punctiform photic stimuli," *J. Neurophysiol.,* 1958, 21:437-464.

13. ———, and Rutledge, L. T., " 'Generalization' between cortically and peripherally applied stimuli eliciting conditioned reflexes," *J. Neurophysiol.,* 1959, 22:428-435.

14. ———, Rutledge, L. T., and Larsen, R. M., "Conditioned reflexes established to electrical stimulation of cat cerebral cortex," *J. Neurophysiol.,* 1956, 19: 401-415, and personal communications.

15. Estes, W. K., "Statistical theory of distributional phenomena in learning," *Psychol. Rev.,* 1955, 62:369-377.

16. Fessard, A. E., "Mechanisms of nervous integration and conscious experience," in *Brain Mechanisms and Consciousness,* Charles C Thomas, Springfield, Ill., 1954.

17. Gavlichek, V., "Electroencephalographic characteristics of the conditioned reflex dominant state," *Sechenov Physiological Journal of the USSR,* 1958, 44:274-285.

18. Giurgea, C., *Studii Cercetari Fiziol. Neurol.,* 1953, 4:41-73, referred to by Doty, R. W., in *Transactions of the First Conference on the Central Nervous System and Behavior,* Josiah Macy, Jr., Foundation, New York, 1959; Doty, R. W., and Giurgea, C., "Conditioned reflexes establishing by coupling visual and motor cortex stimulation," *The Physiologist,* 1958, 1:17.

19. Grastyán, E., Lissák, K., and Kékesi, F., "Facilitation and inhibition of conditioned alimentary and defensive reflexes by stimulation of the hypothalamus and reticular formation," *Acta Physiologica Hungarica,* 1956, 9:133-151.

20. Hernández-Peón, R., and Scherrer, H., "Habituation to acoustic stimuli in cochlear-nucleus," *Fed. Proc.,* 1955, 14:71.

21. Hess, W. R., *The Diencephalon,* Grune and Stratton, New York, 1954.

22. Hodgkin, A. L., and Huxley, A. F., "Currents carried by sodium and potassium ions through the membrane of the giant axon of Loligo," *J. Physiol.,* 1952, 116:449-472.

23. Hugelin, A., and Bonvallet, M., "Étude éxperimentale des interrelations réticulocorticales. Proposition d'une théorie de l'asservissement réticulaire à une systèm diffus cortical," *J. Physiol. Paris,* 1957, 49:1201-1223.

24. ———, and Bonvallet, M., "Tonus corticale et controle de la facilitation motor d'origin réticulaire," *J. Physiol. Paris,* 1957, 49:1171-1200.

25. Hughes, J. R., "Post-tetanic potentiation," *Physiol. Rev.,* 1958, 38:91-113.

26. Hull, C. L., *Principles of Behavior,* Appleton-Century, New York, 1943.

27. Hydén, H., "Thoughts on an intracellular mechanism serving memory," unpublished manuscript.

28. Jasper, H. H., "Functional properties of the thalamic reticular system," in *Brain Mechanisms and Consciousness*, Delafresnaye, J. F., ed., Charles C Thomas, Springfield, Ill., 1954.

29. ———, "Current concepts of nervous inhibition," in *Inhibition in the Nervous System and Gamma-Aminobutyric Acid*, Roberts, Eugene, ed., Pergamon Press, New York, 1960.

30. ———, Ricci, G. F., and Doane, B., "Patterns of cortical neuronal discharge during conditioned responses in monkeys," in *Neurological Basis of Behavior*, Little, Brown and Co., Boston, 1958.

31. John, E. R., and Chow, K. L., unpublished observations.

32. ———, and Killam, K. F., "Electrophysiological correlates of differential approach-avoidance conditioning in the cat," *J. Nerv. Ment. Dis.*, 1960, 131:183-201.

33. ———, and Killam, K. F., "Electrophysiological correlates of avoidance conditioning in the cat," *J. Pharm. Exp. Therap.*, 1959, 125:252-274; and John, E. R., in *Transactions of the First Conference on the Central Nervous System and Behavior*, Josiah Macy, Jr., Foundation, 1959.

34. ———, Killam, K. F., Wenzel, B. M., and Mass, M., unpublished observations.

35. ———, Tschirgi, R. D., and Wenzel, B. M., "Effects of injections of cations into the cerebral ventricles on conditioned responses in the cat," *J. Physiol.* (London) 1959, 146:550-562.

36. ———, Wenzel, B., and Tschirgi, R. D., unpublished data.

37. ———, Wenzel, B. M., and Tschirgi, R. D., "Differential effects on various conditioned responses in cats caused by intraventricular and intramuscular injections of reserpine and other substances," *J. Pharm. Exp. Therap.*, 1958, 123:193-205.

38. Jung, R., "Coordination of specific and non-specific afferent impulses at single neurons of the visual cortex," in *Reticular Formation of the Brain*, Little, Brown and Co., Boston, 1958.

39. Konorski, J., "Mechanisms of learning," in *Physiological Mechanisms in Animal Behavior*, S. E. B. Symposium No. IV, Academic Press, New York, 1950.

40. Kreps, E. M., referred to by Palladine, A. V., and Vladimirov, G. E., in "The use of radioactive isotopes in the study of functional biochemistry of the brain," *First Internat. Confer. on Peaceful Uses of Atomic Energy*, Geneva, 1955, Vol. 12, Paper 710.

41. Lashley, K. S., "The problem of serial order in behavior" in *Cerebral Mechanisms in Behavior*, Wiley & Sons, New York, 1951.

42. ———, "Basic neural mechanisms in behavior," *Psychological Review*, 1930, 37:1-24.

43. Liberson, W. T., Ellen, P., and Cadell, T., "EEG studies during avoidance conditioning in rats," in *EEG Studies of Conditioning in Animals and Man*, Grune and Stratton, New York, in press; and Liberson, W. T., paper presented at APA *Symposium on Cerebral Dysfunction*, Chicago, 1959, to be published.

44. Livanov, M. N., and Korolkova, T. A., "The influence of inadequate stimulation of the cortex with induction current on the bioelectrical rhythm of the cortex and conditioned reflex activity," *Zhur. vysschei. ner. deyatel. im. Pavlova*, 1951, Vol. 1, 3:332-346; as reported in Rusinov, V. S., and Rabinovich, M. Y., "Electroencephalographic researches in the laboratories and clinics of the Soviet Union," *EEG clin. Neurophysiol.*, Suppl. 8, 1958.

45. Livanov, M. N., and Polyakov, K. L., "Electrical processes in the cerebral cortex of rabbits during the formation of the defensive conditioned reflex to rhythmic stimulation," *Bull. Acad. Sci. USSR*, 1945, 3:286-307; as reported in Rusinov, V. S., and Rabinovich, M. Y., "Electroencephalographic researches in the laboratories and clinics of the Soviet Union," *EEG clin. Neurophysiol.*, Suppl. 8, 1958.

46. Loucks, R. B., "The experimental delimitation of neural structures essential for learning: The attempt to condition striped muscle responses with faradization of the sigmoid gyri," *J. Psychol.*, 1935, 1:5-44.

47. ———, "The acquisition and retention of responses conditioned to faradic cerebral stimuli administered through electrodes shielded by barriers," presented at meetings of American Psychological Association, September, 1955.

48. ———, "Studies of neural structures essential for learning. The conditioning of salivary and striped muscle responses to faradization of cortical sensory elements, and the action of sleep upon such mechanisms," *J. Comp. Psychol.*, 1938, 25:315-332.

49. MacIntosh, F. C., and Oborin, P. E., "Release of acetylcholine from intact cerebral cortex," *Abstracts, XIX Internat. Physiol. Cong.*, Montreal, 1953, pp. 580-581.

50. Morison, R. S., in *Brain Mechanisms and Consciousness*, J. F. Delafresnaye, ed., Charles C Thomas, Springfield, Ill., 1954, p. 493.

51. ———, and Dempsey, E. W., "A study of thalamo-cortical relations," *Am. J. Physiol.*, 1942, 135:281-292.

52. Morrell, F., personal communication.

52a. ———, *Annals New York Acad. Sci.*, 1961, 92:860-876.

53. ———, and Jasper, H., "Electrographic studies of the formation of temporary connections in the brain," *EEG clin. Neurophysiol.*, 1956, 8:201-215.

54. Neff, W. D., Nieder, P. C., and Oesterreich, R. E., "Learned responses elicited by electrical stimulation of auditory pathways," *Fed. Proc.*, 18:112, 1959.

55. Nielson, H. C., Doty, R. W., and Rutledge, L. T., "Motivational and perceptual aspects of subcortical stimulation in cats," *Am. J. Physiol.*, 1958, 194:427-432.

56. Olds, J., "A preliminary mapping of electrical reinforcing effects in the rat brain," *J. Comp. Physiol. Psych.*, 1956, 49:281-285.

57. Penfield, W., "Studies of the cerebral cortex of man," in *Brain Mechanisms and Consciousness*, Charles C Thomas, Springfield, Ill., 1954.

58. Pitts, W., and McCulloch, W. S., "How we know universals," *Bull. Mathematical Biophysics*, 1947, 9:127-147.

59. Podsossenaia, L. S., referred to by Rusinov, V. S., in "Electrophysiological investigation of foci of stationary excitation in the central nervous system," *Pavlov Journal of Higher Nervous Activity*, 1958, 8:444-451.

60. Purpura, D. P., "Organization of excitatory and inhibitory synaptic electrogenesis in the cerebral cortex," in *Reticular Formation of the Brain*, Little, Brown and Co., Boston, 1958.

61. Roytbak, A., "Bio-electric phenomena arising in the cerebral cortex under a combination of stimuli applied to two points of the cortex," *Abstracts, XX Internat. Physiol. Congr.*, Brussels, 1956, pp. 787-788; "Bio-electrical phenomena in the cortex of the cerebral hemispheres," Academy of Sciences of the Georgian SSR, Tiflis, 1955, translated by the National Medical Library.

62. Rusinov, V. S., "An electrophysiological analysis of the connection function in the cerebral cortex in the presence of a dominant focus," *Abstracts, XIX Internat. Physiol. Congr.*, Montreal, 1953, pp. 147-151.

63. ———, "Electrophysiological research in the dominant area in the higher parts of the central nervous system," *Abstracts, XX Internat. Physiol. Congr.*, Brussels, 1956, pp. 785-786.

64. Segundo, J. P., Roig, J. A., and Sommer-Smith, J. A., "Conditioning of reticular formation stimulation effects," *EEG clin. Neurophysiol.*, 1959, 11:471-484.

65. Sharpless, S., and Jasper, H. H., "Habituation of the arousal reaction," *Brain*, 1956, 79:655-680.

66. Sperry, R. W., "Cerebral regulation of motor coordination in monkeys following multiple transection of sensorimotor cortex," *J. Neurophysiol.*, 1947, 10: 275-294; Sperry, R. W., Miner, N., and Myers, R. E., "Visual pattern perception following subpial slicing and tantalum wire implantations in the visual cortex," *J. Comp. Physiol. Psych.*, 1955, 48:50-58; Sperry, R. W., and Miner, N., "Pattern perception following insertion of mica plates into visual cortex," *J. Comp. Physiol. Psych.*, 1955, 48:463-469.

67. Stern, J. A., Ulett, G. A., and Sines, J. O., "Electrocortical changes during conditioning," in *EEG Studies of Conditioning*, Grune & Stratton, New York, in press.

68. Tschirgi, R. D., "Blood-brain barrier," in *The Biology of Mental Health and Disease*, Hoeber-Harper, New York, 1952.

69. Ukhtomski, A. A., "Concerning the condition of excitation in dominance," *Novoev refleksologii i fiziologii nervnoi sistemy*, 1926, 2:3-15, abstracted in *Psychol. Abstracts*, 1927, No. 2388.

70. von Foerster, H., *Das Gedachtnis, Deuticke*, Vienna, 1948.

71. Walter, W. Grey, *The Living Brain*, W. W. Norton and Co., New York, 1953.

72. Wedensky, N. E., *Zeitschrift der russ. Gesellschaft für Volkshygiene*, 1897 (Januar), referred to in: Wedensky, N. E., "Die Erregung, Hemmung, und Narkose," *Pflügers Arch. f.d. ges. Physiologie*, 1903, 100:1-144.

73. Yoshii, N., and Hockaday, W. J., "Conditioning of frequency-characteristic repetitive electroencephalographic response with intermittent photic stimulation," *EEG clin. Neurophysiol.*, 1958, 10:487-502.

74. ———, Matsumoto, J., and Hori, Y., "Electroencephalographic study on conditioned reflex in animals," paper presented at *First International Congress of the Neurological Sciences*, July, 1957.

75. ———, Pruvot, P., and Gastaut, H., "A propos d'une activité rhythmique transitoirement enregistrée dans la formation réticulée mésencéphalique et susceptible de représenter l'expression électroencéphalographique de la trace mnémonique," *C. R. Acad. Sci.*, Paris, 1956, 242:1361-1364.

76. ———, Pruvot, P., and Gastant, H., "Electrographic activity of the mesencephalic reticular formation during conditioning in the cat," *EEG clin. Neurophysiol.*, 1957, 9:595-608.

77. Zal'manson, A. N., "Uslovnyie oboronitel'nyie refleksy pri lokal'nom otravlenii tzentrov kory golovnogo mozga strikhninom i kokainom" ("Conditioned defensive reflexes after local poisoning of the cortical motor centers with strychnine and cocaine"), *Vysshaya Nervnaya Deyatel'nost*, Moscow: G I Z, 1929, pp. 39-48.

CHARLES SHAGASS

Explorations in the

Psychophysiology of Affect

The scientific student of mind is constantly confronted with the need to publicize or externalize events which are private and internal. This task seems nowhere so difficult as in the area of feelings and emotions. Because physiological techniques hold forth the promise of objectifying emotions, they have been extensively used in studies of affect. The broad aims of such studies are both applied and basic. On the applied side, they seek to discover objective indicators which might be used to evaluate affects for such purposes as psychiatric diagnosis, appraisal of the effects of psychiatric treatment, and estimation of consumer reactions in market research. More basically, there is the hope that, ultimately, it may be possible to describe with sufficient detail bodily mechanisms which "explain" emotion adequately. This would mean that emotion could be defined in physiological terms without doing violence to the data of subjective experience. We are obviously a long distance from this goal, and some may doubt if it is attainable.

I propose here to review the major findings obtained over a fifteen-year period of psychophysiological research on affect and to discuss some conceptual and methodological problems which are important in this field. The studies in which I have been involved have been concerned mainly with the disturbing emotions, particularly anxiety and depression. These affects represent, however, an important segment of emotional phenomena, and it is hoped that the material to be presented may contribute some perspective to the current status of this problem area.

The Problem of Definition

Although the word, emotion, appears to convey meaning to all, there is no universally accepted definition, and the achievement of one seems unlikely in the near future. As English and English[5] point out in their dictionary, there is fair agreement in classifying as emotion such phenomena as fear, anger, joy, disgust, pity, affection, etc., but definitions tend to bring in conflicting theories. They state that nearly all theories assign important roles to the activities of both the central nervous system and the autonomic, nearly all relate emotion in some way to motivation, and most assign a dominant role to a feeling element.

A major source of difficulty in definition seems to stem from failure to distinguish clearly between the concept, the theories of mechanism, and the indicators of emotion. The concept of emotion is an abstraction based on subjective feeling qualities which are a matter of common experience. The word has meaning because of this community experience. However, as already mentioned, it is very difficult to externalize such experience in a reliable fashion. This difficulty has led workers to devise definitions based on their theory of mechanism. Unless the theory is correct, such a definition can have little lasting value. To some workers an operational definition, based on the functional relation between indicators, seems to avoid the objections inherent in definitions arising from the subjectively based concept or from theories of mechanism. For example, Farber and West[8] recently suggested that emotion be defined as a given kind of functional relation between antecedents (e.g., of environmental or neurophysiological type) and consequents (e.g., bodily reactions and overt behavior). They note that "this criterion would not lead us to ask whether emotions exist." Employing such a criterion one might describe the relationships between threat of failure in a college examination and a tense expression, tachycardia, sweating, etc., with no necessary reference to emotion. In my opinion, however, it seems doubtful that such an experiment will fail to raise the question of emotion, at least in the mind of one who reads the report of it. The operational definition may set aside the question, "What is emotion?" but it does not dispose of it.

My own position on this question is to stay with a conceptual definition of emotion, while retaining the operational definition in specific research. I conceive of emotion as *that aspect of behavior which may be subjectively experienced as feeling.* This view would hold that there may be a feeling aspect to *all* behavior, that there may be several dimensions of feeling, and that there may be variations in intensity along all dimensions. To avoid an endless chain of definitions, feeling can only be defined by an appeal to common experience, by requesting the reader to accept what is being referred to as that quality of experience which allows him to understand the word, "feeling," to inquire about the feelings of others, and to expect others to understand when he talks about his feelings.

There seem to be several advantages to this concept of emotion. It places the problem squarely in the realm of common experience, and does not do away with emotion by defining it. It does not depend upon an explanatory theory of how this experience comes about, and it does not confuse the correlates or indicators of emotion with the concept. It easily encompasses all emotions, pleasurable and unpleasurable. It involves the concept of one or more intensity continua, so that one thinks of more or less emotion rather than presence or absence of emotion. Finally, in any specific experimental situation, this concept of emotion is not incompatible with the use of operationally defined indicators. Indeed, it should help to give explicit orientation and perspective to the results obtained by studying the relationships between indicators.*

It should be emphasized that the concept stated above does not equate emotion with the verbal report of feelings, even though, in many instances, such a report may seem the most trustworthy indicator. Certainly affect labels, such as anger or love, are derived from common verbal formulations of patterns of emotional experience. Implicit equating of the reported feeling state with the observer's concept of the process of emotion frequently occurs, both in investigative and clinical work. The available language probably facilitates this confusion, as the same terms are used for both. For example, depression may refer to a subjective report, a syndrome involving a variety of signs and symptoms, or a nosological entity reflecting the observer's conception of a disease process. In experimental work it is obviously necessary that one specify the way in which an affect label is being used.

Methodological Problems

Some general methodological problems will be discussed in this section. Specific techniques will be considered, where applicable, in discussion of the results of particular studies.

Sources of Data

There appear to be four general classes of data which are used to identify emotions and to study them. These are: (1) subjective report of

---

* Obviously the goal of research is to arrive at a definition, based on complete and detailed understanding of the mechanisms, which could then be stated solely in terms of mechanism. In my view, only such a definition can satisfactorily replace a conceptual definition, such as the one given above.

feeling state; (2) overt behavior, including facial expressions and gestures; (3) bodily reactions, physiological and biochemical; (4) the situational context or environment. Most studies are carried out to determine the relationships between two or more of these kinds of data. Bodily reactions are frequently set up as the dependent variable, while one or more of the other classes serve as independent variables. The way in which subjective report, expressive behavior and knowledge of the situation are combined to arrive at the criterion of affect is often difficult to specify, and some investigators may neglect to make a serious attempt to obtain such information. Yet it is likely that much of the difficulty in duplicating experiments may stem from such a source of variability. For example, the correlation between a response such as the galvanic skin response (GSR) and "anxiety" may be quite different in two studies, one of which uses as the criterion of anxiety only the subjective report of feeling during the period of GSR recording and the other of which uses the patient's history and his observed ward behavior together with his report. It is important that the nature and source of affect criteria be specified.

Problems Involving Time

Every experiment involves several decisions concerning time, some of which may not be explicit. All physiological phenomena have their own time characteristics, such as latency of response, time for recovery of normal responsiveness, duration of response, and possible diurnal fluctuation and cycling. These characteristics must be taken into account in the timing of physiological observations. It is possible to observe a wealth of change in a brief latency response such as the electromyogram (EMG) of skeletal muscle before there is any sign of change in slower responses such as the GSR or stomach motility. If one is attempting to correlate physiological responses with concomitant verbal events, as during interview, the more rapid responses may offer greater opportunities for determining close time relationships. Furthermore, it would not be surprising if the psychological correlates of phenomena which differ tenfold in latency were different.

Most responses arise from a background of activity which may have an important influence on the limits of responsiveness, i.e., the size of the response may be a correlate of the background activity.[18] It is thus necessary to provide for measuring the background activity over an adequate period of time.

The most difficult time problems arise from the fact that one is frequently attempting to correlate phenomena with completely different time bases. Interpretation of such results requires caution. The problem is minor if the investigator wishes to do no more than measure a bodily response to a well-defined stimulus and to relate this to other responses, e.g., feeling state, occurring at the same time. However, he often wishes to relate individual differences in response to some estimate of relatively long-term reaction tendencies, e.g., anxiety-proneness. This may involve several uncertain assumptions. One assumption would be that the stimulus used to elicit the response is representative of "anxiety-provoking" stimuli for the subject. Another is that the response is an adequate representative of the reaction systems involved in the subject's "anxiety" responses. The probability is rather low that both of these assumptions will together approach correctness. Furthermore, the results of such an experiment, whether positive or negative, do not disclose whether only one or both of these assumptions is correct or incorrect. To determine this, it is generally necessary to carry out several experiments, using different stimuli for the same response and different responses for the same stimulus.

Reliability or repeatability represents another problem in which time is important. There seems to be some discrepancy between investigators' expectations concerning lability at the psychological and physiological levels. Most workers subscribe to the view that emotion is dynamic, rather than static. In accordance with this view, one should expect rather wide fluctuations from time to time in any sensitive indicator of emotion. Nevertheless many studies, particularly those involving chemical determinations, use extremely limited sampling, which involves an implicit assumption of stability. Furthermore, if retest studies do not show high repeatability of individual determinations, their reliability is said to be low and they may be discarded. High reliability is desirable, but it must be emphasized that reliability can be assessed only if at least two observations are made under identical conditions. Lack of reliability may mean that a sensitive indicator is varying appropriately. This problem can be handled by serial studies of *both* the indicator and what it is supposed to indicate. If the reliability of a valid indicator is tested in a population which remains relatively fixed at some extreme of emotional reactivity over a long period of time, e.g., a group of severely depressed patients, one may obtain data suggesting greater stability than one would find in another group with a greater range of affective responsiveness. This possibility has to be considered when different populations are studied by the same method.

"Stimulus" Problems

A wide variety of stimulus situations has been used to evoke emotional responses. These have ranged from gross physical "threats," such as

Blatz's collapsing chair,[2] to relatively subtle symbolic "threats" introduced into the interview situation. The deliberate manipulation of interview transactions to evoke particular affects has often been disappointing, the subjects failing to respond as predicted. This was a frequent experience in the Michael Reese studies of anxiety.[11] The same problem may arise with conditions which seem more straightforward. For example, in one of our studies[52] we predicted that the "threat" associated with electroconvulsive therapy (ECT) would evoke more disturbing emotion than when the patient knew he was not to receive a treatment. In fact, several patients became more disturbed in the non-treatment test. One patient said she was upset because she could see no need for an intravenous injection when she was not receiving a treatment. These experiences document the difficulty involved in attempts to predict emotion from one source of data alone. What seems a threat to the investigator may be no threat, or a different kind of threat, to the subject.

Rating Problems

The reliability of ratings is notoriously limited. Nevertheless, they frequently are indispensable, and one can do no more than to try to define their basis and their reliability as accurately as possible. To assess reliability multiple raters must be used, and it is also valuable to check the same rater against himself whenever possible. Our experience has been that different raters will achieve no more than 85 per cent agreement on such apparently simple matters as deciding whether or not a particular person is being talked about in one minute sections of interview transcripts.[50] Agreement was much less, about 60 per cent, in ratings of tension based on the same interview or of personality trend based on examination of case records.[39, 48] When tension of the same subjects was rated in separately conducted interviews, agreement was slight. It thus appears that there may be moderate agreement between ratings based on identical data, but that agreement decreases sharply when the data are elicited at different times.

Experimental Results

A. Studies Using Peripheral Physiological Indicators

The studies to be discussed in this section were carried out in the Laboratory for Psychological Studies of the Allan Memorial Institute of Psychiatry in Montreal in collaboration with Dr. R. B. Malmo, its director, and other members of the staff. Their main object was to discover and validate significant physiological indicators of disturbed emotion in psychiatric disorders. In recent years Malmo has extended his studies to cover the broad range of behavior which may be subsumed under the concept of activation.[21] The data obtained in studies of psychiatric patients have contributed to and are consistent with his general formulations.

Reactions to Standardized Laboratory Stress. In the early phases of this work it was reasoned that differences between individuals suffering from pathological anxiety and those not so afflicted should be more sharply brought out under appropriate conditions of standard stress than under conditions which are assumed to be basal or nonstressful. This assumption was based on the clinical observation that emotional disturbances in psychoneurosis and other disorders are particularly evident during stress. Accordingly, a laboratory stress situation involving the application of a standardized series of painful stimuli by means of the Hardy-Wolff thermal stimulator was devised. In a pilot study,[30] it was shown that this relatively mild stress situation produced a reduction in lymphocyte count, thus indicating that the situation probably activated the adrenal cortex. Also a group of patients, selected for a high level of clinical anxiety, were much more reactive in this situation than a group of nonpatients with respect to amount of finger movement and fluctuation in the GSR. Finger movement was measured by means of a modified Luria tremorgram.[9]

The pain stress situation was then applied to a larger series of seventy-five patients and another nonpatient control group.[22] The patients were divided into three groups: (1) those in whom anxiety was the predominant symptom, (2) those in whom anxiety, if present, was secondary, and (3) a group of early schizophrenic patients. Physiological variables studied were: frontoparietal EEG, EMG from the neck, respiration, GSR, and finger movement. The patients in whom anxiety was predominant displayed a generally higher level of physiologic disturbance than normal controls or patients in whom anxiety was absent or secondary. On the whole, degree of anxiety appeared to be related to the degree of physiologic disturbance. The best indicators seemed to be those in the motor sphere, namely finger movement and neck muscle potentials. In most of the physiologic reactions, the early schizophrenic group resembled the anxiety patient group more than any other. The results drew special attention to the relevance of measures of skeletal muscle activity as indicators of emotion.

Further analysis of the data of this study was carried out in order to test the hypothesis that physiologic responsiveness to stress would tend to be localized in the physiologic system related to particular somatic complaints. From case history evidence, the patient population was divided into those with: (1) "head" complaints, such as headache, tightness in the region of the head and neck, neck tension; (2) "heart" complaints, such as precordial pain, palpitation, tachycardia, hypertension, fainting, and giddiness; (3) both "head" and "heart" complaints; (4) neither. In accordance with the hypothesis it was predicted that the patients with "head" complaints, group (1), would show more reaction than groups (2) and (4) in the neck muscle tracings. It was also predicted that the patients with "heart" complaints, group (2), would show more reaction in pulse rate and respiration than groups (1) and (4). The data supported these predictions and led to enunciation of the principle of symptom specificity. This principle states that, in psychiatric patients presenting a somatic complaint, the particular physiological mechanism of that complaint is specifically susceptible to activation by stressful experience.[23] It may be noted that very few of the subjects in the pain stress experiment actually experienced their symptoms during the test. The correlation was with a reaction tendency elicited from the patient's history, rather than with his immediate reaction during the experimental session.

In a further series of studies, the pain stress situation was used together with two other types of laboratory stress. The physiological indicators studied were: EMG from neck and forearm, finger movement, pulse rate, blood pressure, and respiration. One of the additional stress situations involved mirror drawing. The other was a specially devised discrimination task, which required the subject to state which of six numbered circles exposed on a screen was larger than the other five.[25] There were twenty sets of circles, and each was exposed three times, the duration of individual exposures decreasing from 5 to 2 seconds. This series was designed to explore the previously used indicators in more detail, to study some new indicators, and to determine how well the results with pain stress agreed with those obtained under other conditions of stress.

The results were presented in four papers. Three of these were organized around individual indicators, namely EMG,[29] finger movement,[25] and blood pressure.[24] The fourth brought together all data relevant to the problem of responsiveness in chronic schizophrenia.[32] The results confirmed and extended those found in the earlier studies. They showed that psychiatric patients responded to stress with greater muscular tension, greater disorganization of motor control, and greater and more prolonged elevation of blood pressure than nonpatient subjects. It was of particular interest to find that the differences in EMG and finger movement were manifested even though psychoneurotics, acute psychotics, and controls were practically identical with respect to perceptual performance on the rapid discrimination task. Once again the results suggested that greater attention to the motor aspects of affect was indicated.

We also began to consider the possibility that these differences in motor reactivity reflected central regulatory disturbances, possibly involving the reticular formation.

In the paper on responsiveness in chronic schizophrenia, attention was drawn to the fact that physiological reactivity was not consistently low in such patients. The concept of responsiveness was analyzed into two major components: (1) those which involved background physiological activities, such as heart rate and blood pressure; (2) those which involved purposive acts, such as signaling by pressing a button. The data from all three stress situations gave clear evidence of normal, or greater than normal, background physiological activity in the chronic schizophrenic patients. On the other hand, the purposive acts required by the stress tests were less frequently or less well executed by the schizophrenics. The results seemed to indicate that, in schizophrenia, those aspects of responsiveness which are associated with emotional arousal may remain intact while the mechanisms underlying overt purposive acts may be defective or inoperative. The significance of this observation lies in its apparent contradiction of the idea that the impression of "flat affect" in chronic schizophrenia is physiologically based. It was suggested that such an impression arose more from lack of purposive response to the questions of the examiner than to any general decrease in affective responsiveness.

Studies employing rather different kinds of experimental situations were carried out to explore further aspects of the hypothesis that psychoneurosis is characterized by defects in physiological regulation of reactions to stress. In one,[31] subjects were exposed to seven brief stresses. The first four involved drawing with and without a mirror and the last three were cold pressor tests.[13] Blood pressure was recorded before, during and after these tests by means of a Cambridge Recording Sphygmotonograph. The main finding, which supported the hypothesis, was that over the series of stresses, the blood pressure reaction of psychoneurotic patients was unchanged in magnitude and level while that of the nonpatient controls tended to show adaptation by decreasing.

Two studies used an experimental situation which would really be difficult to classify under the "stress" concept.[3, 28] In these, EMG reactions to strong auditory stimulation were recorded. Comparison of psychoneurotic patients and controls revealed that there was relatively little difference between them in the very earliest phases of the EMG reaction, for 0.2 second after the stimulus. However, following a peak at 0.2 second, the arm EMG response of the controls tended to return to baseline while that of the patients remained elevated for a considerably longer period of time.

These findings lent further support to the hypothesis of defective physiological regulation in psychoneurosis, and suggested that the defect lay in failure of inhibitory mechanisms.

Physiological Studies during Psychotherapy.   Simultaneously with the stress studies it was decided to apply physiological methods to the study of the psychotherapeutic interview. The technique involved voice recordings during interview which were matched with muscle potential recordings taken from several areas simultaneously. The matching was done by simultaneous sound and marker signals introduced into the voice recordings and physiological tracings. In the first of these studies,[26, 27] one of the main aims was to bring the data to bear on the principle of symptom specificity. A few cases were studied over a fairly long period of time. These longitudinal studies appeared to bear out predictions based on the previous cross-sectional group studies. Physiological disturbances in critical symptom areas were noted in response to the stress of interview and in response to discussions of life situations distressing to the patient. There was also evidence of a relationship between diminishing level of muscular tension during interview and general clinical improvement as therapy progressed.

Another study was carried out in order to determine whether localized muscular tension was associated with specific psychodynamic themes being discussed in the interview situation.[50] In a series of interviews with one patient, two major themes, labeled "sex" and "hostility," were identified in terms of life figures being discussed. The interviews were broken down into one-minute segments, and each segment was classified according to whether or not the relevant life figures or objects were being referred to during that time period. The fluctuations in muscular tension, as recorded by EMG's from five different body areas, were then related to the classification of interview content. The data showed a clear association between increased tension in the right forearm and "hostility" content, while "sex" content was associated with increased tension in the right leg. Analysis of interviews with two other subjects showed similar relationships. The data thus supported the hypothesis that particular psychodynamic themes are associated with specifically localized increases in muscular tension. The correlations were interpreted from the viewpoint that the EMG may be regarded as an indicator of the effectiveness of central neural mechanisms for resolution of conflict. There was also some evidence to suggest that the mean level of muscle tension from day to day was correlated with the patient's mood as observed by the ward nurses. Malmo, Smith, and Kohlmeyer later reported an additional case showing specific relationships between increased forearm tension and "hostility" and between leg tension and "sex."[33]

Throughout these various studies of the physiologic concomitants of disturbed emotional states, constant attempts were made to interpret the data in terms of known properties of the central nervous system. The advent of general knowledge about the properties of the reticular activating system during the early phases of this work[14] was most helpful. It seemed likely that the reticular formation functioned mainly in a regulatory capacity and the most attractive interpretation of the deviant physiology of psychiatric patients was in terms of defects in regulatory mechanisms. Malmo later formulated anxiety specifically as resulting from weakened inhibition.[20] He drew on Eccles' hypothesis of a chemical transmitter for inhibition and on the demonstration of an inhibitory substance by Elliot and Florey to suggest that in anxiety the effectiveness of this substance has been reduced. He suggested that anxiety may be produced by keeping the level of arousal very high over long periods of time and stated the hypothesis that such a continuous overarousal may result in impairment of central inhibitory mechanisms.

B. Electroencephalographic and Drug Threshold Studies

A possible approach to the study of central nervous system reactivity in affective states was suggested by the clinical impression that the level of excitement and tension seemed to be related to the amount of intravenous sedation required to quieten a disturbed patient. Should this relationship hold generally, it would follow that the amount of sedative required to attain a specified end point of sedation could be taken as a quantitative index of degree of tension.

The first task was to discover a suitable end point. The characteristic augmentation of fast frequency activity in the EEG by barbiturates provided one. Amobarbital sodium (sodium Amytal) was injected intravenously at a constant rate, the same amount being given at the beginning of a specified time period, while the EEG was recorded. The amplitude of frontal activity of from 15 to 30 cycles per second was measured and plotted against the amount of the drug. This usually yielded a sigmoid curve, containing an inflection point which followed a sharp rise in amplitude and preceded a diminishing rate of increase of amplitude. In the first studies,[39] it seemed that the inflection point corresponded closely to the onset of slurred speech. However, later work indicated that slurred speech was not a reliable criterion, as different observers varied considerably in their judgment of its onset. It was retained as a rough guide to the progress of the drug effect. After some empirical exploration, an injection rate of 0.5 milligram per kilogram every 40 seconds was decided upon. The sedation threshold was defined as the amount of amobarbital sodium required to produce the inflection point in the curve of fast frequency amplitude. Figure 1 illustrates the effect of amobarbital sodium on the EEG and also shows a clear sedation threshold curve.

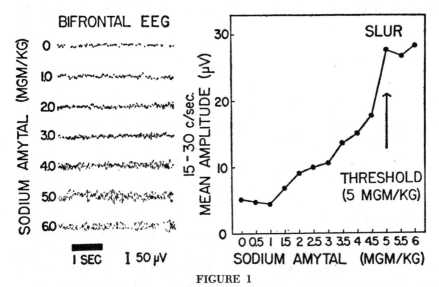

FIGURE 1

Effect of increasing amounts of amobarbital (Amytal) on bifrontal EEG. Note in-flection point in amplitude curve at threshold point.

In the initial study with this procedure, psychiatric patients were assessed as to degree of "tension" on a numerical rating scale. The assessment was made independently by two psychiatrists on the basis of the same interview at which both were present. They agreed rather well, the correlation between their ratings yielding a coefficient of 0.78. The sedation threshold was found to be closely correlated with these ratings of "tension." It thus appeared that an objective indicator of central nervous system activity, which correlated well with clinical assessments of "tension," had been achieved. However, in later work it was found that the assessment of "tension" was difficult to duplicate and upon close scrutiny of the basis of the assessment, it was discovered that it had probably been influenced to a large extent by the diagnosis. In effect, patients with conversion hysteria or hysterical personality disorders gave low thresholds, whereas patients with diagnoses of anxiety state or neurotic depression gave high thresholds and patients with mixed neuroses tended to give intermediate values.[42, 46, 54]

Continued use of the concept of "tension" was troublesome because the sedation threshold findings in psychosis were quite different from those in the psychoneurotic disorders. Patients with acute psychoses, either of schizophrenic or depressive type, almost invariably gave low threshold determinations even though they seemed extremely tense. As the sedation threshold test was applied to all types of psychiatric patients, and to a nonpatient control group, a two-factor concept of its psychological correlates was developed.[42, 53] In nonpsychotic subjects, patients and nonpatients, the threshold appeared to be well correlated with the amount of manifest anxiety which was elicited on clinical examination. It should be noted that this assessment of manifest anxiety was based on all available evidence and not solely upon the reported feeling state at the time of testing. It included observations of the patient's behavior at the time of the examination, his reported ward behavior, and history. In a group of forty-five nonpatient control subjects, who were interviewed for one-half hour before the test, it was found that the sedation threshold, while generally low, was significantly correlated with the number of symptoms of manifest anxiety elicited.[53]

On the other hand, in the psychotic disorders, thresholds showed no relationship with assessable anxiety. Below normal thresholds were found in the patients with organic psychoses, thresholds at about the normal level were found in the acute psychotic disorders, including schizophrenias, depressions, and paranoid reactions, and above normal thresholds were found in the chronic schizophrenic and in "borderline" schizophrenic states. One exception, in the chronic psychoses, was that patients with simple schizophrenia generally had thresholds at about the normal level of 3 milligrams per kilogram. The results in psychoses appeared to make some sense if they were conceptualized as reflecting a dimension of ego-function impairment. It was reasoned that ego function was most impaired in the organic states, whereas impairment would be least in the "borderline" schizophrenias. Acute psychotics would be considered more impaired than the chronic cases, who had reached some level of stability in their relationships with the outside world. If one accepts this kind of ordering of the level of ego-function impairment, then the sedation threshold results show a clear negative correlation with the amount of impairment of ego functioning. The lower the threshold, the greater the impairment. Taking the results as a whole, then, the sedation threshold could be considered to reflect the balance between ego-defensive and ego-disruptive processes.

A mathematical analysis of the primary data obtained in sedation threshold determinations showed that it measured the rate of depressant action of amobarbital sodium. These findings suggested that it measures a time characteristic of neuronal activity, which is probably an important factor influencing cerebral excitability.[43]

From the standpoint of psychiatric diagnosis, a most interesting sedation threshold finding appeared to lie in its capacity to differentiate neurotic from psychotic depressions.[46, 55] Psychotic depressions were associated with normal threshold values, whereas neurotic depressions had elevated thresholds; correspondingly, the threshold was correlated with the outcome of electroconvulsive therapy.[44] It thus found useful application as a diagnostic aid in doubtful cases or in cases where the depression was "masked."[17] The relationship between the threshold and the short-term response to ECT also held for schizophrenic patients.[45] It should be noted, however, that these diagnostic applications did not mean that the threshold was measuring something related to either depression or acute schizophrenia. In these conditions, the threshold was actually normal. It had its use in differentiating states associated with high thresholds from those in which the thresholds seemed to be unaffected.

The association between the sedation threshold and personality variables seemed of particular interest in the light of Eysenck's[6, 7] studies with a dimension of personality which he designated by Jung's term of "introversion-extroversion." It will be recalled that our findings in the neuroses showed that low thresholds were associated with hysterical disorders and high thresholds with anxiety states and neurotic depressions. Obsessional personality trend is a frequent accompaniment of the latter two diagnoses. In view of the fact that hysteria has been considered the neurosis of the extrovert and dysthymia (obsessive compulsive neurosis, anxiety, depression) the neurotic reaction of the introvert, Eysenck and I predicted that the sedation threshold would be correlated with introversion-extroversion and specifically that introverts would show high sedation thresholds. This prediction was borne out in a study carried out with Kerenyi.[16, 48] In this study, the Guilford R and S scales, measuring extroversion and introversion, were administered to fifty psychoneurotic patients. A correlation coefficient of 0.60 between the introversion-extroversion scores and the sedation threshold was found, the relationship being in the predicted direction. In a larger group of patients, a correlation of similar magnitude (0.53) was also found between the threshold and ratings of hysterical-obsessional trend from case history material.[48]

These findings with personality variables seemed to be of considerable importance in attempting to reach a formulation concerning the nature of anxiety. It was suggested that the clinical concept probably encompasses a number of affective reaction patterns mediated by different neural mechanisms. It was considered that the kind of mechanism mediating anxiety in a given individual might be closely linked with his personality pattern. From this viewpoint, the sedation threshold would be seen as a measure of the amount of activity in the mechanism mediating anxiety in obsessional or introverted individuals. This concept would lead us to seek other indicators to reflect the activity of anxiety mediating mechanisms in individuals of different personality type. Ultimately one would hope to be able to classify anxiety objectively by means of neurophysiological test procedures.

The repeatability of the sedation threshold seemed extremely high in initial studies.[54] However, it was shown that this high repeatability is not due to the threshold being a fixed biological characteristic of the individual.[51] When patients who had shown a great amount of clinical improvement were retested their thresholds decreased from high levels toward normal.

The technical facilities required for carrying out sedation thresholds prompted the exploration of other indicators which might replace the EEG end point. As has already been mentioned, slurred speech was not reliable and was found unreliable by others,[1, 9, 57] although one worker has appeared to obtain satisfactory results with it.[15] The onset of unresponsiveness appeared to be a fairly reliable indicator, and it was used as the basis for a "sleep" threshold. The "sleep" threshold correlated fairly well with the sedation threshold and, in an initial study, which compared the diagnostic relationships of both determinations as carried out in the same testing session, the main diagnostic correlations appeared to be approximately the same for both kinds of determinations.[47] However, subsequent experience has shown that the "sleep" threshold is rather markedly affected by the situation and may vary considerably in the hands of different examiners. A second study, utilizing the pre-ECT injection of thiopental to determine the thiopental "sleep" threshold, revealed some interesting relationships with hostility.[52] On several occasions it was noted that the "sleep" threshold rose rather markedly when the patient was angry. This could apparently happen in a short time. The finding suggests that considerably more attention should be paid to the evaluation of hostile affect when the sedation or "sleep" thresholds are measured.

The sedation threshold findings have received varying degrees of confirmation by other workers. Nymgaard appears to have confirmed the differentiation between neurotic and psychotic depressions and, in the course of her work, has developed an apparently useful objective criterion for determining the threshold when the EEG curve is not clear.[34] Seager[38] also confirmed the findings in depression, but he obtained extremely high mean threshold values in his population. Seager and I have recently had the opportunity to determine the reasons for differences in our findings, and these have turned out to be due to a combination of recording conditions, changes in method, and some misinterpretation of the phrase, "tendency to plateau," as meaning actual flattening of the curve rather than a change in slope. Seager was able to obtain results comparable to mine after these differences in technique were resolved. Fink has suggested the use of nystagmus to lateral gaze as the end point for the sedation threshold, but Seager has not found this criterion to be reliable.[37] Ackner and Pampiglione[1] have not been able to verify any of the sedation threshold findings. This failure appears due, at least in part, to differences in technique, insofar as their mean values were very much higher than ours. It is also possible that their criterion of anxiety was mainly in terms of the immediate subjective report and overt behavior of the patient at the time of testing.

It seems worthy of emphasis that the specific sedation threshold procedure, first described by myself, may be far from optimal. However, the results obtained with it indicate that the objective measurement of drug reactivity offers a rather sharp tool for sorting out neurophysiological mechanisms associated with affect and personality. Currently the major problems seem to lie in the technical sphere, namely, the need to find suitable new indicators. This has proved to be rather difficult. One recent attempt by Lipowski and myself[49] was relatively unsuccessful. In this study the effect of methamphetamine (Methedrine) on critical flicker fusion (CFF) was used as an indicator of central nervous reactivity. The idea was to find an "excitation threshold" which would be the reverse of the sedation threshold. The findings did not encourage further use of the CFF indicator.

In an entirely different experimental approach, the effect of intermittent light stimulation on the EEG was used as an indicator. Intermittent photic stimulation produces, over a certain frequency range, rhythmic activity in the parieto-occipital EEG, which corresponds to the frequency of flashing light. This is called photic driving. The photic driving responses of patients with anxiety and depression were compared in one study.[41] This revealed that there was relatively more driving in response to a faster frequency of flashing light than to a slower frequency in anxious patients than there was in depressed patients. A normal control group was intermediate between the two patient groups. Serial studies of two subjects over a period of several months showed relationships between fluctuations in feeling state and the photic driving response which were predicted from the first, cross-sectional, study.[40] One dramatic observation was made when one of the subjects, married to a medical interne and not wishing to start a family, believed that she had become pregnant. Her photic driving responses, on several successive tests, were like those of depressive patients.

Attempts to confirm and extend these observations with photic driving by means of automatic frequency analysis led to variable results. However, these experiments did play an important role in suggesting a new approach to neurophysiological investigation of affect which we are currently pursuing.

C. Direct Measurements of Cortical Excitability

In attempting to relate the results of the various experiments described above to concepts of central nervous system function, it has been necessary to use rather vague formulations, such as "cerebral excitability." This is because, except for the EEG, no direct methods for observing central nervous activity have been available, and the standard EEG has provided little in the way of relevant information. Obviously, a concept such as cerebral excitability would have much more meaning if methods were available for measuring specific aspects of it directly.

The work of Gastaut and his colleagues[10] on cortical excitability cycles in animals suggested a possible approach to the problem. They used the response of visual cortex to light as a measure of excitability. By varying the interval between pairs of light flashes, they were able to plot a cycle of cortical excitability in terms of the response to the second light flash. Such an excitability curve yielded data showing the absolute and relative refractory periods, the time for recovery of normal excitability, and the duration of supernormal and subnormal phases of excitability. Unfortunately, direct application of Gastaut's method to the human is not possible because the visual evoked potential is not readily apparent in the ordinary EEG. This is because the spontaneous EEG rhythms are of much greater amplitude than the evoked potential picked up from electrodes placed on the scalp. However, some years ago, G. D. Dawson[4] showed that it is possible to measure sensory evoked potentials from scalp recordings if one repeats the stimuli many times and averages or summates the electrical activity of the cortex following the stimulus. The summation procedure causes the spontaneous waves to more or less cancel out, whereas the evoked potential, which is a response to the stimulus and locked to it in time, tends to summate. Late in 1956, we conceived of the idea of applying Dawson's method to the measurement of excitability cycles with the aim of determining the relationships between such cycles and affective state.

The major initial problems have revolved about instrumentation, but these now seem to be almost solved. At Iowa, Shipton completed an electronic summator that he used in collaboration with Schwartz in a series of pilot studies. It was found to have several inadequacies and a superior instrument is being made. However, with the first instrument, it was possible for us to demonstrate that human cortical excitability cycles, using the method of paired stimuli, can be measured by a summation technique.

To measure excitability cycles, we have utilized the potential evoked by electrical stimulation of the ulnar nerve at the wrist in the contralateral somatosensory area. Figure 2 shows a series of such responses recorded over two time bases. The primary evoked potential has a latency of 15 to 16 milliseconds, and the peak of the primary response

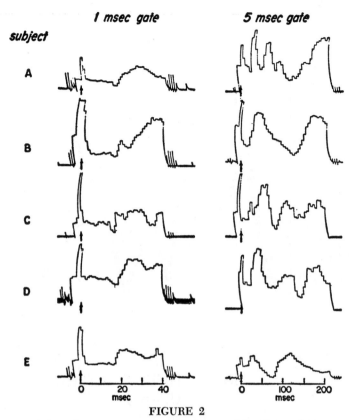

FIGURE 2

Illustrates variations in somatosensory evoked potentials. Note relative consistency of initial "primary" responses on left compared with great variability of later components on right. (Stimulus intensified about twice sensory threshold.)

occurs about 25 milliseconds after the stimulus. When two stimuli are administered, the amplitude of the primary response to the second stimulus will vary in relation to the time between the two stimuli. If the amplitude of the second response is plotted as a proportion of the first response, this ratio depicts the fluctuations in excitability following stimulation. Figure 3 shows two such excitability curves. In both instances, the recovery of normal excitability occurred after about 25 milliseconds and was followed by a series of supernormal and subnormal oscillations. The latter differed in the two subjects whose curves are shown.

The relationship of data such as these to the problem of affect will be the focus of further exploration. However, it is already apparent

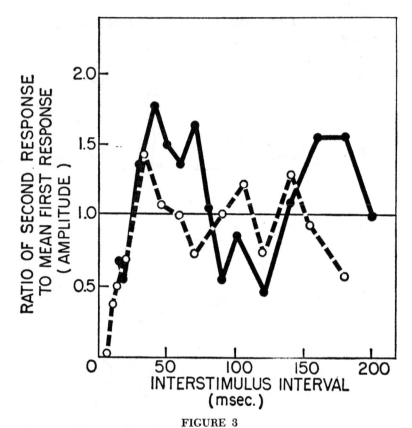

FIGURE 3

Excitability curves for two subjects. Ratio of 1.0 indicates that $R_2 = R_1$ and excitability has returned to normal.

that the method will lend itself to a very large number of applications in the neurophysiological study of human behavior. For example, in an exploratory study, we found evidence that the first sign of a cortical evoked potential, occurred at about the sensory threshold, i.e., when the subject first reported that he felt the stimulus.[56] This observation indicates that the evoked cortical potential may be used as a direct indicator of sensory awareness in the unanesthetized organism. It also demonstrates how much additional meaning a physiological indicator may acquire when it correlates closely with the subjective report.*

* Studies carried out subsequent to preparation of this chapter have demonstrated that those aspects of cerebral responsiveness reflected in the recovery cycle and intensity-response gradient of somatosensory evoked potentials deviate from normal in several psychiatric syndromes.

Conclusion

During the fifteen-year period covered by the studies reviewed here, there have been important advances in neurophysiological knowledge. To name a few, the properties of the reticular formation have been discovered and elucidated,[12] the Papez circuit for emotion has been shown to have some validity,[36] subcortical centers intimately involved in response reinforcement have been found.[35] Methods which will bridge the gap between animal and human data are required to bring the full weight of these advances to bear on the problem of human emotion. It is here that psychophysiological studies seem destined to make a unique contribution. For the gap can only be bridged if the same observations can be made in man and animal. These observations can then be correlated with human behavior, subjective and objective, on the one hand, and with animal behavior under various experimental conditions, usually not permissible in human studies, on the other.

If any trend can be discerned in the studies reviewed, it seems to consist of a shift from the periphery to the central nervous system. This shift is methodological rather than a matter of changing interest. The focus of interest has always been on what is going on in the brain, the place "where vital things happen."[58] However, as new methods become available it is becoming more possible to study brain functions directly. It seems to me that we are just now able to glimpse a coming era of really focused psychophysiological investigation, in which neurophysiological and pharmacological tools will be used to provide some definitive information about affect. In such a development I do not visualize discard of the peripheral physiological approaches. I would rather anticipate that these approaches will gain added significance from the studies of central nervous function. And I would further expect that the physiological information will help to sharpen the insight of psychological observation.

REFERENCES

1. Ackner, B., and Pampiglione, G., "An evaluation of the sedation threshold test," *J. Psychosom. Res.*, 1959, 3:271-281.
2. Blatz, W. E., "The cardiac, respiratory, and electrical phenomena involved in the emotion of fear," *J. Exp. Psychol.*, 1925, 8:109-132.
3. Davis, J. F., Malmo, R. B., and Shagass, C., "Electromyographic reaction to strong auditory stimulation in psychiatric patients, *Canad. J. Psychol.*, 1954, 8:177-186.
4. Dawson, G. D., "A summation technique for the detection of small evoked potentials, *EEG Clin. Neurophysiol.*, 1954, 6: 65-84.

5. English, H. B., and English, A. C., *A Comprehensive Dictionary of Psychological and Psychoanalytical Terms,* Longmans, Green, New York, 1958.

6. Eysenck, H. J., *Dimensions of Personality,* Routledge, London, 1947.

7. ———, *The Dynamics of Anxiety and Hysteria,* Routledge and Kegan Paul, London, 1957.

8. Farber, I. E., and West, L. J., "Conceptual problems of research on emotion," *Psychiat. Res. Rep. Am. Psychiat. A.,* 1960, 12:1-7.

9. Fink, M., "Lateral gaze nystagmus as an index of the sedation threshold," *EEG Clin. Neurophysiol.,* 1958, 10:162-163.

10. Gastaut, H., Gastaut, Y., Roger, A., Carriol, J., and Naquet, R., "Étude électrographique du cycle d'excitabilite cortical," *EEG Clin. Neurophysiol.,* 1951, 3:401-428.

11. Grinker, R. R., Sabshin, M., Hamburg, D. A., Board, F. A., Basowitz, H., Korchin, S. J., Persky, H., and Chevalier, J. A., "The use of an anxiety-producing interview and its meaning to the subject," *A.M.A. Arch. Neurol. Psychiat.,* 1957, 77:406-419.

12. *Henry Ford Hospital International Symposium on Reticular Formation of the Brain,* Little, Brown & Co., Boston, 1958.

13. Hines, S. A., and Brown, G. E., "The cold pressor test for measuring the reactibility of the blood pressure: data concerning 571 normal and hypertensive subjects," *Am. Heart J.,* 1936, 2:1-9.

14. Jasper, H. H., "Diffuse projection systems: the integrative action of the thalamic reticular system," *EEG Clin. Neurophysiol.,* 1949, 1:405-420.

15. Kawi, A. A., "The sedation threshold," *A.M.A. Arch. Neurol. Psychiat.,* 1958, 80:232-236.

16. Kerenyi, A. B., "Sedation threshold, conditioning, introversion—extraversion and manifest anxiety. A neurophysiological and psychological study of personality," unpublished thesis, Dept. Psychiat., McGill University, 1957.

17. Kral, V. A., "Masked depression in middle aged men," *Canad. M. A. J.,* 1958, 79:1-5.

18. Lacey, J. I., "The evaluation of autonomic responses: toward a general solution," *Ann. New York Acad. Sci.,* 1956, 67:123-164.

19. Luria, A. R., *The Nature of Human Conflicts,* Liveright, New York, 1932.

20. Malmo, R. B., "Anxiety and behavioral arousal," *Psychol. Rev.,* 1957, 64:276-287.

21. ———, "Activation: A neuropsychological dimension," *Psychol. Rev.,* 1959, 66:367-386.

22. ———, and Shagass, C., "Physiologic studies of reaction to stress in anxiety and early schizophrenia," *Psychosom. Med.,* 1949, 11:9-24.

23. ———, and Shagass, C., "Physiologic study of symptom mechanisms in psychiatric patients under stress," *Psychosom. Med.,* 1949, 11:25-29.

24. ———, and Shagass, C., "Studies of blood pressure in psychiatric patients under stress," *Psychosom. Med.,* 1952, 14:81-93.

25. ———, Shagass, C., Belanger, D. J., and Smith, A. A., "Motor control in psychiatric patients under experimental stress," *J. Abn. Soc. Psychol.,* 1951, 46:539-547.

26. ———, Shagass, C., and Davis, F. H., "Symptom specificity and bodily reactions during psychiatric interview," *Psychosom. Med.,* 1950, 12:362-376.

27. ———, Shagass, C., and Davis, F. H., "Specificity of bodily reactions under stress. A physiological study of somatic symptom mechanisms in psychiatric patients," Chapter XV, in *Life Stress and Bodily Disease. A. Res. Nerv. Ment. Dis.,* 1950, 29:231-261.

28. ———, Shagass, C., and Davis, J. F., "A method for the investigation of somatic response mechanisms in psychoneurosis," *Science,* 1950, 112:325-328.

29. ———, Shagass, C., and Davis, J. F., "Electromyographic studies of muscular tension in psychiatric patients under stress," *J. Clin. Exper. Psychopathol.,* 1951, 12:45-66.

30. ———, Shagass, C., Davis, J. F., Cleghorn, R. A., Graham, B. F., and Goodman, A. J., "Standardized pain stimulation as controlled stress in physiological studies of psychoneurosis," *Science,* 1948, 108:509-511.

31. ———, Shagass, C., and Heslam, R. M., "Blood pressure response to repeated brief stress in psychoneurosis: A study of adaptation," *Canad. J. Psychol.,* 1951, 5:167-179.

32. ———, Shagass, C., and Smith, A. A., "Responsiveness in chronic schizophrenia," *J. Personality,* 1951, 19:359-375.

33. ———, Smith, A. A., and Kohlmeyer, W. A., "Motor manifestations of conflict in interview: A case study," *J. Abn. Soc. Psychol.,* 1956, 52:268-271.

34. Nymgaard, K., "Studies on the sedation threshold," *Arch. Gen. Psychiat.,* 1959, 1:530-536.

35. Olds, J., "Positive emotional systems studied by techniques of self-stimulation," *Psychiat. Res. Rep. Am. Psychiat. A.,* 1960, 12:238-258.

36. Papez, J. W., "The visceral brain, its components and connections," in *Henry Ford Hospital International Symposium on Reticular Formation of the Brain.* Little, Brown & Co., Boston, 1958, pp. 591-605.

37. Seager, C. P., unpublished data.

38. ———, "Verification of the sedation threshold technique," *EEG Clin. Neurophysiol.,* 1959, 11:606.

39. Shagass, C., "The sedation threshold. A method for estimating tension in psychiatric patients," *EEG Clin. Neurophysiol.,* 1954, 6:221-233.

40. ———, "Anxiety, depression and the photically driven electroencephalogram," *A.M.A. Arch. Neurol. Psychiat.,* 1955, 74:3-10.

41. ———, "Differentiation between anxiety and depression by the photically activated electroencephalogram," *Am. J. Psychiat.,* 1955, 112: 41-46.

42. ———, "Sedation threshold. A neurophysiological tool for psychosomatic research," *Psychosom. Med.,* 1956, 18:410-419.

43. ———, "A measurable neurophysiological factor of psychiatric significance," *EEG Clin. Neurophysiol.,* 1957, 9:101-108.

44. ———, "Neurophysiological studies of anxiety and depression," *Psychiat. Res. Rep. Am. Psychiat. A.,* 1958, 8:100-117.

45. ———, "A neurophysiological study of schizophrenia," Report, 2nd International Congress for Psychiatry, 1959, 2:248-254.

46. ———, and Jones, A. L., "A neurophysiological test for psychiatric diagnosis. Results in 750 patients," *Am. J. Psychiat.,* 1958, 114:1002-1009.

47. ———, and Kerenyi, A. B., "The 'sleep' threshold. A simple form of the sedation threshold for clinical use," *Canad. Psychiat. A. J.,* 1958, 3:101-109.

48. ———, and Kerenyi, A. B., "Neurophysiologic studies of personality," *J. Nerv. Ment. Dis.,* 1958, 126:141-147.

49. ———, and Lipowski, Z. J., "Effect of methedrine on critical flicker fusion and its relation to personality and affect," *J. Nerv. Ment. Dis.,* 1958, 127:407-416.

50. ———, and Malmo, R. B., "Psychodynamic themes and localized muscular tension during psychotherapy," *Psychosom. Med.,* 1954, 16:295-313.

51. ———, Mihalik, J., and Jones, A. L., "Clinical psychiatric studies using the sedation threshold," *J. Psychosom. Res.*, 1957, 2:45-55.

52. ———, Müller, K., and Acosta, H. B., "The pentothal 'sleep' threshold as an indicator of affective change," *J. Psychosom. Res.*, 1959, 3:253-270.

53. ———, and Naiman, J., "The sedation threshold, manifest anxiety, and some aspects of ego function," *A.M.A. Arch. Neurol. Psychiat.*, 1955, 74:397-406.

54. ———, and Naiman, J., "The sedation threshold as an objective index of manifest anxiety in psychoneurosis," *J. Psychosom. Res.*, 1956, 1:49-57.

55. ———, Naiman, J., and Mihalik, J., "An objective test which differentiates between neurotic and psychotic depression," *A.M.A. Arch. Neurol. Psychiat.*, 1956, 75:461-471.

56. ———, and Schwartz, M., "Evoked cortical potentials and sensation in man," *J. Neuropsychiat.*, 1961, 2:262-270.

57. Thorpe, J. G., and Barker, J. C., "Objectivity of the sedation threshold," *A.M.A. Arch. Neurol. Psychiat.*, 1957, 78:194-196.

58. Walter, W. G., "Where vital things happen," *Am. J. Psychiat.*, 1960, 116:673-694.

H A R O L D   E .   H I M W I C H

Emotional Aspects of Mind:

Clinical and Neurophysiological Analyses

After I had accepted the responsibility for writing an article toward an understanding of the mind with special reference to the emotional aspects, I referred to the dictionary for a precise definition and found the following: "Mind—that from which thought originates, the subject of consciousness, that which thinks, reasons, remembers, wills, perceives, feels." Therefore, we see that the properties attributed to the mind are manifold including the entire gamut from perceiving, thinking, and feeling to willing. Each of these characteristics of the mind in turn requires further definition. For example, consciousness may be defined in several ways but shall here be used as awareness, or environmental contact. To quote Bertrand Russell,[59] "When anything happens to me, I may or may not notice it. If I notice it, I may be said to be 'conscious' of it. According to this definition 'consciousness' consists in the knowledge that something is happening to me. What is meant by 'knowledge' in this definition remains to be investigated." The chief aspect of mind for our present consideration is its emotional component. Emotion is here referred to as an organically aroused state characterized by experiences of unpleasantness or pleasantness.

The data that furnish part of the basis for our discussion of emotion have been acquired during the past six years by observations of psychotic patients, and psychotropic drugs were the tools used to produce behavioral alterations. It is true that we were unable to study emotions discretely or to isolate them from the nexus of the other characteristics of mind. For that reason it will be necessary to discuss the emotional aspects of mind in conjunction with other behavioral changes wrought by drugs whether for physiologic or pathologic aspects of the mind.

The material to be discussed will be presented in three parts: first, the behavioral effects of psychotropic drugs on psychotic patients exhibiting pathologically altered moods; second, brain mechanisms involved in the expression and experiencing of emotion; and, third, an experimental analysis of the effects of psychotropic drugs on these brain mechanisms in animals.

The Behavioral Effects of Psychotropic Drugs on Psychotic Patients Exhibiting Pathologically Altered Moods

The purpose of the first part of this paper is to present evidence briefly that we possess in our therapeutic armamentarium drugs which can affect mood so that abnormal emotional behavior can be corrected by psychotropic drugs. There are two great advances that made such therapy possible. The first was the advent of the tranquilizers and the second that of the antidepressants. The first of these began several years ago with the clinical use of reserpine and chlorpromazine. These two tranquilizing drugs have proved valuable in the treatment of patients with disorders of mood or affect especially when pathologically elevated. The advantages obtained from reserpine and other rauwolfia alkaloids as well as from chlorpromazine and the whole family of phenothiazine derivatives, subsequently developed, cut across diagnostic categories. These drugs are employed with salutary results in all types of hyperactive patients who secure benefits from sedative influences. The clinical categories include the schizophrenic patients of the paranoid type who may be in a manic frenzy or catatonic furor, the manic whose disorder is chiefly that of elated mood, and the schizoaffective whose abnormal elation is associated with distortion and deterioration of thought process, as well as patients with toxic psychosis, for example, delirium tremens. Such patients with hyperkinesis, increased initiative, and affective tension have their abnormal activities reduced toward more reasonable levels by these drugs so that they cease to wear themselves out and are no longer trials to hospital personnel and fellow patients.

It is characteristic of the tranquilizers that in general they may exert two kinds of desirable effects. The first is regarded as nonspecific and has just been referred to above. It includes a beneficial dampening of the emotional tone, one of our chief interests at the present moment.

Another drug action may be marked as more specific, the apparent ability to correct or mitigate the abnormal mentation, perception, and thinking of the psychotic patient.

The rauwolfia drugs have been used successfully in exerting an over-all quieting action as they reduce anxiety and hostility and in general produce a calming effect. At the same time they also evoke specific effects in the correction of inappropriateness of hebephrenic and catatonic patients, who may then exhibit a decrease of mannerisms as their speech becomes more coherent and logical and their autism decreases. These two effects of the tranquilizers have also been developed to a high degree in the group of phenothiazine derivatives. The first, the sedative action, results in the reduction of the intensity of emotional expression and of psychomotor manifestations in behavior. As a result of the second, the delusions of the paranoid, the mannerisms of the hebephrenic, and the flight of ideas of the elated schizoaffective patient are corrected to varying degrees.

In contrast with this group of overactive patients, we have another whose outstanding feature is depression. Characteristically, patients with depression are seized by an uncontrollable sadness, and here again we find associated with the affective alterations other changes in behavior, including psychomotor retardation, difficulties in concentration, self-depreciation, guilt, and suicidal impulses. The types of depression are many, for example, the depressive phase of a manic-depressive disorder. Depression is also observed during the period of involution. In contrast to these is still another type, the reactive depression with milder symptoms, termed "neurotic reaction." The descriptive term "agitated depression" is applied to patients who are suffering not only from excessive sadness but also from agitation and tension and therefore exhibit a mixture of symptoms representing both the psychopathology of hyperactivity as well as depression.

Where do we stand in our treatment of patients with one or another of the depressions? We have long passed the stage when general central nervous stimulants are used exclusively in the management of depressed patients. It is true that drugs such as amphetamine, pipradrol (Meratran), and methylphenidate (Ritalin) increase activity, elevate the mood, and counteract fatigue. These desirable changes when applied to patients with delusions and anxieties, however, may worsen their clinical situation and activate their psychotic features, for these drugs act in a global fashion and stimulate all aspects of behavior whether the results are desirable or not. We now have at our command recently developed drugs that seem to be more specific for the depressive processes. One of these is imipramine (Tofranil); and the others are the monoamine oxidase inhibitors with iproniazid (Marsilid) as the prototype of newer members of this group, including nialamide (Niamid), phenylazine dihydrogensulfate (Nardil), phenylisopropyl hydrazine (Catron), isocarboxazid (Marplan), and tranylcypromine (Parnate).

There are many reports that imipramine is satisfactory in the treatment of endogenous depression: the depressive phase of the manic-depressive psychosis, and involutional melancholia. But good results have also been reported in selected cases with reactive depressions.[40] Similarly, in some of our patients in whom depression is secondary to the schizophrenic processes, we have observed beneficial effects.

The monoamine oxidase inhibitors, too, have proved valuable and, like imipramine, have exhibited some degree of specificity in the treatment of various types of affective depression, in psychosis and psychoneurosis associated with sad effect. In many instances depression, and agitation as well, are greatly diminished. Sometimes, improvement is observed with the use of monoamine oxidase inhibitors in chronic schizophrenics who are depressed.[24] We have, therefore, seen that abnormal mood can be significantly altered by psychotropic drugs. In patients with pathologic elation tranquilizers are of value, while in those who exhibit sadness and hopelessness with suicidal tendencies the antidepressants have been used successfully in many instances.

This review leaves us with a picture of the clinical events that represent the consensus of psychiatrists who have used these drugs successfully. Closer examination, however, of the clinical effects reveals that there is no clearly defined border between the tranquilizers and the antidepressants. Rather, they share to a greater or lesser extent certain therapeutic actions in common. A drug that is predominantly tranquilizing may be somewhat antidepressant, while an antidepressant drug may also, to a degree, have a tranquilizing effect.

A contrary opinion exists in regard to the tranquilizers since there is a belief that these drugs can precipitate a depression, a belief that may however be based upon superficial evaluation of the clinical evidence. Ayd[4] examined a group of patients referred to him because of depression that was thought to be due to the use of either chlorpromazine or reserpine compounds. In twenty-three of a total of forty-seven such patients the clinical picture was induced by overdosage with the production of excessive tranquilization. These patients recovered when the dosage of the tranquilizers was reduced and either a stimulant or an antiparkinson drug was added to the medication. Two-thirds of the remaining patients had a significant previous history of depression as well as of a basic obsessional personality make-up. Not only did most of these patients reveal a predisposition to psychic disturbances, but they also had a history of environmental stresses that could have helped to precipitate the current depression; and some of these patients showed frank signs of depression on their first visit to the psychiatrist. In other instances, in schizophrenic patients who also suffer from depression, the use of a tranquilizing drug with relief of the schizophrenic aspects may unmask the depression. Thus, the depression is the result of the interaction between the drug and the personality structure of the patient. By the same token, the use of an antidepressant drug may liberate schizophrenic symptoms previously held back from expression by the depressive processes. The literature notes instances where therapeutic relief of depression has been obtained by the use of tranquilizing drugs. We are not referring to a temporary side reaction of increased disturbance usually called "akathisia," or turbulence[32] appearing early with the use of phenothiazines, and especially with reserpine, but rather to such instances as reported by Litin, Faucett, and Achor,[42] which indicate that mild depressions may be lifted without discontinuing reserpine and thus forfeiting the beneficial effects exerted on patients with hypertension. Ayd[4] remarks that some depressed patients treated with tranquilizers to control their agitation ultimately recover from their depression, and this affords further evidence for our conclusion that tranquilizing drugs may also have antidepressant activities.

We have made a study of a group of psychotic patients in which not only antidepressant actions of imipramine but also some tranquilizing properties were revealed. Of sixty patients with various diagnosis forty-two were schizophrenics, and it is to the latter group that we shall limit the present discussion. In nineteen the results were unsatisfactory, but twenty-three others exhibited various degrees of improvement. It is not so surprising that some schizophrenic patients who also exhibited signs of depression improved with imipramine, but six schizophrenic patients, all with paranoid reactions and elaborate delusional systems and without depressive symptoms, benefited from imipramine. In this last group of improved patients the results of imipramine could not be distinguished from those of a tranquilizing drug. When we turn to the antidepressants, we observed that nialamide, a monoamine oxidase inhibitor, relieved not only the sad affect characteristic of depression but also the agitation, anxiety, and ceaseless pacing of the floor observed in this type of depression. Therefore, we see that the clinical effects of these drugs are more complex than revealed by a first glance and that some of our most successful psychotropic drugs partake to a varying degree of tranquilizing and antidepressant actions.

These drugs are used to treat psychotic patients with a variety of symptoms. The symptomatology of the "functional" psychoses represents a spectrum because, only at the two extremes do we observe uncomplicated clinical pictures either of schizophrenic hyperactivity with pathologically elated emotions or of profound depression with psychomotor retardation. But these two textbook pictures are not representative of other patients whose psychopathology reveals greater or lesser components made up of each of the two extremes. There is a variable mixture of the symptoms of agitation and tension in all states of depression and not only in the so-called agitated depressions. We note a similar mixture of symptoms when a depression is superimposed on a patient with a basic schizophrenic process, but it must also be remembered that a schizophrenic person is not a completely different person from other persons in his feelings, thinking, and behavior and may be partly in a range describable for the depressed patient. Goldman[24] comes to a similar conclusion:

It is clear to experienced clinicians that differentiation of depressive states from certain schizophrenic manifestations is not always possible and many patients, particularly severely psychotic individuals, have mixed symptomatology and functioning. Also the possibility of two simultaneous or consecutive illnesses occurring in one individual must be considered. This problem can be clearly delineated only with detailed case reports indicating mixed symptomatology, such as patients who have alternating depressive and schizophrenic symptoms of classic purity, or depressive patients who suddenly develop paranoid hallucinatory episodes after years of recurring pure depressions.

Perhaps one reason that psychotropic drugs are used successfully is that their actions are characterized both by tranquilizing and antidepressant properties. Beaudry and Gibson[8] found that trifluoperazine can stimulate children with malignant emotional disturbances who are too hypoactive and, conversely, can tranquilize others who are too hyperactive, thus illustrating the complex influences of this phenothiazine derivative. This suggestion is further illustrated by a comparison of chlorpromazine and imipramine. We have seen that both drugs are antidepressant. Chlorpromazine, however, is more calming and exhibits greater antipsychotic powers than imipramine, while imipramine is a stronger antidepressant. In a word, when it comes to tranquilization and antipsychotic action, imipramine may be regarded as a weak chlorpromazine; on the other hand, in regard to antidepressant action, chlorpromazine is a weak imipramine.

One additional point should be made, namely, that there are differences even among the various members of the phenothiazine group. For example, chlorpromazine and triflupromazine (Vesprin), members of the dimethyl phenothiazine group[32] possess greater sedative powers and exert lesser stimulation than do the piperazine phenothiazines: trifluoperazine (Stelazine), perphenazine (Trilafon), thiopropazate (Dartal), and prochlorperazine (Compazine).

Brain Mechanisms Involved in the Expression
and Experiencing of Emotion

Before analyzing the mechanisms of the actions of psychotropic drugs on emotion, we must consider briefly the relationships between the brain and mind, since these drugs affect the mind by acting on the brain. The brain is regarded as the substrate of the mind because without the first we cannot have the second, at least in mammals. On the relationship between brain and mind the philosopher, Bertrand Russell, says: "It becomes possible to think that what the physiologist regards as matter in the brain is actually composed of thoughts and feelings, and that the difference between mind and matter is merely one of arrangement.[59] According to the neurologist, C. Judson Herrick: "The body makes the mind, but the mind is not a product made by the body as gastric juice is made by the stomach. It is the body in action, a peculiar pattern of action of a special kind of bodily apparatus, just as walking is another pattern of action of a different kind of apparatus."[27] Both definitions have in common their monistic attitude, distinct from a dualistic concept separating mind from brain. In our consideration of the effects of the psychotropic drugs upon behavior both in infraprimate mammals as well as primates, including man, we shall avoid the metaphysical viewpoint, which denies a sense of similarity among these organisms, and instead will adopt an evolutionary one that includes both similarities and differences and regards man as the most highly evolved animal insofar as his mental characteristics are concerned. This superiority is, therefore, not absolute for, to a lesser extent, man's mental advantages are shared by his mammalian relatives.

One way to examine mind is to study behavior, for the latter is a physical correlate of the former. As we ascend the phyletic tree, behavior becomes more complex in terms of variability in response to stimuli. This variability is associated with different though not independent brain areas: the more discriminative mental activities with the last part of the brain to develop, the neocortex, and the cruder aspects of awareness with older cortical and subcortical areas. The release from the dominance of inherited patterns in response to stimuli is observed to correlate with the evolution of the neocortex. Mammals, the members of the last phylum to appear, are superior to their phyletic ancestors in acquiring new behavior through learning. The basic experiments of Lashley revealed a positive relationship between the amount of intact cortex in rats and their learning to run a maze.[41] The development of reasoning, foresight, and planning for the future, and communication and spoken language parallels that of the cerebral cortex in the mammals and especially their highest representatives, the primates. The mental differences as we go from rat, cat, and dog to monkey, chimpanzee, and man are related to the number of cells and their complexity of arrangement in the neocortex. In contrast MacLean has emphasized that there are greater similarities in the construction of the rhinencephalon or limbic lobe, which shows similar degrees of development and organization throughout the entire mammalian series.[43] Lashley had previously concluded that the fundamental emotional reactions have undergone little change in the course of mammalian evolution.[41] These similarities render the comparative study of emotions in animals and man more satisfactory than that of the more discriminative aspects of the mind. Another advantage of this type of study is obtained in the bodily expression of emotion. Thought, especially in man, may go on with a minimum of observable behavioral changes, but emotions find expression in easily noted alterations both of the autonomic or visceral organs and of the musculature or somatic structures.

It is true that the neocortex is not required for the expression of emotion as observed in the decorticate dog or cat. Similarly, the schizophrenic patient subjected to the insulin hypoglycemic treatment of Sakel reveals emotional mimetic phenomena, especially marked in the second stage of insulin hypoglycemia with the functional suppression of the cortex.[29] However, it is not unlikely that this activity is largely pseudoaffective.

From other experiments we know that there are elements of awareness contributed by each of these three groups of structures, the reticular formation, the hypothalamus, and the limbic system. It is true that primitive pseudoaffective behavioral expressions can be elicited at the midbrain level and probably by the reticular formation. Section of the brain stem below this level has been reported by Bard to abolish such behavior and further suggests the involvement of the midbrain reticular formation in the mediation of these rather fundamental aspects of emotion.[6] Hess's studies demonstrate the broad range of emotional response patterns selectively elicited from discrete localized electrical stimulation in various hypothalamic areas.[28] Alterations are seen that in normal animals are conventionally associated with fear, anger, pleasure, as well as with such phenomena as exploratory tendencies, cleaning tendencies, and continuous restlessness. Stimulation of either the hypothalamus or the motor cortex leads to integrated autonomic and somatic effects. In experiments in which the cortex had been extirpated, however, the somatic adaptations of the hypothalamus were effected entirely by extrapyramidal pathways.[35] Lesions in the limbic system may produce either tranquilization or the reverse reaction of rage,[31] and the latter especially when, the more forward portion of the rhinencephalon, the septal area and the olfactory tubercle were removed. Bilateral extirpation of the amygdala and adjacent piriform lobe rendered animals easily disturbed, while bilateral removal of the amygdala and hippocampus make for placidity and emotional unresponsiveness. Recently a paper by King and Meyer suggested that the septal region and the amygdaloid nuclei play reciprocal roles in the control of affective behavior.[38] Impulses from the septal and amygdaloid regions may attain the hypothalamus and in the rat, at least, the septal area appears to dampen the hypothalamic activity associated with emotional states while the amygdala may facilitate such hypothalamic mechanisms.

Other studies made on the reticular formation, the hypothalamus, and the limbic system permit the conclusion that under certain conditions they can function as a unit to furnish the anatomic substrate for emotion. The first group of structures in this functional trilogy was delineated and evaluated in the work of Magoun and Moruzzi,[46] Jasper,[36] and Bremer,[10] who studied the reticular formation and the functional

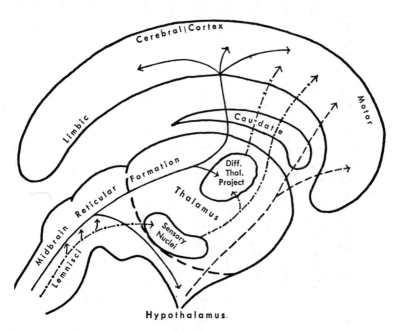

FIGURE 1

Mesodiencephalic activating system. Stimulation of the organism evokes impulses that travel by way of the lemnisci to the thalamic sensory nuclei and then to cortical sensory areas. The lemnisci send collateral nerve fibers to the midbrain reticular formation, and by these fibers impulses advance in the reticular formation to the diffuse thalamic projections and arouse the cerebral cortex. Collaterals bearing stimuli from the midbrain reticular formation pass to the hypothalamus, which in turn sends impulses to the cerebral cortex.[30]

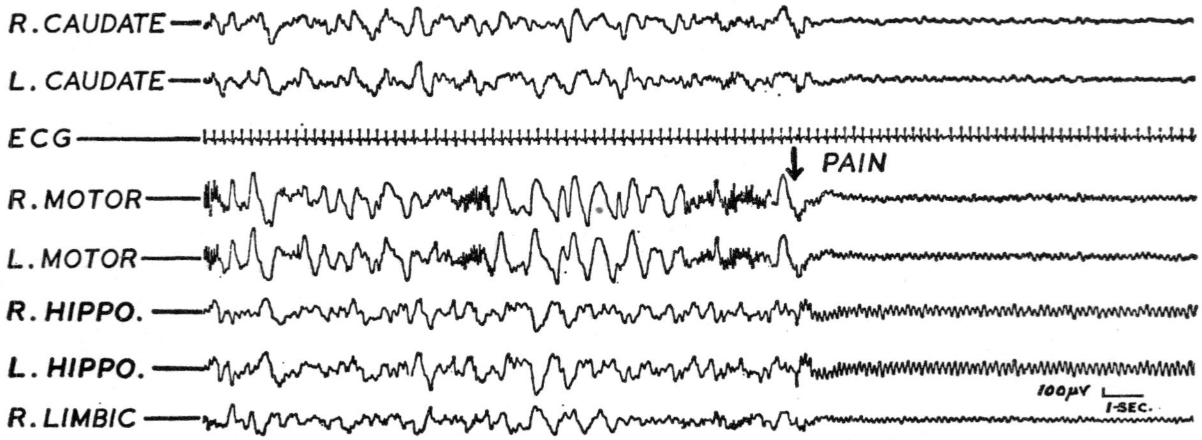

FIGURE 2

Peripheral stimulation arouses activating system. An impulse from the periphery evoked by pain activates the alerting mechanism and changes the drowsy pattern to one of alertness. The left part of the figure reveals the resting pattern of high-voltage slow waves and 14-per-second spindles. The right part of the record shows cortical fast-low-voltage activity and 4-to-7-cycle-per-second rhythm of hippocampal origin. Tracings are derived bilaterally from the limbic cortex, the motor cortex, the caudate nucleus, and the hippocampus. In addition an ECG record is presented.[30]

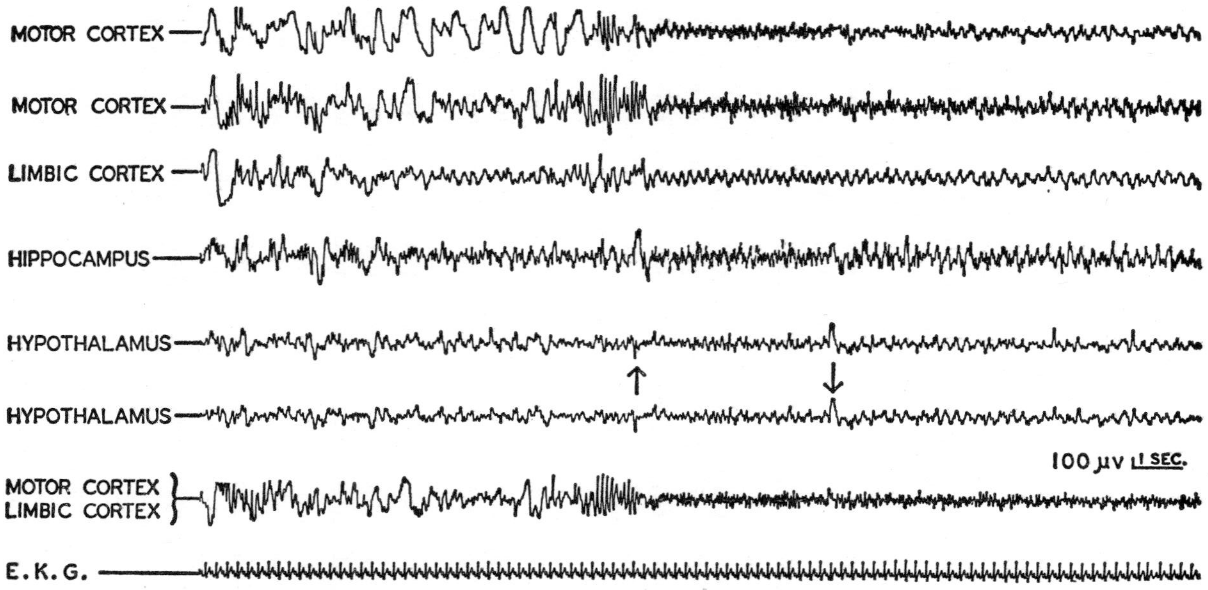

FIGURE 3

EEG arousal evoked by stimulation of the reticular formation. Electrical stimulation of the reticular formation (frequency 250-per-second, duration 1.5 milliseconds, 5.0 volts) is associated with alert tracings from all parts of brain indicated in the figure. Monopolar tracings labeled from above downward are taken from the motor cortex, limbic cortex, and hippocampus and bipolar tracings from the motor and limbic cortex.[66] In the hypothalamus the character of the waves changes to alerting during the period of stimulation indicated by the two arrows. After stimulation has ceased, the hypothalamic patterns are somewhat altered to resemble those of the alerted limbic cortex. The lowest tracing is that of the electrocardiogram.

prolongation of its ascending activities in the diffuse thalamocortical fibers that together form the mesodiencephalic activating system (MDAS).[55, 56]

Because of the basic role of the reticular formation in the physiology of the emotions, it is worth while to recall that it forms a central network of gray matter containing neurons with centrifugal and centripetal pathways extending in both directions through the spinal cord as well as the bulbar, pontine, and midbrain levels of the brain (Figure 1). This reticular system parallels, in a way, that of the lemnisci that brings sensory information to the cortex. A sign of stimulation of the MDAS is the replacement of a light sleep pattern consisting of slow high-voltage waves interrupted at intervals by 14-per-second trains of low-voltage undulations in all cortical leads with the alert pattern of potentials of still lower voltage at 22 to 30-cycle-per-second frequency, chiefly in the cortex. The hippocampus, however, shows 6-cycle-per-second rhythm, extremely regular both in amplitude and in voltage (Figure 2). These electrical changes give evidence of cortical and hippocampal coordination with the reticular arousal process. Perhaps in this manner the MDAS adds the emotional cloak to awareness achieved by the classical sensory pathways. We have no sure means of differentiating between the expression of emotion and the experiencing of emotion, but as suggested by Gellhorn it is not improbable that the neocortex plays an important part in adding the element of experience to the chiefly emotional mimetic functions of the subcortical and paleocortical structures.[24]

The fundamental studies of Cannon[15] and Bard[5] have revealed that the hypothalamus contains patterns for the coordination of visceral functions and muscular activities especially in states associated with the mobilization of the total organism as in "fight or flight" reactions. The activities of the subcortical extrapyramidal motor systems are integrated with the autonomic discharges in such expressions of the emotions. It is true that Masserman[44] has shown that the hypothalamic activity is chiefly of the quality of awareness termed pseudoaffective. On the other hand, as demonstrated by Murphy and Gellhorn,[47] hypothalamic stimulation can evoke cortical excitation. Figure 3 is included in order to show that hypothalamic alerting may be evoked by the arousal of the reticular formation.

We have to thank many investigators for information on the third group of structures called the rhinencephalon or limbic system which has received impetus from the work of Klüver and Bucy,[39] Bard and Mountcastle,[7] Walker and Thomson,[64] Pribram and Kruger,[52] Spiegel and co-workers,[63] Schreiner and Kling,[60] and Rothfield and Harman.[58] The structures associated with the limbic system include the septum, the amygdala, the anterior and midline thalamic nuclei, the hippo-campus, the hippocampal gyrus, and the cingulate gyrus. According to Papez (Figure 4) impulses are transmitted from the hippocampus through the fornix to the mammillary bodies of the hypothalamus.[50] From that area they continue to the anterior thalamic nuclei attaining the cortex of the brain in the cingulate gyrus and returning via the cingulum to the hippocampus. By means of the cingulate area the Papez circuit brings the crude paleocortical emotional substrate of the brain into connection with the more discriminative activities of the mind as displayed by the functions of the neocortex. Thus, subcortical and paleocortical areas making up parts of these three groups of structures all interact with the neocortex. A sign of integrated participation of these three groups of structures is revealed in the effects of the electroencephalogram in re-sponse to noxious stimulus, pinching of the footpad, evokes impulses

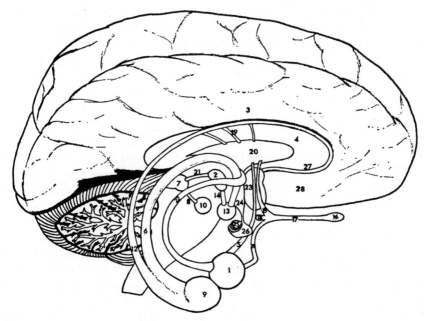

FIGURE 4

Semidiagrammatic presentation of limbic system. 1, amygdala; 2, anterior nucleus of thalamus; 3, cingulate gyrus; 4, corpus callosum; 5, diagonal band of Borca; 6, fornix; 7, habenula, a nucleus of the thalamus 8, habenulopeduncular tract; 9, hippocampus; 10, interpeduncular nucleus; 11, lateral olfactory stria; 12, longitudinal stria; 13, mammillary body; 14, mammillothalamic tract; 15, medial olfactory stria; 16, olfactory bulb; 17, olfactory tract; 18, olfactory tubercle; 19, perforating fibers; 20, septum pelludicum; 21, stria medularis; 22, stria terminalis; 23, subcallosal gyrus; 24, hypothalamus; 25, posterior pituitary gland; 26, anterior pituitary gland; 27, caudate nuclei in depth of brain; 28, septal region. (Adapted from "Physiology and Pharmacology of Emotion," *Scope*, 1955, 4:1.[1])

which ascend the lemnisci, and is relayed by the specific thalamic nuclei to the cortex to bring awareness (Figure 2). At the same time collaterals arising in the lemnisci pass to the reticular formation which in turn excites hypothalamic mechanisms by means of collaterals and also stimulates the cortex via the diffuse thalamocortical projections. Further examination of Figure 2 reveals that both the limbic cortex and hippocampus are simultaneously alerted. Furthermore, tracings from the limbic cortex, which in the rabbit is similar to the cingulate gyrus in man, also shows the participation of that portion of the Papez circuit in the alerting reaction. Figure 3 was included because it reveals that direct electrical stimulation of the midbrain reticular formation can evoke changes in hypothalamic function. The point we wish to make is that these three groups of structures do not necessarily function independently of each other but under certain conditions act together in an integrated way. According to Harris:[26] "The reticular formation, the hypothalamus and the limbic system all seem to be intimately related to the regulation of sleep and consciousness and to emotion." That is not to say that they are the only areas of the brain involved in emotion, and we know that many parts are interconnected on a basis of reverberating circuits. For example, some of the primitive emotions seem to have a thalamic site, especially those evoked by pain and usually allocated to the midline nuclei, those thalamic nuclei which also give rise to some of the diffuse thalamocortical projections. Furthermore, as we have seen, the reverberating circuits include cortical activities and there seems to be no room for doubt that some kind of cortical participation is essential for the normal experiencing of most human mental processes. But because under certain circumstances the reticular formation, the hypothalamus, and the Papez circuit can act in a unified way they will be given the single term, thymencephalon, hereafter, thus avoiding the repetition of the names of the three different structures. Though thymencephalon is a new word, it conforms with the adjectives, thymotropic and thymoleptic which are used synonymously with psychotropic and psycholeptic in describing this new group of drugs. It is worthy of note that among the various meanings of the Greek word, thymos, are: strong feeling and passion. Encephalon means literally that which is within the head and refers to the brain. Thus, the entire word indicates the parts of the brain especially involved with feelings and emotions. We do not know for sure the exact anatomic paths by which these three major systems included under the term, thymencephalon, interact with each other. We have, however, the observations of Nauta,[48, 49] which reveal that fibers originate in the midbrain reticular formation nuclei of Bechterew and Gudden and then pass directly to the hypothalamus and to the septal area, eventually to be distributed by way of the fornix and cingulum to the hippocampus and the cingulate gyrus (Figure 5). These areas return fibers to the nuclear structures of the midbrain reticular formation to complete a reverberating circuit. By another pathway the midbrain reticular formation sends fibers to the Papez circuit via the olfactory tubercle. Adey[2] also suggests two-way pathways between the hippocampus and midbrain reticular formation by way of the thalamus and fornix.

In our conception of the thymencephalon, we must not forget that

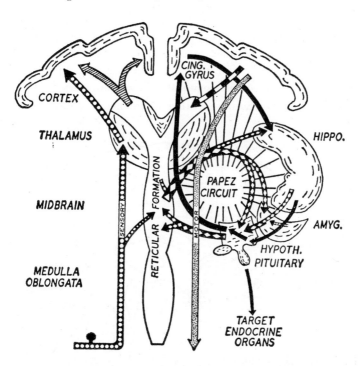

FIGURE 5

Semidiagrammatic illustration of some interrelationships between the reticular formation and the limbic system. The left half of this figure portrays specific sensory pathways to the thalamic sensory nuclei and the cortical sensory areas as well as a collateral (white dots on black arrows) to the reticular formation (white), which is continued to the diffuse thalamocortical projection (shaded). The reticular formation also possesses important descending motor activities. On the right side of the figure is indicated diagrammatically (in black arrows) the Papez circuit connecting the hippocampus, fornix, hypothalamus (mammillary body), thalamus (anterior nucleus), cingulate gyrus, and cingulum returning to the hippocampus. The connections of the Papez circuit with the amygdala and reticular formation are suggested by arrows containing white diamond shapes. Fibers originating in the nuclei of Gudden and Bechterew pass directly to the hypothalamus. The feedback from the cortex to the reticular formation (black and white arrow) as well as the motor pathway from the cortex to the spinal column (stippled arrow) are also included in the right half of the diagram. The figure is adapted from Galambos.[22]

this area is the chief repository of the biogenic amines of the brain, acetylcholine, the indolamines, including serotonin and the catechol-amines, chiefly noradrenaline and dopamine. In contrast the neocortex and the cerebellum contain minimal quantities of these neurohormones (Figures 6 and 7). Whether or not changes of function in the thymen-cephalon include alterations in the metabolism of serotonin and nor-adrenaline is not proved. The roles of acetylcholine in nerve conduction and synaptic transmission in the peripheral system have been studied for many years. Less is known in regard to the function of acetylcholine in the central nervous system, though it seems established that certain areas of the brain are cholinergic in part.[55, 56] We have still less knowl-edge of the parts played by serotonin and noradrenaline. Suggestions have been made that they may be concerned with central transmission[13] or that they may be involved in central transmission perhaps by modify-ing the action of acetylcholine or other neurochemical mediators.[17]

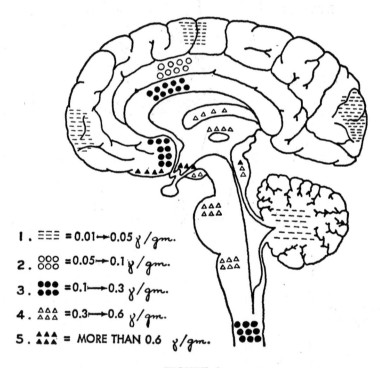

1 . ≡≡≡ = 0.01→0.05 ɣ/gm.

2 . ooo = 0.05→0.1 ɣ/gm.

3 . ●●● = 0.1→0.3 ɣ/gm.

4 . ᴬᴬᴬ = 0.3→0.6 ɣ/gm.

5 . ▲▲▲ = MORE THAN 0.6 ɣ/gm.

FIGURE 6

Serotonin content of the human brain. The areas with the highest concentration of serotonin, an indoleamine, include the hypothalamus. A lower level is observed in the mammillary bodies, fornix, thalamus, and medulla oblongata. Serotonin is found in the cingulate gyrus, hippocampus, and amygdaloid nucleus in greater concentrations than in the neocortex or cerebellum, which contain the least amounts.[19]

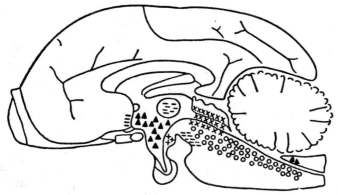

$\Delta = 1.0$ μg/g, $+ > 0.4 < 1.0$ μg/g, $0 > 0.3 < 0.4$ μg/g, $- > 0.2 < 0.3$ μg/g fresh tissue.

FIGURE 7

Medial sagittal section of a dog's brain, showing the distribution of noradrenaline in micrograms per gram of fresh tissue. In the dog brain, the catecholamines, especially noradrenaline, are at their highest concentration in the hypothalamus and then occur in decreasing amounts in the mammillary bodies and the reticular formation. Still lower concentrations observed in the neocortex and cerebellum.[68]

We have thus compared neocortical functions with those of the reticular formation, the hypothalamus, and the limbic lobe, as the latter are the parts of brain involved in the expression of emotion. It is true that they afford crude awareness too, but the discriminative experiencing of emotion is added by the neocortex. We have shown that under the influence of a noxious stimulus the reticular formation, the hypothalamus, and limbic system can act together, and in the term, thymencephalon, we have included the integrated actions of these parts of the brain. We have also pointed out that the thymencephalon contains biogenic amines in contrast with the neocortex which is relatively free of them. As we shall see in the next section, the thymencephalon rather than the neocortex is the part of the brain which is chiefly affected by the psychotropic drugs.

An Experimental Analysis of the Effects of Psychotropic Drugs on Brain Mechanisms

A Comparison of Animal and Human Behavior

We would like to know how the psychotropic drugs act to produce desirable differences in behavior, since such information should be valuable for understanding their mechanisms of action. It is also possible that this knowledge may throw light on the underlying causes of these behavioral abnormalities. At present there are numerous drug actions that are unexplained, especially in the field of human observation. It is the purpose of the third part of this paper, then, to present the actions of psychotropic drugs on animal brain and to compare them with behavioral changes they cause both in animals and in man. For example, the effects of these drugs are not necessarily uniform. A tranquilizer may be of aid to one paranoid schizophrenic patient and not to another. This divergence between therapeutic results and clinical categories appears to an even greater extent with the use of the antidepressants. There may be many reasons for such discrepancies: the different personality structures of the patients involved and their individual past histories. There may even be basic differences between two patients who, because of apparently similar behavior have been placed in the same clinical category, yet, on a biochemical basis may be dissimilar. We are now beginning to make our first exploratory observations in these directions. Toward that end it would be highly advantageous to make neurochemical and neurophysiological studies on the brains of patients. Such studies are difficult to accomplish, and even if successful would prove only that behavior changes and the neurochemical findings are the results of a common cause, the administration of the drug. It would require a large number of such correlations before we could begin to consider that the pharmacologic effects and the behavioral alterations represent cause and effect. We have a better opportunity to examine the brains of animals than those of patients although this brings the additional handicap of difference of species. But the most important disadvantage in the study of the effect of psychotropic drugs on animals is that we cannot be sure whether or not they exhibit aberrant behavior similar to that of psychotic patients. Because we are interested in the emotional aspect of behavior and its expression it is appropos to note that one of the ways in which animals differ from man in expression of emotions is that they are less controlled and not affected to the same degree by previous socializing experiences. Animals in this regard resemble human infants in whom perception cannot be separated from its emotional content. This advantage is, therefore, offered by the study of behavior in animals. The production of abnormal behavior in the laboratory has not been fully realized. It is true that a dog suffering from rabies encephalitis resembles, in some ways, a manic schizophrenic patient with extreme excitement as the animal exhibits indiscriminative biting and apparently purposeless hyperactivity, but such symptoms do not occur in the absence of this disease. We have recourse to the use of psychotomimetic drugs in animals as in the experimental use of these drugs in human volunteers. This method can be used, with proper reservations, as an approach to the study of abnormal behavior, but thus far we have not been able to reproduce behavior identical with that occurring in psychotic patients. Conditions approaching experimental neurotic ambivalence have also been produced in dogs trained to distinguish between a circle and an ellipse as the animals have finally become frustrated as the shape of the ellipse is gradually changed to approach that of a circle. Such an animal loses previously learned behavior, refuses to eat, and exhibits uncontrolled excitement, but all these symptoms characteristically occur in the experimental chamber and the animal is largely free of them when removed to another environment. The observations presented in this paper have been made on apparently normal animals subjected to psychotropic drugs. It is easy to demonstrate in animals the sedative effects of the rauwolfia alkaloids and the phenothiazine derivatives similar to those exerted on man under the influence of reserpine or chlorpromazine. Motor activity decreases and a taming action is seen on the rhesus monkey, a primate frequently exhibiting hostile behavior toward man. These drugs prolong the sleeping time induced by barbiturates. As mentioned above, these changes in animal behavior cannot be compared with human results as far as antipsychotic actions are concerned. On the other hand, they do show a calming influence which is not only observed in psychotic patients but also in human subjects who do not suffer from pathologically elevated emotions.

The antidepressant action of imipramine is different from the stimulating properties of amphetamine, pipradrol, methylphenidate, and other central nervous system stimulants because that of imipramine is more specific as evidenced by results obtained on animals in activity cages. Unlike amphetamine and the other central nervous system stimulants, imipramine does not evoke hyperactivity.[62] On the other hand, animals with drug-induced depression respond to imipramine the same as humans with depression due to disease, since imipramine counteracts the closure of the pupils as well as that of the eyelids, the fall in body temperature, slowed heart rate, and diarrhea induced by the administration of reserpine.[20] Nevertheless, imipramine cannot antagonize the action of reserpine to prolong barbiturate hypnosis. Similar specificity is produced by monoamine oxidase inhibitors, which do not increase motor activity except after prolonged medication. Agreement of results between animals and human patients is noted as comparatively slight stimulating effects are observed in human individuals who are not depressed. When, however, monoamine oxidase inhibitors are given to an animal who had previously received reserpine they resemble imipramine in counteracting myosis, palpebral closure, semiprostration, and decrease of body temperature.[12] The ability of monoamine oxidase inhibitors to reverse the sedative effect of reserpine is much more marked, however, when re-

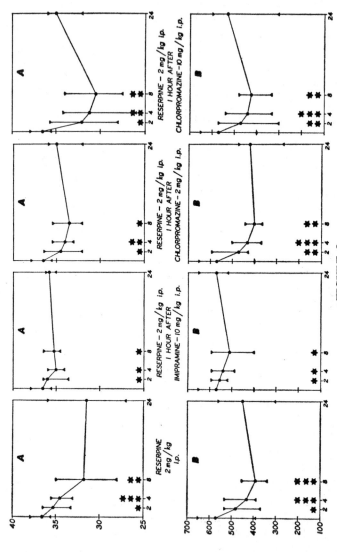

FIGURE 8

Interactions between reserpine, imipramine, and chlorpromazine. (A) Imipramine counteracts the fall of rectal temperature and the diarrhea induced by reserpine. (B) Imipramine counteracts the decrease of heart rate and ptosis evoked by reserpine. (A) Chlorpromazine, 2 mg/kg, counteracts the reserpine-induced fall in rectal temperature and diarrhea but does not antagonize the decrease of heart rate of ptosis. Chlorpromazine, 10 mg/kg does not counteract any of these reserpine-induced effects (A, B).[21] Abscissas = time in hours after reserpine injection ordinates = C – (A), or pulses per minute – (B); * = degree of diarrhea and ptosis evaluated by an arbitrary score (number of stars directly proportional to intensity of symptomatology); A = rectal temperature and diarrhea; B = heart rate and ptosis; vertical bars = range. Each point is the mean of at least 10 rats.

serpine is administered after one of these inhibitors,[16] for then the animals exhibit marked signs of central excitation characterized by piloerection, foreleg clonus, tremors, and penile erection. Furthermore, these alterations are accompanied by a large rise in rectal temperature in rabbits. These stimulating actions are produced by doses of monoamine oxidase inhibitors which by themselves neither evoke pyretogenic effects nor overt signs of central stimulation. To illustrate these antagonistic actions we shall compare the effects of imipramine and chlorpromazine on rats. For these experiments four groups of animals were used.[20] The first received reserpine, 2 milligrams per kilogram; in the second, third, and fourth groups reserpine was followed by imipramine, 10 milligrams per kilogram, chlorpromazine, 2 milligrams per kilogram, and chlorpromazine, 10 milligrams per kilogram, respectively. As presented in Figure 8, hypothermia, diarrhea, bradycardia, and palpebral ptosis all induced by 2 milligrams per kilogram of reserpine were antagonized by the subsequent administration of 10 milligrams per kilogram of imipramine. The results of chlorpromazine are of two kinds depending upon dosage. With 10 milligrams per kilogram of chlorpromazine the reserpine-induced actions were not antagonized. On the other hand, 2 milligrams per kilogram reversed both the fall in rectal temperature and the diarrhea. Thus, under certain conditions chlorpromazine can counteract reserpine in a manner similar to that observed with imipramine. The sedation produced by reserpine is, however, always synergistic with that of chlorpromazine. The animal observations are in accordance with the conclusions derived from our clinical observations that a tranquilizing drug may occasionally reveal antidepressant activities. In an attempt to make an experimental analysis of the behavioral results we shall examine various neurohormonal and electrophysiological alterations wrought by the psychotropic drugs on the brain of infrahuman mammals. Incidentally, if these drugs evoke similar basic results in the human brain they would be suggestive of correlations with behavior in patients receiving these drugs.

Electrophysiological and Neurohormonal Observations on Animals

In Table 1 are presented the effects of some psychotropic drugs on the ability either (1) to block or stimulate the reticular formation, (2) to modify the effects of amygdaloid stimulation on secondary hippocampal responses, (3) to evoke spontaneous rhinencephalic seizures, and (4) to influence recruitment, namely, the activity of the thalamocortical projections. The term MAOI represents any member of the group of monoamine oxidase inhibitors and especially nialamide, phenylazine dihydrogensul-

TABLE 1

Effects of Some Psychotropic Drugs on Evoked and Spontaneous Potentials of Brain

	CHLORPROMAZINE	RESERPINE	IMIPRAMINE	MAOI
Reticular formation	Inhibition[31]	Inhibition followed by stimulation[31]	Inhibition[33]	Stimulation[21]
Evoked hippocampal response	Facilitation[54]	Depression followed by facilitation[54]	Facilitation[54]	No effect[54]
Spontaneous rhinencephalic seizures	Present[51]	Present[37]	Present[67]	Absent[21]
Recruitment	Facilitation[18]	No effects[18]	Facilitation[18]	No effect[18]

fate, phenylisopropyl hydrazine, isocarboxazid, and tranylcypromine. For electroencephalographic examples of the blocking or stimulation of the reticular formation the reader is referred to Figures 2 and 3. Figure 9 illustrates the influences of reserpine, tranylcypromine, and a serotonin precursor on the magnitude of the evoked hippocampal potentials,[54] while examples of amygdaloid and/or hippocampal spontaneous seizure patterns are afforded by Figure 10 exemplifying this action with reserpine.[37] A drug action on recruitment is seen by the facilitation of that function by chlorpromazine in Figure 11.

Table 2 reveals relative effects of various drugs on concentrations of two brain neurohormones. The relative intensities of these changes are indicated by the number of plus and minus signs. Thus, the extents of the fall or rise of serotonin and noradrenaline as the result of the administrations of reserpine and monoamine oxidase inhibitors, respectively, are greater than the increases of serotonin due either to chlorpromazine or imipramine.

A glance at these two tables reveals little in common between the tranquilizers on one side and the antidepressants on the other. These drugs do not act in the same manner, not even on a general basis, but affect the brain in characteristic ways which, at least superficially, have

TABLE 2

Effects of Some Psychotropic Drugs on Concentrations of Brain Serotonin and Noradrenaline

	CHLORPROMAZINE	RESERPINE	IMIPRAMINE	MAOI
Serotonin	+[21]	− −[12]	+[21]	+ +[12]
Noradrenaline	0[53]	− −[12]	0[53]	+ +[14]

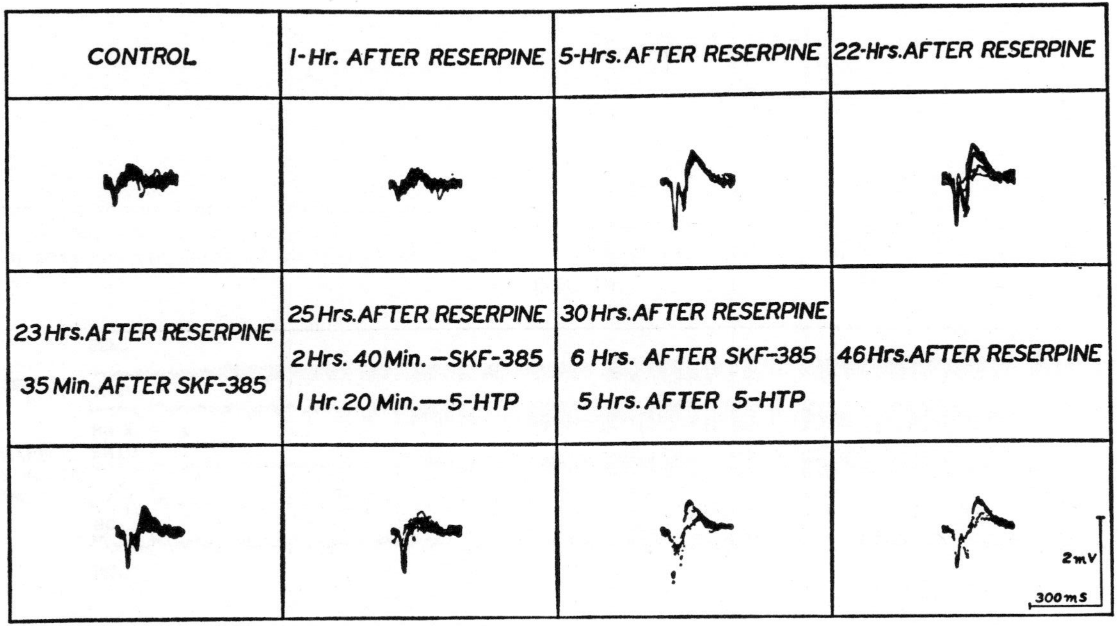

CONTROL	1-Hr. AFTER RESERPINE	5-Hrs. AFTER RESERPINE	22-Hrs. AFTER RESERPINE
23 Hrs. AFTER RESERPINE 35 Min. AFTER SKF-385	25 Hrs. AFTER RESERPINE 2 Hrs. 40 Min. — SKF-385 1 Hr. 20 Min. — 5-HTP	30 Hrs. AFTER RESERPINE 6 Hrs. AFTER SKF-385 5 Hrs. AFTER 5-HTP	46 Hrs. AFTER RESERPINE

2 mV
300 mS

FIGURE 9

Sequential effects of reserpine, tranylcypromine (SKF-385), and 5-HTP on hippocampal-evoked potentials. One hour after reserpine a diminution in the evoked hippocampal potential is observed, while five hours after the administration of the drug a large increase of potentials occurs, an increase still evident twenty-two hours after reserpine administration. Tranylcypromine, a monoamine oxidase inhibitor, reduces for a second time the magnitude of the evoked potentials. A further reduction occurs after the administration of 5-hydroxytryptophan, the precursor of serotonin. Thirty hours after reserpine the potentials again increase in magnitude, and at forty-six hours they approach the control levels. When tranylcypromine is administered without reserpine premedication, no consistent effects on evoked hippocampal potentials are produced.[54]

FIGURE 10

Effect of reserpine (0.1 mg/kg) on rhinencephalic seizure patterns. Records of spontaneous seizures initiated in the amygdala. The seizure patterns appear next in the hippo- campus and entorhinal cortex but spare the median supra- sylvian gyrus and the sensory cortex.[37]

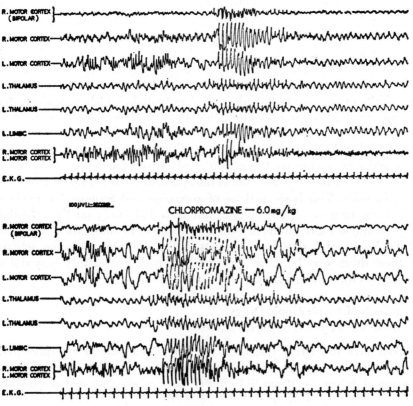

Stimulus = 9 volts, 1.5-m/sec duration, 7/sec frequency for 5.0 sec.

FIGURE 11

Chlorpromazine enhances recruiting responses, the gradual waxing and waning of amplitude in response to stimulation of anterior thalamic nuclei. Note that the duration of recruiting responses is prolonged after the administration of chlorpromazine. The leads are indicated in figure.[66]

little in common. Obviously, then, each drug must be studied separately. For the present, positive conclusions cannot be drawn in regard to any general relationships of the electroencephalographic and neurohormonal changes in regard to behavior either among tranquilizers or among antidepressants. Several minor correlations, however, are suggested by a review of these two tables. The first arises from a comparison of the basic effects of chlorpromazine, a tranquilizer, and imipramine, an antidepressant, and surprisingly we find a general agreement between them. Both block the reticular formation, facilitate evoked hippocampal responses, are associated with spontaneous rhinencephalic seizures, and

facilitate recruitment. Similarly, both cause moderate increases of serotonin without influencing noradrenaline. It is striking that imipramine and
promazine have the same chemical constitutions except for the substitution of diethylene linkage for sulfur. Lest the reader come to the
conclusion that these drugs are exactly alike in their basic effects, it
should be pointed out that the dosages required to produce the basic results are not necessarily of the same order. Moreover, sciatic stimulation
of rabbits evokes contralateral cortical potentials which are of greater
amplitude in animals on imipramine than on chlorpromazine.[67] Thus
imipramine has this enhancing action not possessed by chlorpromazine.
Among other differences, Sigg[62] has noted that imipramine is less effective
than chlorpromazine on the conditioned escape-avoidance response in
rats, in alcohol-induced sedation in mice, and in reducing rectal temperature in mice. The basic actions of reserpine and monoamine oxidase
inhibitors, in general, are diverse, but their influences on the reticular
formation and on recruitment bear resemblances to each other. A review
of Tables 1 and 2, therefore, suggests that the differences in the actions
of these drugs may be more apparent than real, in that they may differ
in degree rather than in kind.

Effects of Psychotropic Drugs
on Rhinencephalic Seizure Patterns

We have previously discussed the power not only of reserpine and
chlorpromazine but also of imipramine to evoke amygdaloid and/or hippocampal seizure patterns.[37, 51, 67] We have also suggested a possible

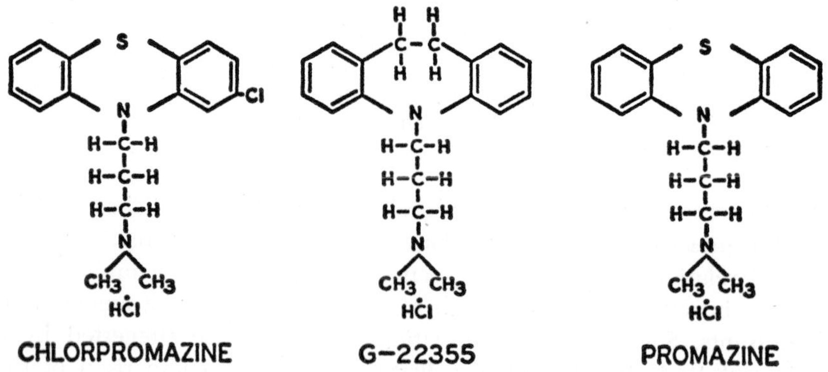

CHLORPROMAZINE   G−22355   PROMAZINE

FIGURE 12

Structural formulas of chlorpromazine, imipramine (G-22355), and promazine.
Note (1) the identical side chains of the drugs; (2) a sulfur atom (S) bonds the
chlorpromazine and promazine nuclei, while an ethylene (—CH_2—CH_2—) bonds
the imipramine nucleus.[67]

influence of rhinencephalic seizures in correction of schizophrenic thought.[31] Seizure patterns of these limbic areas may not only prevent their contribution to the Papez circuit but also interfere with its function in integrating rhinencephalic activity with that of the cortex. Thus the loss of this function of the Papez circuit is a possible factor in the prevention of the morbid thinking of schizophrenia. The tranquilizing influences of rhinencephalic seizures are seen in a cat under the influence of chlorpromazine which will not attack a mouse but instead acts with apparent indifference; yet, motor activity and reflexes of the cat are not changed. Andy and Akert[3] have shown that when the hippocampus is stimulated electrically and the hippocampal discharge is propagated to the amygdala, it renders the cat unaffected by the mouse until after the discharge is completed.

Effects of Psychotropic Drugs on the Reticular Formation

A further suggestion on the strange combination of antidepressant and tranquilizing actions comes out of the basic observations of behavioral effects, and we are again referring to their influence on the reticular formation which has been presented on Table 1.[31] We shall, therefore, mention only briefly that when either chlorpromazine or imipramine in relatively small doses is given to a rabbit the reticular formation is blocked and the alerting response to pain usually seen in the cortex fails to appear. It is safe to assume, however, that the lemniscal functions continue to bring sensory impulses to the cortex. It is of interest, therefore, that chlorpromazine, the phenothiazines in general, and imipramine improve the effects of analgesics in the control of pain. Probably it is the discriminative experiencing of pain that is prevented by blocking the reticular formation. In any event, reserpine, which activates the reticular formation, possesses less sedative powers than chlorpromazine.[31] Monoamine oxidase inhibitors, reserpine, and central nervous system stimulants like amphetamine, pipradrol, and methylphenidate all evoke EEG and behavioral arousal. The central nervous system stimulants cause arousal by exciting the adrenergic receptors of the midbrain reticular formation. The mechanisms of action of reserpine and of the MAOI drugs are unknown but appear to be more complicated that those of central nervous system stimulants. The first effect of reserpine is the transitory production of the EEG sleep pattern later to be followed by a more enduring activation.[31, 45] Perhaps the ability of reserpine to affect serotonin metabolism is associated with these EEG alterations. Rabbits with intracarotid administration of 5-hydroxytryptophan, a precursor of serotonin, exhibit these two EEG patterns. Smaller doses of 5-hydroxytryptophan evoke sleep patterns while larger ones are alerting, as previously reported by Monnier and Tissot.[45] Our work[21] shows in addition that the different patterns appear to be associated with two different levels of serotonin in the brain. Moderate increases bring on sleep patterns and larger ones, above 300 per cent, cause activation.

Neurohormonal Effects of Psychotropic Drugs

We shall next follow clues afforded by a study of serotonin and noradrenaline in regard to the mechanisms of action of the psychotropic drugs. Brodie and Shore[12] have found that after a single dose of 5 milligrams per kilogram of reserpine given to a rabbit the rise and disappearances of the drug in the rabbit brain takes place in approximately twelve hours while the serotonin concentration is reduced to about 10 per cent of the control level for thirty-six hours and thereafter slowly ascends to normal levels in the course of a week. Later work by the same investigators showed that the decrease and subsequent restoration in noradrenaline levels of the brain parallel closely those of serotonin. During the entire period in which the animals suffered low brain concentration of these two neurohormones, they exhibited sedation. These workers logically suggested that the sedation was not caused directly by the presence of reserpine in the brain but by the alterations which that drug produced in the brain neurohormones.

It would seem desirable to determine whether the sedation was induced preponderantly by serotonin or by noradrenaline, and the opportunity to make this discrimination was afforded by the reserpine analog SU 5171 (Ciba). Brodie, Spector, and Shore[13] have shown that this analog in a dose of 0.5 milligram per kilogram decreases noradrenaline by about 85 per cent though with relatively little change in brain serotonin and, most important, there is little change in behavior. An increase of dosage to 2 milligrams per kilogram evokes a 65 per cent fall in brain serotonin, and with it sedation is observed. These authors, therefore, concluded that the decrease of brain serotonin may be the active factor in the therapeutic results of reserpine. It should be noted, however, that there is at least one dissenting voice. Sheppard and Zimmerman,[61] using different experimental procedures, failed to find correlations between brain serotonin and behavior similar to those observed by Brodie, Spector, and Shore.[13]

Most important for our understanding of the action of serotonin is the suggestion of Brodie[11] that sedation is due to an increased concentration of free serotonin in the brain.* It is true that reserpine releases serotonin from its binding sites and because of this release the sero-

---

* See, however, the recent findings of Green and Erickson.[25]

tonin concentration of the body falls, but additional serotonin is continuously elaborated and thus the level of free serotonin in the body is raised above normal despite the diminution of total serotonin. A raised level of free serotonin is probably determined by the rate of the new formation of that amine which is prevented from joining its binding posts by the action of reserpine. Increased concentrations of serotonin may also be attained by the administration of its precursor. Bogdanski, Weissbach, and Udenfriend[9] have injected 5-hydroxytryptophan in members of the various mammalian species and noticed that with low doses, 10 to 20 milligrams per kilogram, or medium ones, 50 to 100 milligrams per kilogram, sedation was evoked while high doses, 120 to 330 milligrams per kilogram, caused excitement and disorientation. Systematic observations made in our laboratory[34] in general confirmed these conclusions. In dogs pretreated with tranylcypromine injections of 2 milligrams per kilogram of 5-hydroxytryptophan indicated sedation, but a dose of 7 milligrams per kilogram of that serotonin precursor produced only temporary sedation which was followed by signs of central nervous system excitement. These signs seem to be individualized from animal to animal, perhaps being conditioned by personality structure. Nevertheless, the following behavioral changes were observed in a series of dogs: motor restlessness, ataxia, obstinate progression, festination of hind legs, aggressiveness, hostility, and a rise in rectal temperature.

All of the above observations were made on animals, but in other studies we compared behavioral and biochemical changes in patients, and, in general, there were suggestive agreements between the results obtained on animals and man. We[14] measured the urinary excretion of tryptamine, its metabolite indole-3-acetic acid, as well as that of 5-hydroxyindoleacetic acid (5-HIAA), in patients receiving reserpine and isocarboxazid separately and together. Soon after starting the administration of reserpine a short period of worsened behavior was observed in three of six patients and attributed to stimulation of the extrapyramidal system with signs of akathisia or motor restlessness and anxiety as well as activation of the psychotic symptoms. It is well known that phenothiazines, and especially reserpine, may evoke disorders of the extrapyramidal functions which are, however, improved with atropine-like antiparkinson drugs; but, whether associated with reserpine or occurring spontaneously, these disturbed periods were preceded and accompanied by increases in the urinary excretion of tryptamine and to a lesser extent by that of indole-3-acetic acid. At the same time the elimination of 5-HIAA augmented in these patients. In view of the fact that 5-HIAA is a breakdown product of serotonin such a result suggests a simultaneous increase of free serotonin and is therefore not unlike that observed in infraprimate mammals on high doses of 5-hydroxytryptophan.

These elevations in urinary constituents became even more marked in five of nine schizophrenic patients during the placebo period immediately following the cessation of combined therapy with reserpine and isocarboxazid. The periods of highest urinary excretion of these three products represent the occasions during which the patients became most disturbed, when extrapyramidal signs, including akathisia, or motor restlessness, and anxiety appeared and when the psychotic symptoms were activated. Thus, both extrapyramidal abnormalities and behavioral disturbances were associated with increased indoleamines. We have thus disclosed relationships between abnormal behavior and the increased elimination of indoleamines and indoleamine breakdown products in the urine. From our results we cannot say which one of the indoleamines, serotonin or tryptamine, is involved in this process. Either of these or other indole derivatives, however, may be factors in the excitation of the extrapyramidal system and the activation of the psychosis.

Though both reserpine and isocarboxazid may increase the concentrations of free serotonin their mechanisms of action are different. With

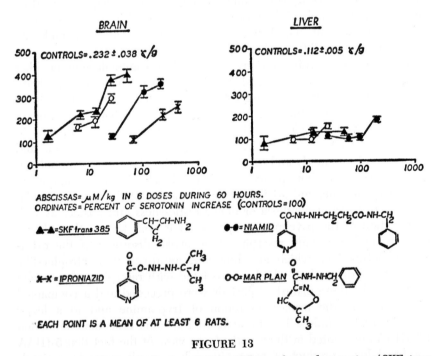

FIGURE 13

Serotonin concentrations in brain and liver. Effects of tranylcypromine (SKF trans 385), nialimide (Niamid), isocarboxazid (Marplan), and iproniazid (Marsilid) on serotonin increases in brain and liver. Because the liver possesses multiple pathways for the metabolism of serotonin, the use of monoamine oxidase inhibitors does not affect significantly the serotonin concentration in that organ.[18]

reserpine, not only does urinary 5-HIAA become greater but also tryptamine and indole-3-acetic acid. But with monoamineoxidase inhibitors 5-HIAA falls and usually to a much greater extent than does indole-3-acetic acid while tryptamine continues at highest levels. The profound diminution of 5-HIAA is caused by the power of isocarboxazid to prevent the breakdown of serotonin which, like tryptamine, rises in the body. Our results with the catecholamines[53] of the urine show that they also increase in concentration with disturbed behavior and especially with anxiety, but the time relationships were different from those noted with indoleamines. The rise of catecholamines seems to follow rather than to precede the signs of increased anxiety.

That the monoamineoxidase inhibitors increase brain serotonin in animals and may do so selectively can be seen by a comparison of the effects of these drugs on brain and liver serotonin made by Costa[18] (Figure 13). The monoamineoxidase inhibitors also increase brain noradrenaline though the rise is delayed and smaller in magnitude in comparison with that of serotonin (Figure 14). In observations of rabbits, following medication of MAOI drugs, Brodie, Spector, and Shore[14] report an association between signs of nervous stimulation and increases in brain

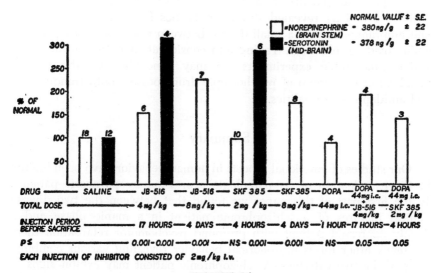

FIGURE 14

Effect of amineoxidase inhibitors and precursors on rabbit brain serotonin and norepinephrine. Changes in the concentration of biogenic amines in the brain after administration of monoamine oxidase inhibitors and biogenic amine precursors. Numbers at the top of the bars represent number of animals in each group. The *p* values express the significance according to the *t* test. Comparison was made between experiment groups and controls. Rabbits given both DOPA and monoamine oxidase inhibitors. NS = not significant, i.v. = intravenous, i.c. = intracarotid. JB 516 is the code name of phenylisopropyl hydrazine (Catron). SKF-385 is the code name of tranylcypromine (Parnate).[21]

noradrenaline. With the administration of phenylisopropyl hydrazine in doses of 2 milligrams per kilogram for four to five days the levels of both noradrenaline and serotonin were raised. Only during the period when the noradrenaline contents of the brain stem were highest was there a marked degree of spontaneous motor activity, increased motor response to tactile stimuli, and constriction of the blood vessels of the ear in rabbits. After administration of the drug had ceased, these signs disappeared with the fall of noradrenaline although serotonin still remained elevated. Thus, the evidence is in favor of a role for noradrenaline as well as for serotonin in abnormal behavior.

Tranquilizing and Antidepressant Effects of Psychotropic Drugs

Our review of the clinical effects of the psychotropic drugs disclosed that the usual classification of tranquilizers typified by the phenothiazine derivatives and rauwolfia alkaloids, and by antidepressants, including imipramine and the MAOI drugs may be regarded only as a first approximation, since tranquilizers may exert antidepressant actions and antidepressants may have tranquilizing influences. Another comparison of the psychotropic drugs made on the basis of animal experiments (Tables 1 and 2) revealed strong similarities between chlorpromazine and imipramine and to a small degree between reserpine and the monoamine oxidase inhibitors. Taking into consideration both clinical observations and basic experiments we may conclude that the various members of this group of psychotropic drugs possess both tranquilizing and antidepressive qualities.

Summary

Our studies of emotional aspects in human behavior have been limited to the examination of its pathologic expression by psychotic patients. In the first part of this paper we found that between the two diverse clinical pictures of a schizophrenic patient in a manic phase and a deeply depressed patient with profound psychomotor retardation there are many other forms of abnormal behavior revealing various combinations of the two extremes. A schizophrenic patient may exhibit signs of depression while a depressed patient may be hyperactive, pace the floor, and show other evidence of agitation, anxiety, and tension. In either case a mixture of symptoms from two different clinical categories is observed in the same patient.

We have also reviewed briefly the clinical results produced by tranquilizers, phenothiazine derivatives, and rauwolfia alkaloids and those of the antidepressant drugs, imipramine and monoamine oxidase inhibitors. These drugs are classified in two apparently diverse groups, but closer scrutiny suggests that they are not so different as indicated by early studies, since drugs that are chiefly tranquilizing may exert antidepressant actions, though to a lesser extent, while medications used mainly to relieve depression also possess some tranquilizing influences. Perhaps the complex effects of these drugs account for their therapeutic successes, especially, in those psychotic patients with symptomatologies expressing divergent behavioral components and partaking to different degrees of abnormal elation and abnormal depression. These drugs, therefore, exert normalizing influences and in favorable instances ameliorate to different degrees psychomotor excitement and psychomotor retardation.

In the second part of this paper we examined the brain areas concerned with the expression of emotion: reticular formation, hypothalamus, and limbic system and found that they also contribute crude awareness of emotion. Because they may act together and also to avoid repetition of these names they are given the single term, thymencephalon. It is realized, however, that the brain acts as an integrated unit and that the various brain areas contribute differently to total behavior—for example, the neocortex adds the discriminative experiencing of emotion.

We have found in the third part of this paper, consisting of examinations of the effects of these drugs on infrahuman mammals, that the major drug actions of the psychotropic drugs are localized in the thymencephalon, although it is also pointed out that these actions are widespread in the brain. We have reviewed the differences in the major effects of these drugs as typified by the sedative effects of the phenothiazines and reserpine and the abilities of imipramine and the monoamine oxidase inhibitors to counteract this sedation. But a comparison of eight different parameters (Tables 1 and 2) reveals similarities between chlorpromazine and imipramine and to a much lesser extent between reserpine and the monoamine oxidase inhibitors. It is, therefore, obvious that the performance of these drugs is complex, influencing the function of many brain structures, which are affected in different ways. Whether or not we shall find a key substance is impossible to say at present, but it would seem that the changes in behavior are resultants of diverse consequences in various brain areas, and especially those which form the thymencephalon. Perhaps this diversity will some day furnish the explanation for the mixed effects of these drugs upon behavior and why some drugs exhibit both tranquilizing and antidepressant actions.

It would seem that, in this study of the emotions, the analysis of the behavior of psychotic patients and the behavioral alterations induced by psychotropic drugs afford additional evidence for the complex and diverse elements in psychotic behavior.

REFERENCES

1. Adapted from "Physiology and pharmacology of emotion," *Scope*, 1955, 4:1.
2. Adey, W. R., "Rhinencephalon and behavior disorders," *Int. Rev. Neurobiology*, 1959, 1:1-41, Pfeiffer, C., and Smythies, J. R., eds., Academic Press, New York.
3. Andy, O. R., and Akert, K., "Seizure patterns induced by electrical stimulation of hippocampal formation in the cat," *J. Neuropathol. Exper. Neurol.*, 1956, 14:198-213.
4. Ayd, F. J., "Drug-induced depression—fact or fallacy?" *New York State J. Med.*, 1958, 58:354-356.
5. ———, "Emotions," *Handbook of General Experimental Psychology*. Clark Univ. Press, Worcester, Mass., 1934.
6. ———, "On emotional expression of decortication with some remarks on certain theoretical views," *Psychol. Rev.*, 1934, 41:309-329, 424, 429.
7. ———, and Mountcastle, V. B., "Some forebrain mechanisms involved in expression of rage with special reference to suppression of angry behavior," *Research Publ. Assoc. Nerv. Ment. Dis.*, 1947, 27:362-404.
8. Beaudry, P., and Gibson, D., "Effect of trifluoperazine on the behavior disorders of children with malignant emotional disturbances," *Am. J. Ment. Def.*, 1960, 64:823-826.
9. Bogdanski, D. F., Weissbach, H., and Udenfriend, S., "Pharmacological studies with the serotonin precursor, 5-hydroxytryptophane," *J. Pharmacol. Exper. Therap.*, 1958, 122:182-194.
10. Bremer, F., "Considerations sur l'origine et la nature des (ondes) cerebrales," *EEG Clin. Neurophysiol.*, 1949, 1:177-193.
11. Brodie, B. B., "Storage release of 5-hydroxytryptamine (HT)," *5-Hydroxytryptamine* (G. P. Lewis, ed.), Pergamon Press, New York, 1957.
12. ———, and Shore, P. A., "A concept for a role of serotonin and norepinephrine as chemical mediators in the brain," *Ann. New York Acad. Sc.*, 1957, 66:631-642.
13. ———, Spector, S., and Shore, P. A., "Interaction of drugs with norepinephrine in the brain," *Pharmacol. Rev.*, 1959, 11:548-564.
14. Brune, G. W. G., and Himwich, H. E., "Clinical and biochemical effects produced by reserpine and isocarboxazid medication in patients." In preparation.
15. Cannon, W. B., *The Wisdom of the Body*. Norton, New York, 1952.
16. Chessin, M., Kramer, E. R., and Scott, C. S., "Modifications of the pharmacology of reserpine and serotonin by iproniazid," *J. Pharmacol. Exper. Therap.*, 1957, 119:453-460.
17. Costa, E., "Analysis of proposed mechanisms of serotonin action in neurotransmission," in press.
18. ———, personal communication.
19. ———, and Aprison, M. H., "Studies on the 5-hydroxytryptamine (serotonin) content in human brain," *J. Nerv. Ment. Dis.*, 1958, 126:289-293.
20. ———, Garattini, S., and Valzelli, L., "Interactions between reserpine, chlorpromazine and imipramine," *Experentia*, 1960, 16:461-463.
21. ———, Pscheidt, G. R., Van Meter, W. G., and Himwich, H. E., "Brain concentrations of biogenic amines and EEG patterns of rabbits," *J. Pharmacol. Exper. Therap.*, 1960, 130:81-88.
22. Galambos, R., *The Central Nervous System and Behavior* (M. A. B. Brazier, ed.), Madison Printing Co., Madison, Wisconsin, pp. 287-293, 1959.

23. Gellhorn, E., *Physiological Foundations of Neurology and Psychiatry*, Univ. of Minnesota Press, Minneapolis, Minnesota, 1953.

24. Goldman, D., "Pharmacologic treatment of depression," *Dis. Nerv. Sys.*, 1960, 21:74-80.

25. Green, H., and Erickson, R. W., "Further studies with tranylcypromine (monoamine oxidase inhibitor) and its interaction with reserpine in rat brain," *Arch. Internat. Pharmacodynamie Therap.*, 1962, 135:407-425.

26. Harris, G. W., *The Reticular Formation, Stress, and Endocrine Activity. Reticular Formation of the Brain* (eds. Herbert H. Jasper, Lorne D. Proctor, Robert S. Knighton, William C. Noshay, and Russell T. Costello), Little, Brown & Co., Boston, 1958.

27. Herrick, C. J., *The Evolution of Human Nature*, Univ. of Texas Press, Austin, Texas, 1956, p. 296.

28. Hess, W. R., *The Functional Organization of the Diencephalon* (ed. J. R. Hughes), Grune and Stratton, New York, 1957.

29. Himwich, H. E., *Brain Metabolism and Cerebral Disorders*, Waverly Press, Inc., Baltimore, 1951.

30. ———, "Prospects in psychopharmacology," *J. Nerv. Ment. Dis.*, 1955, 122:413-423.

31. ———, "Psychopharmacologic drugs," *Science*, 1958, 127:59-72.

32. ———, "Some drugs used in the treatment of mental disorders," *Am. J. Psychiat.*, 1959, 115:756-759.

33. ———, Van Meter, W. G., and Owens, Helen, "Drugs used in the treatment of the depressions," *Biol. Psychiat.*, 1959, 1:27-52, Grune & Stratton, New York.

34. Himwich, W. A., Costa, E., and Himwich, H. E., "Action of 5-hydroxytryptophan on selected arterial sites in the brain," in preparation.

35. Hinsey, J. C., "The anatomical relations of the sympathetic system to visceral sensation," *Research Publ. Assoc. Nerv. & Ment. Dis.*, 1935, 15:105-180.

36. Jasper, H., "Diffuse projection systems: the integrative action of the thalamic reticular system," *EEG Clin. Neurophysiol.*, 1949, 1:405-420.

37. Killam, Eva K., and Killam, K. F., "The Influence of Drugs on Central Afferent Pathways," *Brain Mechanisms and Drug Actions* (ed. W. S. Fields), Thomas, Springfield, Ill., pp. 71-94.

38. King, F. A., and Meyer, Patricia M., "Effects of amygdaloid lesion upon septal hyperemotionality in the rat," *Science*, 1958, 128:655-656.

39. Klüver, H., and Bucy, P. C., "Preliminary analysis of function of the temporal lobes in monkeys," *Arch. Neurol. Psychiat.*, 1939, 42:979-1000.

40. Kuhn, R., "The treatment of depressive states with G 22355 (imipramine hydrochloride)," *Am. J. Psychiat.*, 1958, 115:459-464.

41. Lashley, K. S., "Persistent problems in the evolution of the mind," *Quart. Rev. Biol.*, 1949, 24:28-42.

42. Litin, E. M., Faucett, R. L., and Achor, R. W. P., "Depression in hypertensive patients treated with Rauwolfia serpentine," *Proc. Staff Meetings Mayo Clin.*, 1956, 31:233-237.

43. MacLean, P. D., "Psychosomatic," *The Handbook of Physiology: Neurophysiology* (J. Field, H. W. Magoun, V. E. Hall, eds.), Am. Physiol. Soc., Washington, D.C., 1960.

44. Masserman, J. H., "Destruction of the hypothalamus in the cat," *Arch. Neurol. Psychiat.*, 1938, 39:1250-1271.

45. Monnier, P. M., and Tissot, R., "Action de la Reserpine et de ses mediateurs (5-hydroxytryptophan serotonine et dopa noradrenaline) sur le comporte-

ment et le cerveau du lapin," *Helv. Physiol. Acta*, 1958, 16:255-267.

46. Moruzzi, G., and Magoun, H. W., "Brainstem reticular formation and activation of the EEG," *EEG Clin. Neurophysiol.*, 1949, 1:455-473.

47. Murphy, J. P., and Gellhorn, E., "Influence of hypothalamic stimulation on cortically induced movements and action potentials of the cortex," *J. Neurophysiol.*, 1945, 8:341-364.

48. Nauta, W. J. H., "An experimental study of the fornix system in the rat," *J. Comp. Neurol.*, 1956, 104:247-271.

49. ———, "Hippocampal projections and related neural pathway to the midbrain in the cat," *Brain*, 1958, 81:319-341.

50. Papez, J. W., "A proposed mechanism of emotion," *Arch. Neurol. Psychiat.*, 1937, 38:725-743.

51. Preston, J. B., "Effects of chlorpromazine on the nervous system of the cat: a possible neural basis for action," *J. Pharmacol. Exper. Therap.*, 1956, 118: 100-115.

52. Pribram, K. H., and Kruger, L., "Functions of the 'olfactory brain,'" *Ann. New York Acad. Sci.*, 1954, 58:109-138.

53. Pscheidt, G., unpublished observations.

54. Revzin, A., and Costa, E., "Effects of serotonin and paleocortical excitability," *Am. J. Physiol.*, 1960, 198:959-961.

55. Rinaldi, F., and Himwich, H. E., "Alerting responses and actions of atropine and cholinergic drugs," *Arch. Neurol. Psychiat.*, 1955, 73:387-395.

56. ———, and Himwich, H. E., "Cholinergic mechanisms involved in functions of mesodiencephalic activating system," *Arch. Neurol. Psychiat.*, 1955, 73:396-402.

57. ———, Rudy, L. H., and Himwich, H. E., "Clinical evaluation of azacyclonol, chlorpromazine and reserpine on a group of chronic psychotic patients," *Am. J. Psychiat.*, 1956, 112:678-683.

58. Rothfield, L., and Harman, P., "On relation of hippocampal fornix system to control of rage responses in cats," *J. Comp. Neurol.*, 1954, 101:265-282.

59. Russell, B., *My Philosophical Development*, Simon and Schuster, New York, 1959.

60. Schreiner, L., and Kling, L., "Behavioral changes following rhinencephalic injury in cat," *J. Neurophysiol.*, 1953, 16:643-659.

61. Sheppard, H., and Zimmerman, J. H., "Reserpine and the levels of serotonin and norepinephrine in the brain," *Nature*, 1960, 185:40-41.

62. Sigg, E. B., "Pharmacological studies with Tofranil," *Canad. Psychiat., A. J.*, 1959, 4:S75-S83.

63. Spiegel, E. A., Miller, H. R., and Oppenheimer, M. J., "Forebrain and rage reactions," *J. Neurophysiol.*, 1940, 3:538-548.

64. Thomson, A. F., and Walker, A. E., "Behavioral alterations following lesions of the medial surface of the temporal lobe," *Arch. Neurol. Psychiat.*, 1951, 65:251-252.

65. Valcourt, A. E., "Study of excretion of 5-hydroxy-indole acetic acid in mental patients," *Arch. Neurol. Psychiat.*, 1959, 81:292-298.

66. Van Meter, W. G., unpublished observations.

67. ———, Owens, Helen, and Himwich, H. E., "Effects of Tofranil, an antidepressant drug on electrical potentials of rabbit brain," *Canad. Psychiat. A. J.*, 1959, 4:S113-S119.

68. Vogt, M., "The concentration of sympathin in different parts of the central nervous system under normal conditions and after the administration of drugs," *J. Physiol.*, 1954, 123:451-458.

A. BRADFORD JUDD

MILTON GREENBLATT

One Aspect of Mind

In this paper the authors would like to suggest several hypotheses for bringing closer together the clinical and experimental observations of various investigators concerned with nervous and mental function. These hypotheses form a model for a developmental psychophysiology, that is, an ontogenetic physiology of mental phenomena which parallels the growth and experience of the individual.

The nature of the anatomical development of those structures of which the individual mind is a function continues to be a central issue in any discussion of mental phenomena. Investigation of the anatomical and physiological changes accompanying a permanently acquired alteration of behavior ("the search for the engram"[10]) has for several decades occupied inquiring minds in the field. This search has not been unrewarding. Riesen[19] and others have demonstrated irreversible structural alterations in a sense organ deprived of stimulation for prolonged periods. The very early observation by Gudden in 1870 of atrophy of developing central nervous structures following destruction of their neuronal afferent source focused attention on the possibility of growth with function; yet there has been no adequate demonstration of decrease or increase in number of central neuronal elements as a result of functional deprivation or stimulation. Levine[11] observed a decreased rate of cholesterol formation (and therefore, presumably, a decreased rate of myelinization) of certain central nervous structures in the rat when the infant animal was raised in a stimulus-poor environment. This does not suggest an alteration of neuronal synaptic structure, but it is clear that the metabolism of neuroglia and, in turn, of neurons of the central nervous system are influenced by endocrine and general metabolic function, which are influenced by the stimulus environment. Relatively short-lasting changes in synaptic resistance of central neurons have been reported, and Burns[3] lists the mechanisms proposed by various investigators to account for these changes. These long-term neuroendocrine influences and short-lasting changes in synaptic resistance are important variables in the development of central nervous function. But the first principle upon which the present discussion will be based is that nerve cell types and their synaptic associations are determined by genetic and cytologic principles which do not differ from those of general cytology and that new synaptic associations are not formed as a result of function. There is a wealth of evidence suggesting this principle, and it appears that the problem of accounting for the plasticity of behavior in a fixed neuronal structure has been the main reason for the continued search for a permanent anatomic alteration accompanying behavioral change.

Since the definition of the mind is made more difficult, rather than easier, by the first principle, the second had best be stated immediately. It is that learning is a differentiation and integration of electrical excitation within the nervous system, neuroendocrine influences excepted. It should be stated immediately that this distinction between nervous and endocrine elements is itself spurious, since each nerve element is also an endocrine element having its specific neurohormonal output by which an alteration in biochemical activity of an adjacent nerve element is effected (synaptic transmission) and self-propagating biochemical reactions achieved (neuronal transmission). But we will here be largely concerned with the electrical phenomena accompanying these changes. The mechanisms by which the differentiation and integration of nervous excitation are accomplished will form the body of this paper.

Let us start by considering the origin of this electrical activity. It is an unanswered question whether activity may arise "spontaneously" within the central nervous system,[4] but at least central nervous structures are not primarily originators of activity and seem principally concerned with increasing and decreasing the rates of discharge of sensory receptors (intero- and exteroceptors) and of motor and endocrine effectors. The past century has seen the discovery and description of the "centers" and "pathways" connecting input and output, and many different structures have been in vogue as centers of memory, learning, emotion, and other behavioral concepts. In the past fifteen years a beginning knowledge of the anatomy and physiology of central systems having widespread inhibitory and facilitory influences throughout the central nervous system has been gained. Knowledge of these systems remains sufficiently limited that they continue to be called mesencephalic and thalamic *reticular* formations, and much work toward the definition of their component elements remains to be done. But already they are a great addition to the understanding of how central integrations are accomplished. There exists an extensive literature on this subject, but a few examples may serve here. One investigator[5] demonstrated that stimulation of the olivocochlear bundle in the cat resulted in inhibition of activity in the cochlea. He and others[6] then demonstrated that an apparent focusing of attention on a new stimulus, e.g., a series of clicks, resulted in an increase of activity in the first central receiver, the cochlear nucleus, while a shifting of attention to a different stimulus, e.g., visual, resulted in a decrease of activity in the central receiver. Similar phenomena have been demonstrated at most every level in the central nervous system and in a variety of experimental animals and in man. These systems are intimately concerned with the mechanisms for attention and the wakeful state.

The extensive works of W. R. Hess and others have described the role of the hypothalamus and other central structures in mediating certain basic self- and race-preserving behavior, e.g., licking, swallowing, defecating, urinating, ejaculating, and related postural behavior. Whereas in lower animals these inherited or unlearned nervous integrations are many and include cerebral cortical neurons in their patterns, in the human they appear to be few and largely mediated by subcortical structures. For example, very shortly after birth most lower animals show good visual pattern discrimination, in contrast to the very slow acquisition of patterned vision in the human, a finding well illustrated by patients reported by Sendon[20] and others who, following removal of congenital cataracts, labored months to recognize visually simple objects which they already knew well by other senses. Man has a far greater capacity for acquired integrations and is less "stimulus-bound" than lower animals, but he requires a more complex nervous apparatus for the performance of the simplest functions. Removal of the visual cortex in the rat results in an animal capable of sufficient remaining visual capacity in subcortical structures to solve simple mazes learned prior to the defect, whereas removal of the primary visual cortex in the human results in total blindness. Having fewer inherited integrations, those integrations acquired by man, i.e., all that he learns, may be integrated with a diversity of inherited patterns arising in subcortical structures. It is in general true, as first pointed out by Hughlings Jackson, that higher structures serve as modifiers of the simpler patterns of lower structures. What is remarkable in man is the degree of elaboration of the highest structures and the relative functional independence of cortical and subcortical structures in the immature state. It is worthwhile pausing for a moment to consider some of the ways in which those inherited patterns mentioned above might influence cortical function.

The primary projection areas of the cerebral cortex have rich associations with the thalamus and other subcortical structures and with other cortical structures. Integration of these cortical areas is, however, dependent upon excitation via the lemniscal and extra-lemniscal systems from the specific receptors of which they are the cortical "projections," as is clear in the case of the visual cortex from the observations, commented upon above, of the congenitally blind who have gained sight as adults. Visual capacity does not mature in the absence of visual experience. It is becoming increasingly apparent that integration and elaboration of patterned cortical excitation arriving via the lemniscal and extra-lemniscal systems is dependent upon other structures not usually thought of as part of the sensory system. An understanding of the extra-lemniscal system has scarcely begun and has largely grown out of the study of the reticular formations mentioned above.

A great deal of interest has recently been focused on the hippocampus and related structures, which are often spoken of as "the site of memory." Situated as it is with its rich allocortical afferent sources and its abundant outflow to the hypothalamus and mesencephalon, the hippocampus seems well suited for a role of central integrator. Papez[15] very early called attention to the possible role of rhinencephalon in the mediation of emotion. Recent investigations of the electrical phenomena accompanying the establishment of conditional reflexes[2] have further implicated this structure. Clinical material indicates that bilateral hippocampal lesions may result in almost complete, permanent anterograde amnesia.[13] That the hippocampus may, and probably usually does, play an important role in establishing central integrations seems clear, but it would be unfortunate were it to be thought of as *the* site of memory formation. (Absence of amnesia following bilateral fornicectomy[7] and apparently normal mental development in the congenital absence of fornices[14] would seem to indicate that the role of the hippocampus is a sometime affair.) It has been noted above that structures within the mesencephalic reticular formation may inhibit or facilitate patterned excitation arriving in central structures from a peripheral sense organ. The large hippocampal efferent supply to the hypothalamic structures which give rise to those simple, inherited behavioral reaction patterns described by Hess and others may serve a similar function in the inhibition and facilitation of the neurons of the hypothalamus and mesencephalon which mediate the basic integrations which serve the preservation of the individual and the species.

In passing from receptor organ to projection cortex to association cortex, stimuli acquire "significance" for the individual. This significance represents an integration of patterns of excitation which are more largely acquired, the exteroceptive-bound excitation, with patterns of excitation which are more largely inherited, the interoceptive-bound excitation. Although the neuronal structure is fixed, and although all integrations are, in one sense, inherited, in that they are limited to the pathways that exist in this structure, there is a vast interconnectedness of the central structures, and many different functional states are possible. The nervous system forms a suitable substrate for the multistable functions described by Ashby.[1] Out of the immature state of relative functional undifferentiation, that of the infant, that of the occipital cortex of Sendon's patients when their first postoperative bandages were removed, or that functionally unbalanced state of the acutely brain-damaged patient, in which states a sudden change of stimulus context results in a disordered consciousness and primitive, massive defensive reactions, are elaborated stable sets of patterned excitation which are the experience of the individual. Integration proceeds by facilitation and inhibition of excitation patterns which have previously been differentiated, so that excitation which was at first widespread (a "novel" experience) becomes channeled and abbreviated in its circuits as it acquires specific significance for the individual. The structures which accomplish this integration are the mediators of "consciousness," and their integration into stable patterns is the development of the "self." These structures are only in a general way function-specific within the species, and certain central anatomic structures may serve different level integrations in different individuals, insofar as their experience is different. For example, forniceal section produces no demonstrable postoperative defect in one patient[7] and severe anterograde amnesia in another.[21]

Perhaps the most interesting work which remains to be done is that which describes the maturation of integrations and the alternate possibilities in development. The European school of naturalists, often called ethologists, has made significant contributions to the study of hierarchy of integrations in lower animals.[9] The phenomenon of a specific inherited integration, e.g., following behavior, becoming associated with an acquired integration, e.g., a large object moving in a visual field, only during a specific period of the organism's development, e.g., the third day of a duckling's life, and persisting for the remainder of life has been described by them and called imprinting. Such observations provide dramatic examples of processes which proceed to greater or lesser degree throughout the life of the organism. The study of human psychopathology, despite its inexact nosology, has made great contributions to the understanding of mental phenomena. Freudian "apertural" psychology has attempted to define maturation of integrations in the human in terms of "erogenous zones," focusing attention on the integrations achieved around body areas that have strong inherited integration patterns associated with them. That the early integrations are formed about the stimulus patterns of another human being, called "object relations," is by now a psychiatric commonplace, and schools of psychiatry have been formed about an understanding of "interpersonal relations."

As an interesting sidelight, the phenomenon of hypnosis may be cited as providing an excellent illustration of the tenet of the relationship of early integrations to significant persons and offers interesting facts about these integrations. Detailed recall of early life events may be achieved most easily by the hypnotic subject when the hypnotist assumes the role of a significant object present at the age which the subject is suggested he recall.[18] Release from present consciousness seems facilitated when the real object of the hypnotist assumes the role of an object present at the earlier age. Most interesting research into the nature of the relation of functional integrations and organic substrate is provided by the work of Teitelbaum[22] and others. A subject was given the single post-hypnotic suggestion that he "forget everything you know about your hands." In the post-hypnotic period the subject demonstrated not only a lack of knowledge of his hands, but also a left-right disorientation, an inability to count, a lack of recognition of many other body parts, and difficulty in spontaneous writing, all of which are the distinguishing symptoms of a destructive lesion involving the angular and supramarginal gyri, called Gerstmann's syndrome.

Atypical development in children[17] is the result of failure of maturation of early developmental integration and behavioral aberration resulting from continued maturation of part functions. The destructive effects of overwhelming stimuli (darkness and electric shock to the foreleg) on the infant sheep separated from its mother with resulting retardation of development and behavioral abnormality has been well substantiated by Liddell.[12] The requirement for specific stimuli in order for normal maturation to occur has been demonstrated in a large number of infant mammals. Man may rightly be proud of his "thalamus-free" cortical expansions,[23] but he is, in one sense, the most stimulus-dependent animal, for he, more than others, relies upon his environment to provide him with specific stimuli around which he can integrate his behavior. Either too few or too many stimuli result in the disorganization of highly integrated behavior and emergence of primitive defensive reactions. Although the process which underlies this "disorganization" is the very essence of learning, experiences at the extremes result in defensive reintegrations which leave the individual less well able to adapt to a range of stimuli. The more severe the disorganization, the more will earlier, more primitive integrations emerge to be reintegrated. The existence of both purely representational (hallucinations) and purely somatic (psychosomatic disorders) defensive reintegrations indicates that every level of nervous system function may be effected. It is tempting to speculate that the relatively thalamus-free neocortical expansions allow the elaboration of already complex integrations without the interference or need for integration of simpler, more primitive patterns arising in subcortical structures. The prefrontal lobes in man (Pribram's "intentional" cortex[16]) may so operate,[8] and their great elaboration in the "playful" porpoise may allow this animal to divert the stream of strong, recurring excitation arising in the diencephalon and by this means to prevent the inhibition of the structures mediating consciousness and thus to enjoy a sleep-free existence. Present understanding of the time and place sequences of maturational integrations is so rudimentary that the electroencephalogram and other electrical recording procedures are principally employed in research and are of limited application for diagnosis, prognosis, and therapeutic planning in human mental development.

It would be wrong to conclude that in studying the mechanisms underlying the development of the individual mind we arrive at any ultimate definition of "mind." Beyond the development of the individual mind, there evolve the social institutions governing group behavior that increasingly determine that human environment on which the development of the individual mind is so dependent. One hesitates to speak of "group mind," but the study of any particular "mind" cannot be comprehended in isolation from the study of these cultural institutions.

REFERENCES

1. Ashby, W. Ross, *Design for a Brain*, 2nd ed., Chapman and Hall, Ltd., London, 1960.
2. Brazier, Mary A. B., editor of *The Central Nervous System and Behavior*, Josiah Macy, Jr., Foundation First and Second Conferences, Macy Found., New York, 1958 and 1959.
3. Burns, B. Delisle, *The Mammalian Cerebral Cortex*, Edward Arnold, Ltd., London, 1958, p. 84.
4. ———, *ibid.*, p. 60.
5. Galambos, R., "Suppression of auditory nerve activity by stimulation of efferent fibers to the cochlea," *Fed. Proc.*, 1955, 14:53.
6. ———, Sheatz, S., and Vernier, V. G., "Electrophysiological correlates of a conditioned response in cats," *Science*, 1956, 123:376-377.
7. Garcia-Bengochea, F., Corrigan, R., Morgane, P., Russell, D., Jr., and Heath, R. G., "Studies on the function of the temporal lobes: I. Section of the fornix," *Tr. Am. Neurol. A.*, pp. 238-239, 1951.

8. Greenblatt, M., and Solomon, H. C., "Studies in lobotomy," *ARNMD*, 1956, 36:19-34.

9. Kortland, A., "Aspects and prospects of the concept of instinct," *Archives Neerlandaises de Zoologie*, 1955, 11:155-284.

10. Lashley, K. S., "In search of the engram: Physiological mechanisms in animal behavior," *Symposia Soc. Exper. Biol.*, 1950, 4:454.

11. Levine, Seymour, "Stimulation in infancy," *Scient. Am.* (May), 1960, 202:80-86.

12. Liddell, Howard S., *Emotional Hazards in Animals and Man*, Charles C Thomas, Springfield, Ill., 1956.

13. Milner, Brenda, *The Memory Defect in Bilateral Hippocampi Lesions*, Psychiatric Research Report No. 11, American Psychiatric Association, edited by D. E. Cameron and M. Greenblatt, pp. 43-52, 1959.

14. Nathan, P. W., and Smith, M. C., "Normal mentality associated with a maldeveloped 'rhinencephalon,'" *J. Neurol. Neurosurg. and Psychiat.*, 1950, 13:191-197.

15. Papez, James W., "A proposed mechanism of emotion," *Arch. Neurol. and Psychiat.*, 1937, 38:725-743.

16. Pribram, Karl H., "The intrinsic systems of the forebrain" in *Handbook of Physiology*, edited by John Field; Section I, Neurophysiology, 1960; II: 1323-1344.

17. Rank, Beata, and Macnaughton, Dorothy, "A clinical contribution to early ego development," *Psychoanalytic Study of the Child*, 1950, 5:53-65.

18. Reiff, Robert, and Scheerer, M., *Memory and Hypnotic Age Regression*, Int. Univ. Press, p. 72, 1959.

19. Riesen, Austin H., "Effects of stimulus deprivation on the development and atrophy of the visual sensory system," *Am. J. Orthopsychiat.*, 1960, 30:23-36.

20. Sendon, M. v., *Raum- und Gestaltauffassung bei operierten Blindgeborenen vor und nach der Operation*, Barth, Leipzig, 1932, cited by D. O. Hebb, in *Organization of Behavior*, John Wiley & Sons, Inc., New York, p. 18, 1949.

21. Sweet, W. H., Talland, G. A., and Ervin, F. R., "Loss of recent memory following section of fornix," *Tr. Am. Neurol. A.*, pp. 76-78, 1959.

22. Teitelbaum, H. H., "Psychogenic body image disturbances associated with psychogenic aphasia and agnosia," *J. Nerv. & Ment. Dis.*, 1941, 93:581-612.

23. Yakovlev, Paul, in Brazier, *op. cit.*, p. 405, 1958.

R A L P H   W.   G E R A R D

Material Aspects of Mental Disease

For any behavior there must be some material substratum. For any change in behavior there must be some change in the material substratum. A nerve impulse can exist only when there is a nerve to carry it; and a change in the second nerve impulse, as the result of the passage of the preceding one, depends only on a change left behind in the nerve by the nerve impulse, not on a change directly from one nerve impulse to another.

Similarly, the functioning of the brain in general, which is behavior, must depend, in a broad sense, on the architecture of the brain. Any change in behavior whether induced by nerve impulses as the result of psychotherapy or by a changed chemical milieu as the result of pharmacotherapy or in any other way, must be associated with a change in the material situation. I have said nothing new so far, but am perhaps pointing out that "nature is a structure of evolving functions." Perhaps I am introducing an intervening variable, such as inhibition or excitation in the Pavlovian sense, which contributes nothing to the phenomena being described until the new correlate is analyzed further. The problem is, of course, to keep such a broad consideration from being vacuous, as Malamud well put it; and the way to keep it from being vacuous is to put in the particulars.

This means, especially I think, to ask at which level, which things

Reprinted from *Diseases of the Nervous System*, Monograph Supplement, Vol. XX, No. 5, May, 1959.

For this paper the author, jointly with others, was awarded the R. Thornton Wilson annual award for his contribution to psychiatric research and treatment.

are important. "Level," which no longer needs definition, includes the molecular level; the integrated, coordinated organization and function-ing of molecules to give the cellular level; the patterned working to-gether of cells to give the organ level; organs to give the individual; the individuals to give the group; and groups to give the society. (One can put in more levels if desired.) I think, in principle, that we will ultimately understand what happens at the social level in terms of indi-vidual psychology; individual psychology will be understood in terms of the gross behavior of the nervous system and of the interaction of neurons; and the way the individual synapse and individual neuron behaves will depend upon the population of molecules and other subordinate units that constitute it. It is, however, patently impossible, in the foreseeable future, to perform such an act of reduction; and it is pragmatically not desirable to do so in many cases. So that the real question, again, for each situation, is at which level is attack most profitable. Sometimes this will be at a higher level, sometimes at a lower one.

When do changes that occur in the system become irreversible and when do they remain reversible? I have heard Bevan over the radio and always wondered why such a distinguished and eloquent speaker had a speech defect—a peculiar sort of lisp as it seemed to me. I spent a week in Wales last summer and discovered that this was not a speech defect; this was English spoken with a Welsh accent. The attribute was not an individual but a cultural one. Nonetheless, although originally Nye Bevan could have learned to speak any tongue in any form, I am sure that at this stage of his life he would be quite unable to speak, say, American English. Whatever the higher level sociopsychological factors that brought about this way of speaking, they have left a nervous system which today speaks that way and cannot speak otherwise—or we should not find so many intelligent people retaining a strong accent after decades of use of a different language in the country of adoption. It might be possible by hypnosis, by intensive psychotherapy (which means pouring in nerve impulses in certain patterns), by light sedation, by I don't know what manipulations, to change these traces in the nervous system so as to cure this way of speaking. But I am not too optimistic that one can do a great deal about it after a person is grown up.

Something can certainly be done at an experimental level. You will recall the work on chimpanzees raised in total darkness for the first months of their lives. Although the eyes and brain were unmolested, the animals never acquired the ability to use pattern vision. During the maturation process certain things, that should have happened in the nervous system as the result of functioning, just didn't happen. The nervous system developed in some other direction than in the normally guided one and it was then too late to re-establish the correct connections. Something very similar to this undoubtedly happens in the child with strabismus who suppresses one visual image. Here also time is of the essence. If the divergence from normal is caught at the beginning, one can correct it; later, it is irremediable.

So here at these higher levels, involving the psychosociological components, the primary problem is the kinds of patterns laid down between neurons. This involves synaptic fields, electric fields, chemical fields; I don't know which in detail, of course, but the interrelations and interactions of neurons at the cellular level account for behavior at the organ and individual levels. I have been so bold as to suggest that the neuroses probably constitute this type of disturbance in the nervous system while the psychoses are more disturbances at lower levels, with the molecules and the cells themselves out of kilter, quite aside from any defects at the interaction level. Let us turn to these lower levels.

When one blacks out in low oxygen or goes into hypoglycemic coma, or diabetic or renal coma, or goes into convulsions because of parathyroid hypocalcemia, or is under sedative drug action, or when the functioning of the nervous system is grossly disturbed in a thousand other ways, it is perfectly clear that we are dealing with something not patterned in the fine sense that I have been considering. Here is a more general effect, hitting at the cellular and molecular level.

The examples that I have chosen above are secondary in relation to the nervous system, which is not the primary site of the lesion, but rather the victim of changes due to disturbances in other parts of the body in which it is one of the organs. (I shall consider more primary disturbances later.) Here the changes are largely unpatterned. True, there are marked differences from one disturbing situation to another; the whole nervous system does not rise or fall as a unit in its functional level. But you would probably accept the interpretation that these functional differences depend on simple quantitative differences—in blood supply, the blood-brain barrier, metabolic rate—and qualitative differences—in metabolism, architecture, connection—from one group of neurons to another; so that, although all cells are affected, certain ones show a particular effect much more easily or strikingly than do the others. Oxygen lack causes degeneration in the striatum; carbon disulfide destroys the caudate, streptomycin lesions involve the vestibular nuclei, acetylpyridine knocks out the hypothalamus, hypoglycemic convulsions start in the amygdala and hippocampus, so on and on. In each instance, if the disturbance is pushed a little further the rest of the brain goes too.

Here we have the more general cellular, molecular disturbances in contrast to the organ and individual ones. Where there is a patterned pathology, involving disturbed interrelations above the cellular level, the indications are for a patterned therapy, the kind available through psychotherapy or sociotherapy. We are trying to hit differentially into particular neural networks, even without knowing what they are. This must be the situation that justifies the lovely phrase describing some neuroses: "By the group have they been broken, by the group shall they be healed." Conversely, when disturbances are more general, at the cellular and molecular levels, the attack has also to be more general and at these levels and so more chemical or physiological. The latter is not now so convenient or practicable, although it is by no means excluded in the future. Certainly with the growing use of the buried electrode, which can deliver stimuli or produce localized lesions, and of the micropipette, for injection of chemicals, the hope remains that biologically it will prove possible to trace specificity down through the molecular level.

It is implicit in what I have said, that speed in attacking any divergence from normal is of the essence. If one can catch the perturbation that is still functional and reversible before, through repetition, continuation, and fixation, it has become irreversible and therefore structural, the better the chance of correcting it. This, of course, corresponds to the fact that the early and persistent experiences are most difficult to alter. As to just when one moves from a reversible change—as in increased adrenal cortex secretion or the appearance of a facultative cellular enzyme—to a maintained change has to be worked out in each particular condition.

If hamsters are allowed to learn a maze or to act to avoid danger, the conditioning situation being presented each day, and are also given electroshock every day, they learn practically on the normal curve if the shock comes several hours after the experience. But if the shock is given a few minutes after the learning experience, the same amount of shock and the same amount of experience now leads to no learning. Clearly, there must be an interval between impulses entering the nervous system and their leaving a relatively indelible trace. We have gotten the temperature coefficient of fixation time and we have studied the influence of some drugs on it. My interpretation is that an impulse must go round and round in a neuron loop for a few minutes in order to leave an engram. This would involve tens of thousands of repetitions over the same elements—enough to change a physiological response into a structural residue.

There is great variability in the time during which reversibility is still possible. Animals injected with hemoporphyrin develop severe behavioral changes and degenerative lesions of the nervous system. A third as much of protoporphyrin, the normal heme precursor (to which the hemoporphyrin is a metabolic competitor) will completely protect if injected as much as three hours after the hemoporphyrin, but is useless after five hours. Studies on phenylketonuria show that early correction of the diet is helpful; later it is not. Only early treatment can correct cretinism. Incidentally, notice that I am mentioning a number of hereditary diseases; it is possible to do something for such subjects, to achieve a considerable therapeutic success.

Fortunately, in schizophrenia there is much reason to believe that there is a relatively long period of reversibility. Whether we achieve really preventive measures or only restorative ones, at least it is possible over years or decades, rather than hours or days, to re-establish good functioning of the nervous system. A variety of maneuvers, all the way from Loevenhart's carbon dioxide inhalation, or insulin coma, or electro-shock, or carbon dioxide in its newer use, to psychotherapy, or group discussion or putting a pile of dirt in the ward and letting the subjects play with it—whatever the appropriate one be in each case—can restore, at least for a brief time, the chronic burned-out schizophrenic to more or less normal function. So the neural apparatus has not been too irreversibly damaged in this sense. Of course, from a broader viewpoint, the brain probably is and remains abnormal throughout.

One could develop at some length a causal chain of events from disturbed molecules to disturbed behaviors. It is only in the present sense that my phrase which has had such a vogue, "No twisted thought without a twisted molecule," was meant. It is obviously changes in the functioning of neurons—whether they discharge or not, what their thresholds are, how long it takes them to recover from activity, how long the fixation process lasts—which immediately determines behavior; but this, in turn, is determined by their chemistry.

For example, consider the neuron threshold, which is related to the question of excitation and depression, to convulsive disorders, to coma. It is quite clear that the threshold of a neuron varies with the potential across its membrane. Further, at least in the case of muscle which we studied, and it must be equally true for nerve, the magnitude of the membrane potential varies regularly with the cellular concentration of creatine phosphate. The synthesis of creatine phosphate, in turn, depends on adenosine triphosphate, which is formed by a series of enzymic reactions with the aid of energy from oxidations.

We were not surprised, therefore, to find that audiogenic mice and rats, strains which are highly sensitive to sound and can be given lethal convulsions by, say, jingling keys, had a lower concentration of ATP in their brains than did normal related strains. Moreover, the sensitivity is greatest at around thirty days after birth, and it is between the third and sixth weeks that the development of ATP and its related enzyme lagged in the brain of the audiogenic animals as compared with normals. Just during the period of susceptibility to fatal seizures was there a low ATP, presumably a low creatine phosphate, a low membrane potential, a low threshold, and oversusceptibility to bursts of activity spreading through the nervous system.

I would have liked to examine in some detail the types of molecular changes in cells and the appropriate therapeutic maneuver for handling each. Time permits only some summary statements. We are concerned here with molecular morphology—too many or too few of a given kind at some particular place; or too many or too few altogether. The distribution of molecules or ions, especially of inorganic ones which are not formed or destroyed in the body, depends on their penetration across boundaries, on their transportation, on whether they are given off or taken up by some other organ, and ultimately on their supply in food and the manner of their excretion from the body. A disturbance at any of these levels—input-output, interaction between organs, or movement across limited regions within an organ and into or out of a cell—can alter the distribution. Indeed, the effect of an electric field on ion movements is crucial to the whole functioning of the nervous system. The way change in membrane permeability enables nerve fibers to conduct impulses, and the many changes in the relation between organs are also important.

All these interactions are obvious enough; more interesting, in a way, are the changes due to altered balance between production and destruction of metabolic intermediates. All substances in the body, except those that enter as such, are formed from other substances and are in turn changed into still other substances. If A forms M, and M forms B, what alterations can occur? Most common is some blocking of the enzyme-coenzyme mechanism that allows A to change to M or M to change to B. The former decreases the amount of M, the latter increases it. Much effort has been directed to finding out, in particular cases, which is involved. Actually, since there is always a chain of increases and decreases, the difference is not so sharp as it may seem. Decrease of M may block some other reaction and lead to excess of X or deficiency of Y, and increase of M might do the same, and so on.

Many emphasize the accumulation of some blocked intermediate. My own strong impression is that we end up sooner or later with a deficit of something. Suppose we accept that the ammonia increase in hepatic disease causes coma; the question remains how does ammonia do this? Similarly, how does phenylpyruvic accumulation lead to the oligophrenia? Each acts on some other metabolic link, and could increase or decrease other substances. It could speed, divert, or block reactions, so that an almost unlimited matrix of chemical-metabolic interactions is possible.

Each case must, therefore, be analyzed before a rational treatment for it is clear. Yet, if one clear step is the accumulation of a particular substance, any maneuver to prevent its accumulation—by withholding its source or blocking its precursor—may solve the problem. And if the deficit of a particular substance is a clear link in the sequence, supplying this missing intermediate may correct the trouble. This is frequently the case in genetic defects—as in Neurospora mutants or human cretinism. Finally, the blocked catalytic mechanism, the enzyme and coenzyme system, might be restored so that the metabolic flow is restored to normal.

All these are possible. The biochemist is rapidly filling our test tubes with the critical components of living catalytic systems. The main problem is to get them into the cells, where permeability is so limited. Even on this score, there is encouragement. The blood-brain barrier, for example, normally will not let in glutamic acid, but when it is disturbed as the result of hypoglycemia, glutamic acid does pass. Proteins do cross cell walls, and many conditions—hypoxia, hypoglycemia, drugs—favor their passage. So the situation is by no means an impossible one.

I mention these items because, I think, the tremendous feeling of empathy of the physician and therapist with the patient has colored judgment about mental illness. The doctor has felt that any disease due to an hereditary organic defect is hopeless and therefore he preferred to emphasize other factors. I submit that there are many hereditary metabolic defects for which more can be done today than for some of the unidentified or even identified environmental determinants of behavior. It is easier to correct an infant's cretinism than an adult's accent. Something can be done about these metabolic errors, and two examples will point up my position.

One is phenylketonuric oligophrenia. In our own lifetime, over the couple of decades since the disease was recognized, it has moved from the great unknown to a precisely known and reasonably manageable disturbance of the nervous system. Fjølling first noticed a color reaction in the urine of certain feebleminded children and related this to phenylpyruvic acid. This phenylketonuric oligophrenia is hereditary. Further work showed that phenylpyruvic acid in the blood as well as in the urine is high, and that in the blood not only phenylpyruvic acid is high but also phenylalanine, the amino acid which gives the phenylpyruvic acid on deaminization. Phenylalanine is normally changed to tyrosine by putting oxygen in the molecule. These patients, when loaded with phenylalanine, could not increase blood tyrosine as the normal does, but simply accumulated phenylalanine. There was clearly a block somewhere in the oxidation of phenylalanine to tyrosine. Biochemists worked out the mechanism of this reaction; phenylalanine plus triphosphopyridine nucleotide (TPN) plus potassium plus a coenzyme plus two enzymes constitute the active system. In the phenylpyruvic subjects there is no decrease but an actual increase in coenzyme, and TPN and potassium are present. Clearly it is the enzyme that is lacking. Further, of the two enzymes involved, the one present in the liver proves to be lacking.

Thus, a disease that started as a form of feeblemindedness has become an inherited metabolic error involving the lack of a specific enzyme in the liver. Moreover, there is some evidence that feeding phenylpyruvic acid to animals, raising the blood concentration to levels that appear in humans, interferes with their learning behavior. So, whatever the secondary mechanism may be, here an excess of a specific substance can bring about the important symptomatology. Cutting down the excess should be beneficial and the ideal way would be to get the missing enzyme back into the cells and keep it there. Maybe this will become possible, but we are not up to it yet. What has been done is to develop diets which contain minimal amounts of phenylalanine. This is effective, since the substance is not made in the body; it is one of the essential amino acids. Current clinical reports indicate that children put on this diet sufficiently early get along much better than otherwise. If given phenylalanine for a while, they deteriorate rapidly and improve again when it is removed.

The other example of my thesis, schizophrenia, has not yielded such concrete biochemical results. Here, we still need a definitive criterion, like the urine color test, to give greater nosological definition. I am not going into the evidence for believing that biological and hereditary factors are important. Everybody knows Kallman's work. When I first began to talk about it I found but few psychiatrists who knew it and most did not believe it. Bodily differences have been described and related to behavioral differences—sluggishness of response, poor reaction to stress, "stenosis" of behavior(a term I use as particularly descriptive), and so on and on. But we will not be on safe diagnostic ground until there are reliable objective criteria. Whether they be biochemical, physiological, or behavioral makes no difference. The material ones are more easily objectified and "sold." I will just remind you of some at present on the horizon. And I might as well say now that every one of these, at least those on hand long enough for checking, has been rejected by some investigators.

Substances specific to the urine of schizophrenics, isolated chromatographically, when injected into rats markedly interfere with their rope climbing performance. Patients have been controlled as to diet, etc. Schizophrenic blood injected into rats also interferes with their speed in climbing a rope. We, as others, checked that and got nowhere. Yet Dr. Winter, who developed this test and is scrupulously honest and careful, assured us at a recent conference in Strasbourg that he had been highly successful in diagnosing patients by blind runs on blood sent him from three hospitals.

Schizophrenic blood has also been reported to facilitate the blood pressure response to local application of adrenalin to the rabbit cortex. We are testing this now.

There are reports that the ability of insulin to increase the glucose utilization of isolated rat diaphragm is prevented by schizophrenic plasma; and indeed some Norwegian workers find an alpha globulin which specifically combines with the insulin. This finding, reminiscent of Meduna's early claim of anti-insulin action, is also being examined.

Early reports on changes in phosphate turnover of red blood corpuscles from schizophrenics, were extended by Boszermeny-Nagy, working in my laboratory at the University of Illinois, and Gerty, who showed a difference in insulin effect. More recently Gottlieb's group reported greater changes in phosphate turnover under an emotional or insulin stress in schizophrenics than in normals. Dr. Ling and I are finding a consistently greater amount of guanosine torphosphate in schizophrenic corpuscles than in normal ones, but the full controls are yet to be completed.

As I have said, for every positive report there have been counter reports, and even when the findings are real they may not be due to the disease schizophrenia but to all sorts of secondary factors. An obvious example is the decrease in some phenolic acids in the urine of schizophrenics, as shown by several workers. This has now been proven conclusively by Kety's group to be the result of less coffee drinking. The substances are metabolites from coffee, vary with the coffee intake, and are low in schizophrenics because they drink less coffee.

There is much smoke; we have yet to find the fire. But I have every confidence that with advance of the life sciences we will soon see some flame, just as I am confident that advance in the physical sciences will soon show us things we have not previously been able to see. Whitehead once told me a quatrain, attributed to a cook, which ran as follows:

> Moon, lovely moon, bathed in fire sublime,
>   Careening throughout the far boundaries of time,
> Whenever I see thee I ask in my mind,
>   Shall I never, oh never, behold thy behind?

Discussion

DR. FURST: I would like to ask Dr. Gerard to comment on monamine oxidase and its relationship to emotion and primary depression.

DR. GERARD: First, manic and hallucinatory states were attributed by Canadian workers to the accumulation of abnormal or excessive oxidation products of epinephrine which lowered neuron thresholds. When this was questioned, the New Orleans group said the catecholamines were not increased but the enzymes that oxidize them were different in schizophrenics, so that oxidation was slower or due to abnormal products, and so on. National Institute of Mental Health workers recently reported no difference in these reaction rates or products in schizophrenic plasma. They even offered evidence that adrenolutin, adrenochrome, and the like are not in the normal path of metabolic breakdown of adrenalin or noradrenaline. Nonetheless, it is not often possible to explore the total conditions under which processes occur. Abood, indeed, offered evidence that adrenochrome is formed from the catecholamines when oxidized by ceruloplasmin rather than by monoamine oxidase; and so on and on—without entering the serotonin arena.

I also am guilty of putting forward a hypothesis involving the catechols. Adrenalin certainly can lower the thresholds of neurons. (It can also raise thresholds and inhibit in larger amounts; but we showed conclusively for the motor cortex and elsewhere that application of adrenalin increased excitability.) It is nice to think of a possible modulation of neuron thresholds throughout the brain, depending upon the level of circulating adrenalin, as well as on the activity of the reticular formation. This is a kind of extension of Cannon's emergency theory of epinephrine liberation, to include effects not only on the soma but also on the brain, on the level of the tension of the psyche. It is a long story, but the amino oxidases may help determine what happens to the adrenaline liberated, whether other stimulating or inhibiting compounds are formed, and the like.

DR. AZIMA: I would like to make one point and ask Dr. Gerard two questions. If your philosophy is reductionistic, my impression is that in the present state of epistemology this implies the fallacy of infinite regression and this fallacy is based upon two other fallacies. One is the fallacy of misplaced concreteness and the other one is the fallacy of linear causality. This means if anything affects B then it affects C and so forth.

DR. GERARD: You are perfectly correct. I meant to accept positivism. I am aware of all of the difficulties you raise but I still cannot think otherwise than in terms of cause and effect. Neither could Einstein.

DR. AZIMA: The second question I want to ask, do you believe in the concept of linking and in the concept of emergence?

DR. GERARD: I think very few would be interested in pursuing this very far. If you have not seen it, may I commend to you the April issue of *Behavioral Science*. This monograph, also separately published by the National Academy of Sciences, on "Concepts of Biology" is the report of a three-day symposium in which a dozen leading biologists participated. Many of these issues are discussed, and since I had the responsibility of preparing the preliminary organizing article and the final summary, my views are available there.

Specifically as to emergence, my view is that there is no emergence, in the sense of some supernatural aspects appearing with new combinations. But with every additional level there are new kinds of relationships possible and some are not directly extrapolatable from the older ones. A square equation does not give the mathematics of a cubic equation. However, having seen the more complicated situation one can always understand it in terms of the interrelations of simpler ones. It is just too big a job intellectually to consider all the variances possible in going up levels; whereas it is relatively easy to come back down and to develop the understanding that gives predictive control. This is what I would equate with the term causality, to avoid the philosophical problem. I think that, sooner or later, one must get to the micro level for control; but first many relations must be established at the macro level. I do not say that sociological, psychiatric, psychological, or neurophysiological formulations are not good because they are not down to the molecular level. As to infinite regression, as long as the physicists are giving us subnuclear and smaller units, I am willing to regress too.

DR. MARVIN K. OPLER: I find myself much interested in and curious about this last flurry of discussion. Various positions are described and criticized, but it seems to me that the criticism must be more specific than it appears when we merely talk about the general history of science. I might say that, as an individual, Dr. Gerard has a right to regress, as he laughingly puts it, and to conduct his impressive research at any point along the line of regression he chooses. I have no fear that he will be involved in his own work in infinite regression or even with what the Freudians call regression. However, both of the preceding speakers, in their disagreement, have each commented on the general history of science. And I think it is high time to leave that generalized argument and to talk about social and preventive psychiatry, which is the scheduled topic of this meeting. The thing that bothers me is not the reductionism, as was just suggested, but rather what that reductionism implies about the direction of research which Dr. Gerard, somewhat cavalierly, insists must begin on an organicist level.

Those who insist we begin on any one narrow level, whether it is simply the organicist level, or among other thinkers the "purely psychological" level, are guilty not only of an insistent reductionism as suggested here, but also guilty of an attempt to split apart relevant aspects of research. The human problem, for instance in schizophrenia, neither begins nor ends on the organic level. The human condition or "human predicament," as some French existentialists have called it, is by definition not something that can be understood by separating the different approaches and going on from there. The organicists, if they are fervent purists, study such conditions as schizophrenia, alcoholism, and other highly generalized or presumptive illness entities by such a segmented approach. Their assumption always is that you will reach important conclusions on one level or another. But we all know that schizophrenia is not a unit psychosis, that alcoholism is not necessarily an illness entity, and that both may develop in a framework of socially or culturally derived stresses and strains which affect persons of widely different organic make-up. The assumption that you always hit "pay dirt" on one level or another disregards everything we know to date about the etiology and dynamics, and the overgeneralized character of our psychiatric nomenclature for these disorders.

Incidentally, I entirely agree with Dr. Gerard's diagram of levels, but so far as the human being is concerned and so far as the psychiatrist's effectiveness is involved, I would insist with him that these social, cultural, psychological, and organic levels are always interrelated. To say they are not interrelated is to become mystical and insist upon a dichotomy of mind and body. But Dr. Gerard wishes to say, on the one hand, that there is not a separate development of such levels, and then wishes to add, on the other hand, that one will arrive at the neatest experiments and the most revealing data only on one level (the organic) and through attention or application to that one level alone. He seems to me to contradict the first proposition when he adds his second proposition.

To say that success will be achieved on one level only is naive when we look at specific discoveries in the general history of science. For instance, the discoveries about pellagra, beriberi, and such deficiency disorders as kwashiorkor were very useful to psychiatry. In these examples, there is a link between a specific disease entity and an organic system of causality. The same is true of toxic psychoses and such scattered examples of the organic disorders as Korsakoff's syndrome. I was always impressed when I read the original documentation of Dr. Alfred Hess and others on vitamins. Everyone knows that Hess found out about deficiency situations affecting New York school children by learning something about their social status and ethnic group backgrounds including what they ate. He was interested in knowing in what population rickets had a high incidence. This is what led to the biochemical and other research. Dr. Walsh McDermott is currently studying the epidemiology of tuberculosis among a population of Navajo Indians to achieve the same kind of initial insights in regard to alarmingly high incidence rates.

To cite an instance, concerning the epidemiology of a nonorganic condition, the Puerto Ricans in New York City and New York State have high rates of schizophrenia per capita according to Malzberg's published data. In my own epidemiological studies in this group as reported for an area of the East side of New York City, we found that Malzberg's data, if anything, had probably understated the case, for we encountered considerable numbers of ambulatory schizophrenics. Malzberg's is of course a study of treated prevalence. We studied not only treated cases but also Puerto Ricans who had never been in treatment, so that we had a prevalence study of both the treated and the untreated. Besides the epidemiological surveys in this group, we decided to study Puerto Ricans who were hospitalized because of schizophrenic disorder. We also studied neurotic Puerto Ricans who appeared in a randomly sampled population. Some people claim that neurotics do not develop into full-blown psychotics, but my colleague, Dr. Thomas Rennie, earlier proved that this was not the case and that concepts about the unit psychosis were extremely dubious. We found a continuum of stresses and strains upon the Puerto Rican population which in some cases led to neurotic behavior and in others to a case history where psychoneurosis had grown out of a florid neurotic background.

We also found "well" Puerto Ricans. But how were we to explain the greater prevalence of mental disturbance in this population when compared with other ethnic groups of New York City? The answer is that the normative community, the social and cultural backgrounds of Puerto Ricans in New York City, and their typical problems were used to produce hypotheses which we could test in samples of hospitalized Puerto Rican schizophrenics. These hypotheses were best called biosocial. They necessitated joint research by social scientists, social psychiatrists and psychologists. Ideally one would add on neurophysiological and biochemical research. But neither neurophysiological nor biochemical research will necessarily tell us anything about why Puerto Ricans have more schizophrenia in New York City per capita than any other group. Further, their problem is not merely a neurophysiological and biochemical problem. The definitions of a life process like schizophrenia require us to include the social and cultural strains upon a population that are reflected in epidemiology and which, even if they have neurophysiological and biochemical correlates, are problems which do not in any sense begin on such organic levels.

DR. GERARD, *in response to Dr. M. K. Opler*: I thought I was going to be able to say I agreed with you and stop, but your last sentences indicate an area of conflict. Our philosophical orientations seem to fit well until we come to grips. I think of the story of the man explaining socialism, who said, "If you have two yachts, that means you keep one and give me one."

"Yes, that is clear."

"If you have two automobiles, you keep one and give me one."

"Yes, I agree."

"If you have two shirts, you keep one and give me one."

"Wait a minute! I *have* two shirts."

We agree in principle all the way until it comes to schizophrenia and the question of how much is horse and how much is rabbit. Here, I think, each of us is expressing a faith. At this stage we don't know the answers; if we did know them, and are rational beings, we could not argue about them. It is because so much is still unknown that my judgment, on looking over the total evidence, can be that the biological component is a larger one, yours puts the weight more on the social level.

DR. OPLER: You seemed to when you said the others are concomitant variations. In any event, if you don't we have no disagreement. The only difference this judgment makes is that it determines where one puts his chips, how he will direct his research effort to solve schizophrenia. The one thing you said that I would vigorously disagree with, and maybe you will disagree with it yourself if I paraphrase what I thought you said, is that all these factors enter and that it is meaningless to try to analyze further.

DR. GERARD: Good. Then I am not disagreeing with you. This is the same thing Malamud said. Granted that there is a heredity and an early embryological development and a past group experience and a current life stress—a mother-in-law coming to dinner or whatever it is. Granted that all these factors enter, one gets no further unless he asks; so far as this particular variation is concerned, to what is the variance attributable, how much to this, that, and the other factor. The answer is a matter of experiment and what we are all seeking.

I am reminded of my friend, I can say "friendly enemy," Mortimer Adler, with whom I have often crossed swords. He loved to give a sweeping talk and point out that science did not face the grand questions of the universe; only philosophy could face them. I would then point out that science did not as yet answer, and perhaps never asked, the grand questions of philosophy; but science does answer the questions it asks and philosophy does not. So let us hope that science gets around to them!

HOWARD LIDDELL

The Biology of the "Prejudiced" Mind

A simple experiment with a sheep will disclose the essential features of the prejudiced mind, although a great deal of time and patience are required of the observer. For our purpose the sheep is far superior to man and monkey, since these mentally gifted animals are too erratic and fidgety. Charles Chaplin, in *Modern Times,* displayed artistic intuition by beginning his picture with a flock of sheep running down a lane as a preface to the hero's struggles with assembly-line living.

A middle-aged ewe is brought to the laboratory and prevented from escaping by a comfortably wide web strap around her chest passing through a cleat in the wall. After a brief period of struggling she remains quiet and chews her cud or nibbles from a bucket of oats. Shoe laces soaked in brine are wrapped around one foreleg and electrodes clipped to the shoe laces delivers a brief shock of about seven volts at the experimenter's convenience. This mild electric shock can be felt only by the most sensitive observer as a mild tingling of the fingers or as a slightly disagreeable experience when the electrodes are applied to the tip of the tongue.

For the sheep, however, this brief electric current to the foreleg is a menacing event to which she reacts with vehement struggling, suggesting panic. Repetition of this experience brings apparent composure and after ten or twenty repetitions her reaction is a brisk, energetic flexion of the stimulated forelimb followed by nose licking, grinding of the teeth, and yawning as signs of ill-suppressed excitement.

Our animal has given up further attempts to escape and, except for her perfunctory forced reactions to the occasional mild shocks on the foreleg, remains quietly at her place against the wall. A metronome adjusted to click once a second (M 60 is a convenient abbreviation) is placed out of sight near the animal. After the metronome clicks for a few seconds a shock to the foreleg follows. When the clicking has continued for five to ten seconds on ten occasions a conditioned reflex, *or prejudice,* will have been formed: but not firmly. However, after 100 coincidences of metronome beats and the alarming, disagreeable shocks to the foreleg *the sheep will be prejudiced against the sound of the metronome for life.* Over thirty-five years of experimental work in our laboratory confirms this seemingly dogmatic statement. The animal can never again listen to the metronome with equanimity. Indeed, the clicking of a typewriter visibly disturbs her.

Many of our prejudices arise from such seemingly innocuous coincidences. In extreme cases, where this conditioning experience has been long continued, the sound of winding a watch proves alarming. The human neurotic's extreme sensitivity to sound (hyperacusis) confirms these observations of sheep and goat behavior.

In conditioning, as we are describing it and as Pavlov investigated it for half a century, animal, or man, is compelled to behave ineffectually in response to the inevitable. This is the origin of anxiety, and anxiety results in prejudice. The sheep whose behavior is being described illustrates this generalization. After two or three coincidences of metronome and shock the clicking of the metronome evokes startle at the first click, then vague restlessness with movements of head and ears, bleating and tentative movement of all four limbs preceding the shock. However, at about the tenth sounding of the metronome the foreleg, to which the shock is soon to be applied, is precisely flexed one or more times in response to the clicking. At the next trial or two the sheep may visibly tense at the sound but remains motionless until the shock.

When the thoroughly stabilized conditioned reflex, at least a hundred trials old, is elicited by sounding the metronome the sheep's behavior is highly stereotyped. At the first click it raises its head and pricks up its ears, then lowers the head with extended forelegs and within two or three seconds begins to execute a series of precise flexion movements of the foreleg once a second, in time with the metronome. The nicety of its movements suggest the deportment of a ballet dancer.

These movements of the foreleg preceding the shock increase in vehemence and precision as the moment of shock approaches. Often, when the electrodes have been accidentally disconnected from the leg the observer is deceived by the reaction to the final metronome click. From the rapid and vigorous flexing of the leg he falsely assumes that the sheep is flinching from the disagreeable shock.

But this stereotyped conditioned behavior is ineffectual. Regardless of how many times or how precisely the leg is withdrawn the shock is sure to follow. It will require some argument and illustration to support the view that all conditioned reflexes are ineffectual in adjusting to actual situations. This attempt will, however, be made.

All the operations involved in the formation of conditioned reflexes, either positive or negative, take place on the threshold of intelligence, i.e., at a basic or primitive biological level. The more complex cognitive operations, which we call reasoning, emerge later in evolution.

Our middle-aged ewe, who is now prejudiced for life against the sound of the clicking metronome, has generalized her prejudice to include all rates of the clicking metronome, all such noises as typewriting or winding a watch, and even tones of various pitches.

The expressions of this prejudice can be modified in intensity and in patterns of behavior as clearly appears in the formation of a negative conditioned reflex.

We now set the metronome to click at twice a second (M 120), but when it sounds no shock to the leg follows. At first the sheep reacts exactly as before. But after a few coincidences of rapid clicking with no shock to follow her pattern of behavior changes. Soon she alerts at the first click but does not flex her foreleg. When the metronome ceases, however, she vehemently withdraws her leg as if the shock had actually been applied.

This intense "off-reaction" at the cessation of the clicking is observed for three or four tests and is succeeded by the final stabilized phase of the negative conditioned reflex. Now the animal alerts at the first click, remains motionless but with labored breathing while the signal for no shock continues, but when the clicking ceases she exhibits the usual signs of restlessness already described. The picture is one of letdown or release from tension.

A further characteristic of the newly formed negative conditioned reflex is the already familiar appearance of generalization. Although our sheep becomes obviously tense and disturbed at the rapid clicking (M 120) she does not lift her foreleg. Instead, she often stiffens it as if firmly resolved not to flex it. Now, if the metronome is again set to click once a second the sheep no longer withdraws her leg at the slow clicking noise but maintains the new negative response. However, her reaction to the now unexpected shock is unusually vehement.

By contrasting the two metronome rates, M 60 and M 120, on a few occasions an accurate differentiation or discrimination between them has been achieved and it seems reasonable that this should be so. But further observation clearly shows that there is a fundamental difference between a psychophysical judgment (as when one compares two lifted weights to decide which is the heavier, or two tones as to which is the louder or higher) and the establishment of a stable differentiation between positive and negative conditioned reflexes. In the case of psychophysical judgments we are dealing with "pure-culture" cognitive operations. In the establishment of positive and negative conditioned reflexes and the limits of discrimination between them, we are deeply involved with the visceral machinery of emotion and *prejudice*.

Negative conditioned reflex action is emotionally upsetting for any animal. In our experience the chronic emotional disorder that I. P. Pavlov called experimental neurosis may befall the sheep during the experiment on negative conditioning just described. In a number of cases the animal repeatedly subjected to M 120 without shock is unable to prevent the anticipatory flexion of the foreleg which it had previously been trained to make in response to M 60.

Within a few days, after thirty or forty repetitions of M 120 without shock, our sheep resists being led to the laboratory. In its restraining harness it is unable to maintain the customary self-imposed restraint. Moreover, it exhibits a diffuse agitation with frequent startle reactions, bleating, urinating, defecating, irregular rapid respiration and heart aciton and, in addition, persistent small tic-like movements of the trained foreleg.

Once precipitated by this reiteration of the rapid metronome always without shock the sheep's neurotic condition, like its formerly less intense prejudice against the sound of the metronome, persists for life. In this neurotic state the animal's rest at night is disturbed and its normal gregariousness is severely damaged. Now, it no longer benefits from its natural gregariousness, or "flock instinct," and becomes an easy prey to marauding dogs.

It is interesting to speculate about the relation of neurotic traits to conditioned reflexes. According to our present view *all conditioned reflexes, both positive and negative, are prejudices and, hence, neurotic traits*. A severe neurotic attack in the experimentally neurotic animal as just described and an anxiety attack in man both originate from the operation of our coincidence principle. These speculations are in accordance with Sigmund Freud's view of character traits where in "Moses and Monotheism" he wrote:

Our researches have shown that what we call the phenomena or symptoms of neurosis are the consequences of certain experiences and impressions which, for this very reason, we recognize to be etiological traumata. We wish to ascertain, even if only in a rough schematic way, the characteristics common to these experiences and to neurotic symptoms. . . .

What features are common to all neurotic symptoms? Here we note two important points. The effects of the trauma are twofold, positive and negative. The former are endeavors to revive the trauma, to remember the forgotten experience, or, better still, to make it real—to live through once more a repetition of it, if it was an early affective relationship it is revived in an analogous connection with another person. These endeavors are summed up in the terms "fixation to the trauma" and "repetition-compulsion." It will thus be seen that to understand the problems of neurosis enables us to penetrate into the secrets of character-formation in general.

The negative reactions pursue the opposite aim; here nothing is to be remembered or repeated of the forgotten traumata. They may be grouped together as defensive reactions. They express themselves in avoiding issues, a tendency which may culminate in an inhibition or phobia. These negative reactions also contribute considerably to the formation of character. Actually, they represent fixations on the trauma no less than do the positive reactions, but they follow the opposite tendency. The symptoms of the neurosis proper constitute a compromise, to which both the positive and negative effects of the trauma contribute; sometimes one component, sometimes the other, predominates. These opposite reactions create conflicts which the subject cannot as a rule resolve.

The second point is this: All these phenomena, the symptoms as well as the restrictions of personality and the lasting changes in character, display the characteristic of compulsiveness; that is to say, they possess great psychical intensity; they show a far-reaching independence of psychical processes that are adapted to the demands of the real world and obey the laws of logical thinking. They are not influenced by outer reality, or not normally so; they take no notice of real things, or the mental equivalents of these, so that they can easily come into active opposition to either. They are as a state within a state, an inaccessible party, useless for the common weal. . . . In any event, changes of the personality remain like scars.

The deletions in this quotation are to spare the reader from Freud's preoccupation with the psychosexual origin of neurosis derived from the strong clinical impressions of his practical life as a physician of his day and culture. Pavlov, in the introduction to his numerous lectures on the conditioned reflexes frankly confesses that his investigations began as the consequence of a *"strong laboratory impression."*

These strong impressions cannot be ignored if we are to examine the biological origins of prejudice. It is of first importance for any serious investigator of behavior to attempt to harmonize the strong impressions of such venerable and dedicated truth-seekers as Pavlov and Freud. In the first place, it must be recognized that both men were fixated in their speculations upon two different segments of the life span. A deleted portion of the previous quotation from Freud portrays his fixation on the earliest period of human development:

All these traumata belong to early childhood, the period up to about five years. Impressions during the time when the child begins to speak are found to be especially interesting. The period between two and four years is the most important. How soon after birth this sensitivity to traumata begins we are not able to state with any degree of certainty.

In our present investigation of maternal-neonate relations in sheep and goats we are able to give a definite answer to Freud's question. Sensitivity to psychic traumata begins at birth in both sheep and goat.

Pavlov subjected his dogs to the strong bodily experiences or perceptions of the conditioning laboratory at late adolescence or maturity—six months or older. Although his approach to the understanding of behavior was as clinical as Freud's, it required many years of observation for him to realize that conditioning was essentially traumatizing (or, as we would now say, prejudice forming).

Beginning his conditioned experiments about 1900, it was not until 1916 that he encountered the phenomenon of experimental neurosis in a dog. This animal was attempting a too difficult discrimination between a luminous circle as a signal for food and a more and more circular oval as a no-food signal. The breakdown point came when the semiaxes of the ellipse were in the ratio of seven to nine—a slightly flattened circle. The symptoms Pavlov observed were those previously described in our neurotic sheep whose breakdown occurred during its unsuccessful attempt to "say no" (that is, not lift its foreleg) in response to M 120, the signal never followed by shock. Here the experimenter was attempting to inculcate a negative prejudice.

In the early years of our work we followed Pavlov in employing mature, or nearly mature, sheep and goats. Typically, our animals were about three months of age at the beginning of conditioning. Their life span is about ten years.

Upon reflection it becomes clear that the tardy recognition of the close (even symbiotic) relationship between psychoanalysis and conditioning is the result of clinical and laboratory accident. Freud was led to center his attention upon traumatic happenings early in life as disclosed by psychoanalysis in the human species. Pavlov attempted to analyze in physiological terms the dog's hunger—or as he describes it, "the dog's passionate longing for food." He was forced to conclude, as a physiologist, that "appetite is juice" and this can be measured. Hence, he chose as subjects dogs of convenient size and age to stand quietly in harness upon the laboratory table while the gastric juice or saliva was being collected and measured. This simple laboratory requirement is the accidental origin of the restraining harness (or Pavlov frame) and of "self-imposed restraint," since the dog must be induced not to fight and break the glassware used to collect the digestive juices.

In Freud's case, his patients presented diverse symptoms. These, upon analysis, turned out to be disabling bodily expressions of infantile traumata or prejudices which he attempted to combat (or "cure") through the relearning accomplished during psychoanalysis. (In passing, it is worthy of note that the analytic couch and the Pavlov frame, so similar in function, are both products of clinical and laboratory accidents, becoming in time fixed *clinical and laboratory habits of mind* (or prejudices).

In Pavlov's case (and we fall into his error) his adult animals exhibited the traumatic consequences of their conditioning only with the passage of months or years. It was easily overlooked by him (as by ourselves) that *the very process of conditioning is traumatizing or prejudice forming*. Like the positive and negative manifestations of human neurosis, so clearly described by Freud, the conditioned reflexes "remain like scars" on the animal's personality. Conditioned reflex action, like neurotic human behavior, is stereotyped and compulsive. It does not adjust the animal to the realities of the presenting situation. Hence it is basically ineffectual. The more highly conditioned the animal, the greater its frustration in facing the demands of daily living.

We return at last to our interrupted experiment with the middle-aged ewe. She has now acquired a positive conditioned reflex to M 60 and, with some difficulty, a negative conditioned reflex to M 120. We are now prepared to attempt more and more difficult discriminations between M 60, always terminated by shock to the foreleg, and slower and slower rates (M 100, M 92, M 87, and M 72) never followed by shock. Paradoxically, less and less time is required to establish successively more difficult negative conditioned reflexes. For example, a negative reflex to M 92 is more quickly established than the negative response to M 100. Our sheep has gained, through practice, a greater facility in withholding a leg flexion at the progressively slower negative rates, although her perturbation at the more difficult negative signals has been steadily and visibly increasing.

This situation reminds one of the increasing fluency of the hypochondriac in relating his symptoms as he "shops around" from physician to physician. He has gained practice by consulting various doctors.

A final experiment may be described. Our sheep can now reliably distinguish the long familiar M 60 as a positive conditioned stimulus from M 72, negative; that is, never followed by shock. If the experiment is to be demonstrated before a class of a hundred students, the sheep, confined to a portable "Pavlov frame" (a piano box, with the front removed), is wheeled into the lecture room in her demonstration cabinet, and is allowed to nibble for a few minutes from a bucket of oats.

For the success of the demonstration it is necessary to space all signals, positive or negative, from three to five minutes apart. At M 60 the sheep alerts, crouches, and after the usual latent period of three to five seconds flexes her foreleg in time with the metronome. After a five-minute pause we sound the metronome at seventy-two beats per minute (M 72)—a rate never followed by shock. She tenses and with obvious effort prevents her foreleg from being flexed by forcibly extending it. When the metronome ceases, she heaves a sigh of relief. We now wait another five minutes and sound M 60 again, to which she responds with the usual stereotyped, mincing flexions of the foreleg in time with the clicking, ending with a vigorous terminal flexion in response to the brief shock. After another period of waiting three, four, or five minutes we sound M 72 once again, and our animal once more refrains from flexing her foreleg with the usual signs of intense effort.

Now for the crucial test! We wait only a minute after M 72 before sounding M 60 again. Visibly in distress, she alternately raises and lowers her head and appears to be making every effort to lift her foreleg from the floor, which she seems unable to do. Loud grinding of the teeth is often audible at some distance during the ordeal. The shock now elicits a motor explosion in which she leaps upward. This explosion suddenly relieves her tension.

That this account is in terms of human behavior is not accidental. Many years ago we received the strong laboratory impression that our experimental animal was trying to say: "*Remember you are not studying physiology, you are studying me.*"

At this point a digression is necessary. What about reward and punishment? The biologist, in our opinion, is not concerned with, and knows nothing of, reward and punishment. Specifically what about food prejudices? These have little or nothing to do with reward or punishment. They are basically a consequence of the action of our *coincidence principle*. It is naive to think of shock as punishment and food as reward in the conditioning experiments we have been discussing.

For example, in Pavlov's early conditioning laboratory the dog stood in his restraining harness (Pavlov frame) on a table in a testing room, and the experimenter observed him from outside through a peephole in the door. The secretion of saliva could be observed and recorded at a distance by a special arrangement which does not concern us here. All stimuli were presented to the dog automatically because the experimenter's presence in the room was found to be a focus of the animal's attention. This requirement made it necessary to feed him at the end of the positive conditioned stimuli such as a metronome by the following simple mechanical arrangement: Pulling on a string outside the door swung a food pan in front of the experimental animal. But after fifteen seconds the string was removed and the action of the spring snatched the pan from under the dog's nose, thus abruptly interrupting his greedy eating. In certain dogs of nervous temperament, this seemingly innocuous procedure aroused so strong a prejudice against the feeding situation that further conditioning experiments had to be abandoned.*

An amusing and more specific example of food prejudice during conditioning was observed by W. Horsley Gantt in the twelve-year investigation of his experimentally neurotic dog Nick. In his monograph, *Experimental Basis of Neurotic Behavior,* Gantt related the origin of Nick's violent prejudice against a particular brand of dog biscuit, namely, "Spratt's Ovals." The circumstances of the origin of this food prejudice are briefly as follows:

Nick was subjected to a grueling conditioning routine in which he was compelled (through self-imposed restraint) to choose between two pairs of tones sounded in succession. When there was a rise in pitch a Spratt's Oval biscuit dropped into the food pan, but when the higher tone was followed by the lower, no food was given. When this discrimination was mastered the tones were moved nearer together in pitch until Nick's neurotic breakdown occurred. In addition to the usual positive and negative signs of neurotic disorder the dog tried to avoid the whole laboratory situation including absolute rejection of food on the premises.

But his aversion to Spratt's Ovals was more specific. When presented with this brand of dog biscuit either in the laboratory building or on Gantt's farm he typically reacted in one of three ways. He barked at them. He took one in his mouth and dropped it or he urinated on it. He would readily accept dog biscuits of another shape.

In concluding our digression, it is necessary to expose the fallacy of "electric shock as punishment" in the experiments we have been discussing.

Our goat, "Cuthorns," had been carefully trained for more than a year in making longer and longer delayed responses to M 60. Finally she was accurately reacting in anticipation of the one hundred first click of the metronome which was always accompanied by shock to the foreleg. We were recording her heartbeat electrically, and regularly observed the following conditioned cardiac reflex. At the first few clicks her heart accelerated, then slowed a little, then accelerated, then slowed, but steadily increased in a saw-tooth kind of progression. At about the seventy-fourth click she began flexing her foreleg, and these flexions increased as her heart rate mounted until the moment of shock. At the shock she gave the usual vigorous flexion of the leg but within two or three seconds her heart abruptly slowed to the rate preceding the first

---

* These facts do not appear in Pavlov's writings. They were related to me by Professor P. S. Kupalov while he was a guest in my laboratory in 1929.

metronome click. Using the heart rate as a sign of emotional excitement, the actual shock after 100 seconds of waiting served as a striking relief of her previous mounting tension. In this specific experimental environment *shock was a reward.*

On the other hand, while Cuthorns was standing in her Pavlov frame tensely, but quietly, awaiting our pleasure an accidental and hence unsignaled shock caused, along with the leg flexion, an immediate racing of her heart which required about half a minute to resume its former rate. Here in the same laboratory situation and with the same animal, *shock was a punishment.*

Thus far the discussion has dealt with positive and negative conditioned reflex action in the adult experimental animal. It is now time to bridge the gap between Freud's concern with traumatic experiences in the very young child and Pavlov's fixation upon the traumatizing effects of positive and negative conditioning in the mature animal.

An accidental experiment subsequently repeated with both sheep and goat mothers first turned our attention to the prepotent influence of the maternal-neonate relationship upon the behavior of our experimental animals. Our goat, Cuthorns, had a newborn kid. When it was a few days old we allowed it to follow its mother into the laboratory for her daily test. As the mother stood in the Pavlov frame her kid frisked about, nursed briefly, and was continually on the go. The kid repeatedly bleated and its mother replied. At the first click of the metronome, however, Cuthorns' reaction was now suddenly appropriate to the situation and hence realistic and effective. She attempted gently to butt her kid away from her—obviously to get it out of harm's way.

At this point, our thoughts were directed to Freud's pleasure principle in relation to our "coincidence principle." Our understanding of the pleasure principle is that it is concerned with the impulsive, omnivorous id—"a seething cauldron of excitement"—seeking gratification from the external world without regard for the limitations of reality. Observing the "unbridled" behavior of Cuthorns' kid as it cavorted about its mother impelled us to try out conditioning on this young animal. We constructed a miniature Pavlov frame mounted on a high stool (a Pavlov high chair), and attempted the usual conditioning to the metronome. The kid's perpetual squirming, followed by utter fatigue, convinced us of the uselessness of our attempts to develop self-imposed restraint in this youngster under these artificial circumstances.

We have been engaged in the investigation of sheep and goat behavior for almost forty years. During this period we have come to appreciate our fortunate choice of these experimental animals. They are of conveniently large size for physiological experimentation. They are relatively inexpensive to maintain, and their life span of ten to fourteen years is favorable for long-term studies. And most important for purposes of our present discussion, the production of twins is common to both species. One twin of the same sex can be employed as a control for the other. This has proved to be a vital consideration in our investigation of the behavioral consequences of the establishment of adequate or faulty maternal-neonate relationships in these simple mammals.

To determine the influence of the mother's presence on the conditioning of her offspring a series of experiments was planned which has now been in progress for fifteen years. These experiments have already yielded startling results—startling in their implications as to the baleful influence of positive and negative conditioned reflexes (or prejudices) upon physical and mental health.

The difficulties encountered in attempting to condition Cuthorns' kid in the Pavlov's high chair were surmounted by allowing the little animal complete liberty of locomotion in the laboratory room with the mother *present* or *absent*. The standard procedure for analyzing the maternal-neonate relations involved in conditioning the lamb or kid is as follows:

The little animal in confined in a room where it is allowed complete freedom of movement. A light cable suspended from the center of the ceiling is attached to a strap about the animal's chest. Electrodes from this cable are fixed to the foreleg to which a very mild electric shock may be delivered.

The plan of the investigation was simple. We selected sheep and goat mothers with twins of the same sex. One twin was tested in the laboratory room in the presence of its mother, while, at the same time, the other twin was subjected to an identical training routine in an adjoining room, alone. The same conditioning schedule was followed each day. Since sheep and goats are "afraid of the dark," this has been found to be the most effective conditioned stimulus for them. The lights in the room were dimmed for ten seconds followed by shock to the foreleg. Twenty of these darkness signals spaced two minutes apart and each followed by shock comprised the daily session of fifty minutes.

In every case, the little animal with its mother showed no restriction of locomotion during the tests. It would run and jump on her at the shock, cuddle up beside her, and wander about exploring even though she was lying down and seemingly paying no attention. We observed no evidence of self-imposed restraint.

The twin, alone in the adjoining room, soon became immobilized (a maximum of self-imposed restraint). If the observer were seated in a corner of the room, it would face him, cautiously advancing a little, then retreating, as if both attracted and repelled by his presence. This ambivalent behavior was observed in both lamb and kid.

In these young animals, as their solitary training continued, experimental neurosis supervened but pursued a different course from that observed in the adults. The lamb, for example, first passed through a stage of diffused agitation with rapidly repeated small tic-like movements of the forelimb—often as many as eighty a minute. But finally it lay down soon after entering the laboratory room, with chin on the floor and made no visible response to the dimming of the lights, not even ear movement. At the shock it rolled a little on its side but made no effort to rise.

With the mother in the room the little animal was seemingly immune to this stress of monotonously recurring apprehension.

We found that the newborn lamb or kid could be conditioned at a very early age, as early as four hours following birth. It occurred to us that the same trauma inflicted upon the young animal by this stressful, early conditioning in isolation might also be inflicted upon it by interfering with the maternal-neonate relations. This conjecture marked an important turning point in the work of our laboratory. We were soon engaged in the fascinating study of the *natural history of prejudice.*

The studies on early conditioning showed that the period of greatest vulnerability to the stress of Pavlovian conditioning is from four hours to three weeks of age when the animal is deprived of its mother's presence in the testing room. It is as if she serves as a *security signal* indicating that all is well.

We conditioned ten kids in isolation at four to fourteen hours of age *for just one session of about an hour* with twenty darkness signals at two-minute intervals. Of the ten subjected to this early training, two had died within a week. All but one of the remaining eight died in the summer pasture at less than a year of age. Only one out of those ten survived.

We also conditioned ten pairs of twin kids at one month of age. Five of these twins were trained in isolation and five with the mother. Four of the five that were conditioned in isolation died within the year, while only one of the five that were conditioned with the mother present died within the year.

It is clear from these results that *prejudices* formed by Pavlovian conditioning in young animals *are not only disabling, they can be lethal.* The reader may be tempted to speculate upon the lethal effects (suicide) in man of the formation, early in life, of disabling prejudices and their fatal organization in later life.

As a next step in our pursuit of the natural history of prejudice we tried the effect of simply removing the kid from its mother. We had under observation twenty-two control kids in which there was no separation from the mother following parturition, and twenty-one experimental kids separated from the mother five minutes following birth and kept away from her, alone in an adjoining room for half an hour to two hours. Nineteen of the twenty-one experimental kids separated from the mother for a short time after birth had died in the summer pasture at less than a year of age, but only two of the twenty-two control kids died that summer. *None of these forty-three kids were subjected to any form of conditioning or training.*

In view of these sinister findings it would appear that the *human baby is emotionally extraordinarily tough.*

Let us now turn to the discussion of the *constructive* role of prejudice. In the thinking of Freud and Pavlov both positive and negative manifestations of neurosis and both positive and negative conditioned reflexes are compulsive and, hence, disabling. On the other hand an optimistic view of prejudice should be considered.

In view of the previous gloomy subject matter it is necessary to broaden our conception of Pavlovian conditioning. In mutual conditioning between mother and newborn, the mother's presence becomes a conditioned security signal to her offspring. This mutual conditioning establishes a stable pleasure organization between mother and newborn which promotes its healthy growth and development.

The intricate details of the dynamics of this brief interrelationship following birth is summarized by Francis Moore. As the result of many months of "round the clock" observation of the sheep and goats in our laboratory she writes:

Mutual conditioning in the sheep and goat is accomplished through all the senses; smell, taste, body contact, hearing, seeing, and by the place sense as well. That is, animals become used to where to find their young, and the young to where the mother is. Any disarranging of the population of a group of mothers and young is very disturbing to the orientation of both mother and young.

When mutual conditioning is accomplished in the normal manner, no inhibiting is required of the young by the mother during the first few days of life. When inhibiting is eventually required by the mother not allowing the young to nurse, the process is very gradual and it is done in such a way that the young expects satisfaction in the near future. Refusal is indicated by clearcut signals such as a motion of the leg that covers the udder. There is never any confusion as to what is indicated.

Body contacts with the mother are never refused. She at all times permits the young to make contact with her in any way it may desire. It may sleep close to her or in play jump on her, or after nursing may stand under her head or body.

Termination of the mutual conditioning is very gradual and is effected by a widening circle as the young become less dependent for food up the nursing process.

The key to this mutual conditioning seems to be an interplay of pleasurable behavior patterns so that mutual pleasurable stimulation is involved throughout. The signals for the food to be offered are consistent and always followed by what they imply. This results in digestive readiness.

Resting periods are completely relaxed since no ambivalence has been aroused.

Another example of mutual conditioning, derived from natural history, is the phenomenon of *imprinting*. Here, the newly hatched gosling sees and follows the first moving object. If it happens to be a man that man becomes imprinted upon the little bird's brain. Henceforth, human beings will be accepted as fellow geese. Konrad Lorenz has related how a goose upon whose mind he was imprinted allowed him to help build her nest. As he told us, he had become an *honorary goose*. Imprinting, then, appears to be the most striking example of the unadulterated operation of the *coincidence principle* in nature.

A few final reflections upon *pleasure organization* in relation to *mutual conditioning*. Many years ago Sandor Rado anticipated our interest in happy prejudices in his exciting notion of pleasure organization.

According to him, man in the exercise of pleasure functions derives excitation from stimulating the sensitive spots available in his mind and body:

These pleasure functions interact and combine with one another to make up the individual's entire pleasure organization. The latter is obviously neither sexual or non-sexual, but an entity of a new order brought about by integration on a higher level. It undergoes typical changes during the life cycle, and is characterized at every stage by a measure of functional flexibility, working in the service of one then another of the biological systems. . . . This pleasure organization requires a term that reflects its biological nature and avoids confusion between the superior entity and its component parts.

The notion of mutual conditioning leads into the sphere of sociology which embraces all of the manifestations of group processes. The goat in the process of mutual conditioning occurring during the mothering of her newborn is at the same time involved in necessary interactions with the rest of the flock. The pleasure organization which she and her offspring establish is a simple instance of Rado's broader conception. By contrast, the members of an amateur string quartet establish a transitory and vulnerable pleasure organization at a highly complex level.

As a tentative step toward a definition of mind we have discussed the biology of prejudice and, in so doing, have omitted certain fundamental considerations. Three aspects of man must be involved in a definition of mind. Man is at the same time an *organism,* a *mind,* and a *social being* (or socius*). Through the process of historical screening, we think of Jim Thorpe as a superior organism, Descartes as a mind, and Buddha as a social being. This discussion has been limited to the attempt to make some inferences concerning man's nature as organism and socius.

* *Socius* is the conception of Charles Horton Cooley, a worthy of American sociology. See his *Social Organization,* 1918.

J A M E S   G .   T A Y L O R

J O S E P H   W O L P E

Mind as Function of Neural Organization

I. Introduction

In the past, behavioral scientists who have insisted on a monistic objective account of the subject matter of psychology have found mind an awkward fact to be glossed over or explained away; and, except in general terms, they have not been able adequately to meet the objections of idealists and dualists (though well able to criticize *their* positions). A recent book by Taylor (1962) has provided the behaviorist with a complete answer to his critics. The application of learning theory to a new range of facts has brought to light the biological mechanisms of perception and consciousness.

The present paper delineates Taylor's behavioral theory of mind and then indicates how several important kinds of abnormal behavior are related to mind thus conceived. It will be shown that neurotic behavior is a particular variety of conditioned responding quite unrelated to any abnormality of mind, and that in the context of the theory the agnosias are the most elemental examples of abnormalities of mind.

We define mind as *a set of functions of learned behavior*. We shall in due course explain the precise character of those functions and why we refer to a set of functions rather than a single function. But first we consider it necessary to state certain philosophical implications of our definition.

The term "function" here implies that an element of mind is a

218

dependent variable. That is, we do not recognize *any* form of mind that exists autonomously or independently of some behavioral substratum. Hence we reject every form of psychophysical dualism, and all derivatives and unacknowledged relics of dualistic theory. Our definition implies also that we reject all forms of philosophical idealism; that is, all theories that start from the assumption that the primary reality is mind, and postulate that the physical universe as we experience it is a set of functions of mind. On the contrary, we take as our starting point matter in all its aspects, from the electrons, protons, neutrons, and other particles to the vast array of compounds formed by their combination that provide the content of experience.

We believe, with Samuel Alexander (1920), that as the organization of matter increases in complexity, new properties emerge. These are properties that could not exist without the higher level of organization involved; but, on the other hand, this higher level is itself a direct outcome of properties inherent in the less highly organized substances that unite to form the new compound. Thus, the molecule of nucleic acid has the property, not possessed by any of its component parts, that it can generate other molecules of nucleic acid from suitable material in its environment. This property of self-reproduction, possessed by a large number of highly complex organic compounds, is a necessary prerequisite for the emergence of a still higher property—life-characteristic of self-maintaining organisms. The essence of life, or self-maintenance, is that there is a continuous interchange of matter between the organism and its environment, the transaction being invariably initiated by the organism, but in such a manner that the living substance retains its chemical and structural identity.

In the simplest organisms interchange takes place largely as a result of random encounters with suitable substances in the environment. But even in such organisms, as Jennings (1906) demonstrated long ago, behavior is by no means rigidly predetermined. The unicellular stentor (Jennings, pp. 174-175), enveloped in a cloud of carmine grains, first takes the slightly irritating particles into its mouth, then progressively modifies its responses until finally it contracts into its tube, remaining there for about half a minute. If the water currents now again bring carmine grains, the contraction into the tube is seen to be the animal's *immediate* response. This change of response, a manifestation of a primitive form of learning, persists for several minutes.

As organisms become more complex in structure and more diversified in function, there is an increase in the number, variety, and complexity of the responses that can be acquired by learning. Structural organization must be increasingly supplemented by a superimposed organization that comes into being through learning, since the inherited structure of a complex organism is not in itself sufficient to guarantee survival. Among the most important of the means by which the complexity of the super-imposed organization is increased is the development of sensory surfaces in the form of specialized receptors distributed over an area such as the skin or the retina, together with the development of specialized cells that can rapidly signal the responses of the receptors to distant parts of the body and thereby initiate appropriate actions. This is accompanied by an enormous number of neuronal ramifications in the central nervous system, allowing for multitudinous combinations of stimulus and response to be connected to each other by the learning process. In the most complex of organisms this has a remarkable outcome—the capacity to learn to respond *not merely to stimuli, but also to objects*—so that adequate response can be made to an object no matter which aspect is presented to the organism; i.e., despite the fact that the sensory stimulus compounds from the object making their impact upon the organism are various. As will be seen below, this is the result of highly complex compound conditioning of exteroceptive stimuli in conjunction with relevant proprioceptive stimuli.

It will be shown that the property whereby one aggregate of matter, at a highly complex level of organization, is automatically adjusted to any aspect of another piece of matter, and similarly to all other pieces of matter that make impact upon it is none other than the property we call *consciousness*. From the days of Johannes Müller, psychologists, physiologists, and neurologists have tended to think of consciousness as being some kind of essence secreted by neurons, and varying in quality according to the particular group of neurons involved. Alternatively, they have thought of it as being some kind of physical energy generated by certain highly specialized groups of neurons. But the supposed essence is chemically unidentifiable, and the energies generated by neurons do not enable us even to guess, let alone assert with confidence, that this neuron is generating a perception of red and that one the perception of the tone of an oboe playing B flat. In short, the known variation in the chemical and physical behavior of neurons is much too restricted to explain the rich variety of consciousness. So if we insist that consciousness is something generated by neurons, we are forced to accept the hypothesis that the neurons have some mystical or supernatural power that is beyond the reach of science. We emphatically reject any hypothesis that implies that the neurons have metaphysiological powers.

Now, let us go back to the stentor. Presumably, no psychologist would maintain that the stentor must first be conscious of the harmfulness of the carmine grains before it reverses the action of its cilia and subsequently retreats into its tube. Most scientists would agree that physiological and biochemical principles will prove sufficient to account for the observed facts. But if a unicellular organism can learn without consciousness, there can be no logical objection to the notion that a multicellular organism can do likewise. In short, we maintain that the ability to learn is a property of matter at a lower level of organization than that required to generate consciousness.

Consciousness, then, follows the emergence of a higher level of organization. In order to give a full and adequate description of this organization, it is necessary to specify not only the acquired reactions of the organism, but also the objects to which these reactions are directed, and, in particular, those properties of the objects and their spatial and temporal relations to the organism that have served to reinforce the organism's reactions and confer on them the status of conditioned responses. The environment compels us to abandon this kind of behavior and to adopt that; for this kind involves us in encounters with substances that are damaging to the life process, while that kind involves encounters that promote the life processes. The organism is molded by the environment to constancies of neural response that yield consciousness—not as a self-sufficient "entity" but as a relating of the organism to the environment. The organism is conscious when it has developed mechanisms that enable it to respond in an appropriate way to objects from every angle of approach. All this will be amplified below.

As a background to our main exposition, it is necessary to give a brief outline of some central principles of modern learning theory.

II. Basic Principles of the Learning Process

Modern learning theory may be said to have had its formal beginning with Pavlov (1927). His experiments on dogs revealed that practically any response, including involuntary responses like salivation, can be connected at will to practically any stimulus—that is, can be made the conditioned (learned) response to a chosen stimulus. Pavlov devoted the major part of his life to defining and quantifying the factors that influence conditioning. A general implication of his work was that learning proceeds *automatically* when the relevant mechanisms are brought into play and does not require the intervention of any kind of mind-entity. He deemed this to apply as fully to the most complex instances of learning as to the conditioning of simple habits.

Quantification of the factors involved in learning with a view to formulating laws of learning was pursued even more systematically and with greater rigor of definition by Hull (1943). Hull's methodology for dealing with problems of learning (and of behavior in general) has been adopted by most experimental psychologists during the past two decades, and has led to a great accumulation of facts about the learning process.

We shall briefly state some basic propositions of modern learning theory that have been established by experimental investigation. Upon these propositions the theory of perception described in this paper has been built.

The behavior of organisms that concerns us depends on the functioning of the nervous system. The basis of this functioning is the transmission of impulses by neurons. When an organism is exposed to particular stimulus conditions, its response is determined by the neurons activated by the stimulus conditions. The response, therefore, depends upon the particular functional connections (synapses) that exist between neurons. Many functional connections are formed in the course of organismal growth. Others are established by learning—the outcome of interactions between the organism and its environment.

The following operational *definition of learning* was proposed some years ago (Wolpe, 1952). Learning may be said to have occurred if a response has been evoked in temporal contiguity with a given sensory stimulus and it is subsequently found that the stimulus can evoke the response, although it could not have done so before. If the stimulus could have evoked the response before but subsequently evokes it more strongly, then, too, learning may be said to have occurred. This definition is narrower than it need be, and for the words "sensory stimulus" the words "stimulus conditions" should be substituted.

That learning depends upon the setting up of specific neural connections was demonstrated by a striking experiment by Culler (1938). He showed that when a conditioned response had been established to an auditory signal, stimulation of a particular spot on the cortex of a dog elicited the same response. It did not elicit this response either before conditioning or after extinction. There is no reason to suppose that when learning is of a more complex kind, involving associations between words and images or between complex concepts, the basic process is different in any way. There may be vast multiplication of instances of the basic process, with great variety in the elements combined, or it may integrate two or more complex neural patterns of activation.

An individual act of learning—an individual event that has the effect of strengthening a functional neural connection—is conveniently called a reinforcement. We shall briefly mention some of the most important factors concerned in reinforcement. Controlled experiments in simple situations have shown that the details of time relations between stimulus and response affect in an important way how much learning occurs. In motor learning, the optimal time interval is in the region of half a second, while in some experiments on emotional learning it has been found to be in the region of five seconds. The amount of learning increases directly with the *number* of reinforcements, according to a simple positive growth function.

The strength that accrues at a given reinforcement to the connection between a stimulus and a response varies directly with the magnitude of the reduction of a state of *drive* (central neural excitation) that follows the response, and inversely with the length of the interval by which the drive reduction follows the response. The drive reductions that have been mainly studied have been those associated with the satisfaction of primary needs such as hunger and thirst, but quantitative relations have also been established in the case of such secondary drive states as anxiety. In some cases, such as the learning of words, drive reduction must obviously be of an exceedingly low order of magnitude, being a consequent of the drop in sensory excitation upon termination of the stimulus (Wolpe, 1950). Certain experiments have suggested that sometimes reinforcement is related to drive *increment;* for example, experiments showing that *increases* in illumination can be reinforcing (e.g., Hurwitz, 1956). Apparently there are circumstances in which drive increments fulfill the usual role of drive reduction as a reinforcing agent.

Unlearning—the weakening and elimination of established habits—implies the weakening of synaptic connections which previous learning has formed between neurons. The process of unlearning which has received most study is called extinction. This means the more or less smoothly progressive weakening of the learned response to a stimulus when this response occurs a number of times without drive reduction. There is some evidence that this process is based upon reactive inhibition —inhibitory impulses emanating from muscle and associated with fatigue. Another mechanism by which habits are weakened depends upon reciprocal inhibition—the elicitation of responses that are incompatible with and therefore inhibitory to the learned response. An important illustration of the operation of the reciprocal inhibition mechanism will be described in Section IV, where it will be shown that this is the usual process by which neurotic habits are overcome.

When a response has been conditioned to a defined stimulus, it may also be evocable by similar stimuli, to a degree that varies directly with the measure of similarity to the conditioned stimulus. This phenomenon is known as *primary stimulus generalization,* and may be observed in a large number of "dimensions" such as intensity, size, shape, position, color, or pitch—depending upon the sensory modality concerned. For example, if a response is conditioned to a red light of given size and intensity, weaker responses may be elicited to an orange light of the same size and intensity, to a smaller red light of similar intensity, or to a feebler red light of undiminished size. What ultimately determines the magnitude of a response to a generalized stimulus is the degree of similarity of its effects in the afferent part of the nervous system to those produced by the original conditioned stimulus.

III. The Behavioral Basis of Perception

There is a picturesque Scottish saying that "facts are chiels ye canna ding," which, freely translated, means "facts are indestructible." As applied to science it may be stated thus: whenever there is a conflict between theory and fact, it is the theory that is destroyed. In the following paragraphs we present a small selection of experimentally established facts that will serve to overthrow any theory of perception that fails to account for them.

A. When a patient suffering from bilateral cataract has his crystalline lenses removed, light can penetrate to the retina; but the images are not in focus, and correcting lenses must be fitted. If, as is usually the case, the lenses are not inserted in the eyes themselves but are held in front of them in a spectacle frame, the retinal image of any object suffers a transformation which has the following main effects:

1. The diameter of the image is multiplied by a factor of approximately 1:3.

2. There is a marked spherical aberration.

3. The passage of the image across the retina is no longer the same function of the position of the eye as it was before the operation.

This last effect is a direct result of the first two plus the fact that the lenses do not move with the eyes.

By any standard theory of perception it is easy to deduce from these facts that when the patient looks through his spectacles for the first time, he sees objects magnified by 30 per cent; straight lines in the periphery of the field are seen as curved; and under movements of the eyes the shapes and positions of objects are perceived as unstable. But there is more to be explained. If the patient is not discouraged and decides to make the best of this strange new visual world, the spherical aberration presently disappears, the constancies of position and shape are restored, and ultimately the enlarged world contracts to its true size (Vail, 1952). There is, of course, no change in the physical properties of the retinal image, nor in the distribution of fibers from the retina to the striate area.

B. Spectacles that reverse right and left were worn continuously for periods of several weeks by two subjects in Innsbruck. After about a fortnight, each subject reported the occasional occurrence of brief periods when the right-left ordering of the world was correctly perceived. Those periods increased in frequency and duration until, finally, correct perception was continuous. But there were anomalies. Thus, a building on the right-hand side of the street was correctly perceived as being on the right, but an inscription on it was perceived as mirrored. A book, opened to show an illustration on one page and letterpress on the other, produced a strange effect. Picture and print were perceived in their correct relative positions, and the perceived ordering of the several parts of the picture was correct, but the printed page appeared to be mirrored within itself. One of the subjects ended the experiment at this stage, but the other continued for some days longer and ultimately perceived print as running from left to right.[*]

C. One of us (J. G. T.) wore spectacles in the form of 20-degree prisms with bases left for four and a half hours on each of thirteen consecutive days. One of the effects of such spectacles is that horizontal surfaces below the level of the eyes are perceived as sloping downward to the left with an increasing gradient. At the end of the experiment this was no longer true, but the perceived shape of a horizontal surface depended on whether the subject was standing or sitting. If he stood or walked on level ground, the ground was perceived as having a level path about a yard wide stretching in front of his feet, with a gentle upward slope to the right of this path and a steeper downward slope to the left. If he sat at a table, the top of the table was perceived as sloping down to the left but there was no trace of curvature throughout its whole area. There was no evidence of a level section in the middle. Presumably the retinal stimuli were much the same in both cases, but it is evident that this identity does not enable us to deduce the perceived shape of the table from that of the floor, or vice versa.

The above facts, as well as the better known facts of everyday perception, have elsewhere (Taylor, 1962) been accounted for in detail. A summary is given in the following paragraphs.

The infant at birth has no learned responses to the objects around him. It will emerge from our exposition that this implies that he has no perception of the spatial ordering of his environment, and will not achieve such perception until he has acquired at least a number of well-established conditioned responses. But the neonate already has a number of unconditioned responses available to him. For example, he can turn his eyes and he can move his hands. Let us ask how he acquires such organized responses as turning the eyes toward an object and stretching out the hand to grasp it.

To a mature person it seems as if all that is required to initiate a movement of the hand toward an object is a visual stimulus, but since the eyes and the head are mobile, and the initial position of the hand is variable,

[*] Personal communication from Professor I. Kohler.

simple geometrical considerations show that, even when the trunk is immobilized, this action involves no fewer than eleven variables, all of which must be represented by afferent impulses in the nervous system. These variables are functions of:

The positions of the images of the object on the left and right retinas. (Variables 1 and 2.)

The horizontal angular deviations of left and right eyes from their central position. (Variables 3 and 4.)

The vertical angular deviation of the eyes from the central position. (Variable 5.)

The position of the head relative to a standard position. (Variables 6, 7, and 8.)

The initial position of the hand related to a suitable coordinate system. (Variables 9, 10, and 11.)

Since the positions of the retinal images are jointly determined by the position of the object relative to the body and the orientation of head and eyes, it is clear that afferent functions 1 to 8 are all required to determine the terminal position of the hand when it makes contact with the object. Further, since the hand may start from any one of a large number of positions, afferent functions of its initial position must collaborate with the first eight functions to determine the path of the movement.

A neonate is unable to make such responses, but by the time he is able to sit without support he can grasp any object within reach of his hands. This development can be explained on the basis of conditioning as follows. Accidental contact with an object evokes the grasping reflex unconditionally, and this has the effect of establishing temporary connections between the preceding eleven-dimensional pattern of stimulation and the response of moving the hand from the initial position to the goal. For any one position of the object the number of possible patterns of stimulation is colossal, and if each pattern had to be separately conditioned to the appropriate response, a million lifetimes would not be sufficient to complete the task. But there are two factors that accelerate the process.

If a bright light stimulates the periphery of the retina, it sets up impulses in fibers that, running directly to the superior colliculi where they synapse with fibers to the oculomotor nuclei, are the pathway to a reflex fixation response. This reflex is subsequently also conditioned to weaker stimuli, such as the light reflected by objects. When a sufficient number of conditioned reflexes of this type has been established, the number of eleven-dimensional patterns that have to be conditioned to manual responses suffers a spectacular reduction, since for each of the first two variables we need now consider only one value—the central (fixation) position on each retina. If a successful manual response is evoked while the object is under fixation, this response is conditioned not only to the eleven-dimensional pattern of stimulation in operation at fixation, but also, by Pavlov's principle of the short-trace reflex, to other preceding patterns in which the retinal images were peripheral.

The second accelerating factor is stimulus generalization (see above). To understand how this operates it will be convenient to think of a pattern of stimulation as a point of an eleven-dimensional space. Given that the goal object and the infant's body are both stationary, it is evident that the patterns of stimulation involving this object are all contained within an eight-dimensional subspace of the eleven-dimensional stimulus space. Hence, generalization will spread in the first instance to other points within the eight-dimensional subspace. Thus a single reinforcement may have the effect of conditioning the appropriate response to thousands of potential patterns of stimulation involving the same goal-object.

The establishment of innumerable conditioned responses of this kind implies an important change in the organization of the system consisting of the organism and its immediate environment. At the beginning of the process the system is characterized by a one-many relation between the position of an object and the pattern of stimulation to which it gives rise, and also by a one-many relation between afferent and efferent events. Conditioning has the effect that only one efferent event is evoked by each compound afferent event, but as each efferent event involves making contact with the source of the exteroceptive components of the afferent event, the final result is the establishment of one-to-one correspondence between the positions of objects in the environment and the terminal positions of responses directed toward those objects.

Conditioning implies the establishment of temporary connections between the afferent and efferent portions of the cortex. We shall use the term *engram* to designate such a connection. In view of the multidimensionality of the afferent events, it is evident that the engrams are structurally very much more complex than has hitherto been supposed. And it is not surprising that Lashley (1950), using the crude technique of extirpation, was unable to discover any evidence for their existence.

When a conditioned response is evoked, it is evident that the temporal sequence of events involves (1) a compound afferent event, (2) the activation of the engram mediating the response, and (3) the transmission of the appropriate impulses to the motor system. We may say that completion of the first two stages of this sequence has the effect of putting the organism into a state of readiness for the third stage. But for various reasons, the final stage may fail to be completed. For example, if two or more engrams, mediating mutually incompatible responses, are simul-

taneously active, only one of them can succeed in gaining control of a
final common path. However, this success does not imply that the other
engrams fail to establish states of readiness for their relative responses.
Our conception of the engram is such that each of them must be considered as a unique structure; consequently, activity in one of them does
not in general inhibit the simultaneous activation of others. Thus, the
several objects in the immediate environment can all simultaneously
arouse states of readiness for responses directed to them, although only
one, or even none, of those responses may actually be evoked.

It is evident that this state of simultaneous readiness for actions
directed to objects in the vicinity implies that the infant has acquired
knowledge of the positions of those objects, since each engram mediates
a response that establishes contact with the object. The form that this
knowledge takes can be none other than the perception of the *spatial*
ordering of the environment. But at first it is a very restricted knowledge.
It is three-dimensionally accurate only with respect to objects that
are within reach of the hands. Objects beyond that range can only be
perceived as a two-dimensional array at an indeterminate distance, since
the only responses conditioned to such objects are two-dimensional movements of the eyes. Analogously, the night sky presents to a mature
subject a two-dimensional projection of objects distributed in a four-
dimensional time-space continuum. The transformation of this two-
dimensional array into a four-dimensional array requires a vast amount
of additional information that can be obtained only by the systematic
observations of astronomers. Similarly, the infant extends the range of
his perceived space by acquiring additional information in the form of
engrams mediating responses to more distant objects.

The first expansion takes place when the infant learns to sit without
support. His new mobility adds fresh sources of variation to retinal
stimuli, but it also adds new dimensions of proprioceptive stimuli, in
which the pressures due to gravity play a more important part than
they have done hitherto. Although the system appears to have increased in complexity, it is actually not as complex as the system that
is in operation at the beginning of life, since a substantial proportion
of the eleven-dimensional patterns of stimulation of the earlier stage
have already been conditioned to responses that can be completely
defined in terms of a three-dimensional continuum. They are, in fact,
stimuli that give rise to perception of a space that is three-dimensional
within a narrow range, and two-dimensional beyond that range. By
virtue of this conditioning the complexity has, in the language of Samuel
Alexander, gathered itself together and expressed itself in a new simplicity. The new patterns of afferent activity, enlarged by new proprioceptive components, but simplified by the existing organization of the

original eleven-dimensional patterns, are available for conditioning to new responses, involving an inclination of the body together with a stretching out of the hand, that result in an enlargement of the radius of the child's perceived environment.

These new responses involve repeated shifting of the child's center of gravity, threatening loss of balance, and the child must therefore learn to make compensatory movements enabling him to change the angle of his body without falling. Thus his responses are simultaneously adjusted not only to the positions of objects in his vicinity but also the direction of the gravitational axis; and this implies that his perceptual world acquires a horizontal-vertical frame of reference which does not arise from retinal stimulation alone.

These developments prepare the way for a further dramatic expansion of the perceptual world when locomotion makes it possible for the child to acquire responses to the directions and distances of objects far beyond the reach of his hands. The most important effect produced by locomotion on the afferent system is that the retinal image of an object changes as a continuous function of its distance. Thus, the visual angle subtended by a fixed object increases with positive acceleration as the distance diminishes. It is unlikely that the rate of change can itself become an effective stimulus, since it is measured in infinitesimals; but the continuously changing stimulus is punctuated, so to speak, by the regularly recurring cycles of proprioceptive and pressure stimuli that are incidental to locomotion whether by crawling or by walking. The successive locomotor cycles carve the continuously changing retinal stimulus into temporal slabs, each of which is characterized by a greater proportional expansion than its predecessor.

For any given object the proportional expansion that results from reducing its distance from $n + 1$ to n paces is unique, and this expansion, therefore, constitutes a stimulus that can be conditioned to a unique response, such as taking $n - 1$ paces to bring the object within reach of the hands. Repeated application of this operation in numerous situations has the ultimate effect that when the child is confronted with an ordinary three-dimensional scene, a single pace produces varying degrees of expansion according to the distances of the objects, and these arouse activity in engrams mediating appropriate responses to all the objects. Here again we have a state of simultaneous readiness, and since the prepared-for responses vary with respect to the distance through which they carry the body, the state of readiness can only mean that the child perceives the scene in depth.

While the changes in stimulation induced by locomotion are of primary importance for the development of perception of depth, there are also momentary patterns of compound stimulation that are uniquely determined by distance, and these too can become conditioned to the appropriate responses. For example, if definite values are assigned to variables 1, 3, and 4 listed above, then the distance of the object that is responsible for variable 1 exactly determines the value that variable 2 must have. Hence, for each set of values that can be taken by variables 1 to 4 (that is, for each state of this four-variable system) there is one and only one *distance* of the object producing the retinal stimuli, and this remains true no matter what values may be assigned to variables 3 and 4. If, then, the several states of the four-variable system that can arise from an object at a fixed distance can all be conditioned to a response appropriate to that distance, binocular parallax can generate perception of depth which will operate even when the body is stationary. Without going into any details we shall simply say that the circumstances are eminently favorable for such conditioning.

The process we have outlined generates a whole crop of perceptual constancies. This is implicit in our earlier statement that, although there is a one-many relation between the position of an external object and the patterns of stimulation to which it may give rise, conditioning establishes a one-to-one correspondence between the position of the object and the terminus of the response conditioned to it. Generalizing, we may say that whenever there is a one-to-one correspondence between some property of objects and a response adapted to that property, a perceptual constancy will be found. Here is a common example. The size of a stable object is such that the movements required to grasp it always require the same separation of the fingers or hands. The action of grasping is invariably the terminal stage of a response that is subject to a wide range of variation with respect to the amount of locomotion required to bring the object within reach. But since all these varying responses have a constant terminal component, it is evident that the stimuli which evoke the variable component of the response are also conditioned to the constant terminal component, provided the time elapsing between the presentation of the stimulus and the beginning of the terminal response is not too long. By virtue of the variable component of the response, the stimulus generates perception of the distance of the object; by virtue of the constant component it generates perception of its size, and this size is constant over a wide range of distances.

Our contention that perception is molded by commerce with objects is supported by the fact that size constancy is abolished when we look *down* on familiar objects, such as people and vehicles, from the top of a tall building. Most of us have no readiness for responses that will carry us safely down the wall to a level where a terminal manipulation can be initiated. In situations that do not evoke the relevant behavior, there is no size constancy. It is as simple as that.

Thus, in different contexts there are differences in the character of perception of things. In this sense, mind is a *plurality*. That is, if we choose any set of stimuli and record the responses that are conditioned to them, we thereby define a subsystem that generates certain elements of mind. Each subsystem has a measure of independence. This is strikingly manifested in the second example at the beginning of this section in which the subject still saw printing reversed after his general visual field had been righted. By any of the standard theories of perception it is quite unthinkable that perceived space should be correctly ordered with respect to right and left, and at the same time a part of the field should be perceived in reversed order. To the behavioral theory this presents no difficulty. For each of the plural aspects of the environment has its own behavioral basis. There are several classes of responses that are conditioned to compound patterns of stimulation including retinal components, and when reversing spectacles are worn there is no reason to suppose that those classes of responses will all be corrected at the same rate. In particular, the responses of reading are likely to be corrected rather slowly, partly because reading is likely to be severely restricted until the more fundamental problems of movement and locomotion have been solved, and partly because the spectacles are external to the eyes, with the result that when the head is held in a fixed position, reading requires movements of the eyes from right to left instead of from left to right. Engrams mediating two apparently contradictory modes of behavior can thus be simultaneously activated by one and the same total pattern of stimulation.

Our third example (in which the shape of a horizontal surface differed according to whether the subject sat or stood) is more straightforward. The two different forms of perception occurred at different times, and it is easy to see that different proprioceptive and pressure variables are operative in the two cases, as well as different sectors of the response mechanism. The main point of interest is that in each situation perception was partly correct and partly distorted, and this is explained by the fact that in each of them the subject's behavior was directed to a restricted aspect of the environment. Locomotion, for example, was directed to a narrow strip of ground, and never to ground to the right and left of this strip. Initially, the distorted retinal stimuli caused some disruption of walking, and, as the subject is a cripple, this exposed him to a risk of falling and provided a strong motivation for the correction of errors. Appropriate responses were soon conditioned to the new stimuli and as these were, of course, exactly the same responses as those evoked under normal conditions, the perceived shape of the ground was normal. But as no new responses were conditioned to the rest of the ground, it continued to be perceived as distorted.

Two predictions from the theory have been exactly confirmed. The first was in July, 1953, when Dr. S. Papert undertook to act as subject in an experiment involving the wearing of spectacles that reverse right and left. At first he wore them continuously, but on the fifth day he predicted, from the behavioral theory, that if he wore them for only half of each day he would ultimately be able to put them on or take them off without producing any change in the perceived ordering of the environment. About a fortnight later this prediction was triumphantly vindicated when he rode a bicycle while wearing the spectacles, took them off while riding, and put them on again without experiencing any switching of right and left. Exactly the same responses were conditioned to both normal and reversed retinal stimulation, and the perceptual field consequently came to have the same properties in both cases.*

The second prediction was made in July, 1959, when J. G. T., then a guest in the home of J. W., wore a contact lens incorporating a prism of nearly 12 degrees. One of the effects of this lens is that straight lines are perceived as curved. Before the lens was made, it was predicted that such a curved line would be made to appear straight by sufficient repetition of the mere act of scanning it. The basis of this prediction was the assumption that the perceived shape of an object depends on the simultaneous activation of engrams mediating fixation responses directed to all parts of the object. The lens distorts the retinal image, but because it moves with the eye and therefore changes the pattern of distortion as it goes, fixation responses are subject to error. But for the same reason exactly the same fixation responses are required as in normal vision. Hence, when the errors are all corrected, the changed retinal pattern will arouse engrams mediating exactly the same set of fixation responses as in the normal case, and the object will be perceived as having the normal shape. The prediction was fully confirmed. Curved lines began to straighten at once, although the subject only sat and looked. A vertical line in one part of the room became completely straight after scanning it for twenty seconds, but lines in other places, requiring different settings of head and eyes, were still curved, and each had to be separately straightened. One horizontal line obstinately remained curved even after two minutes of continuous inspection. It actually was curved, although the subject had no direct means of knowing that at the time. This experiment shows in the most convincing way how intercourse with the environment "molds" visual perception to conform to spatial reality; and when conformity has been dislocated the parts have to be refashioned separately.

---

* A film describing this experiment was shown at the 15th International Congress of Psychology, Brussels, 1957.

Thus, our knowledge of the world is a function of the activation of engrams that are the product of repeated occasions of learning in varied spatial relations to objects. The engrams are complex integrated neural response-systems, arousable by systematically variable combinations of sensory inputs, providing, within specifiable limits, constancy of perception despite variations in sensory stimulation. Since there are constancies with regard to all parts of all perceptual fields, consciousness of the environment involves a simultaneous activation of engrams related to all objects present at a given time.

The learning process can connect any engram to any other in such a way that activation of the first leads to activation of the second. Imagery without perception is thus elicited; and this is the basis of thinking.

IV. Reorientation to Some Varieties of Abnormal Behavior

Our theory of mind calls for a reappraisal of the functional status of many varieties of abnormal behavior. This cannot be systematically undertaken here, but a few comments will be made with regard to some important categories of abnormal behavior. To begin with, we shall deal with and correct the widespread belief that abnormal mental processes are responsible for the neuroses. We shall also briefly review those abnormalities of behavior that involve perceptual integration, and show how some instances of visual agnosia may be understood in terms of our theory.

We have avoided any consideration of the major psychoses because of a strong presumption based on several kinds of evidence (e.g., Kallmann, 1953; Frohman, *et al.*, 1960) that these conditions depend at least in part on biochemical abnormalities and therefore cannot be accounted for solely in terms of behavioral integration.

A. Abnormal Response Habits: The Neuroses

To characterize the neuroses as abnormal response habits and not as the result of malfunctions of mind is, of course, directly contrary to the teachings of the psychoanalytic *Zeitgeist*. Below we shall present facts that support this position, and show that there is no room for supposing that neurosis is a disorder of mind. The perceptual synthesis of the neurotic subject is characteristically normal, and his imagery corresponds with reality.

Despite wide differences of belief regarding many aspects of the neuroses, the identity of the clinical conditions they comprise is a matter of general agreement—anxiety states, phobias, hysterias, obsessions and compulsions, and various combinations of these. It would also be widely agreed that the behavior characteristic of these conditions is inappropriate and unproductive (unadaptive).

Behavior that in its unadaptiveness and in other ways resembles that of human neuroses can easily be conditioned in animals by subjecting them, while in confined space, either to ambivalent stimulus situations (e.g., Pavlov, 1927) or to noxious stimulation (e.g., Wolpe, 1952). The enduring states of disturbance thus produced are generally manifested by symptoms that are also observed in human anxiety states, (e.g., tachycardia, tachypnea, muscular tenseness) but several variations suggestive of other syndromes have also been noted. Just as in humans, the disturbance, e.g., anxiety, is not "endogenous" (like the symptoms of an organic illness), but "stimulus-linked," i.e., evoked only in response to the impact of particular stimulations. The experimenter can condition to the neurotic responses any stimuli he chooses, but at the same time, incidental conditioning may occur to other stimuli that happen to be present in the situation. The essential point is that the animal learns to respond with anxiety to all manner of objectively harmless stimuli—bells, flashes of light, rabbits, enamel dishes, wire mesh, etc.

As mentioned earlier, generally speaking, the repeated evocation of a response that leads to no benefit ("reward") for the organism results in a progressive weakening (experimental extinction) of the habit of responding thus to the evoking stimulus. High-intensity conditioned anxiety responses are an exception to this rule because they involve a mechanism, discussed elsewhere (Wolpe, 1958), that counteracts the usual process of extinction; and this is what makes neurotic habits extraordinarily tenacious. However, they can be overcome if conditions are arranged so that a neurotic response is inhibited by a simultaneous response that is incompatible with it. In animal neuroses this is done by giving food to the hungry animal immediately after the presentation of a stimulus evoking a feeble degree of anxiety (i.e., a stimulus slightly resembling one of the original stimuli to which anxiety was conditioned). The act of eating inhibits the anxiety and weakens the anxiety response habit so that on subsequent occasions stimuli increasingly similar to the relevant conditioned stimulus can be made to precede the introduction of the food without inhibiting eating. This progression depends on the phenomenon of stimulus generalization. (See Section II.) When the anxiety-evoking potential of a generalized stimulus is weakened, the potential is also weakened of all stimuli that resemble the conditioned stimulus in the same general direction. Eventually, the conditioned stimulus itself is deprived of all power to evoke anxiety. This piecemeal breaking down of the anxiety response habits is apparently due to the gradual development of conditioned inhibition of the anxiety responses following on their *reciprocal inhibition* by opposing responses (Wolpe, 1952).

Allusion was made above to the fact that human clinical neuroses and animal experimental neuroses share the feature of unadaptiveness besides having other outward similarities. This in itself does not necessarily mean that the same causal process underlies both; and, in fact, the contrary has been dogmatically asserted (e.g., Glover, 1959). It has been said that whereas animal neuroses are a matter of conditioning, human neuroses are due to a malfunction of mind[*] and that therefore any similarities must be coincidental. However, the presence of common features compels a careful examination of the alternative hypothesis— that the two have a common basis. It is possible to settle the issue by testing predictions generated by the opposing hypotheses. Thus, if human neuroses are really the same as animal neuroses, lasting cure will be expected to follow the elimination of specified habits of response by conditioning methods. This will not be expected if human neuroses are due to a disturbance of mind, for then some kind of reordering of mind will be the essence of therapy.

What is needed, then, is a comparison of the effects of operations dictated by the two opposing hypotheses. It is important to note that each group of theorists will predict *some* therapeutic success to be yielded by the methods of the other group; for it can reasonably be held that sometimes in the course of conditioning therapy there may be incidental change of mental forces and, equally reasonably on the other side, that during psychoanalysis there is sometimes inadvertent reconditioning. But clearly when a principle is valid, its deliberate application will produce a higher proportion of favorable results than can be expected to emerge when it comes into play only now and then, by chance as it were.

The following are the relevant facts. In human neuroses the outcome of psychoanalytic therapy has been no better than that of simple methods such as employed in general hospitals—since usually between 40 and 60 per cent of patients in both groups are either apparently cured or much improved.[†] The failure of psychoanalytic methods to register superior measures of success speaks against the presumption that psychoanalytic mechanisms are the crux of the therapeutic process and suggests instead that the mechanisms of recovery are active in equal measure in psychoanalytic and hospital settings, although unperceived by both

[*] It is important to realize that when Glover and other psychoanalysts speak of mind, it is in a dualist frame of reference—as an *entity* distinct from, though intimately bound up with, the physical organism.

[†] For comparative statistics, see Knight (1945) and Eysenck (1952).

groups of therapists. By contrast, therapeutic procedures based on conditioning principles derived from the successful treatment of experimental neurosis in cats, mentioned above, have been notably more successful than the traditional methods. Employing a variety of responses that, like feeding, are physiologically antagonistic to anxiety but more readily applicable to human subjects, one of us (Wolpe, 1958) in a series of 210 neurotic patients has obtained a recovery rate of 90 per cent apparently cured or much improved in a mean of thirty-one sessions. Lazarus (1959) has reported no failures in eighteen cases of phobias in children, in a mean of just over nine sessions per patient. In answer to the usual claim that psychoanalysis alone ensures *lasting* freedom from symptoms, it must be pointed out that statistical studies have consistently shown that when nonanalytic methods result in marked improvement such improvement is almost invariably lasting. For example, in a five- to fifteen-year follow-up study, Hamilton, Varney, and Wall (1942) found evidence of relapse in only one of sixty-seven patients.

The crucial point is that, as far as the evidence goes, it supports the view that an intrinsically simple conditioning process and not a malfunctioning of mind is the basis of human neuroses. Such beneficial effects as are brought about by psychoanalysis and other methods that do not deliberately make use of conditioning principles are apparently due partly to reciprocal inhibition of the patient's anxiety responses (evoked verbally and in other ways in the consulting room) by antagonistic responses evoked by aspects of the interview situation, and partly to their reciprocal inhibition in association with changed behavior in the life situation prompted (not always intentionally) by the interviews.

B. Abnormalities of Perceptual Integration

We must now turn to those deviations of behavior that are characterized by abnormalities of imagery, and examine to what extent they can be better understood in the light of our theory of perception. The following phenomena* invite our attention:

1. Optical illusions
2. Hallucinations
3. The visual agnosias

* At first glance, *delusions* would seem to deserve listing here too, but this would be incorrect. A delusion is a persistent systematized false conception of a sector of reality. Perceptual impressions themselves are intrinsically in keeping with reality, but there are "wrong" connections that are impervious to the normal processes of correction through experience. A pathological process is evidently at the root of this, but it involves not perceptual synthesis but the interaction of formed sectors of experience.

Of these the last group appears to be by far the most relevant to our subject, and we shall content ourselves with brief comments on the first two.

1. An *optical illusion* is a visual perception that does not accord with objective reality, occurring under special circumstances in a subject whose perceptions generally reflect reality. Some of the facts outlined in Sec-III show how certain optical illusions depend upon engrams based on motor habits. Admittedly the errors of perception discussed there are of a special kind, but it would be easy to show that even common illusions such as the Muller-Lyer have the same basis.

2. A *hallucination* is an internally evoked image which the subject mistakes for a perception. Hallucinations occur in (a) certain cases of cerebral pathology, (b) psychotic states, (c) emotional stress in neurotic or even normal subjects, (d) deeply hypnotized subjects, by suggestion, and (e) subjects deliberately conditioned. It would seem that in each of these groups of cases the image is well integrated and the error is related to whatever ordinarily discriminates the imaginary from the real. The hallucinated image is evoked with vividness and other features that usually belong to a perception. When hallucinations are produced by conditioning, something approaching the *totality* of perceptual experience is conditioned to a particular stimulus. In the hallucinations of hypnosis it is likely that "perceptual qualities" are added to the image by the suggestions of the hypnotist. It is possible that abnormal neural discharges have the same kind of effect in pathological cases. Detailed investigation alone can identify the precise processes. It would seem, however, that these are related to the fact that *sensory input* is present in every perception, and in a hallucination the effects of such input are added to an imagined image. There is apparently no other abnormality of the factors of perceptual synthesis.

3. In *visual agnosia*, though there is no visual defect, there is an inability to integrate visual stimuli or imagined visual images in such a way that the perceptions of the person accord with his environment. Though cases are rare, a good many have been described from which it is clear that integration may be faulty in a number of different ways. Many of the impairments that have been observed are listed below, systematized from cases referred to by Critchley (1953).

A. *Space Dimension Impairment*
1. Loss of distance judgment
2. Loss of size judgment (can arrange by color when not by size)
3. Visual field flat, not stereoscopic
4. Lost directional relations (cannot decide which way around to put cardboard letters, e.g., E)

5. Loss of directional relations evoked by words (e.g., asked to say which people in a picture are *below*, points *behind* the picture

B. *Impaired Topographic Synthesis*

1. Inability to cull up topographic or geographic images (e.g., able to describe wife's appearance but not area where he has lived ten years)
2. Inability to recognize topography (e.g., recognizes bed only by placing colored object on it)

C. *Loss of Coordination between Vision and Movement*

1. Pointing inaccurate
2. Loss of coordination between idea and movement (when advanced unable to point to parts of own body)°

D. *Limitation of Recognition Based on Functional Characteristics*

Recognizes lighted cigarette but not smoker, window-latch but not window, handbag but not wife.

Plainly, the above disabilities present problems of great complexity for neurology, whose working out would be a major undertaking. It is our view that our theory of perception provides a functional basis for studying them. It is not possible here to demonstrate the relevance of the theory for each variation, but we shall show in relation to some instances how it offers a rational approach to phenomena previously incomprehensible. In each instance we shall suggest not only what element in the integration of perception is at fault but also by what operations our suggestion may be tested.

(a) **Loss of Size Judgment.** In learning to compare the sizes of two visible objects, an essential part is played by eye movements. If the objects are of the same shape and also at about the same distance from the subject, the eyes will make greater excursions in tracing the contours of the larger object. The movements of the eyes produce proprioceptive impulses that vary according to the size of the excursions and influence the development of the relative engrams. When the engrams have been established, size can be judged on the basis of visual stimuli alone. (In a patient with marked ocular paresis recently ob-

° N.B. a. Some spatial tasks only may be affected.
　　 b. Only one side may be affected. There may be imperception of one side of space, so that, e.g., the patient may make only right turns. In advanced cases he may be able to touch ear, etc., of doll on one side only).

served by J. W., it was doubtful whether there was even slight impairment of size judgment.) But if a lesion interrupts the pathways carrying the ocular proprioceptive impulses from the midbrain to the cortex the character of the engrams will gradually change due to the omission of the proprioceptive component upon which size judgment depends.

Two kinds of observations could be used to test the above proposition. A behavioral test could be done by applying a prismatic contact lens to one of the eyes of the patient. It would be predicted that the vertical curvature could not be removed as in a normal subject (see above) by movements of the eye. Postmortem examination should reveal lesions involving proprioceptive eye muscle projection paths.

(b) **Loss of Stereoscopic Visual Perception.** To some patients the visible scene appears "flat as a colored picture" (Critchley, 1953, p. 329). Depth perception depends upon engrams based on an integration of visual and proprioceptive stimuli from the muscle systems of the body. If the proprioceptive stimuli are totally cut off from the higher centers, it may be expected that for a time, as a result of previous conditioning, the three-dimensional quality of vision will persist; but, gradually, as the subject's daily tasks are no longer accompanied by proprioceptive input, new engrams will be formed based on visual stimuli alone, and these engrams will lack spatial depth. In Dr. Brinton's case quoted by Critchley (p. 329) a few weeks elapsed between the occurrence of a parieto-occipital lesion and the onset of loss of stereoscopic vision.

It would be predicted of such a case that a loss of stereoscopic quality would also affect imagined images; but this would develop more slowly than in the case of perception, and, in so far as the subject would not have experiences relevant to certain engrams, would perhaps never be complete. It is also to be expected that there would be impaired judgment of position of all limbs passively moved. At autopsy, extensive bilateral damage to proprioceptive projection paths would be expected.

(c) **Loss of Topographical Sense.** This means an inability to find one's way about in a familiar environment. For example, whenever a certain patient left the ward to go to the bathroom, she had to place her blue bedjacket across the bed in order to identify it; and leaving her usual hairdresser's she turned right instead of left to get home (Critchley, p. 339). In a case like this, there is clearly an inability to form or arouse topographical engrams. Since vision is intact, it must be presumed that there is a defect in proprioceptive input to the higher centers from the muscle systems involved in locomotion, i.e., especially the legs. Walking itself would be normal, but it is predicted that on being tested such patients would be unable to say how far they had walked, and that they would show impaired ability to recognize the position of legs passively moved by the physician. Position sense of arms might be relatively unaffected. Lesions involving the cortical projection pathways of proprioceptive impulses from the inferior extremities would be expected at autopsy.

REFERENCES

Alexander, S., *Space, Time, and Deity,* Macmillan, London, 1920.

Critchley, M., *The Parietal Lobes,* Arnold, London, 1953.

Culler, E. A., "Observations on direct cortical stimulation in the dog," *Psychol. Bull.,* 1938, 35:687.

Eysenck, H. J., "The effects of psychotherapy: An evaluation," *J. Consult. Psychol.,* 1952, 16:319.

Frohman, D., Luby, E. D., Tourney, G., Beckett, P. G. S., and Gottlieb, J. S., "Steps toward the isolation of a serum factor in schizophrenia," *Am. J. Psychiat.,* 1960, 117:401.

Glover, E., "Critical notice," *Brit. J. Med. Psychol.,* 1959, 32:68.

Hamilton, D. M., Varney, H. I., and Wall, J. H., "Hospital treatment of patients with psychoneurotic disorders," *Am. J. Psychiat.,* 1942, 99:243.

Hull, C. L., *Principles of Behavior,* Appleton-Century, New York, 1943.

Hurwitz, H. B. M., "Conditioned responses in rats reinforced by light," *Brit. J. Animal Behav.,* 1956, 4:31.

Jennings, H. S. *The Behavior of Lower Organisms,* Columbia University Press, New York, 1906.

Kallmann, F. J., *Heredity in Health and Mental Disorders,* Norton, New York, 1953.

Knight, R. P., "Evaluation of the results of psychoanalytic therapy," *Am. J. Psychiat.,* 1941, 98:434.

Lashley, K. S., "In search of the engram," in *Biological Mechanisms in Animal Behavior,* J. F. Danielli and R. Brown, eds., Cambridge University Press, London, 1950.

Lazarus, A. A., "The elimination of children's phobias by deconditioning," *Med. Proc.,* 1959, 5:261.

Pavlov, I. P., *Conditioned Reflexes,* Oxford University Press, London, 1927.

Taylor, J. G., *The Behavioral Basis of Perception,* Yale University Press, New Haven (in press).

Vail, D., "The adjustment to aphakia," *Am. J. Ophthalmol.,* 1952, 35:118.

Wolpe, J., "Need-reduction, drive-reduction and reinforcement: A neurophysiological view," *Psychol. Rev.,* 1950, 57:19.

———, "Experimental neuroses as learned behavior," *Brit. J. Psychol.,* 1952, 43:243.

———, *Psychotherapy by Reciprocal Inhibition,* Stanford University Press, Stanford, Calif., 1958.

PART TWO

Mind as Participation

Definitions: Humane, Psychiatric, & Cybernetic

HAROLD KELMAN

Toward a Definition of Mind

Mind is a creating, emerging, evolving process. In formulating and communicating the premises inherent in such a notion, the experiences and concepts, implicit and evident, will come alive. Concurrently, an image of man, of the cosmos, of therapy, the therapist, and of living and dying as human processes, will become manifest.

We have no word for mind alive. " 'Life' may be regarded as the spreading of a pattern as it pulsates!"[44] Being active, phasic, rhythmic, and changing, having form and direction are some of the attributes of living processes. Our language structure, subject/predicate in form, dichotomizes and hypostatizes processes. It is noun-oriented and makes propositions about things, among them the static objects into which processes have been made. Other languages, like Burmese, Japanese, and Eskimo, verb-oriented, make propositions about events, or more accurately eventing, which minding is. They are better suited to describing the inner and outer structure or form of processes.

Contacting, being contiguous and continuous with immediacies and manifesting more of the emotive and aesthetic components in knowing as minding and being, is more effectively possible with ideographic languages such as Chinese. Indo-European languages, phonetic, alphabetic, and syllabic, which focus on the theoretic component of knowing, are better suited to writing prose than poetry and to formulating scientific laws. They not only are poorer for prompting spiritual responses and for describing the inner and outer structure and form of processes but increase our dissociation from our organicity.

Mind functioning as verb, in its present participle form, namely as minding, would formulate and communicate the process to which I shall devote myself. Minding, as being and manifestation of it, points at ontological aspects of my orientation and beyond to an attempted creative synthesis of what East and West may have to offer in our current total context.

I shall continue with the verb form, minding, sufficiently to embed the fact that we are dealing with the processes, creating, emerging, evolving, minding, and to contrast processes with and call attention to their having been hypostatized into creative, emergent, evolving mind. Only briefly shall I use the term minding experienced in the tension created and the, shortly thereafter, total rejection of what I am presenting by audiences and readers, unfamiliar with being in and experiencing these living categories. I have faith and hope that at later dates I could assume more general familiarity with process language and less feelings of being naked and exposed when bereft of conceptualized, static, dualistic, illusory but nonetheless constricting formulations.

Starting with the phenomenologically neutral statement "There is minding" or "Minding is obtaining," the focus of our attending could be on the center or periphery, surface or depth, and on all points in between. Attending, neutrally, phenomenologically and nonteleologically describes another process and aspect of minding. Using the concept levels, without dualistically attributing a positive value to the top and a negative one to the bottom, we would, so to speak, be slicing the what and the that being investigated at many levels, while attending and describing the forms of these processes and the direction of their moving. The focus of our attending might shift, moment to moment, from the individual, to the societal, to the cosmic aspects of minding, of which all are sources and manifestations.

At all levels of minding this phenomenologically neutral question prompts responses as more detailed describing. "What are the inner and outer forms of processes in minding?" Otherwise formulated, "What are the what and how of minding?" or more accurately "What are the whating and howing of minding?" Posed in this form we avoid the falsely created, hypostatized, oppositional dichotomy of form versus function and experience that forming is functioning and functioning is forming. Whating is a sequence of whats in duration and space. A sequence of whats is the functioning of that what, in this and all instances, is minding.

We could then ask, "In what ways and how can the processes in minding be formulated?" For this we have the new germinative idea, form. "The 'form,' in the sense of the underlying structural pattern, is more important than its material components, which lack individuality.

. . . 'Structure' is a name for the effective pattern of relationships" (Whyte,[44] pp. 27, 28). Matter, mass, and force are adequate concepts to a point. In subatomic and astrophysics, the notions of energy, behavior, and direction are essential for explaining nature as moving fields. Later these ways of looking at reality may be found to be special cases of wider and deeper conceptions. We move rapidly into a world where the form is the phenomenal appearance of a something that does not exist and the effective relationships between those forms has reality only in someone's imagination. For Jeans, "The universe is a thought in the mind of a Supreme Mathematician" and Eddington concluded, "In the end, mind faces itself."

Schroedinger, Nobel physicist, speaks in this oriental metaphysical or Alice in Wonderland language in answering the question "What is life?" with: "It feeds on 'negative entropy.' . . . Living matter evades the decay to equilibrium."[35] He then adds:

When you come to the ultimate particles constituting matter, there seems to be no point in thinking of them again as consisting of some material. They are, as it were, *pure shape,* nothing but shape; what turns up again and again in successive observations is this shape, not an individual speck of material. . . . We do not claim that this "something" is the observed or observable facts: and still less do we claim we thus describe what nature (matter, radiation, etc.) really *is.* In fact we use this picture (the so-called wave picture) in full knowledge that it is *neither.*[36]

On the basis of these wave pictures he calculated his probability curves, aware of Heisenberg's uncertainty principle. Nineteenth century scientific optimism required that its so-called laws fulfill the criteria of certainty and exactness. More humbly we now accept approximations and probabilities. And if the universe is governed by laws, "They execute themselves" (Emerson). From 1905 (Einstein's special theory of relativity) on, the faith cum credo, that it was only a matter of time before science would know everything about everything, waned. What is time? What is everything? are questions we leave for later. But what is knowing? "*Eastern cognition is interested in consciousness itself. Western cognition is interested in the objects of consciousness. . . . Being equals knowing* and *no knowing without the corresponding adequate being.*"[9] To formulate and communicate being, knowing and minding more on form is necessary.

Form is forming, is structuring. Form is disforming, reforming, forming. Form neutrally describes. By neutrally is meant minimally value laden as to aesthetics and morality and maximally as to fact. Arrangements of form we neutrally name order. The process and sequence are ordering, disordering, reordering. Ordering has direction, toward greater and lesser symmetry. According to the second law of thermodynamics, in ideal isolated systems, the movement is toward maximum entropy, maximum disorder, maximum sameness, perfect symmetry.

"It is essential for an objective theory of probability and its application to such concepts as entropy (or molecular disorder) to give an objective characterization of *disorder or randomness, as a type of order*."[32] Popper insists we "develop a theory which allows us actually to construct ideal types of disorder (and of course also ideal types of order, and of all degrees in between these extremes)."[32] Popper's ordered disorder sounds paradoxical as does his ideal disorder because of implicit moral and aesthetic valuations. Unwittingly order and symmetry have positive values attached to them and negative ones to disorder and asymmetry. Randomness and sameness do not have as negative attributions. Actually, perfect symmetry, the Platonic ideal, which is a perfectly ordered order, a permanent monotony of sameness, is spiritual death, is maximum entropy, is cosmic "heat death."

Order is a free creation of the human mind, a form of human intuition. We expand its possibilities in minding by clearly delineating to what and at what points we attach factual, moral, and aesthetic valuations in the ordering process.

"The idea of the Order of Nature—and the grasp of its importance, and the observation of its exemplification in a variety of occasions are by no means the necessary consequence of the truth of the idea in question."[42] Whitehead warns those whose vision becomes blurred by repetitive natural recurrences that "Nothing ever really recurs in exact detail."[42] "The metaphysical faith in . . . *the immutability of natural processes*" which the "scientific method presupposes . . . and without which practical action is hardly conceivable" (p. 252)[32] Popper says is no more logically arguable than is the conceiving of a theory subject to logical analysis. There are no inductive methods in empirical science nor is there an inductive logic. There is no justification "in inferring universal statements from singular ones" (p. 27).[32] Theories are "neither *true* nor *false* but instead more or less *probable*" and capable of a "*degree of corroboration*." Popper purposely selected the "neutral term corroboration. By 'neutral' I mean a term not prejudging the issue" (p. 251).[32]

Einstein's affirmation is beautiful in its simplicity:

The supreme task of the physicist is to arrive at those universal elementary laws from which the cosmos can be built up by pure deduction. There is no logical path to these laws; only intuition, resting on sympathetic understanding of experience, can reach them. . . . [The scientist's] religious feeling takes the form of a rapturous amazement at the harmony of natural law, which reveals an intelligence of such superiority that, compared with it, all the systematic thinking and acting of human beings is an utterly insignificant reflection. This feeling is the guiding principle of his life and work, in so far as he succeeds in keeping himself from the shackles of selfish desire. It is beyond question closely akin to that which has possessed the religious geniuses of all ages.[7]

Spiritual feelings, religious values, faith, "the state of being ultimately concerned" have often been confused with belief:

Almost all the struggles between faith and knowledge are rooted in the wrong understanding of faith as a type of knowledge which has a low degree of evidence but is supported by religious authority. One of the worst errors of theology and popular religion is to make statements which intentionally or unintentionally contradict the structure of reality. Such an attitude is an expression not of faith but of the confusion of faith with belief.[40]

Tillich uses the word "spirit" to mean that which characterizes "Man as man, and expresses itself as moral self-realization, as cultural production, and as religious self-transcendence. It is a power which gives liberation from the binding quality of law, culture and religion."[41] He urges the re-establishment of this doctrine of man as spirit, as the unity of all the dimensions in man.

Northrop asserts that there are many scientific methods requisite to different phases of inquiry of all human concerns and disciplines from the exact sciences to theology. He formulates the basis for "an adequate religion for the contemporary world" and gives us a scientific methodology for distinguishing "trustworthy unseen factors . . . from erroneously inferred ones."[31] In Bridgman's "The Way Things Are" (1959), introspectional language finds a place. The role of the individual knower becomes increasingly important as we pass from abstractions of logic to the value judgments of the social sciences. The concrete individual is Bridgman's point of departure as it is for the Existentialists and the linguistic analysts.

The thinking of many disciplines regarding "The Search for Meaning"[34] converges on the problem of existence at the individual level. There is a deep concern for values and the consequent release of creative energy. Where it extends beyond an individual search for wholeness it becomes a religious quest for an "all-inclusive *Weltanschauung* and a fullness of being. In this sense all men are religious by definition, that is, by virtue of being men."[34] Royce suggests "that meaning is primarily a matter of how an individual organizes his 'self' and his environment, and that perception is a focal point in this organizing process. . . . The more structure is provided outside and inside the organism, the more meaning there is for the organism."[34] His statements hold for human

developmental phases and for Western man. He errs by generalizing to all
people as do workers carrying on isolation experiments. Ancient religious
practices in Tantric Hinduism were almost identical with the latter
aiming at greater religious depths through letting go of attachment to
the values and meaning put on external and internal forms and to many
of the forms themselves.[22] An inscription from an ancient Hindu scrip-
ture in a temple in New Delhi informed me that one of the greatest
sins was attachment to form itself.

Faith in the notion of order, become belief, distorts it into dogma.
The individual has perpetrated an indignity on his human authenticity.
Lacking faith and being faithless to oneself are one of the greatest sins
according to certain Eastern religions. Now, instead of spontaneously
wanting order, that person is compulsively driven to have it. The more
insecure he is the more must this order be one of permanence. What he
is seeking as an ultimate is a perfectly ideal order of ordered sameness,
maximum entropy, death.

To orders of form, the notion plan or pattern may be applied. Both
assume that the universe fits into some kind of over-all arrangement.
Plan suggests something contrived in the mind of a super-being. Aristotle postulated an unmoved-mover, God, and the plan, a universal
scheme born in his mind. The split between the Greek ideal of what
ought to be and what is was codified into Roman law. Centrifugal
impetus was added to Western man's dissociation from his organicity,
started by Plato's exaltation of reason and disparagement of the poetic.
Order as plan has the attribute of permanence and later that of revelation was attached to it. Man the subject, God the object. The moral
dualisms, of good/bad, right/wrong, human/divine, became immutables.

With their new tool, Reason, the Greeks searched for the final
irreducible substance. Democritus suggested atoms. Anthropomorphized
divine forces, Love and Strife, were given the powers of attraction and
repulsion by Empedocles. Under their influences the elements were
combined. Atomistic and dualistic thinking had come into being as did
the notions of causality and teleology. Science took dualism as a given
fact as did Freud. Subject versus object, nature versus nurture, individual
versus environment, became an embedded part of our thinking. Our
moral and aesthetic estimates are two-valued, black/white, good/bad,
beautiful/ugly, instead of being multivalued as are those of the Chinese, who experience life in shades of gray. Moderation, not our extremes
and absolutes, is their guide.

Order as pattern can be one of permanence or impermanence.
Heraclitus said, "All is flux and change." The Greeks felt threatened and
had to bury that Delphic riddler with his "harmony of oppositions." It
was two thousand years before such unitary process thinking again be-

came manifest in Goethe. Orders of permanence, as plan and pattern, have the attributes of being static, final, absolute, perfect, and closed, are automatically in opposition to orders as patterns of impermanence characterized by being dynamic, transient, relative, imperfect, open, plastic, and flexible.

Form as sequences of changing patternings is process. Process has the attributes of being rhythmic and phasic, and having direction. The pattern of process may be neutrally described as integrating. The sequence is integrating, disintegrating, reintegrating. Unwittingly moral and aesthetic valuations of good and beautiful are attached to integrating and reintegrating and bad and ugly to disintegrating. For defining process the logical genus relation was adequate to a point. Later it was realized that for an adequate description of processes another concept was essential, namely that of system. This became more evident in the biological and social sciences and ultimately in physics. Unitary process thinking made possible the describing of open systems in flux.[15]

Even though the second law of thermodynamics always wins, we physically die, while living we can spiritually deepen. Lindsay suggests the maximum consumption of negative entropy as, a "thermodynamic imperative, a normative principle which may serve as the basis for a persuasive ethic." It should have special appeal for the quantitatively minded in our society, which becomes more dominated by numbers. "The qualitatively minded may find satisfaction in looking on the principle as another way of expressing that 'reverence for life' which made Schweitzer's ethical view so satisfying. For all life is entropy-consuming."[28] Another expression of Lindsay's viewpoint is Simpson's assertion that a non-moral evolutionary process produced "a moral animal" who "is responsible to himself and for himself. 'Himself' here means the whole human species."[37] Hoyle confronts the explosion cosmology of Gamow and Lamaitre with his steady-state theory of the universe and offers evidence for enclaves of continuous creation which each human being on this planet is and has the ability to increasingly manifest. Keosian disagrees with the hypothesis of a single original case of successful bio-poesis and offers his conjectures to support the notion of repetitive biogenesis.[13] These expressions of faith confront Biblical fundamentalism. They are manifestations of enclaves of continuous, creating, evolving, emerging, cosmic minding.

Teilhard de Chardin, paleontologist and Jesuit, in neglecting the creator aspect of God, omitting original sin and Christ's redeeming sacrifice, and side-stepping descent from Adam and Eve, confronts us with an emergent evolutionary cosmology in his *Phenomenon of Man*,[5] for which Julian Huxley wrote the introduction. "The religiously-minded can no longer turn their backs upon the natural world . . . nor can the materialistically-minded deny importance to spiritual experience and religious feeling." Father Teilhard submitted to the Church's prohibition of the book's public appearance. On publication (1959), four years after his death, Divinitas devoted a whole issue attacking his ideas but not applying "The mark of heresy . . . because of his good faith." In 1960, *Christian Hatha Yoga*[6] by Benedictine Father J. M. Déchanet appeared, complete with *nihil obstat* and imprimatur. Its aim is to make the body an obedient servant to help "practice fully even virtues as great as faith, hope and Christian charity" with built-in safeguards against turning toward "the Self, the It, the Wholly-One, the vague 'Ungraspable' of Hindu mystics" instead of toward "the God of Abraham, Isaac and Job, the living God, my Creator and Father."

Zen and Existentialism, Father Teilhard using "scientific knowledge merely as factual imagery in which to expound his vision" and writing "an epic poem that keeps closely to the facts," Catholic *Hatha Yoga* and Japanese moving from Shintoism and Buddhism, to find a new home in Judaism, make a partial picture of the ferment and direction of our current cosmic minding, pregnant with possibilities and on the verge of a new evolutionary leap for which the time is only just ripe.

Quantum physics represents a radical break with the past. The "quantum jump" is an evolutionary leap. A continuous pattern again becomes possible if we allow in Schroedinger's probability curves, Heisenberg's indeterminacy, and Bohr's complementarity; i.e., the mutually exclusive contiguous pictures of an electron as a particle and as a wave become contiguous. "By playing with both pictures . . . we finally get the right impression of the strange kind of reality behind our atomic experiments. . . . The probability function combines objective and subjective elements. It contains statements about possibilities or better tendencies ('potentia' in Aristotelian philosophy)."[11]

Heisenberg further states that we may fruitfully discuss ideal experiments that we cannot carry out. Also, the situation is helped by a mathematical formalism called matrix mechanics based on nonlinear equations. We have assumed linearity as a given in nature and symmetry as an ideal. Kovach brilliantly and humorouly informs us that "Life Can Be *So* Nonlinear,"[26] and P. Curie adds, *"C'est la dyssymétrie qui crée le phénomène."* Heisenberg agrees with the Copenhagen interpretation of quantum theory which "starts from a paradox" from which "we cannot escape."

From Zen, to Catholic Yoga through to the so-called exact sciences, as sources and manifestations of cosmic minding, we are seeing increasing congruence in language and aspiration, in faith and humility. The spiritual in science and the spiritual sciences find the gap between them lessening abruptly. More men of truth and wisdom are feeling at home in the purposes of *World Perspectives*. "To help quicken the 'unshaken heart of well-rounded truth' and interpret the significant elements of the World Age now taking shape out of the core of that undimmed continuity of the creative process which restores man to mankind while deepening and enhancing his communion with the universe" (Preface).[11]

Children, persons with brain defects, and beginners in searching for the nature of nature and their nature find order essential and preferably one of permanence. Order expresses a human need for a frame of reference, for meaning. A constantly present loving mother is an essential environment for a child; for a person with a brain defect, one of ordered permanence to protect him from catastrophic reactions; and an ordered world of permanence for the Greeks to explore their newly exalted tool, Reason. Concomitant will be the drivenness and the need to clutch onto the old, the tried, the so-called true, the known, the familiar, the permanent, the static, and to oppose the new, the untried which may be truer, the unknown, the unfamiliar, the impermanent, the dynamic. Human history and that of individuals reveals that with increasing knowledge and self-knowledge a moving from needing an order of permanence to wanting to chance more disorder and impermanence occurs. Then being spontaneous is more obtaining.

Neutrally described it is characterized by the appearance, disappearance, and reappearance of forms in sequences of arrangements of form as orders, as patterns, changing with great rapidity, emerging from and being absorbed back into the source from which they came and having the quality of evanescence. With the experience of being spontaneous are associated feelings of well-being. Derivative and expressive are feelings of being potent, being able, being confident, self-reliant, playful, moral, being wise.

With feelings of well-being go feelings of ampleness, of being pregnant, of abundance. As people become healthier their being reflects more an economy of abundance. The sicker people are the more their unnatural and constricted world is filled with being terrorized by an economy of scarcity. Nature is profligate in its abundance. This is evident in children with their naturalness and their spontaneity. Their charm is their spontaneity, their visibly manifesting constant plays of forms in and through all aspects of their being and in their playfulness with these forms. They reflect an essential of being, namely nonattachment to forms, to appearances, to foregrounds, to phenomena, to their contents. In adults who are truly children, we find spontaneity, authentic maturity, and genuine morality because of their nonattachment to forms and their contents.

This is evident to the artist for whom forms are his medium, his tool, his product. Klee, musician and mathematician, interested in forms of primal being in all of nature, in African and peasant art, attracted to the vitality and fresh perception in children's drawings, to the weird in Nordic and Oceanic productions, and to the drawings of psychopaths playfully bursts these truths in on us. He was a genius. He had rigorous training in the underlying laws of nature and art. Many times his depths were tempered during his tragic life. These deceptively naive and apparently simple doodles are no product of a novice. Klee's childlike, not childish, forms embody much wisdom. They are filled with paradoxes and the absurd. They are and express his philosophy. "Satire is not an excess of ill-humor but humor resulting from a vision of something higher. Ridiculous man, divine God."[24]

Klee was not interested in static forms. His genius was reflected in the ways he broke through them and made them come alive. In his wittily condensed diagrammatic drawings he illustrated the kinetic properties of lines and the principles of an art based on "forming" rather than on static forms. Klee and his work are outstanding exemplars of my main thesis that forming is functioning and functioning is forming, that the more there is being spontaneous which is being childlike, moral, wise, the more there is approximating toward human ultimates possible in forming, in creating, emerging, evolving cosmic minding. Faith in such communion of all dimensions of human possibility is being spiritual. Here, the notion in certain Oriental religions, that having little faith in oneself and being faithless to oneself is sinning against oneself, touches us with immediacy.

Through what processes does genuine spontaneity and authentic morality come about? Through sequences of forming, disforming, re-forming of orders of forms, of phenomena in patterns being dismantled of their contents. Ultimately the forms themselves disappear. Then "there can be awareness without anything of which awareness is aware—hence a state of pure lucidity" (p. 187),[9] also named pure consciousness and absolute subjectivity. Such Eastern notions are not so alien to us. In discussing the experience and process, "communing" in life and in therapy, in nature and with people, I presented a variety of familiar experiences, in a continuum to "pure lucidity." They included the "aha" phenomenon, clinical insight, the creative process, unio mystica, communing, satori and nirvana experiences.[18] *The Zen Doctrine of No-Mind*[38] is an Eastern way toward the attainment of pure lucidity. Psychoanalysis can be a Western one.[23]

Another form of the process by which spontaneity happens is called the search for truth. How East and West approach and participate in this questing points up some essential differences. There is awareness of a problem or problematic situation (Dewey). A question is the West's immediate response, its first step in dealing with the problem. The questions are asked and answered in terms of reason in the context of a subject/object dichotomy. Knowledge is sought *about* an aspect of reality that is made into an object, including consciousness itself. "The way a question is asked limits and disposes the ways in which any answer to it—right or wrong—may be given. . . . A question is really an ambiguous proposition; the answer is its determination. . . . In our questions lie our *principles of analysis,* and our answers may express whatever those principles are able to yield."[27] Implicit in the forms of our questions are assumptions which should be made explicit. "Each generation criticizes the unconscious assumptions made by its parents. It may assent to them, but it brings them out in the open" (Whitehead).

Only from other ground do we become aware that our questions assumed a world of permanence or impermanence, a universe considered as a plan conceived and carried out by a super-being or as a pattern of flux and change. Only after we have evolved system thinking to better understand and formulate unitary processes do we fully realize the limits of the logical genus relation. From the ground of the subject-other relation of the East we see how the West sought knowledge through asking questions, asked and answered in conceptual frameworks.

It took the tough-minded Greeks with their love of discussion to move from the utilitarian question "What is the use of it?" asked by the Egyptians, to listen to Thales of Miletus (*c.* 630 B.C.), "What is the stuff of nature and how is it ordered?" But with revelation proved by Thomistic reason, questioning and questing in such directions became dangerous. It meant doubting a world of permanence created by God's will. The Enlightenment with its emphasis on the individual and reason produced Descartes. "*Cogito ergo sum.*" He not only bifurcated nature (Whitehead), he stood it on its head. Western man's dissociation was reaching its apogee, a far cry from the Lord's "I am that I am" and even further from the East's "*Tat tvam asi*"—that art thou. Existentialism's response is to help Western man back to "I am, therefore I think."

Wider and deeper experiencing cosmic minding confronts us with "aming is ising, is minding, is thinking"; Buber's I-Thou and I-It are phenomenal manifestations of ising. They still lack the immediacy of Job's confrontation of the Lord with "I will maintain my ways before him." This Old Testament Jew is a man of flesh and bone in vital immediate contact with someone, something greater and at the same time maintaining his human dignity. This felt immediacy of Job and his God is a close approximation to the East's subject-other relation with the gap between the human and the divine, the one and the all, still too evident. It is short of the East's juxtaposition and identity of what is named the finite and infinite and is one: *Atman = Brahman,* but *Deus Factus Sum* (I have become God) does not equal Atman = Brahman.

Individuals and groups who cannot tolerate questions and questioning by themselves or others, of nature and of human nature, are people compulsively driven to have a nonexistent safety. They cannot admit that there is no final, absolute, perfect answer, that life is filled with uncertainties, doubts, and imperfections, that the world and man are better understood in terms of open-system thinking than by the closed-system variety characteristic of nineteenth century science.[21] Questioning means being questioned, doubted, criticized; feelings they cannot bear.

Individual and group insecurities, in the context of and supported by the Western mind-structure, drive people to ask the why?[15] It puts the problem out there and makes it into an object. It fosters the illusion that it is a thing that can be picked up and looked at from all sides. The evidence is we do not grasp problems. Life and problems seize us. The assumption in the why? is that a right answer is available, arrived at by reason and formulatable in concepts. The why? implies cause, an efficient, material, and final cause. God willed it that way. The tubercle bacillus is *the* cause of tuberculosis. Everything must be seen in simple cause-effect relations. Anxiety demands the oversimplification of the intricate and complex and begs for false simple answers available from demagogues.

The layman's or common-sense view of causality is of a relation between objects and of situations and processes made into objects. The water filled the empty glass. The war made him neurotic. Scientifically the situation is seen as a relation between "different states of the same object or the same system of objects at different times." Given a system of objects at two different times we must distinguish different kinds of successions. Mere temporal and/or spatial succession, with no necessary or even probable causal connection or predictable outcome, is a neutral phenomenological description of inspective and/or introspective data. This is the point of departure of contemplation and meditation and of the various forms of phenomenology. It is Buddha's teaching; timeless and universal; *ehipassika*, the come-and-see doctrine; *paccattam veditabbo*, to be realized by each man for himself; *opananika*, the goal being the discovery of truth; and truth is "that which is as it is." We possess knowledge when "we see things as they really are."[29] This is the ultimate toward which we move in freer and freer associating.[14] It approaches a-causality, nonteleology, and nondualism. Sequence is not necessarily consequence.

Another relation between sequences is a necessary one but to predict what will be we must have known it from previous experience. This form of causality is teleological. The "changes of the system with time are determined by the final state or goal of the system . . . Aristotelian physics affirmed that all causal relations are teleological" (Introduction).[11]

Mechanical causation assumes that if the initial state of an isolated system is known, its future state can be deduced. When the concept of probability is included in the defined state of the system, a non-deterministic type of mechanical causality is meant and where "no independent variables referring to probabilities appear in the state function" the stronger or deterministic type of causality is defined. "In Newtonian, Einsteinian and quantum mechanics, mechanical rather than teleological causality holds. Causality in Newton's and Einstein's physics . . . is both mechanical and deterministic, in quantum physics . . . mechanical but not deterministic" (Introduction).[11]

Clearly to be distinguished are historical genetic from ontologic genetic, the former emphasized by the West as in the conception of evolution and in Freud's methodology, the latter being the main focus of the East and increasingly so for modern psychoanalytic theories and of course Existentialism. The terms genetic, causal, deterministic, and purposive often are used without explicitly stating that they are meant in the neutral descriptive sense of based upon the outcome of and following upon but not the consequence of. In so-called psychosomatic medicine this confusion is compounded. Physiological processes are psychologized, psychological processes are neurologized, and all manner of psychophysical parallelism creeps in. Of course, thinking would not be possible without a brain, and of course mind has an organic substrate. To speak of organicists and functionalists is naive. The issues are methodological and epistemological.

Genuine desire to know may seem at first to prompt the why? Soon other patterns, more neurotically tinged, become evident; a compulsive need to know, to maintain contact, holds the other's attention, keeps the problem out there, the focus away from the questioner, to argue and to attack. Although the form may be why, it is soon evident that the who? is being asked. It started with why, to judge, justify, blame, and excuse who did what to whom and for what. The what, an instance, is seen as a static thing and final. The who? serves also to keep the problem out there and the who commonly criticized for why they are that way are parents, authorities, society, the analyst, God, but it can also be a what, like fate or the past experienced as a who.

Associated with the why and who?s are the where and when?s which are asked because of the need for answers which come in the there and then form. The need is to find the cause which means to put blame on others out there and then to pin it down. Freud did not originate his genetic approach. His genius was in seeing it in our Western mind structure and in formulating it. While he emphasized the there-then of the past and the cause as a traumatic experience, theorists who emphasize aims and goals are just as teleological, only future-oriented. Both reflect an aspect of Western time notions that can be compared to an arrow. It moves through space and time and has direction, starting back there-then, whizzing through here-now, to a future there-then.

The East's focus is on here-now. Waves, created by a pebble dropped into a quiet pool, moving to the shore to return and be resorbed, point at the East's experience of time. In this context we can understand that being and becoming are aspects of process, here-now. Becoming is being to which we have attached a future time form. Close inspection reveals that becoming is past, present, and future, as being is past ontologic possibility seen as future ontologic actuality viewed in the here-now context.

The notion of forms emerging to be resorbed back into that from which they came has its reflection in the Indian cosmic conception of time with its boundless and numberless worlds having their eternal and unchangeable rhythm, taking 311 trillion years to complete their cycle, to be absorbed into the Absolute, and then to begin over again. These mystic metaphors begin to acquire some scientific status as astrophysicists remind us that in ten to twelve billion years the sun will cool, contract, and die and that a similar fate awaits the whole universe, all life.

The hypothesis of Gold, Cornell astronomer, sounds like something out of Indian cosmology. He believes that life did not originate on earth where it has existed only one billion years, but perhaps it was brought here in spaceships from other planets, where it took about that time to evolve intelligent enough forms to travel deeper into space. This fits with Hoyle's steady-state theory, which holds that, as old galaxies move apart, more galaxies form between out of freshly created matter. Already the first two laws of thermodynamics have been contradicted, and now Gold contradicts the West's notion of time, history, and evolution and affirms that of the East. "When, then, did life begin? The steady-state theory holds that space has no boundaries, and time has no beginning or end. If life spreads from old to new galaxies with the flow of time, its history may extend backward forever. It may live forever, too, renewing itself at intervals of many billions of years by planting seeds on planets in galaxies not yet created."[8]

Sciama, influenced by Hoyle, Bondi, and Gold, suggests a hypothesis, in *The Unity of the Universe* (Doubleday, 1959), which is almost a scientific documentation of Hindu cosmology. Bogoliubov and Shirkov bring us

     . . . to the very threshold of a real four-dimensional realm of matter . . . without rest-mass. . . . The actual organization of the entire wave-structured, quite supersensory, yet objectively real world begins to be a possibility, and

a non-local field a necessity and a reality. . . . Presently we may be allowed—
or even compelled—to accept the existence of a matrix without any obstacles
to universal intercommunication.[1]

Scientifically we have approached form without content, identity without substantially, psi-phenomena validated, levitation adumbrated, continuity affirmed, and contiguity an epi-phenomenon. Channakesavan
elaborates much of the above with frequent references to Western psy-
chologies and philosophies in *The Concept of Mind in Indian Philosophy*
(Asia Publishing House, 1960).

The what and how are an expression of system thinking with answers
formulated in process language.[15] The focus is on orders as patterns in
flux. They act as correctives to the why, who, where, when, and effect
some movement from there-then to here-now. Though formulated as explanation, this direction of thinking brings the West closer to understanding and experiencing whatness and howness, whating and howing
in the moment and as the moment. What is is. Ising is being. "As circumstances mature things happen" no longer sounds like nonsense but
wisdom to become one with. The truth is "that which is as it is."

The differences between judging and evaluating, between a distorted
and a whole sense of responsibility, between moral dividedness and
wholeness become clearer. Judging implies static oppositional dualisms
in the moral, aesthetic, factual spheres as well as in space and time;
negative criticism by someone who presumes, consciously or unconsciously to have the absolute, final, perfect vision of truth in all spheres,
the right and responsibility to excuse, accuse, and punish all those, including himself, who fall short. Benevolence only thinly veils this
tyranny. Judging is destructive by intent and consequence.

Evaluating approaches in attitude and method the phenomenological
operation of the *epoche*. It obtains on the background of moral compassion and moral toughness, firmness that requires confrontation, the
acceptance of pain as pain and pleasure as pleasure, sympathy, tolerance,
and understanding which are not condoning. It maintains an aliveness of
rational discontent, an openness to the awareness of continuing imperfection which functions as a stimulus to further searching.

Responsibility in its distorted usage is synonymous with fault, blame,
criticism. When understood in its root sense, to respond, the fullness of
its meaning emerges. It is in the nature of all nature to respond to
stimuli. Responses are prompted, not caused, by stimuli. The forms of
the responding are the flux of the phenomena, emerging into signs and
symbols as questioning and answering. Heinemann, who introduced the
term *Existenphilosophie* (1929), offers a philosophy of response.[10] *Res-
pondeo ergo sum* is his key symbol rather than *existo ergo sum*. Existence

as appeal, as subjectively regulative idea remains but "as a constitutive principle is dead." "Challenge and response" is one of Toynbee's key-ideas. Being more and more responsive is being more and more respon-sible. Being responsive, as evaluating and containing the process and results in evaluating, is remaining open to more possibilties. The more this process obtains, the more freer associating there is. The more loosen-ing of attachments happens the more wholeness on all levels comes into being. This ultimate becomes more possible on the analytic couch,[16] and as it happens the subject-other relation of the East is approached.

In the West the search for truth is centrifugally oriented, sought for in objective reality, while locomoting in the erect position, in fact or in attitude, with the objective of mastery and acquisition while being dominated by dualisms in will, thought, feeling, and action, while disregarding bodily processes. The aim of the East is immediate contact with the Real rather than the acquiring of conceptual knowledge. Ques-tions and answers and the intellect as ways to the truth are used to expose their inadequacy. *The Zen Doctrine of No-Mind*[38] expresses an ultimate of this attitude. In his search for truth the Easterner sits cross-legged, on the floor actively at rest in the most solidly earth-rooted position a human being can be. His attitude is contemplative, his attention is directed inward, being guided to his depths over the bridge of the rhythmicity of his breathing. His orientation is centripetal and his aim, the letting go of attachments to acquisitions and ultimately to form itself. Then he is the truth, the Real, a sage whose spontaneity is childlike, morality genuine, and wisdom authentic. Then pure lucidity, absolute subjectivity, are more frequent happenings.[23]

We have become acutely aware of the limitations of our Greek heri-tage *"to save the phenomena through"* (p. 173).[9] A succession of epis-temologies have attempted to guide us to real reality via these bits of so-called objective reality. For Schroedinger they are nothing but "pure shape." Heisenberg says that a neutron is a "probability function. But then one sees that not even the quality of being (if that may be called a 'quality') belongs to what is described. It is a possibility for being or a tendency for being" (p. 70).[11] The objectifying mind of the West is finally confronted with itself as its object, with the imagery it called real reality created by it, with its being and its inherent possibilities and tendencies, all as cosmic minding and manifestation of it.

This is the paradox, the point of creative tension and creative possi-bility. In *Freer Associating: Its Phenomenology and Inherent Paradoxes*,[14] I delineated the process and the content of these paradoxes, their form-ing, disforming, and reforming as the essential in freer and freer associating. The creating and absorbing of these forms back into from what they came is the process and the product in creating, emerging, evolving, cosmic minding. For a Westerner—not given to the lotus position—the ultimate possible through freer associating on the analytic couch[16] can be more moments of being wordless, mindless, selfless, being silent, being quiet, being still, and maybe being serene and peaceful. These are approximations to moments of pure lucidity. As they happen, attachments to the phenomena and their contents lessen.

The ultimate of nonattachment is pictured in the being of the sage. This ultimate "describes a more accessible aspect of the state of freedom because the continuing phenomena are present only as empty frames and do not affect pure consciousness. So there may be action without the real participation of the subject, such action consisting merely of its outward sign and result. This ingenious and felicitous effort brings the fulfillment of worldly duties into accord with the spiritual state without contaminating it" (p. 260).[9]

The road toward this childlike wisdom of the sage is the process of creating, containing, and absorbing of paradoxes, of subject/object dichotomies, of Western created oppositional dualisms, of phasic sequences of hanging onto and letting go of both arms of the conflict, of the struggling against the struggling and finally of letting go of the struggling itself in exhaustion, and despair with feelings of meaningless, emptiness, and nothingness.[23] Only by containing the energies invested as forms in these paradoxes, are they conserved. Those manifested in forms unavailable for product work are transformed into forms available for more creative living. Negative entropy has been diminished and positive entropy increased geometrically in a human enclave of continuous creation. The unwisdom in attempting to overcome, leap over, or transcend our problems is evident and impossible. We take our problems along with us and in attempting to deny this fact we waste energies that could be transformed to become available for productive work.

These phases of exhaustion, despair, and meaninglessness Camus described as a characteristic of our age, in which there is a gap between the formulas and institutions we automatically adhere to and the more or less covert assumptions by which we live. "In that gap, between the mask and reality, lies the fertile realm of our indifference—indifference to life, indifference to death (ours and that of others), indifference to suffering."[3] Indifference, out of the context, can be misunderstood and reacted to with abhorrence, as being amoral, as the Eastern notion of nonattachment is usually seen as inhuman passive resignation. Christians often forget that "Man's extremity is God's opportunity." This indifference, despair, and emptiness are the fertile realm, the essential prerequisite to letting go, falling, and ultimately leaping over the precipice into the unknown, into formlessness, which is spontaneity. The ensuing

increment is courage, which is choicefully entering foreknown painful
situations, and ultimately being open to pain as pain and pleasure as
pleasure, neither to be exalted nor degraded.

East and West descended from the magic world. The East emphasized the subject, maintained its close relation to all otherness through
the subject-other relation, and experienced all otherness as continuous,
contiguous, and juxtaposed. Wisdom came through immediate contact
with the Real. The way open to it, to absolute subjectivity, to pure
consciousness was open, immediate, available, and desirable.

The West moved away from the subject and kept increasing its
distance from it. All environment was made into an object, including
consciousness itself. A subject/object dichotomy became an oppositional dualism on a conceptualized plane. Unity in variety became the
guiding mind principle, and unification was brought about through
concepts from on top. Knowledge was what could be obtained through
concepts. The process by which Western man became increasingly dissociated from his organicity becomes evident.

Western ethic, based on Biblical cosmology, made the acquisition of
knowledge a sin, while in the East wisdom is a virtue. Eve was made
from Adam's rib and for thousands of years has fought for equality.
Man and woman, Yin and Yang, are in the East, two aspects of one,
complementary, not opposing. For knowledge carried to the ultimate,
as science and the atom bomb, the West now has a horror, as the East
rushes headlong toward technology. While the East is now revolting
against the deterioration of its wisdom into false cults and empty rituals,
the West is just awakening to the East's ancient understanding of the
Real. I believe we are entering a phase in human history in which there
will be a unification of "the contributions of East and West in ways
heretofore not existent or envisaged."[23]

Whorf's "linguistic relativity principle" suggests that "users of markedly different grammars are pointed by their grammars toward different
types of observations and different evaluations of externally similar
acts of observation, and hence are not equivalent as observers but must
arrive at somewhat different views of the world."[43]

In Japanese, the term for objective is pronounced "kyokkan," while the term
for subjective is pronounced "shukan." The character (shu) has the basic meaning of host or master while the character (kyaku) has the basic meaning of
guest. The second character (kan) has the basic meaning of perception. Subjective phenomena are phenomena perceived in the objective mode, and objective phenomena are phenomena perceived in the objective mode. Experiencing
is polarized into a subjective mode, symbolized by the host, and an objective
mode symbolized by the guest. Thus, formerly, when Orientals sought to establish the concept of objective reality, they still approached it not as something

out there independent of our psychological processes, but rather as a mode of experiencing.*

The Japanese mind holds them in contact with all otherness as being experienced and not as having an objective reality out there independent of their psychological processes. We also start with that from which all forms emerge, with pure lucidity, but instantly and unconsciously set a process in motion. Experiencing is dichotomized into subjectifying and objectifying. Objective processes are subjectified and subjective processes are objectified, both concomitantly. The sequence from subjectifying proceeds through introjecting, internalizing, and ultimately being the objective processes, with the real objective world extinguished, as separate, i.e., as having contiguity. The objectifying proceeds through projecting, externalizing to the point of being emptied of subjective processes with the total-actual self being exhausted of contents and extinguished. With total world and total actual self-extinction, by a process of continuing alienation[12] from what is humanly and externally real, and by the total solution of magic, which means that by order of the supreme mind[12] everything is possible, such people ultimately experience themselves as the world, as the cosmos. Others and objects are not experienced as extensions or appendages of them but as them, identical and continuous with them, and having no identities of their own. Even the sanest among us has elements of such psychotic perceptions and conceptions of self and world.

No more did Freud originate *de novo* his concepts of introjection and projection than did Newton discover absolute time and absolute space. Their genius was in sensing the grammatical structure of Indo-European languages and concretizing certain aspects into concepts. One of my patients suddenly realized in a session that as far back as he could recall a picture of himself as a head on a stick would float in and out of awareness. He believed everything could be figured out. His superior intelligence supported him in this, and that being reasonable was the highest good. An extremely alienated woman began having analytic relationship dreams a few weeks after analysis began. Years of therapy with her and other such experiences helped me to a formulation of this baffling phenomenon. It became clear that she felt she was the cosmos, had appropriated me, everything, and everyone connected with me and had treated me as herself. Only then did many of the bewildering things she said, did, and dreamt begin to fit into place.

These formulations and some understanding of Eastern languages

* Personal communication from Professor Moses Burg, Toyo University, Tokyo, May 25, 1959.

and philosophy helped me understand certain intense responses to the East. People who seek self-extinction, like an opiate, find most seductive the notion of submerging oneself in the All. Egocentric individualists find such an idea abhorrent. Those materialistically and action-oriented see nonattachment to things of this world as a piece of insanity and contemplation in the lotus position as slothful passive resignation. Thinking, become belief, become dogma, that one is the cosmos, whether aware of it or not, makes one a vastly different person from the sage, in contact with the All, and not attached, being one with the All and a profoundly spontaneous identity.

What is the that from which all forms emerge and back into which they are absorbed? Northrop calls it pure fact. For years he has been emphasizing the need for a synthesis of what East and West have to contribute to each other. By what he calls epistemic correlations he shows how the aesthetic component in knowing characteristic of East can be joined with the theoretic component emphasized by the West. Pure fact is "that portion of our knowledge which remains when everything depending on inference from the immediately apprehended is rejected. . . . Strictly speaking . . . we can say nothing about pure fact. . . . Words point it out; by themselves they do not convey it. . . . Pure fact must be immediately experienced to be known. . . . Its elementary constituents cannot be conveyed by symbols to anyone who has not experienced them. . . . This is to affirm that pure fact is ineffable in character. The ineffable is that which cannot be said, but only be shown, and even then only to one who immediately experiences it. . . . Since ineffability is the defining property of the mystical it follows that the purely factual, purely empirical, positivistic component in human knowledge is the mystical factor in knowledge. The pure empiricists are the mystics of the world, as the Orientals who have tended to restrict knowledge to the immediately experienced, clearly illustrate" (pp. 36, 39, 40).[31] Understandably, when Perry arrived in Japan (1853), they had no words for abstract or philosophy in the Western sense. They had to invent them.

Northrop attempted to diminish the subject/object dualism, the aesthetic/theoretic dichotomy by his epistemic correlations. But these are still concepts, mind thinking thoughts. Existentialism came into being as a response to Western man's increasing dissociation from his organicity and as an attempt to undercut the subject/object dualism. The difficulty of communicating what is underneath Gabriel Marcel recognized when he attempted to define being. This would be Existentialism's that from which all forms emerge. "Being is what withstands—or what would withstand—an exhaustive analysis bearing on the data of experience and aiming to reduce them step by step to elements increasingly devoid of intrinsic or significant value." He suggested "this method of approach" after admitting that "defining the word 'being' . . . is extremely difficult."[30] This sounds much like an attempt to dismantle the phenomena of their contents and of "their intrinsic value." It has the flavor of the negative form of Oriental metaphysics which is not Western speculative philosophy.

In Marcel's Catholicism, even in unio mystica, the split between the finite and the infinite, the mundane and the divine, remains. God is still an external object. Northrop recognized that the East, in restricting "reality to the immediately apprehended . . . identifies the Divine with the timeless undifferentiated aesthetic continuum," his pure fact (p. 100).[31] However, Northrop and Marcel, brought up in a thought world structured in conceptualized dualisms in which they must communicate, cannot function on the basis of the subject-other relation and the mind principle of juxtaposition and identity, both characteristic of the East. The same must obtain for any Westerner attempting to communicate the what from which all forms emerge. I have discussed this issue in terms of blocks to communicating communing[18, 20] caused by our language and grammar and by the Western mind structure.

Hsing in Chinese philosophy, *chit* in Hindu philosophy, and *tathata* in Zen are the names of what the East calls that. We must not mistake the apparent similarity of their definition with those for being and pure fact as indicating identity or even similarity while at most pointing in a similar direction. The definition of *hsing* will also point at many of the attributes of *chit* and *tathata*.

Hsing is the dominating force over our entire being; it is the principle of vitality, physical and spiritual. Not only the body but also the mind in its highest sense is active because of *hsing* being present in them. . . . *Hsing* is not a logical *a priori* but an actuality which can be experienced, and it is designated by Hui-neng as *tzu-hsing*, self-nature or self-being, throughout his *T'an-ching*. . . . *Hsing* means something without which no existence is possible, or thinkable as such. As its morphological construction suggests, it is 'a heart or mind which lives' within an individual.[39]

At the beginning and end is that from which all forms come, absolute, still but not static, responding, emanating, and resorbing. Like Japanese architecture it contains "the impulse to form . . . to pattern making . . . into a series of patterns and radiating rhythms that create a dynamic order of the whole . . . in which is found evidence of a larger order to which they feel inexorably linked."[4] In and through it Klee's art based on "forming" becomes manifest and Heisenberg's particle becomes an abstraction defined as a "probability function . . . a possibility for being or a tendency for being."

What kind of model can define the forming process from pure lucidity, formlessness, absolute positive entropy, through the emotive and the aesthetic to the theoretic and the highest order of abstraction? What kind of picture of patterning that can see and define the Immanent in the phenomena and the Transcendent in the continuum? The model must be bidirectional, oscillating, and taking into account the particular and the general, the individual and the cosmic. The cosmic dimension is essential not only because of the implication of our space age but because many of our notions about isolated systems and autonomous regulation are being questioned. "The unequivocal evidence . . . is that . . . organisms under so-called constant conditions . . . derive their . . . observed persistent rhythms" from the subtle and pervasive influencing natural geophysical cycles.[2]

The model of the forming process I am suggesting can give us a picture of cosmic minding, of the ways of becoming alienated from and returning toward *hsing*, of which these processes are aspects, manifested in individuals, groups, nations, East and West. Also, as aspects of and ways toward and away from *hsing*, in terms of this notion of forming, theories and therapies of human nature, teleological and nonteleological, dualistic and nondualistic, can and have been formulated. This would include the range of psychoanalytic positions from Freud's original formulations through the range of so-called deviationist positions and include formulations reflecting Existentialistic thought and Eastern philosophies. Such a model of forming would also define the limits currently possible with constructs of form, i.e., as theoretical structure and where further movement toward closer and wider contact with *hsing* would have to be via forms of intuiting and emoting, cognizant that at some point all forms must be left behind for moments of pure lucidity to obtain.

The forming process is metaphorically a spiral, constituted of an intimately connected sequence of levels or a continuum of transformations with movement possible from depth to surface and vice versa.[17] The helix is of crucial import in Indian cosmology. "Nature moves in a helical pattern in time, so that spiral forms get ingrained at many levels. . . . This is all part of a galactic rotation in which a Cosmic Field plays an important part in transmitting spin (angular momentum) to matter."[33] This is one facet of Reiser's concept of cosmic imagination which moves in similar directions to my ideas on cosmic minding.

X-ray crystallography reveals DNA as a double-stranded alpha helix.[25] It directs protein synthesis and heredity. What was intuited thousands of years ago regarding life and living is being confirmed by science or science confronts us with ancient truth. Furthermore, research reveals that a gene is not a discrete entity but a place in a complex structure.

The form itself is not significant but derives its importance from the place in a pattern, as manifestation and source of its own substrate.

The starting and ending point of the spiral is in *hsing*. It is before, beside, and includes the forms created by sense impressions and intellection. The moment the vaguest awareness of form is adumbrated, that form is already an abstraction from the formless. Abstraction here is used not in the sense of a theoretic postulation but as "the consideration of certain immediately apprehended factors apart from their immediately apprehended context" (p. 96).[31] In this sense each level of the spiral is an abstraction, a creation, a reintegration from the one below formed through the latter's disintegration. While forming from depth to surface and surface to depth, man can create but also miscreate, because in moving from level of abstraction to another there can be error as well as verification. This is the danger inevitable in creative freedom.

Prior to and essential for intellection in the human sense, starting with *hsing* and moving upward, are many levels of the spiral which are pre-rationative. Intuition, empathy, insight, hunch, flash-feelings, aspects of fantasying and dreaming, communing, psi-phenomena, mystic participation, all are pre-rationative until the moment mentation takes over, to order these forms dualistically into logical sequences and to label them. We can see how much of the forming process is prelogical. Considering *hsing* as the first and last level, two further pre-rationative levels might be defined. With *hsing* the first, the second would be made up of sense-impressions. Awareness of sensing or feeling means forming has already taken place. When the form can be named it represents a high-order abstraction. In this sense, feelings as such cannot be had in consciousness. The label attached is to an aspect of the feeling, is a higher order concept of it. The third level of the spiral I call the Helen Keller level because it was what obtained in her before she could "talk." These first three levels are pre-rationative not prerational. They are forms of a dimension prior to those necessary for thought and essential to intellection.

The next higher level, the fourth, might be approximated by hypnagogic reverie, the first level in which we begin to get defined images of sight, sound, movement, etc. The next higher level would be dreams, i.e., the formulations of the dreaming process, and still higher come flash-feelings defined, flash-thoughts and feeling-thoughts. At the top are fantasies and thought processes, each being of a different order of abstraction with the latter ranging to the unattainable ideal of the West, pure thought thinking itself.

When a dream is reported, it is an end product of forming. It can be reinserted into the stream of thought processes by implicit and explicit associations to it. Mutually working with a dream is attempting to arrive at an interpretation. Essentially this means working our way down the formative spiral to make deeper and wider associative experiential connections with the sources of the dream.

Awareness is primary since "there can be awareness without anything of which awareness is aware—hence a state of pure lucidity." The moment lucidity ends there is an experienced dualism, a somebody aware of forms. The very first emergence of forms from the forming process I call images and the process of their forming imagizing. They are after *hsing* and before the first level of the formative spiral. Images are the first evanescence having identifiable form, prompted by stimuli affecting the special senses—vision, hearing, taste, etc. There are also thermal, tactile, and kinesthetic images, those prompted by stimuli from viscera and by the emergence of still poorly identifiable feelings.

When imagizing is prompted by internal and external objects and events present to the senses, the process is called perceiving. Imagining obtains when the images formed are of objects or events not spatially or temporally present to the senses or not perceivable because of the nature of the human organism. As these images evolve, i.e., ascend the metaphorical spiral, they become symbols. Those formed through perceiving are called perceptual images and symbols, and those through imagining, conceptual images and symbols. Feeling or conative images emerge into emotive or conative symbols.

Four aspects of symbol functioning can be identified. Because of the nature of discursive thought, they have to be separated out by a process of abstraction while factually all four aspects participate inextricably. They are subject-symbol-conception-object. Symbols are not proxies but vehicles for the conception of objects and events. The lumping together of symbol and conception and of substituting symbols for the objects they stand for have created all manner of human havoc.

Symbols manifest these attributes. Since forming is an aspect of *hsing* and forms as symbols are one of its products, it becomes more understandable how they come to have these attributes and to be most evident in dreaming. While dreaming we are closer to *hsing* than during waking life, to essentials and with what is essentially concerning us. Symbols, in addition to reflecting essentials, are also truthful to what they are representing because they are formulating essential truths about ourselves including the truth of our falsehoods. Symbols are creations, a product of the creative process in symbolizing. They are artistic because they are abstractions from *hsing*, a continuum of ineffable, aesthetic and emotive moving fields. Symbolizing and hence symbols, as an expression of self-realization,[19] of cosmic minding, formulate and favor the process of cure and hence are curative. They express the organism's tendency to integrate with economy; hence symbols are economical, precise, concise, condensed, and adequate. They are also appropriate, pertinent, timely, and relevant. It is not in the nature of the organism to expend itself on what is not relevant to the tendency toward self-realization.

Man's freedom of choice in selecting symbols, in realizing his nature, is limited in four regards. He can only choose those symbols that will transform energy in himself and coming to him from without. He can only choose symbols from the sensate world and only those that he can perceive, imagine, synthesize, and extrapolate. Thirdly, because energy seeks suitable forms, he can only choose those forms which will aid in his self-realization. This is saying that form does not select meaning but the meaning to be conveyed will select the form suitable to convey it. The last limiting factor to symbol choice is the rigidity of a person's character structure[19] and the narrowing effect it has on him in his living resulting in fewer kinds of experiences and limited experiencing of them. As a person is more spontaneously *hsing*, this last limiting factor becomes absorbed and the forms that happen in and through him become more his meaning, his wisdom.

From the moment of birth learning begins and maybe also in utero. Learning is the process and effects in participating before and after awareness is possible, awake and asleep and while conscious and unconscious of such participating. It proceeds through sequences of organismal environmental occurrences. Some time between twelve and eighteen months, when the infant becomes capable of forming symbols, it begins to form a symbolic self. The symbolic self contains the individual's conception of his body, of his thinking, feeling, willing, acting, his conception of his work and leisure, of his relation to himself and to others, his philosophy of life, of his world, the cosmos, and of himself as an aspect of it. I feel this concept of the symbolic self, in the context of my motion of the forming process and of *hsing*, includes and goes beyond what is subsumed under the Existentialist concepts of *eigenwelt, mitwelt,* and *umvelt.*

To be differentiated from the symbolic self are a feeling of self, the physical self, the actual self, the empirical self, and the self-system. The whole is constituted of a hierarchy of systems which make up the self-system of which the symbolic self is an aspect. The formed aspect of the self-system is a sub-whole of more and less rigid systems and the forming aspect is constituted of more and less plastic ones. To the extent that a person becomes sicker, more to most of his available energies become invested in the formed aspect. That person becomes more and more irrational, i.e., out of ratio with what he would be if he were spontaneously *hsing*. As more of a person's wholeness participates in the forming aspect of the self-system and approximates toward its attributes, the more rational that person becomes. The term rational derives from its root, ratio, and the term rational refers to a two-term vertical relationship. Rational and irrational are used in a purely descriptive sense neutrally applicable to physical and psychological processes, to the organismic and environmental aspects of the unitary process organism-environment, and to that process as a whole.

Just as an oscillating equilibrium obtains between organism and environment so it does between the formed and the forming aspects of the self-system constituted of cooperating and conflicting systems. The conflict between the formed and forming aspects of the self-system I call the essential conflict. It is another formulation of the human paradox. The inevitable juxtaposition of the formed and forming aspects is cyclically tension producing and tension reducing. Among the paradoxes is that immediate tension and pain increase, which a sick person fears, is prerequisite to ultimate tension decrease which he wants. A further paradox follows. As the ratio of tension due to irrational sources diminishes and the general tension level lowers, immediate tension-producing situations are chosen not primarily toward the end of tension reduction but as an accepted concomitant of, and as a stimulus and source of energy for, self and world creating. The area of juxtaposition of the formed and the forming is the area of becoming in the context of being. Although ultimately there will be moments of pure lucidity, of formlessness, always there will be tension because tensioning rhythmically is essential to living. Below a certain tension level, even in a sage, death would ensue.

Through the symbolizing process, an aspect of the universal forming process, man delimits disciplines for understanding nature and his nature. They extend in a continuum from subatomic physics, through biochemistry, psychology, theology, ecology, astrophysics. Through the symbolizing process he can formulate epistemologies, methodologies, and theories requisite to each discipline. He can change human history, the history of human knowledge, his personal history by being more open and alert to them as they emerge and to new ways of seeing his past, his present, and his possible future.

Theories having wider and deeper embeddedness in *hsing* and approximating toward the ultimates in *hsing* being manifest will more accurately reflect the reality of nature and of human nature. Such theories will be characterized by unitary process thinking and will be open-ended. Their validation will be their invalidation. As spontaneous as their emergence will be their resorption. Such theories will manifest increasing congruence, congeniality, and continuity in the theoretic, aesthetic, and emotive aspects of knowing and being. This means they will increasingly reflect man's spirituality. Ultimately there can be neither opposition nor gap between science and religion, since both are cosmic minding, of it and through it.

As long as man is aware of himself as an aspect of cosmos and of cosmic minding, here-now, and that his living and his formulations of it are manifestations of the cosmic forming process, he will be more choicelessly aware, passively alert, and threshold conscious to what is, moment to moment, emerging and being resorbed within and without himself as aspects of cosmic minding. As he moves more in that direction he will approximate toward being ultimate Reality, toward being the wisdom of the sage. "Free from attachments to fruits of works, everlastingly contented, unconfined, even though he be engaged in work he does not work at all. Bhagavadgita, lesson the fourth."[26]

REFERENCES

1. Bogoliubov, N. N., and Shirkov, D. V., *Introduction to the Theory of Quantized Fields,* Interscience Publishers, Inc., New York, 1959. Reviewed in *Main Currents,* Vol. 16, No. 2, Nov., 1959.
2. Brown, F. A., Jr., "Living clocks," *Science,* 1959, 130:1535-1544.
3. Camus, A., by Germaine Bree, in *The New York Times Book Review,* Jan. 24, 1960.
4. Carver, F. N., Jr., *Form and Space of Japanese Architecture,* Shokokusha Publishing Co., Tokyo, 1955.
5. Chardin, P. T. de, *The Phenomenon of Man,* Harper & Brothers, New York, 1959.
6. Déchanet, J. M., *Christian Yoga,* Harper & Brothers, New York, 1960.
7. Einstein, A., quoted in *The New York Times Magazine,* April 24, 1955, p. 17.
8. Gold, T., "Life without end," in *Time,* Jan. 4, 1960, Latin American Edition, Science Section, p. 38.
9. Haas, W. S., *The Destiny of the Mind: East and West,* Macmillan, New York, 1956, pp. 165, 167.
10. Heinemann, F. H., *Existentialism and the Modern Predicament,* Harper Torchbooks TB28, Harper & Brothers, New York, 1958.
11. Heisenberg, W., "Physics and Philosophy," *World Perspectives,* R. N. Anshen, ed., Harper & Brothers, New York, 1958, Chap. III.
12. Horney, K., *Neurosis and Human Growth,* W. W. Norton, New York, 1950, Chaps. VI, VII.
13. Keosian, J., "On the origin of life," *Science* (Feb. 19), 1960, 131:479-482.
14. Kelman, H., "Freer associating: its phenomenology and inherent paradoxes," *Am. J. Psychoan.,* 1962, XXII:No. 2.
15. ———, "Psychoanalysis and science," *Am. J. Psychoan.,* 1953, XIII:38-58.
16. ———, "The use of the analytic couch," *Am. J. Psychoan.,* 1954, XIV:65-82.
17. ———, "Life history as therapy. Part I, Evaluation of literature," *Am. J. Psychoan.,* 1955, XV:144-162; "Part II, On being aware," *Am. J. Psychoan.,* 1956, XVI:68-78; "Part III, The symbolizing process," *Am. J. Psychoan.,* 1956, XVI:145-169.
18. ———, "Communing and relating. Part I, Past and current perspectives," *Am. J. Psychoan.,* 1958, XVIII:77-98; "Part II, The mind structure of the East and West," *Am. J. Psychoan.,* 1958, XVIII:158-170; "Part III, Examples:

general and clinical," "Part IV, Communing as therapy," *Am. J. Psychoan.*, 1959, XIX:73-105; "Part V, Separateness and togetherness," *Am. J. Psychoan.*, 1959, XIX:188-215.

19. Kelman, H., "The holistic approach (Horney)," in *American Handbook of Psychiatry*, ed. by S. Arieti, Chap. 71, pp. 1434-1452, Basic Books, Inc., New York, 1959.

20. ———, "Communing and relating," *Am. J. Psychotherapy*, 1960, XIV:70-96.

21. ———, "Current approaches to psychoanalysis," in *Theoretical Approaches*, ed. P. Hoch and J. Zubin, Grune and Stratton, New York, 1960, pp. 63-78.

22. ———, "Existentialism: A phenomenon of the West," *Int. J. of Social Psychiatry*, 1960, V:299-302.

23. ———, "Psychoanalytic thought and Eastern wisdom," in *Science and Psychoanalysis*, Vol. III, ed. J. H. Masserman, Grune and Stratton, Inc., 1960, pp. 124-132.

24. Klee, P., *M.D.*, May, 1960, pp. 110-114.

25. Kornberg, A., "Biologic synthesis of deoxyribonucleic acid," *Science*, 1960, 131: 1503-1508.

26. Kovach, L. D., "Life can be *so* nonlinear," *Am. Scientist*, 1960, 48:218-225.

27. Langer, S. K., *Philosophy in a New Key*," A Mentor Book, The New American Library, New York, 1955, pp. 1-2.

28. Lindsay, R. B., "Entropy consumption and values in physical science," *Am. Scientist*, 1959, 47:376-385.

29. Malalasekara, G. P., "Nirvana: Extinction or fulfillment?" *Main Currents*, 1960, 16:51-57.

30. Marcel, G., in May, R., Angel, E., and Ellenberger, H. F., *Existence*, Basic Books, New York, 1959, p. 40.

31. Northrop, F. S. C., *The Logic of the Sciences and the Humanities*, Meridian Books, M71, New York, 1959, Chap. XXIII.

32. Popper, K. R., *The Logic of Scientific Discovery*, Basic Books, New York, 1959, p. 359.

33. Reiser, O. L., *The Integration of Human Knowledge*, Porter Sargent, Boston, 1958, p. 140.

34. Royce, J. R., "The search for meaning," *Am. Scientist*, 1959, 47:515-535.

35. Schroedinger, E., *What Is Life?* Cambridge University Press, London, 1945, pp. 70, 71.

36. ———, *Science and Humanism*, Cambridge University Press, London, 1952, pp. 21, 40.

37. Simpson, G. G., "The world into which Darwin led us," *Science*, 1960, 131:966-974.

38. Suzuki, D. T., *The Zen Doctrine of No-Mind*, Rider & Co., London, 1949.

39. ———, *Selected Writings*, ed. William Barrett, Anchor A90, Doubleday & Co., Garden City, New York, 1956, pp. 172, 173.

40. Tillich, P., *Dynamics of Faith*, Harper & Brothers, New York, 1957, pp. 31-34.

41. ———, in "Toward a new image of man," *Main Currents*, 1960, 16:114-116.

42. Whitehead, A. N., *Science and the Modern World*, A Mentor Book, M28, The New American Library, 1948, p. 5.

43. Whorf, B. L., *Language, Thought and Reality*, Wiley & Sons, New York, 1956, p. 221.

44. Whyte, L. L., "Accent on form," *World Perspectives*, ed., R. N. Anshen, Harper & Brothers, New York, 1954, p. 104.

A N A T O L   R A P O P O R T

An Essay on Mind

1. Introduction—An Analysis of the Question

Our task will be to discuss the question "What is mind?" from the point of view of the so-called scientific outlook. That is to say, in our attempt to answer the question we shall want to be sure of two things: first, that we understand the question; second, that our answer will be at least in part supported by the kind of evidence that deserves the name in scientific investigations. Of these two principles of self-imposed discipline, the second is easy to apply, because the rules of evidence in scientific argument are fairly explicit. It is more difficult to apply the first principle so as to achieve clarification of the question and to comply with the standards of *meaningfulness,* as it is understood in scientific discourse.

Indeed, the temptation occurs simply to dismiss the question, since, on the face of it, it automatically falls outside the scope of scientific inquiry. If one asks, "What is mind?" we could counter with "What do you mean by mind?" If he says he doesn't know what he means by it, that is why he is asking the question, we could reply that if the nature of something is to be investigated, the "something" must first be pointed out, so that it can be examined. If we are not shown the object or event or a class of events to be examined, we cannot be expected to begin.

This is an easy way out. A whole school of thought (logical positivism) which arose in our century made short work of all the traditional questions of philosophy by showing that such questions had no meaning according to the criteria of meaning proposed by this school of thought.

Since those criteria of meaning are actually the criteria used in scientific discourse, the logical positivists contributed toward unifying the philosophical and the scientific outlooks, which had been separated in European thought for several centuries. Therefore, the service performed by the logical positivists in bridging the gap between science and philosophy cannot be overestimated. Still the price exacted for this synthesis, namely, the dismissal of traditional philosophical speculative activity as at best a sort of poetic exercise, at worst as symptom of mental disturbance, may have been steep.

There is another way of reacting to a question formulated in typical philosophical form (like "What is mind?") which does not violate the tenets of the scientific outlook but which aims at getting whatever value may be inherent in the question. That is to ignore for the moment the strict criteria of "meaning" imposed by the logical syntax of science and to try to share the questioner's inner state. Something must be bothering him if he asks the question. One cannot ascertain what it is by trying to pin down concrete meanings any more than one can in this way ascertain what someone feels when he tells us that he has a toothache. But only a pedant would argue that because pain cannot always be demonstrated *outside the person who feels the pain* (that is what is involved in giving concrete objective meaning to terms), that the statement "I have a toothache" has no meaning.[1] It has a perfectly definite meaning for anyone who has had a toothache. Evidently besides the meanings derived from objectively demonstrable referents, there are meanings of another kind. To understand fully the meaning of a question like "What is mind?" (or of an assertion like "I have a toothache") it is necessary to share somehow the inner state of the questioner, to feel as he feels.

For artists, mystics, poets, and metaphysicians, but also, I suspect, for most people without special training, this type of understanding (call it "empathetic") is the only one worthy of the name, and the only criterion of "meaning" is, accordingly, a direct experience of an intuitive grasp. In science, however, to establish the meaning of a concept or of an assertion, one must exhibit a chain of operations, demonstrations, or logical deductions that ultimately connect the term or the assertion in question to concrete, sensually perceived referents (objects or events) existing in time and space. The chain may be very long, and so no restriction is placed on the degree of abstraction of a meaningful

---

1. The line between meaningful and meaningless assertions is not always easy to draw. We readily agree that human beings feel pain and that stones feel no pain. We assume that animals resembling us also feel pain. With regard to remote animals like oysters or polyps, we may say we do not know. But how can we find out? If no conceivable procedure of verification can be established, assertions on this subject are technically meaningless. But at what stage do they become meaningless?

term or assertion; but the chain must be continuous: its links must consist *only* of performable operations, demonstrations, or, in the case of theoretical constructs, of rigorous logical deductions from a set of postulates.

Therefore, before attempting to answer the question "What is mind?" from the point of view of the scientific outlook, one must first undertake a translation from the language of direct intuitive appeal, in which answers are usually given to questions of this sort, to a language whose terms can be connected to objective referents and whose assertions can be corroborated or refuted by concrete demonstrations.

The logical positivist tends to eschew this sort of translation wherever questions of speculative philosophy or introspective psychology are involved. It is, of course, his right to declare this job outside the scope of his competence or interest. But the propensity of the hardheaded operationalist to declare that the job cannot be done often has the consequence that it is not undertaken. And this has, in turn, one of two further consequences: (1) either questions like "What is mind?" and others of the same sort are expelled from philosophy altogether; (2) or these questions are left to traditionally oriented philosophers or metaphysicians.

The logical positivists welcome at least the first of these consequences. In my opinion both are undesirable. I do not think that speculation should be sterilized, that is, purged of all questions which cannot satisfy the strictest criteria of meaning. Nor do I think that philosophy should confine itself to the job of carrying out such sterilization. I would like even less to leave "metaphysical" questions to the metaphysicians. I believe that, in addition to the job of determining whether a question has operational meaning, the philosopher should also undertake the job of attempting to *impart* meaning to questions which seem to have none. This job is neglected both by the metaphysicians, who take meaning for granted once they have experienced an intuitive grasp, and by the operationalists, who simply discard those questions which appear meaningless by the usual criteria. In attempting to impart rigorous meaning to a vaguely stated question, the philosopher should help the questioner to reformulate the question by scanning the possible range of answers which satisfy the requirements of meaningfulness in the scientific sense. In short, vague thinking, stemming from genuine intellectual tension, characteristic of traditional philosophy and of common-sense speculation, often can and should be made more precise, and this task is a proper one for the modern semantically sophisticated philosopher.

Let us, therefore, start by deliberately assuming a naive pose. Let us do what "the man in the street" might do in looking for an answer to a question of the form "What is *X*?" Let us look up *X* in a dictionary. Of course, we will not take the dictionary answer seriously. The dictionary is only a record of current usage. Its "definitions" do no more than indicate the contexts in which the terms defined are likely to be used. But as we have outlined our approach to the question "What is mind?" this is just what we are after. Recall that our first task is not to answer the question but to understand it. We should, therefore, form some idea of the context in which the word "mind" is generally used, since we have no direct contact with a specific questioner.

So we turn to a dictionary and look for the entry "mind" in the expectation of finding a summary statement of how the term is currently used. We read ". . . that which thinks, feels, and wills, exercises perception, judgment, reflection, etc., as in a human or other conscious being.[2]

The definition reveals a great deal: not, to be sure, of what "mind" is, but of the way people think about "thinking," "feeling," and "willing." It reveals first that people project their inner states on others. If I think (and of course I know what it means to "think"; I have *direct* experience with thinking), then *he*, who is like me in so many ways, must think too. If I feel, he feels; if I make judgments, he does. Moreover, what thinking, feeling, judging is to me (a direct experience) must be the same to him. It is to him *his* direct experience, which I can never share, but nevertheless which I know is *there*, in him.

Secondly, the dictionary definition reveals that our language habits do much of our thinking for us. If there is "thinking," the dictionary definition of mind implies, there must be "something" which does the thinking. "To think" is a verb, and our language habits prescribe that a verb must have a subject. Hence, "mind"—a noun to serve as a subject of "to think"—is defined as that which thinks.

Most people accept definitions of this sort as answers to questions of the form "What is X?" without difficulty and without further reflection. Such definitions cater to both types of tacit processes inherent in common-sense philosophy, namely, projecting inner directly felt awareness upon objects outside of oneself, particularly upon objects similar to oneself; and the invention of entities to fill the slots where certain grammatical categories are called for.

Some people, however, will wish to reflect further and pursue the question concerning "that." What is the "That" which thinks? Linguistic analogy plays an important part in the reflection. If verbs describe activities, subjects of verbs describe agents. What is the agent that "does" the thinking? (Like "What is the bird that hoots at night?" or "What is the substance that is spreading this fragrance?") The currently

2. *The American College Dictionary*, Random House, New York.

accepted "scientific" answer is that the brain is the thing that does the thinking.

But most of the philosophically inclined people will reject the suggestion that the mind is identical with the brain. A long philosophical tradition derived from an even longer religious tradition demands that a distinction be made between the material brain and the supposedly immaterial mind. To be sure, most will agree that an organism deprived of a brain is thereby also deprived of a mind. But they will insist that even though the mind may have its seat in the brain, it is not identical with it. If pressed to explain, such people may go on to point out that a person may retain a seemingly intact brain, as indicated, say, in an autopsy, but may nevertheless have lost his "mind."

Others will go further and attribute a mind to entities which have no identifiable brain. They may speak, for example, of a "group mind." Some will go still further and assert the existence of a mind or an analogue of a mind (a "psyche," a "soul") in an even more diffuse entity, say, a nation, a culture, a civilization. Finally, some will go to extremes and assert the operation of a "mind" (an "intelligence," an "idea") independently of the existence of matter. They will assert that a "mind" existed prior to matter and indeed has created matter and is guiding the evolution of the tangible world—the cosmic, the biological, and the social. Hegel, for example, held such views.

We have swept over the materialist-idealist spectrum. At one end is the extreme materialist position, which in its vulgar version puts forward the simple-minded notion that the brain *is* the mind and secretes thought in quite the same way that the gallbladder secretes bile. At the other end is the extreme idealistic position with its mystical belief in a dematerialized intelligence.

However, wherever on this spectrum the questioner may be, if he asks the question "What is mind?" seriously, he has already made the tacit assumption that because a word exists, a referent exists behind it. It is upon this assumption that the logical positivist trains his big guns. To demolish a position based on assuming that the existence of words implies the existence of referents, it is only necessary to call attention to some well-known terms without referents. Once some such terms have been acknowledged (werewolves, square circles), the burden of providing a referent for "mind" can be immediately shifted to the questioner:

"If you admit that there is not necessarily a referent behind every term, then there may be no referent to correspond to 'mind.' Therefore in order to be sure that we are not wasting time, we should first ascertain whether there is one. Since you have used the term, not I, it is up to you to find the referent. Once you have found it, but not before, we

can take up the problem about what kind of a thing (or whatever) this
referent may be."

Now while it is true that many terms do not have objectively identifiable referents, I think it can be argued that every term which enjoys
general usage does have a referent in some *shared experiences* of the
users or else the term would not continue to be used. But if experiences
are shared, they must have components outside the people who have
the experiences, even though these components may be nothing but the
communicative acts themselves. The referent for "unicorn" can be taken
to be the imagined animal. As such, it is internal to the person who
imagines and therefore not subject to scrutiny by others. But when
belief in unicorns was shared, there were communications about these
beasts, i.e., stories, pictures, etc. These communications are objectively
identifiable events and can therefore be taken in their totality as the
objectively identifiable referent of "unicorn." The same can be said
about the terms used in theology, mythology, and metaphysics: God,
grace, karma, nirvana, first cause, quintessence, Atlantis, Valhalla, etc.
As long as the referents of these terms are taken as certain inner states
of the users, they are not amenable to scientific investigation. But in
communications about some such terms and in other events which may
have instigated the communications, we do have a class of identifiable
events to be subsumed as the referent of the term in question. This
referent can then be studied like any other referent. Such a study
enables us to say something about the referent and so to give some
kind of answer to the question about what "it is."

In short, in tracing the "meaning" of mind, we should look for
objectively identifiable events which may have given rise to the notion
that there is such a thing or, at least, may have instigated certain communicative acts, in which the referent of mind is tacitly assumed to
exist. It seems to me that this method is a compromise between the
standards of scientific rigor which demand that referents of terms be
objectively identifiable events "in their own right," apart from private
or cultural notions; and the aspirations of philosophy to deal with
questions involving terms without such referents. We still demand that
objective referents be found before the "nature" of something is investigated; but we shall admit real events as referents of possible fictions
if we have reason to believe that these events gave rise to the fictions.

2. The Separation of Living and Nonliving Worlds
and Their Partial Reunion

Following our plan, we shall examine notions (or concepts) *related*
to the notion central to this discussion, namely, "mind," by examining

the events which have probably given rise to them. The first such notion we shall examine is "life," more specifically, "that which distinguishes the living from the nonliving."

Even though a common-sense distinction between animate and inanimate objects probably is made in all cultures and appears quite early in children's perception, a sharp *philosophical* distinction is of comparatively recent origin in Western thought. By a philosophical distinction I mean one which assumes qualitatively different explanations of behavior of living and nonliving objects. The animistic orientation of preliterate cultures is well known. During the Middle Ages, even though formal distinctions between living and nonliving things might have been made in philosophy, the "natural philosophies" of the two worlds were much more alike than they became in modern times (excluding the very recent period). For example, the acceptance of teleological causation in physics made possible the far-reaching analogies between the causes of motion of living and nonliving objects. Falling stones were thought to be "seeking their natural position" at the center of the earth, while rising flames and smokes were seeking their natural positions in the fiery regions of the heavens, quite as the birds were seeking to reach their nests (hence their ability to fly) and rabbits were seeking to reach their holes.[3]

As the mechanistic philosophy of Galilean physics displaced the teleological philosophy inherited with Aristotelian physics, a sharp break occurred between the scientific views of the world of inert matter and the world of living organisms. The separation widened, until in the second half of the last century it became complete when the impossibility of obtaining life from inert matter (which had been believed possible until that time) was demonstrated. But even as the methodological division between physics and biology widened, a contrary trend was starting. It can be traced to the synthesis of urea by Wöhler in 1828—a momentous date, marking a demonstration that a substance hitherto thought to be producible only in a living organism (hence the name "organic") could be produced in a laboratory from "inorganic" substances. The first success was followed by many others until there was no doubt that any substance identifiable in a living organism could be *in principle* synthesized. The limits of the chemist's ingenuity seemed the only (temporary) obstacles to such "acts of creation."

However, this closing of the gap between living and nonliving *matter*

3. Cf. Moritz Schlick, "Philosophy of Organic Life" in H. Feigl and M. Brodbeck, eds., *Readings in the Philosophy of Science*, Appleton-Century-Crofts, New York, 1953; Ernest Nagel, "Teleological Explanation and Teleological Systems" in S. Ratner, ed., *Vision and Action: Essays in Honor of Horace Kallen on His Seventieth Birthday*, Rutgers University Press, New Brunswick, N.J., 1953 (reprinted in Feigl and Brodbeck, *op. cit.*); P. Frank, *Einstein, His Life and Times*, Alfred A. Knopf, New York, 1947.

did not by any means bring about a unified view of the nature of living and nonliving *processes*. Indeed, as the difference between the two kinds of matter disappeared, the Cartesian dualism dominant in European philosophy *re-enforced* the view that there was something about life which was irreducible to physical concepts. Since the difference did not lie in the kind of matter that was involved, it was clear to those who had internalized the dualistic view that something about life that was not matter, not even a property of matter, was responsible for the special character of the living process. Thus, the view known as *vitalism* emerged in the philosophy of biology.

The history of vitalism is a history of successive retreats, one is almost tempted to say to previously prepared positions. But it would be misleading to call the complementary advance of the opposite view an advance of "mechanism," as the antivitalist view is sometimes called. The early mechanistic view of animal behavior, as proposed, for example by Descartes, who thought that animals were complicated clockworks, did not "advance." On the contrary, Descartes' view was revealed to be sterile. What did "advance" was not the pedantic view that "the laws of mechanics" were sufficient to explain the behavior of living things, but rather a method of investigation. This method started with phenomena which were most amenable to description and explanation in terms of known laws and progressed to the study of more complex phenomena. As the investigations progressed, the method was modified and enriched. Thus, the early successes were not in "mechanics" of living things at all (e.g., descriptions and explanations of the motions of animals) but in chemistry, a field of knowledge which was initially quite autonomous from mechanics. It was shown, for example, that many of the chemical reactions which took place in living tissue could be replicated in a nonliving environment under properly controlled conditions. Even though many such reactions could not be reproduced, no chemical reaction taking place within a living organism could be shown definitely to *violate* the known laws of chemistry.[4]

Biophysics advanced alongside of biochemistry. It was shown that the electrical processes in living organisms, of which nervous excitation is the most conspicuous example, were no different from the electrical processes known in physics. It was shown that the law of conservation

4. At one time there were serious discussions of the question whether living organisms did not violate the second law of thermodynamics, inasmuch as they are able to increase their internal organization instead of succumbing to "disorder" as the second law prescribes. Since an explicitly stated condition for the operation of the second law is that the process in question proceed in a closed system, it is obvious that the law does not apply to a living organism through which matter and energy constantly flow. It is hard to see why it was ever necessary to make this obvious argument.

of energy was obeyed in the living organism, in particular that the energy of motion of living things did not spring from some source peculiar to life but from well-known sources, that it could be traced through metabolic chains in a series of conversions and could be fully accounted for by a balanced bookkeeping involving the energy of food ingested and the energy dissipated in mechanical work and in heat losses.

None of these corroborations of the antivitalist view could be possible if the method of investigation had been pedantic, i.e., if it were limited to the application of the "mechanics" to observed phenomena. In Descartes' time the principle of the heat engine was unknown, and chemistry as we understand it did not exist. Physics was practically identical with mechanics, and clockworks were the only known mechanical "organisms." A physicist of that time, if he made a serious attempt to construct a theoretical model of a living organism, based on the principles he knew, would have got nowhere—he would have failed to discover the activating springs in his "clockworks" and hence could not continue with his program.

Thus, the continued advance of the antivitalist view throughout the nineteenth century was due not to a rigid adherence to a *metaphysical* position (such as that the laws of mechanics underlie all phenomena) but rather to a steadfast consistency of its *epistemological position*. This can be stated somewhat as follows:

There are regularities in nature. These regularities are discoverable and describable in terms of general principles. The statement of the general principles and rigorous deductions to show how they apply in specific cases are the content of scientific knowledge. Knowledge advances to the extent that the general principles become fewer in number and to the extent that the specific cases to which such principles can be shown to apply increase in number and variety. Knowledge does not advance when special words are invented to serve as explanations of events unaccounted for, if these words serve no other purpose in the scheme of cognition.

I say this is an epistemological position, not a metaphysical one. The judgments expressed are not about the principles underlying phenomena but about what it means to know such principles and, by implication, how one should proceed to accumulate knowledge. One should proceed from the known to the unknown. One should attempt to show that many seemingly different kinds of events are actually consequences of a few principles. However, no *a priori* commitment to the principles is recommended, and no principle is too sacred to discard. Thus, the way is open to the discovery of new principles and a modification of old ones. But new principles, if they are discovered, must be really demonstrable. One should not accept *names* of principles for actually operating laws of nature.

The objection of the antivitalist against the vitalist's notion of "life force" or the like is not so much on the grounds that this supposed principle does not fit in with the known laws governing the behavior of matter (it would be foolhardy to assume that we know all such laws), but on the ground that the proposed "life force" is not a "principle." It explains nothing. It is only a name for a supposed principle and will remain only a name until the vitalist says more about how this life force is supposed to operate.

3. The Problem Still Remaining—Regulatory Activity— and Its Solution

At this point a defense which deserves a careful examination can be made of the use of terms like "vital force." One could point out that "magnetism" was also used to "explain" certain peculiar ways, not otherwise explainable, observed in the behavior of certain kinds of iron. Certainly magnetism was an important new principle discovered in nature. Cannot "vital force" or some such term be accorded similar status with respect to peculiar events observed in living organisms, not otherwise explainable?

I think the argument carries weight but only to the extent that the "peculiar events" with which the proposed term is to be associated are clearly identified. Most of the time this is not the case. For example, when the vitalist says that certain living organisms are characterized by "consciousness," and that this property necessitates a postulate of a special principle, he has not really identified the "peculiar events." No matter how direct is our awareness of our own "consciousness," this term has no objectively identifiable referent. The same argument applies to such vague formulations as the contentions of the vitalists that the behavior of living organisms is guided by goals and purposes or, on the evolutionary scale, by adaptive strivings (the Lamarckian view), unless the events to be explained in this way are actually pointed out.

Occasionally, however, an outspoken vitalist clearly identifies the class of events which, he submits, are not explainable by known laws governing the behavior of inert matter. When he does this, the challenge to the antivitalist position is genuine and must be met.

Such a challenge was offered, for example, by Hans Driesch.[5] Driesch used the Aristotelian term "entelechy" to describe (and supposedly to explain) specific events observable in the living world and, as Driesch

5. Driesch, H., *The Science and Philosophy of the Organism*, A. and C. Black, London, 1908.

assumed, only in the living world. We do not think that the use of the term "entelechy" explains anything. But to the extent that specific events are subsumed under the term, "entelechy" may have theoretical significance. Driesch's argument must be taken seriously, because he does refer it to a specific class of events.

Most of these events are taken from experimental embryology. It is known that an embryo of an organism (not too high on the conventional evolutionary scale) can be seriously mutilated, for example, cut in two, without affecting the end result of its development. Thus, when the fertilized egg of such an organism has already divided, say into four cells, it is possible to separate the embryo into two halves and have each develop into a complete organism. When the embryo is left intact, the two halves develop into the two halves of a single organism. As Driesch saw it, the development of the embryo is guided not by immediate determinate "causes," such as seem to guide the behavior of inert matter, but rather by "goals," what Aristotle called "final causes," in this case the future whole organism into which the embryo supposedly strives to grow. Whatever be the merit of Driesch's argument, he has thereby indicated the class of phenomena to which the term "entelechy" is supposed to apply. Thus, the matter can be examined.

Is it true that "goal-seeking" behavior is observed only in living organisms? If we follow the actual usage of the term "goal seeking" (or equivalent) we see that this is by no means the case. Indeed, as we have already said, "goal seeking" was normally attributed to inert matter in pre-Galilean physics. Remnants of this terminology still persist. We still say that water "seeks" the lowest level. Crude observations confirm this view. Place obstacles in the way of flowing water, and it will flow around them, still "striving" to attain lower levels. Of course, the mechanistic formulation made it possible to dispense with this teleological explanation. It has been supplanted by the "strictly causal" one where the local *gradient* of gravitational potential instead of the distant existence of a "lowest level" is the assumed underlying "cause" of the water's "striving."

What prevents us from dispensing immediately with entelechy in biology is the fact that the analogues of a gravitational gradient (or other force fields) are hard to discover. The problem is to explain the "world line," i.e., the successive temporal cross sections of a living thing, say the development of a zygote through the embryonic stages into an organism, without reference to a final state, that is, in such a way that each temporal cross section becomes an inevitable consequence of the preceding one in view of known *general* principles.

Now there is no lack of situations where just such a process can be accounted for. For example, mechanical systems which have a configuration of equilibrium will seem to "seek" that configuration no matter what the initial configuration may be. A thin flexible string suspended from two fixed points will always come to rest in the shape of a catenary; each type of crystal will assume its characteristic spatial pattern, etc. No reference to "final goals" is necessary to explain these events. They proceed in strict accordance with mechanical causality.

What is true of genuine equilibria is also true of dynamic steady states. Here a system is not in equilibrium but rather seems to be "maintaining" certain peculiar gradients. Such is the case of "open" systems of chemical reactions, those where steady sources and sinks are maintained. It can be shown that such systems will not only maintain nonequilibrium gradients of concentrations, temperatures, etc., but also that the maintained steady states will depend only on the system parameters (geometric configurations, presence of catalytic agents, etc.) and not on the initial concentrations of the substances involved. Such systems will exhibit clearly "regulatory" behavior. It will seem that they have "goals," namely, the steady states which will be finally achieved independently of the initial conditions.[6] They can, therefore, be subsumed under systems possessing "entelechy" in Driesch's sense. But we know that their behavior can be explained in terms of known principles of physics and chemistry. The thing that makes these systems peculiar is the fact that to explain their behavior in terms of known principles of physics and chemistry it is necessary to make detailed references to configurations which determine the system. For example, it is possible in principle to calculate the steady state distribution of temperature in a solid conductor of any shape, if constant temperatures are maintained in fixed regions. But theoretical physics has so far dealt with only the simplest configurations. Exact calculations have been made only in special cases—for a cylinder in contact with heat reservoirs at both ends, for a sphere whose entire surface is maintained at a constant temperature, etc. Similar calculations for an irregular body or for irregular boundary conditions are enormously difficult. If the boundary conditions themselves vary in time, the problem becomes utterly unmanageable, and the flow of heat in the body will seem unpredictable. Yet the determining role of the general principles of heat flow need not be abandoned on that account.

A similar position can, I think, be maintained with regard to bio-

6. L. von Bertalanffy puts great emphasis on the self-regulatory characteristics of "open" as contrasted with "closed" systems. This point of view is developed in several papers, e.g., "General System Theory," *Main Currents in Modern Thought*, 1955, 71:75, reprinted with detailed annotations in *General Systems*, 1956, 1:1-10. For a review of pertinent literature, see C. Foster, A. Rapoport, and E. Trucco, "Some Unsolved Problems in the Theory of Non-isolated Systems," *General Systems*, 1957, 2:9-29.

logical processes. The configurations known as daisies, giraffes, oysters, paramecia, and mushrooms are so complex geometrically and chemically that it is hopeless simply to try to extend the methods of classical physics (the physics of regularly shaped bodies in an idealized environment) and classical chemistry (the chemistry of systems involving only a few components and phases usually in near-equilibrium) and hope thereby to arrive at deterministic laws governing the biological events in those systems. Yet one cannot on that ground alone demonstrate that these laws are in principle unable to account for the events. Therefore, the antivitalist continues to assume that the laws of physics and chemistry underlie those of physiology. If the connection continues to elude him in particular instances, he seeks to establish it. He has already demonstrated that homeostatic mechanisms are not peculiar to living organisms, and can indeed be artifically constructed. Having demonstrated the connection between a biological principle and known principles of more general type, he can then use this biological principle to explain physiological and embryological events. He has not thereby succeeded in effecting a "reduction," i.e., a total explanation leading from fundamental physical principles to the observed event, but at least he has kept his lines of communication open. The gaps can be filled later. He can go on to study biological events in the light of specifically biological concepts, but he has not invented these concepts *ad hoc* or cut them off from the rest of natural science.

It seems, then, that the question "What is life?" need not lead us into metaphysical speculation. True we will never be able to give a neat definition-like answer. But in the pursuit of the answer we can keep within the main stream of natural science.

This discussion of matters pertaining to the philosophy of biology was undertaken to exemplify the method we shall pursue in attempting to answer the analogous question, "What is mind?"

4. Goal-Seeking Behavior, Conditionality of Response, Mechanization of Learning and of Logical Reasoning

From what has just been said, it should be clear that faced with the question "What is life?" we must first ascertain what sort of things or events the questioner has in mind. At one time the question concerned the stuff from which living things are made. The stuff was studied, and as the techniques for studying stuff improved, it became apparent that the matter in living things was no different from other matter except that it was more complex.

Next the question might apply to the processes in living things. To the extent that the processes were sharply identified (e.g., chemical reactions), they were shown to be no different from other such reactions, except that they were more complex.

Next the attention was centered on the peculiarly "organized" manner in which the processes occurred. Again it has been shown that in all the instances where an organized or regulated process is fully understood, it is a consequence of a particular arrangement of parts in which simpler processes go on.

In this sense, the vitalist view can be said to have been in continuous retreat. But in so retreating it sometimes performed a useful function, namely, searching out new aspects of life to which the reductionist technique, hitherto successful, failed to apply. In other words, in refusing to yield *in principle,* the vitalists, by offering new challenges, instigated the advance of biology based on the nonvitalist view.

I think that psychology (popularly defined as the science of the mind) has traveled or is destined to travel along a similar road.

First, it is necessary to single out specific events which lead people to postulate the existence of "mind." To the extent that the events are objectively identifiable, they are "behavioral" events. Here we use the term as derived from behaviorist psychology, defined in the broadest sense as the part of psychology which examines only objectively identifiable events. However, we shall now give another meaning to the term "behavior." We will exclude from behavior those processes which can be completely described in terms of measurable physical quantities and include only those processes which, although more or less identifiable, cannot be so described.

For example, statements like "the boy is skating" or "the girl is smiling" are descriptions of behavior. These instances of behavior are readily identifiable, but it is difficult or impossible to reduce them to statements about physical events. To do this in the case of "smiling" would be, I suppose, to indicate a certain range of the inclination to the horizontal of the corners of the mouth within which we identify the position of the mouth with a "smile." But in all probability such a definition would not be satisfactory: it would subsume under smiles many facial expressions which would not be recognized as smiles and would exclude many which would be recognized as smiles. A description of skating would be even more difficult—impossible for all practical purposes. On the other hand, "the man's temperature rose to 38° C" or "the soprano sounded a high C" or "the patient's urine contained such and such concentration of sugar" are statements about measurable variables *only* and so are not statements about behavior, as we here use the term.

Now the first striking difference between the class of things to which the possession of a "mind" (or something analogous) can be properly attributed and the class to which a "mind" cannot be properly attributed is the fact that the statements about behavior are normally made with respect to the first class and not with respect to the second.

We can say about a man that he went home or that he kissed his wife or even that he became embarrassed. All or most situational referents of such simple statements are readily identifiable but practically irreducible to specific physical events. We can make similar statements about most of the familiar animals: dogs perform tricks; cats chase birds; horses neigh; birds build nests. All of these are easily identifiable actions, but none of these can be *specifically* described with any accuracy. By contrast, the things we can say about inanimate things (raindrops fall, iron rusts, wheels turn, the moon rises, dynamite explodes) can be specifically described in terms of measurable quantities alone. There are, of course, very complicated physical events involving inanimate objects, but to the extent that they are complicated, they are not only difficult to describe but also difficult to recognize. The outstanding feature of *behavior* is that it is often quite easy to recognize but extremely difficult or impossible to describe with precision.

Driesch makes a similar point when he ascribes "actions" to living organisms and only to those. "Actions," according to Driesch, can be recognized and described only as wholes, not in terms of their elementary constituent parts.

Here, then, is a seemingly fundamental difference between two classes of things. Those that "behave" or "perform actions" and those that only participate in processes. The first class includes only living organisms and not all of these. To this class we may perhaps attribute the possession of a "mind"—not as an explanation of their ability to perform actions, since mind is only a name invented to distinguish this class, but as a distributive term (like "magnetism" discussed above).

The first task, then, of the antivitalist's opposite number in psychology is to try to find a transition area between processes describable by time functions of measurable quantities (as physical processes are described) and "behavior," i.e., events recognizable as successions or combinations of "action" units.

Such a transition area does indeed exist in the processes characteristic of servo-mechanisms or goal-seeking machines. In the simplest machines of this sort, the goal is some physical state, say a steady temperature maintained by a thermostat or a steady speed of rotation maintained in a flywheel by a governor. To a naive observer, a furnace controlled by a thermostat seems to be guided by a "goal" to keep the temperature of a room within comfortable limits. The furnace seems to "know what to do" and when to do it. But it is still easy to describe the process in purely physical terms. The furnace can be only "on" or "off," and each condition is determined by a range of temperature. Thus, the "behavior" aspect of the furnace is readily reducible by simple inspection to a complete description in terms of physical variables.

However, in the case of very complex servo-mechanisms, this is no longer the case. For example, a target-seeking missile or an automatic chemical plant will seem to a naive observer to be "behaving," and he will not be able to specify the "behavior" in terms of deterministic statements involving measurable quantities. The target-seeking missile will seem to him to be "chasing" the target; the automatic chemical laboratory will seem to him to be "doing what is necessary" to bring about an end result, that is, the production of a required chemical, regulating the various processes in just the way they need to be regulated, even if the conditions vary in an unpredictable manner. Such processes are easily recognizable but not at all easily described. Just as it is easy to see that a cat "is chasing" a mouse but practically impossible to state what a cat does in response to every possible situation that may arise in the chase, so it is easy to see that a target-seeking missile "is chasing" the target but practically impossible to describe its behavior in all possible circumstances in concrete quantitative terms.

Nor does the engineer who constructs the servo-mechanism prescribe *specifically* the behavior of the mechanism in all conceivable circumstances. What he builds in is a set of "general rules," physically realized by a network of connections which determine how inputs into the mechanism shall be converted into outputs. The cardinal principle of a servo-mechanism—feedback—is the circumstance that discrepancies between performance and preset goal are also inputs. Outputs resulting from these inputs become then corrective or adjusting actions with the result that the output of such devices begins to resemble "behavior" rather than a determinate physical process. Nevertheless, the principles of operation of these devices depend exclusively on determinate physical processes subject to laws which govern inert matter. Therefore, it is reasonable to conclude that the fundamental difference between "actions" (as Driesch has called them) and determinate physical processes does not really exist. There is only an apparent difference resulting from the ease with which actions can be named by their end results and the difficulty of describing them in terms of series of sequentially determined events.

Those who accept the extention of the antivitalist view to psychology believe that these examples are sufficient to establish in principle the objective equivalence of determinate physical process and behavior. If such equivalence is established, one can proceed to the analysis of behavior on the next level. That is, one assumes that behavior is composed of determinate physical processes. The actual reduction is too difficult to carry out in specific cases, but it can be by-passed at the next level of analysis, namely, that involving the conditional relations among the actions themselves. When we do this, we pass to the level of experimental psychology.

The task here is to find relations between the inputs to an organism and the outputs by the organism. The inputs, however, are no longer physical processes. Rather, they are situations; the outputs are, of course, actions. It is assumed that situations are "recognized" by the organism as units and that the actions are performed as units. The problem now is to see whether we can make further inroads into the concept of "mind" on this level of analysis.

Again let us recall Descartes' explicit differentiation between animals and men. He held the former to be automata, the latter the possessors of minds or souls.

The only automata known to Descartes were clockworks. The "behavior" of a clockwork is entirely prescribed. Once it is wound up, its parts go through a predetermined sequence of motions determined by a fixed arrangement of the parts. It is not clear whether Descartes thought of the behavior of animals in this way. Today we would dismiss such a notion as absurd. A clockwork does not even have inputs in the usual sense, that is, the outside world cannot influence the course of events prescribed by the inner mechanism of a clockwork except to start the mechanism, to stop it, or to destroy it.

One would think that in the case of a living organism at least the dependence of outputs upon inputs should be recognized. A juke box is a good example of an automaton whose mechanism ensures a one-to-one correspondence between a range of inputs (selections) and outputs (records played). This model already exhibits a form of behavior of which a simple clockwork is not capable, namely, a conditionality of response. It has a *repertoire* of inputs which it "understands" (i.e., is able to translate into corresponding outputs) and a *repertoire* of outputs.

However, even a superficial reflection shows that no matter how large the repertoire of such an automaton may be, it cannot simulate the simplest type of behavior which we intuitively associate with "intelligence," i.e., the possession of mind. For the first symptom of intelligence is a plasticity of response, the ability to modify the response to a given stimulus.

Pavlov's studies on the conditioned reflex showed that an animal's response to a given stimulus is indeed modifiable and, be it noted, in a predictable way. However, the first conditioning experiments did not connect the modification of response with an adjustment process, that is, did not show that the new response is somehow "better" for the ani-

mal than the old one. Classifical conditioning was explained simply by
the temporal contiguity of the conditioned stimulus and a response,
which before conditioning had been elicited only by its own (unconditioned) stimulus. It was not long, however, before these experiments
were extended to real learning situations. Animals learned to respond to
stimuli with "correct" actions reflecting a facilitation of "rewarded responses and an inhibition of "punished ones."

At the time when conditioning and learning experiments were being
conducted, the role of the nervous system in channeling excitations and
inhibitions associated with stimuli and responses was already fairly well
understood Accordingly, "quasi-neurological" models were soon postulated to account for conditioning and learning phenomena. The characteristic feature of learning models was that the outcome of each response
was included in the situation as a stimulus. Thus, a "feedback loop" was
closed in the schematic representation, and the learning organism was
shown to be comparable to a servo-mechanism whose preset goal was
the adjustment of "proper" responses to proper stimuli. The connection
between learning (a feature of intelligence, hence presumably of mind)
and in principle objectively identifiable events was thus also established.

The behavior of a learning system can therefore be described in "if
so . . . then so" terms, provided the "if so" part includes not only events
impinging at a given moment of time, i.e., the "state of the world," but
also events which had impinged on the system at previous times. The
range of conditionality of response is thereby significantly increased.

We shall illustrate by the simplest example. Suppose a system has a
repertoire of two stimuli (situations), S_1 and S_2, and two responses, R_1
and R_2. A simple automaton in which there is a rigid one-to-one correspondence between stimulus and response, say $S_1 \rightarrow R_1$; $S_2 \rightarrow R_2$, can be
constructed very simply by connecting the stimulus-activated (afferent)
element S_1 to the response-activating (efferent) element R_1, and similarly
for S_2 and R_2. If we further demand that R_1 and R_2 never occur together,
we can ensure this by "cross-inhibitory" connections as shown in Figure 1.[7]

Now, suppose we wish to endow our system with some "plasticity" of
response. If the repertoire is to remain unchanged, only one significant
variant of behavior can be introduced, namely, the (only) other corres-
pondence between stimulus and response, to wit: $S_1 \rightarrow R_2$; $S_2 \rightarrow R_1$. Call
the two possible forms of behavior B_1 and B_2. Suppose that the one or
the other form of behavior is elicited, depending on a previous experience

7. This paradigm of the stimulus-discriminating model is at the basis of a mathematical theory of the central nervous system developed largely by N. Rashevsky,
H. D. Landahl, and others of the "Chicago School" of mathematical biophysics.
For a discussion of related topics see N. Rashevsky, *Mathematical Biophysics* (Chapters 39, 41, 44, and 45), University of Chicago Press, Chicago, 1948.

E, which is also of two kinds, E_1 and E_2. That is to say, if E_1 has impinged on the system, then B_1 obtains: S_1 elicits R_2, and S_2 elicits R_1. But if E_2 has impinged, then B_2 obtains: S_1 elicits R_2 and S_2 elicits R_1. An automaton realizing these conditions is shown in Figure 2.

This automaton can be said to exhibit a very primitive form of "intelligence." Not only does its response depend on the stimulus, but also the *way* it responds depends on a preliminary stimulus. If in our simplest automaton (A_1, shown in Figure 1), the stimuli S_1 and S_2 are interpreted as "instructions" on how to respond, the stimuli E_1 and E_2 in A_2 (Figure 2) can be interpreted as instructions on how to interpret future instructions.

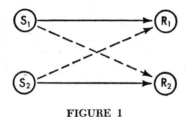

FIGURE 1

Automaton A_1. Schematic representation of a "neural net" that leads a stimulus-activating (afferent) element S_1 to elicit a response by the efferent element R_1 and similarly for S_2 and R_2. The dotted lines indicate inhibitory connections. Thus, R_2 cannot occur when S_1 is activated, because the element S_1 inhibits the element R_2 and similarly for S_2 and R_1.

Now "learning" can be viewed formally in just this way. We can say we have learned something when we have acquired the ability of selecting a proper response to each of a set of stimuli. We can also relearn, that is, we possess plasticity of behavior patterns. To relearn means to change the associations between stimuli and responses. Finally, we store in our memory certain sets which we "plug in" as responses to situations. Thus, the proper response to the self-induced stimulus "when" may be "can I see you?" or "in the course of human events," depending on whether we are asking for an appointment or reciting the Declaration of Independence.

The principles just described can be used to construct automata of arbitrary complexity and plasticity. It follows that the mere complexity and conditionality of responses in supposedly intelligent organisms does not force us to postulate the operation of an extramaterial principle. As far as we have gone, activities usually attributed to mind can be brought about by proper arrangements of material components. It has been shown mathematically that as long as the pattern of responses can be specifically described, including the changes brought about in these patterns by specific events impinging on a system, the behavior of a

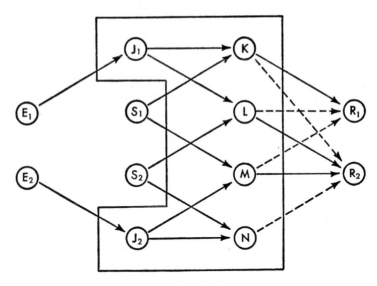

FIGURE 2

Automaton A_2. Schematic representation of a "neural net" in which the correspondence between the afferent elements S and the efferent elements R depends on a prior activation of elements E. To an observer ignorant of the boxed-in section of the net, it will appear that the system "follows instructions" (coded through E_1 and E_2) on how to respond to stimuli S_1 and S_2. Elements K, L, M, and N can be activated only if two elements impinging on one of them (that is, two from set J_1, S_1, S_2, J_2) are activated simultaneously. Thus, if E_1 is activated followed by S_1, then J_1 and S_1 will be activated simultaneously. In this case K and consequently R_1 will be activated; but if E_2 precedes S_1, then M will be activated (via S_1 and J_2) and consequently R_2. As previously, dotted lines indicate inhibitory connections. It is assumed throughout that a constant interval of time elapses between the activation of successive elements in a chain.

system can be realized in an automaton.[8] Hence, the plasticity of behavior attributed to organisms possessing minds or analogous features need not place the behavior of such organisms beyond determinate physical processes as long as the implications of this plasticity are spelled out in terms of specific patterns and specific changes of patterns of which the organism is capable.

The recently developed technology of servo-mechanisms and automata has successfully simulated many types of behavior which had hitherto been thought to be possible only in living or even intelligent beings. Indeed the activity of these devices has replaced corresponding activity of human beings, activities involving regulatory actions, e.g., the piloting of aircraft, adjustment of outputs of machines; and decision processes,

8. W. S. McCulloch and W. Pitts, "A Logical Calculus of the Ideas Immanent in Nervous Activity," *Bull. Mathematical Biophysics,* 1943, 5:115-133.

e.g., mathematical calculations. Logical deduction is likewise entirely within the scope of automata. This is obvious today since the structure of ordinary logical operations has been shown to be strictly isomorphic to certain mathematical systems, e.g., Boolian algebra, with which certain networks of relays or electronic devices can in turn be made isomorphic. The existence of calculating and "logically reasoning" automata is the concrete consequence of these theoretical results. We should keep in mind, however, that only a little more than a century ago, some esteemed philosophers ridiculed the idea that logic could be formalized as a mathematical system.[9] Logic, they maintained was "qualitatively different" from mathematics and therefore related to an entirely different "capacity of the mind." It is safe to assume that those philosophers would have dismissed the demonstration of an automaton performing logical operations and deductions as a charlatan's stunt. Whether they would have modified their view if they were convinced that such devices are genuine, we cannot say. But we cannot help being impressed by the fundamental difference of outlook induced respectively by metaphysical speculations on the nature of mind and by attempts to spell out just what it is that the mind is supposed to do.

5. The Problem Still Remaining—"Creative Thinking"— and the Proposed Solution

The analogy sometimes drawn between logical and computing automata on the one hand and the human brain on the other is an extremely touchy subject. Discussions of the philosophical questions which such an analogy naturally suggests have been characterized by more emotional involvement than is usual in scientific discussions. The publicity attending the building and operation of high-speed computers with the usual exploitation of sensational angles did not help the situation. The nickname "giant brains" calls to mind the awry climate of science fiction, especially the nowadays frequently recurring theme of the sinister use of power conferred by scientific knowledge. One sometimes gets the impression from reading popular accounts that the question "Do electronic brains really think?" is a foremost philosophic question of our day. Again, we shall be careful to avoid metaphysical blind alleys and will try instead to pursue our inquiry further step by step. We shall ask instead:

"If one says that machines are (or are not) capable of performing

9. See the Preface to the centennial edition of George Boole's *The Mathematical Analysis of Logic*, Philosophical Library, New York, 1948 (first published in 1847, Macmillan, Barclay, & Macmillan, Cambridge; George Bell, London.)

mental operations, what does this statement imply about the speaker's conception of mental operations?"

For if one *specifies* the nature of mental operations, then the question of whether a machine can perform them becomes an empirical question —not to be argued about but to be verified. One thing is certain: if one associates mental operations with one's direct (introspective) experience of these operations, then the question "Do machines think?" is unanswerable. But then the question "Does my brother think?" is equally unanswerable. One does answer the latter question, of course, usually in the affirmative, but this is only because the convention that someone who is very much like me "feels" like me is a convenient and wholesome social convention. Except for the general satisfaction provided by such a convention, there is no compelling reason for making it. Similarly, to say that "a machine does not really think" is also to adhere to a convention, which is probably also wholesome in the sense that it forewarns against idolatry, especially technological idolatry, which many feel is a serious threat to some values we cherish.

But if the question is unanswerable when thinking is conceived only introspectively, has the question any sense at all? I think it has. One can impart sense to the question by trying to spell out in terms of objectively identifiable events what one means by "thinking." However, what we mean by thinking is not unchanging. Indeed, changes in our concept of thinking are instigated to a great degree by the advances of automaton technology. I would even go so far as to assert that in this philosophical re-evaluation of the nature of thought lies the greatest potential contribution of automaton technology to our culture. The material rewards of technological achievements eventually reach the point of diminishing returns. At a certain state we cease to profit by becoming richer and more powerful. But we can always profit by becoming wiser.

Let us now think of a way of constructing an adding machine, that is, an automaton which will respond to an input consisting of two positive integers with an output which is the sum of these two integers. One (very foolish) way to proceed would be to connect the input and output elements in such a way that the output corresponding to the sum of every two inputs would be activated by a special connection. Automation A_3 can add any two positive integers, each of which does not exceed two. Even for this limited capacity, the circuitry is involved. If we were to extend the capacity to sums up to ten thousand, the circuitry would become still more involved. If we were to demand that not only pairs of integers but arbitrarily large sets of integers should be summable simultaneously (i.e., column sums), the complexity would transcend all reasonable bounds.

Obviously this is not the way to build a practical adding machine.

The simple desk calculator, on which any set of integers can be added up to, say, 999,999, works on a different principle. It has built into it the rules of decimal addition. Numbers have positional representation. Addition of digits is accomplished by rotating corresponding wheels through corresponding angles, and an arrangement of gears ensures that each complete revolution of a wheel (adding 10) results in a revolution of the wheel representing the next decimal through one unit. Having built a desk calculator of this sort, it is a very simple matter to enable it to subtract as well as add. It only takes a reversal of the direction of rotation to do this.

Perhaps it is a good idea to refrain from asking whether a machine thinks. But the following question seems fruitful: "Does the desk calculator just described resemble something that thinks to a greater degree than the automaton A_3 (Figure 3)?"

In my opinion, the answer must be yes. The construction of the automaton A_3 provides separately and independently for an answer to every possible question that it "understands." There is nothing left for the automaton to "do" than to respond in the way that it had been specifically "instructed" (constructed) to respond. This is not the case with the desk calculator. All the possible sums which it can be asked to do were not even listed, let alone provided for specifically in the construction. Instead, the *principle* of addition was built in. The calculator gives us the specific sums by "applying" the general principle. It is

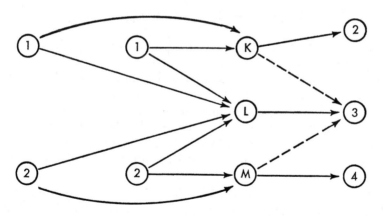

FIGURE 3

Automaton A_3. A simple-minded adding machine, in which each sum is provided for by a separate set of connection. As in A_2, K, L, and M can be activated only by two elements simultaneously. Addition is performed by activating one of the elements on the extreme left together with one in the next column. Thus, 1 and 1 will activate both K and L; but K will inhibit 3 (dotted line), and so only 2 will be activated. If 1 is combined with 2 (or 2 with 1), only L will be activated, and consequently 3. Two 2's will give 4 in the same way that two 1's give 2.

not our intention to call this translation from general principle to specific response "thought," but we submit it is more like thought than the rigidly circumspect set of responses of A_3. In order to build A_3, the builder himself had to know all the sums. But he did not need to know all the sums to build the desk calculator. All he needed to know was *how to add*. The calculator, after it is built according to the principles of addition can then tell the *builder* what a column of figures adds up to. Conceivably, then, the calculator could "know" more than the builder.

The last conclusion seems bizarre. If we know a general principle, it seems we should know all the specific cases where it applies. Thus, if we know the principle of addition, we know by implication all possible sums. Therefore, to conclude that the desk calculator may tell us something we do not know seems farfetched. It should be understood that we are here ignoring the well-known facts that computers can "work" far more rapidly than human beings, may be less subject to errors, etc. It is not quantity or speed or accuracy of thought that interests us here but the "quality." Can an automaton truly tell us something we do not know? In the case of a routine operation like addition, the answer should, after all, be no; for if we know how to add, then we do "know" in principle all possible sums, and, given time and patience, we could state them.

But consider how far we ought to go with such a conclusion. If there is no limit, then we ought to assert that we know all the theorems that will ever be proved on the basis of the postulates of the present mathematical systems, because all of those theorems are implied by (contained in) the postulates. But this conclusion is even more bizarre than the previous one. Evidently to "know" truth A is not at all the same as to know truth B, which can be deduced from A.

It takes "genuine thought," as we understand thought today, to pursue complicated chains of deduction. It takes even more "genuine thought" to reverse the process, i.e., to make a creative induction in the sense of finding a small set of premises from which a given large number of propositions are consequences. We shall examine this problem of creative induction below. For the moment let us return to deduction as currently practiced by machines.

There is no principle which makes it impossible to construct an automaton that would deduce theorems from postulates.[10] In fact, at least one machine is in existence which deduces theorems found in Whitehead and Russell's *Principia Mathematica* and one which deduces theorems of Euclidean geometry. The builders of such machines are

10. A. Newell, J. C. Shaw, and H. A. Simon, "The Logic Theory Machine," *IRE Transactions IT-2*, 1956 (Sept.), pp. 61-79.

fairly confident that some will be built which can through their own process of deduction come up with new mathematical theorems of sufficient interest to be published.[11] Question: Are we willing to concede "thought" to such machines? This is not a rhetorical question. We are not implying that it should be answered in the affirmative. But we are reminding ourselves that unless we wish to take recourse to a purely introspective conception of thought (which enables us to deny thought to the machine, no matter what objective evidence of thought is marshaled), it behooves us also to answer the question, "If not, why not?"

In a way, the discovery of new truths by the processes of deduction can be called "creative" thought, because that is what the research mathematician does. Yet, we wish to draw the line somewhere so as to exclude "trivial" new truths from what we will take as evidence for thinking. For example, an adding machine, constructed so as to select at random arbitrary sets of numbers as inputs to be fed into itself, can grind out sums of these sets. Since it is likely that some of these sums have never been done before, this adding machine would be, formally speaking, "discovering new truths." Unless we restrict the definition of "new truth," we have here reduced the concept to a triviality.

Consider, however, a culture which knows some sums but not the rules of addition. If this is hard to imagine, consider a child who knows the multiplication table but not the rules of long multiplication. To such a child a multiplying calculator will seem to be discovering "new truths." Or, still better, consider the state of mathematical knowledge in Mesopotamia about 1800 B.C. This knowledge encompassed the solution of several algebraic problems, including the solution of some specific quadratic equations. But there is no evidence that the solution of the *general* quadratic equation was known at that time. A computing machine programed to solve quadratic equations by the general formula would certainly have seemed to the mathematicians of that time to be discovering new truths.

The most common objection to identifying such processes in automata with thought lies in dismissing the notion that any device whose principles of operation are completely known is capable of thought. This criterion seems objectively verifiable, not introspective, and, therefore, falls within the scope of our argument. According to it, no automaton thinks (hence, possesses a mind), because every automaton was constructed according to blueprints; therefore, its principles of operation are completely known.

1. Is the principle just proposed always unambiguously applicable?

11. H. A. Simon and A. Newell, "Heuristic Problem Solving: The Next Advance in Operations Research," *Operations Research,* 1958, 6:1-10.

2. If the principles of operation of the human brain should ever become "completely known," shall we then abdicate our self-appointed title of thinking beings?

3. Is it conceivable that we can never decide which of the following alternatives is true: Either the principles of operation of the human brain can in theory become completely known or these principles can never become completely known?

Discussion of the last two questions will be undertaken in the concluding section. Here we shall undertake to examine the first. It appears that automata can be definitely excluded from the class of thinking beings because their designers must be assumed to know how they work from the way they were built. However, does the complete knowledge of the principles of the construction always imply complete knowledge of the principles of operation?

To illustrate, let us examine the principles upon which we might build a chess-playing machine and compare them with the principles on which a ticktacktoe-playing machine could be built. In ticktacktoe it is possible to say specifically what the best move is in response to any given position, because the number of positions is not large, if the symmetry of the grid is taken into account. For example, there are only three positions resulting from the first move, namely center, corner, and side. The best answer to either corner or side is center, and the best answer to center is corner. Hence, there are just three positions that will appear on the second move. If the opponent of the machine has the first move (we assume this in our example), the third move is not controlled by the machine. Hence, all possibilities must be examined on this move. Of these there are twelve, etc. The number of possible situations to the end of the game remains manageable. Thus, a perfect ticktacktoe player can be easily constructed. It will never lose, and if its human opponent makes a single bad move, it will win. An observer ignorant of the principles of circuitry, watching the automaton play, might well conclude that it has a mind and makes judgments.

According to the criterion proposed above, however, this conclusion would be rejected. In fact, it is hard to imagine anything *less* resembling thought than a process of countering each situation with a rigidly fixed response determined in advance.[12]

Now a *chess*-playing machine could not be constructed in this way, because here the number of possible positions is too immense. Nevertheless, chess-playing machines exist. They operate not by built-in prescribed moves but by built-in general rules, "heuristics," as they are

---

12. Resemblance to thinking can be slightly improved here by having the machine choose variants of responses on successive plays wherever more than one best move is available.

sometimes called. A heuristic is a rule which prescribes how to evaluate each chess position according to certain criteria. The positions examined are the positions which can result from a given position after a certain small number of moves, say two by each player. Although the number of such positions can be very large, it is not unmanageable for a high-speed computer. The move selected can then be the move which will lead to the most valuable position after two moves, assuming that the opponent will make the best moves available to him.

Now let us see how the evaluation rules can be assigned. Obviously if a contemplated move provides the opponent an opportunity to check-mate, the contemplated move must be eliminated. Thus, immediate checkmate threats are parried. Next, if the machine can "see" a check-mate to the opponent on the immediate or on the next move, regardless of what the opponent does, this move (or moves) will be assigned the greatest value. Thus, the opportunity to impose checkmate will always be utilized.[13] If none of these situations is imminent, the quality of future possible positions will be evaluated by various general considerations. Some of the obvious ones are:

1. Material. Each piece in chess has a certain well-established average value. Exchanges which result in gain of material will be made, those which result in loss of material will be avoided.

2. Control of center.

3. Mobility.

4. Advancing a passed pawn.

5. Pressure on opponent's weak points.

Etc.

Each of the positions can be given an exact numerical value to the extent that the above desiderata are more fully realized for the machine and less fully realized for the opponent. This value is compounded of a weighted sum of the values of the position by the listed criteria. The set of weighting factors for the several criteria used obtaining this sum con-stitutes a particular heuristic. Once a numerical value is assigned to each of the foreseen positions, the machine will choose the move which will certainly lead to the most valuable position for itself, assuming that the opponent makes *his* best moves.

Now the automaton built on these principles has not been "told" what move to play in every conceivable situation. It has only been told what rules to apply in choosing moves, that is, it has only been told *how* to play. It does its own evaluations of specific situations. It is, there-

---

13. Extending this principle to two moves ahead will automatically enable the machine to solve all "mate in two" problems ever constructed and ever to be con-structed.

fore, a step removed from the ticktacktoe machine, and, it must be admitted, this step is in the direction of "thought," at least according to certain understanding of thought.

It may be pointed out that the designer still knows the principles which completely determine the behavior of the machine. So we are still obliged to deny "autonomy" to the automoton.[14] But now consider a further modification. Suppose after each game the machine adjusts the weighting factors which determine the relative importance of the criteria for evaluating positions. Suppose, moreover, that it makes such adjustments at first in a random fashion, as if conducting a "search." If it loses too many games, it will make adjustments roughly opposite to the ones preceding the losing streak; if it has a winning streak, it will make further adjustments in the same direction.[15] This machine will behave like a learning organism, making variations in its behavior pattern which are at first random, then more and more systematic, leading finally to the elimination of "punished" patterns and the fixation of "rewarded" ones.

Now if the designer himself did not know the "best" weightings for the criteria, while the machine, as a result of its "experience," arrives at such weightings, then the machine will be operating on principles not known to the designer, although the designer had built into the machine some other principles, which enabled the machine to achieve its "wisdom." This machine was not "trained"; it was "educated," that is, taught how to find out things for itself. We have now carried the "thinking" process still further. It is now possible to credit the machine with at least an aspect of creativity. Of course, the designer's "creativity" appears of a higher order, since he foresaw the *way* in which a machine may be endowed with the ability of "thinking creatively." But what has been

14. Again we are neglecting the superior speed and accuracy of an electronic computer.

15. Since the "search" is conducted in multidimensional space (where the coordinates are the weighting factors), it is not easy to specify what is meant by an adjustment in the same or in an opposite direction. The problem is not unlike that faced by an evolving species which can be viewed as making simultaneous progressive adjustments in all the "coordinates" of its genetic complex. The tremendous number of organisms which make up the species allow the species to move simultaneously in many possible "directions," so that natural selection can guide the genetic complex along the "right" direction. Of course, we do not have a comparable population of chess-playing machines. A simple machine would have to make its adjustments sequentially. However, there are only a few weighting factors, not thousands (like genes), and so the number of directions of adjustment can remain manageable. For example, if there are four weighting factors and if the adjustments occur in small steps of constant size, there are sixteen different directions to try out at each adjustment. After a "successful" adjustment, those directions will be tried first which are most positively correlated with the preceding one and vice versa.

done once, can be done again. The next step is to design a machine which would design a machine which would "think creatively" about chess and many other things.

6. The Problem Remaining

I would expect any reader seriously concerned with our central question "What is mind?" to feel thoroughly dissatisfied at this point, and I entirely share this feeling. For there is no sense in deceiving ourselves. We may have tried to capture something which perhaps by its very nature cannot be captured. We may have embarked on a pursuit like trying to find the horizon. We go where the horizon seems to be. But we do not reach the horizon. Perhaps the only possible answer to our question is "Whatever we say the mind is, we will discover that it is not." Our method has been to spell out the sort of behavior which we would be willing to attribute to a mind. Our analysis revealed that this behavior could often be simulated in a system subject only to laws which govern physical processes. So for a moment we could perhaps be tempted to conclude that mind is reducible to special spatiotemporal patterns of events. But as soon as we have done this, we are dissatisfied. It appears to us that we have not really captured the *essential* aspect of mind. If this vague feeling of dissatisfaction were our only grounds for rejecting each "model," we could attribute our reluctance to prejudice; and, indeed, there is no denying that some people's stubborn insistence on viewing mind as something beyond the scope of scientific analysis is largely a manifestation of prejudice. But the fact is that we *can* point out the specific results of mental activities which we have no idea how to "program" into an automaton, even if unlimited time and resources were at our disposal.

For example, let us try to imagine an automaton whose input would be everything that was ever written on physics before 1905, and let the output (of course, not specifically arranged for) be a paper outlining the special theory of relativity. Let us imagine an automaton whose inputs would be all the sensory inputs that impinged on William Shakespeare or Michaelangelo or Bach and let it then produce a *Hamlet* or a *Moses* or a *B Minor Mass*. These are the usual examples. They are obviously selected to make it appear that the job of spelling out what the mind does is an impossible one. The enormous gap from "mechanized intelligence" to creative thinking, as we usually understand it, seems indeed unbridgeable.

But we need not invoke the creations of genius to illustrate our point.

Consider the twenty questions game. To reduce its difficulty, let the things thought about be confined to those expressible in phrases containing no more than 100 letters, and let the number of questions allowed be 2000. Our problem is to design a machine which will play a good guessing game. Let the object to be guessed be "the egg from which came the goose from which came the quill with which Chaucer began to write the *Canterbury Tales*."

From a certain joint of view, this is a trivial task. The following automaton will do the job very well. It exhibits the letters of the alphabet in succession asking whether each is the first letter in the phrase thought of. When the answer is yes, it does the same for the second letter. Also each time a letter is guessed, it asks, "Is this it?" Eventually the phrase will be constructed and guessed.

Among human players, this method of guessing is specifically disallowed, since it makes the game entirely trivial. The rules of the game allow only questions about "categories." Of these a few conventional ones will always occur: Real? Material? Does it exist now? Has it once existed? Has it existed in the Eastern Hemisphere? etc. All these categories can, of course, be included into the repertoire of a computer, together with the rules of making the next dichotomy, once one has been established. Still I doubt whether a computer can be programed which would "zero in" on the egg from which came the goose from which Chaucer's quill was taken and on *any other* subject which can occur to the human mind.

If this conjecture is correct, why is this so? The phrase can be guessed by a machine if the universe from which the building blocks for the construction of the guess is strictly circumscribed, in our example, the alphabet. In all probability, the phrase cannot be guessed if the universe is coextensive with the concepts which we can *potentially* form. In one case, we can completely specify the rules of sequential selection; in the other we cannot.

A similar problem is raised in the modern theory of syntactic structure.[16] Almost all children learn to speak their native tongue so that they are recognized as native speakers. This means that they make utterances recognized by other native speakers as acceptable utterances (sentences) in the language (or dialect). Suppose now we wish to construct an antomaton that will do the same. What shall we have to "teach" it? Listing *all* possible utterances is out of the question. Indeed, the essence of having learned a language is revealed in the speaker's

16. In what follows, I have drawn heavily on ideas put forward by Noam Chomsky, some of which are developed in his review of *Verbal Behavior* by B. F. Skinner in *Language*, 1959, 35:26-58. Any misinterpretation that may have crept in is, of course, my own responsibility.

ability to make *new* utterances which he has in all probability never heard but which are nevertheless recognized as acceptable ones. Evidently not a listing is required but a set of rules for constructing such utterances.

Now the rules we see in grammars are useless for this purpose. The rules mention terms like noun, verb, preposition, subject, predicate, gender, number, etc. These terms are defined with reference to other equally abstract terms: nouns with reference to "names of persons, places, or things" (is "wisdom" a place, person, or thing?), verbs with reference to "actions" (is "to contain" an action?). Definitions of prepositions, conjunctions, and articles are even more vague. To see this, try to define them so that the properties of "if" or "the" will be the consequences of the definition. The definitions we find in grammars and dictionaries are at best hints, which can be utilized by an adult mind either in the study of a foreign language or in bringing his own utterances closer to the usage peculiar to some social class (e.g., one can "improve" one's English). But these rules are useless for teaching an automaton to generate acceptable utterances on its own, even if we do not ask that the utterances are related to each other by a continuity of meaning.

Specific *and exhaustive* rules of syntax have evidently not been discovered.

There remains, however, the possibility of teaching an automaton to make acceptable utterances in the same way we have proposed for the automaton which is to learn to play acceptable chess—by selecting "heuristics" for making utterances which lead to a greater proportion of "acceptable" utterances and by eliminating other heuristics. But there is a fundamental difference. Whereas the chess automaton could register each game as won or lost, according to explicit criteria, there seem to be no rigid criteria which we can apply to decide whether an *arbitrary* given utterance is acceptable or unacceptable. *We* may be able to decide in each particular case, but we cannot yet build a *decision principle* into the machine. Thus, the machine can learn to improve its language only if a feedback loop is passed through it and a human speaker of the language. But if this is done, it is the man who guides the selection, not the machine!

If the set of explicit and exhaustive rules of syntax continues to elude us, i.e., if it continues to be impossible to build a machine which can learn to "speak grammatically" with an unlimited repertoire of utterances and without a human link in its learning circuit, then here is indeed a relatively simple example of the kind of evidence which puts "mind" definitely beyond the present scope of explicit analysis (hence of simulation) without recourse to tasks of unreasonable difficulty, such as writing dramas or creating new scientific concepts. The example appears to be indeed a simple one when we remember that *referential* meaning (i.e., meaning as translation of nonverbal experience into verbal utterance) has been excluded from the task. We do not ask of our machine to do what most three-year-olds can do—make judgments about the current, past, and future events, use veiled symbols to denote inner affective states, make "logical" grammatical mistakes which are not mere sound analogies but are indicative of deep internalization of metaphysical categories, such as time sequences, causal relations, anthropomorphic conjectures, projections of inner awareness, etc. In other words, although we ask of our machine considerably more than of a parrot, we do not ask nearly as much as we expect from a normal child just learning to speak. And even this seems entirely beyond our present automaton technology, hence beyond our present capacity to analyze mind in objective terms.

Another area of thinking which still seems beyond analysis (therefore beyond simulation) is induction as the inverse of deduction. In elementary textbooks on logic induction is illustrated by statements of general propositions on the basis of special examples: "This green apple is sour; this green apple is sour . . . ; all green apples are sour." This sort of reasoning is easy to simulate. All we need for a mechanized generator of elementary induction is a learning mechanism of a conditioned response type which will fixate a response to special cases. But consider a more sophisticated type of induction. Given a number of mathematical theorems labeled as "true," to find a system of postulates from which the theorems can be deduced. If a repertoire of such systems is specified, the job can be done by trying each system in turn until the deductive rules lead to the theorems. But suppose the repertoire of postulate systems is not given. It was not given to Newton. Yet he was able to find the system (the three laws of motion and the inverse square law of gravitational attraction) from which the empirically discovered Kepler's laws of planetary motion appeared as strictly deduced consequences.

The problem of the servo-mechanism capable of performing "actions" (pp. 285-286) also suggests an inverse problem: the problem of recognizing "situations." A "situation" is to an input variable what an action is to an output variable. Certain patterns of inputs must be classified together to recognize a situation. Again, the problem of pattern recognition has a trivial solution: one can simply list all the inputs which are to be subsumed under a single situation. But, of course, such a solution misses the point of the problem. The problem is to find the *rules* which govern the recognition of situations, so that an explicit listing becomes unnecessary.

Pattern recognition in automata is an important current problem of research.[17] It has proved, as one would expect, much more difficult, than the problem of goal-seeking action. For in the latter, goals can be specified, but not in the former. We do not know explicit criteria for "good" classification (except in very specific instances) and so cannot build them into Gestalt-recognizing machines.

Perhaps the most fundamental recognition problem is that of meaning recognition. A meaning-recognizing machine should be able to apply *general* rules to decide whether two given sentences do or do not say the same thing. Some of these rules may be simply grammatical transformation rules and so seem in principle mechanizable. "Peter hit Paul" and "Paul was hit by Peter" say approximately the same thing, and this identity of meaning is attributable to the grammatical transformation rule from active to passive verb form. There are also very simple semantic transformation rules. "Peter is taller than Paul" and "Paul is shorter than Peter" say the same thing in virtue of one such simple rule. But what is the transformation rule which enables any bright ten-year-old to recognize that "Every rose has thorns" and "There are no unmixed blessings" say approximately the same thing? Here we have gone beyond grammar and beyond formal semantics. We have entered the area of symbolic transformations, a jungle whose depth psychologists have been valiantly attempting to chart. Psychoanalysis, for example, is one attempt to understand the working of the human mind by discovering the rules of symbolic transformation according to which early childhood experiences are embedded as the components of the adult personality.

Whatever the merits of a particular postulated system of such transformations (e.g., the Freudian system relies heavily on sexual and proto-sexual experience as the source of the transformation rules), the importance of such attempts cannot be overestimated. For they strike at the frontier: the manifestations of the human mind which still defy rigorous analysis.

These, then, are the current problems, related to the problem of understanding the mind: syntactic and semantic analysis of language; creative induction; recognition of situations; the role of symbolic transformations in personality formation and behavior. In arriving at these problems, we believe, we have arrived at the frontier, separating the aspects of mind which we have understood from those which still elude our understanding. The frontier is further out today than it was even recently, well within our memory. Therefore, it appears that those

17. See, for example, O. G. Selfridge, "Pattern Recognition and Modern Computers," and G. P. Dinneen, "Programming Pattern Recognition," in *Proceedings of the 1955 Western Joint Computer Conference, IRE.*

who maintain that mind is in principle unanalyzable in scientific terms have been retreating, just as the vitalists have been retreating in biology. But the complementary "advance" can continue only if the frontier is always kept in sight. As some aspects of mind are "explained away," we must immediately focus on others, which are sure to appear, like the retreating horizon.

It may, therefore, happen that the problem of "mind" will always be with us; that the working of the human brain will never be "completely" understood, because as understanding increases, more questions will inevitably appear than have been answered.

The last statement is not about the mind but about our future knowledge (and ignorance) *about* the mind. Logicians say that such statements belong not to an object language (which contains statements about some objectively identifiable portion of the world) but to a meta-language (which contains statements about what we say or can say in the object language). We might also define meta-languages of higher order, related recursively to each other. The existence of meta-languages offers special challenges in epistemology, in particular problems related to the existence of undecidable propositions. We might, for example ponder on the question of whether question 3 on page 296 implies a decidable proposition or not, and whether the question which we have just raised itself implies a decidable proposition.

Question 2 is of a different sort. There the possibility of "complete knowledge" of the human *brain* is admitted. Such complete knowledge might be claimed, for example, if a one-to-one correspondence between physically identifiable events in the brain and descriptions of directly perceived inner states can be demonstrated.[18] The question pertains, then, to the fate of our future self-concept in the light of such knowledge. A reasonable answer might, perhaps, be the following. As detailed knowledge of the physicobiological basis of our mental apparatus increases, the questions concerning the nature of mind will become less charged with affect and anxiety. Perhaps in due time our title as beings endowed with a mind will come to mean considerably less to us than it does today; just as occupying the center of creation has come to mean considerably less to men as they have acquired appreciation of the vastness and grandeur of the cosmos.

18. Occasional experiments indicate that we may be on the verge of such discoveries. See, for example, W. Penfield, "The Interpretive Cortex," *Science*, 1959, 129:1719-25.

W. ROSS ASHBY

What Is Mind?

Objective and Subjective Aspects

in Cybrenetics

The advent of cybernetics has thrown a good deal of light on some of the old problems of the relation of mind and brain, and the time has undoubtedly come when we may usefully begin to ask how the old concepts appear in the light of the new facts. We shall find that some of the old concepts require drastic revision.

The cybernetician is concerned essentially with behavior, with what a system *does*. When asked about its "mind," therefore, he becomes uneasy. "Mind," to him, starts by being a word of four letters, to which he will admit meaning only as it is shown to have reference to some demonstrable feature of behavior. Yet the cybernetician is also human, and he knows that he has subjective experiences—a sight of greenness, or the emotional effect of a musical chord—that he cannot demonstrate *directly* to others. He finds, therefore, that his approach to the subject falls at once into two aspects; there is the objective—mind as it may be seen in others, and the subjective—mind as he experiences it in himself. These two aspects seem to be profoundly different and to involve two universes of discourse so separate as to have, at present, no common ground. Since this separation (much as one may regret it) seems to me to be undeniable, at least as we see it today, I shall discuss the question: "What is mind?" in two separate sections.

I

Let us, then, set the introspectional aspects on one side for the moment, and consider mind as it is shown in others, whether in man, animal, or machine. Here, the outstanding fact today is that our understanding of these matters has been immeasurably clarified and deepened by the advent of the general purpose digital computer. Let me hasten to add that I refer to it not for the various tricks it can perform in mimicking elementary human functions but because its advent has forced the development of *a complete logic of mechanism*. Until it came, "mechanisms" were just the heterogeneous devices, mostly of metal, found in the inventor's workshop. Since its advent we have been forced to clarify our thinking, and to develop an adequately *general* theory of mechanism.

The computer's essential feature, from this fundamental point of view, can be easily described. It is a machine in which the operator can prescribe, for any internal state of the machine and for any given condition affecting it, what state it shall go to next. This power of the operator may seem trivial, but allow him to use it as frequently and with as great variety as he chooses, and the power becomes total, within the realm of behavior. All behaviors are at the operator's disposal, subject only to practical limitations of time and money. Name the behavior, and the logic of mechanism leads inexorably to a program that, with the machine, forms a whole mechanism that will show the behavior.

The relation of mechanism to behavior is thus today understood with a completeness that was quite lacking even twenty years ago. In those days the question "can a machine do it?" could be answered in only a few cases, and then only when some device had been invented actually to do the job. In those days a philosopher could reasonably maintain that certain forms of behavior were quite beyond a merely mechanistic system. Today the question "can a machine do it?" is dead, for we know the answer to be always "yes." The reason is that the specification of the behavior gives to the operator all the information he needs for programing the general computer to do it. (Most of the difficulties that remain today are difficulties in defining clearly what it is we want the machine to do. The request "what is the square of this matrix?" defines clearly what is wanted, but the request "find a neater proof of Pythagoras' theorem" leaves undefined what is meant by "neater"; nor is an unambiguous definition easily decided on.) Meanwhile, however, the statement that a machine can produce *every* well-defined form of behavior is uncompromising, and must stand unless a specific example to the contrary can be produced.

The reader who is unconvinced may wonder whether the statement holds for the various activities known loosely as "intelligent" or "adaptive." Here the problem has been clarified by the works of Sommerhoff and the writer. Sommerhoff showed, in 1950, how the basic concepts of adaptation, coordination, integration, purpose—essential in the biologist's working set of concepts—could all be given completely objective definitions in terms of behavior. And since the general computer can produce *any* type of behavior, we are now able to specify the program, or the machine, that will produce such behaviors as show adaptation, coordination, integration, purpose. The present writer's work, published independently in 1952, solved essentially the same problem with essentially the same answer, by showing that "adaptive" behavior corresponds to certain forms of "stability" in a mechanism, and by showing that "stability" could be related directly to the nature of the mechanism showing it. Thus today the position is that the building of a machine of any required power of adaptation is bounded only by the sheer quantity of work that must be done if the program, or the machine, is to show adaptation in major degree. Thus, so far as "mind" has an aspect of "adaptability" or "intelligence," shown objectively in behavior, all of this aspect can be shown by mechanism, which shows the aspect by its *way of behaving.*

Another unconvinced reader may raise the question whether the power of the general computer to produce all forms of behavior extends to the emotional; can a machine produce rhetoric, music, art?

Before answering, let us postpone till Section II those subjective aspects that would be raised by the question: can a machine feel? Here we ask only: can a mechanism *behave* in a way appropriate to various emotions? Again the answer must be yes; for the reader who asks: Can the machine produce rhetoric? must be prepared to define or specify what he means by rhetoric; and as fast as he produces his specification in terms of behavior, so fast can the machine be programed to do it.

The proposition that *all* forms of emotional behavior can be produced by the general computer can perhaps be made intuitively more obvious if one remembers that mere celluloid, silver grains, and dyes, in the hands of such a programer as Walt Disney, can be made to represent practically every form of emotional behavior known to drama. So it seems that the *emission* of that aspect of mind that transmits emotion to others is possible to mechanism, for ultimately it means simply that the emitter must produce a particular way of behaving.

It is perhaps now clear that those who think of "mind" and those who think cybernetically are approaching the same phenomena with somewhat different basic ideas. Modern studies in the logic of mechanism have shown exhaustively how every concept properly applicable to a dynamic system (whether human, animal, or mechanical) has reference ultimately to various ways of behaving. The possession of "mind," therefore, must come ultimately to the identification of certain ways of behaving. But the four-letter word "mind" is a noun, a substantive, referring to a thing or substance. Clearly the person who uses the noun and the person who thinks of ways of behaving are somewhat at cross-purposes in their basic concepts. Can we resolve the confusion?

We have now left the world of mechanisms and their logic and have come to that of semantics. It seems to the writer that we can regain our clarity by the following considerations.

The English language allows a great variety of conceptual types to come to the noun form. Brown gives brownness, to act gives action, quickly gives speed, and so on. The flexibility is often convenient, but it has dangers. Thus, if we say: The dog runs, the statement is clear and simple. We can also say: The dog runs quickly, and also: The dog runs with a bone, and each of these sentences is simple and natural. But we can also say: The dog runs with a bone with speed, and the semantic trap is set. By using a noun form—with speed—for what is essentially adverbial—quickly, as a *way of running*—we are in danger of being led to thinking about speed in ways that are really appropriate only to bones, and if we persist in the analogy we may go on to ask such questions as: How does the dog hold on to the speed? or: What is the speed made of? or: What sort of stuff *is* speed?

Put in this way, and in this example, the whole semantic muddle may sound trivial and contemptible, but we must remember that when Descartes posed to himself the question: What is mind? he lived in a century in which great discoveries were being made, of the type in which some property of a body was demonstrated as due to its *containing* some*thing*. Ethyl alcohol had been separated from wine, and the intoxicating quality of wine had quite reasonably been attributed to the alcohol it contained. The heaviness of litharge was shown to be due to the lead it contained, and the briny taste of sea water had long been known to be due to the salt it contained. In such a context he might well ask: And what is contained in the brain that will explain its remarkable properties? Whatever it is, said Descartes, let us assume its existence and give it a name: I suggest we call it—mind. He saw ways of behaving, and deduced a substance. He saw an adverb, and deduced a noun.

The change, from adverb to noun, has led to a great deal of confusion. We can restore order by noticing that the transition can be made properly only when certain conditions hold. The chief of these is that the ascribed property must have noun-like properties, i.e., it must behave as a substance or a thing behaves. The alcohol extracted from wine certainly has these properties: it can be stored in a bottle, passed from hand to hand, remixed with water, reseparated, and so on. It persists unchanged in time, and it does not change as it is moved from place to place. (The same applies to the lead from litharge and the salt from sea water.) This double *invariance* shows at once that we are dealing with something of unusual simplicity, so far as the communication of its property to the observer is concerned. Contrast this invariance in time with, say, the *pattern* of waves on a piece of sea; its changeableness shows that "pattern" lacks one of the elementary properties of substance or thing. So too do those properties of the shadow of a moving body which change as the shadow falls on surfaces of varying shape or position.

The fact is that we human scientists, shaped by evolution, are rightly impelled by our nature to take advantage of every simplicity that our environment offers. One such simplicity is the behavior called "thing-like." When it is shown by certain *parts* of our environment (by a rattle, a toy horse, a slide rule), we seize on the simplicity and make our thinking about it correspondingly simple, and thereby efficient. But our drive for the simple may be overdone, and we may try to force the assumption of thingness or substance on to phenomena or systems that do not have the necessary simplicity.

Sometimes the assumption that a system has a property because it "contains" some "substance" can be sustained, but only at the cost of some artificiality, and the need to remember that "contains" and "substance" must be understood in some restricted sense. The physicist makes much use, for instance, of the idea that a system or body shows certain forms of behavior because it "contains energy." And the energy does show some of the properties of a substance, in that its total quantity is invariant, so that what disappears from one place must appear somewhere else. But the system "contains" energy in a sense that no longer has the special simplicity in which wine "contains" alcohol.

The "containing" can show in weaker forms till it becomes quite inapplicable. A spinning gyroscope is difficult to turn; we can say, without too much distortion of our thinking, that the difficulty is due to its "content" of angular momentum. We can say of the atmosphere on a stormy day that it conducts heat well because of its "content" of turbulence. But when we say of a sponge that it behaves as a sponge does because it "contains" a lot of holes, tempting us to think of the holes as a sort of "substance," then we are obviously reaching the point at which the analogy is breaking down.

Finally, in the general computer we reach a system that manifestly has so many possible behavioral properties (for it can do anything thinkable) that the invocation of some "substance" to account for each property would be merely ridiculous. Hence, we reach the really general case, in which each behavior is a fact in its own right, so that our discussions about it must be *in terms of the behaviors themselves*—they cannot be conducted in terms of some hypothetical underlying "substance."

To talk of mind, as a substantive, is thus as dangerous as talking of electricity as a fluid. To speak thus of organisms' ways of behaving is to use the inappropriate model of substances and things. Within some small range such a model may be appropriate, but over the whole range known today it is quite clearly inappropriate. Those who persist in using it are as mistaken as those who use an obsolete map, or Faraday's theory of electricity. Today we must use the truly valid concept of "ways of behaving."

II

So far as mind shows in objective behavior, then, we have today an *exact* understanding, for the modern logic of mechanism is complete in itself. But what of the subjective aspect, the inward self-awareness that is an inseparable part of the whole concept of mind? I can do little more here than record my conviction that cybernetics, while providing a brilliant light for the objective, has thrown absolutely no light on the subjective—has only made us even more acutely aware of how different are the objective and the subjective, and how different are their relations to the classic scientific methods.

(In this connection I must clarify the confusion that sometimes arises when experiments, on animals perhaps, study the animals' changes between somnolence and alertness. Such studies, in our present context, are purely objective, as objective as the study of the different responsivenesses shown by a portable radio set when connected, or not connected, to its battery.)

Returning to consideration of the subjective, of the facts given to a person by his own introspection, we can see that we are making a fundamental change from the point of view held in the first section. There we discussed the general theory of systems, but always from the point of view of an observer *outside* the system. Now we are considering the general theory of the system that "observes" itself internally. Such a branch of general system theory has hardly been started, though D. M. MacKay has insisted on the great importance of the distinction, and has given a dramatic example of its profundity. He points out that a prediction about a system, to be verifiable, must not itself act on the system (i.e., reach it as an effective communication), lest it act as a new factor affecting the system, falsifying itself. (A classic example occurred when the Gallup poll, predicting an election result, reached the public and upset the election severely.) Now if a person enters a situation to which his response may be predicted, an outside observer may make a prediction and see it verified, but the person himself, as soon as he makes the prediction about himself, is likely to be upset by the prediction itself. So of the person in the situation, the outside observer may say that he *is* predictable, while the person may say of himself that he is *not* predictable, and these two contradictory statements may be both true simultaneously —because one is made by an outside observer and the other by the system about itself. There can thus be no doubt, in the general theory of systems and knowledge about them, of the greatness of the change occurring when the observer changes from speaking of another system to speaking of himself.

The reader will have noticed that the essential feature of MacKay's example is that when the system makes predictions about itself there is feedback: the system produces the prediction, and then the prediction acts on the system, which may then produce a revised prediction, and so on. Now there seems to be a widely held intuitive notion that self-awareness has something to do with feedback, although at present the facts are few and obscure. I will try to indicate what seem to be the main points, none of them amounting to more than a hint, yet all of profound interest.

There is the fact, for instance, that most observers saw the point when W. Grey Walter demonstrated that his tortoise would produce a special form of behavior ("dance") when, and only when, it saw its own reflection. Furthermore, a moment's consideration of its machinery assures us that the dance can be produced only when the system is subjected to its *own* reflection—that of others does not sustain the necessary phase-relation. Most of us have felt that this demonstration was a major contribution to a most difficult subject.

Yet the contribution itself raises difficulties. Arranging the machine to see its own reflection is simply a particular case of the very general operation, on any system: Couple one of its outputs to one of its inputs. Now the general logic of mechanism assures us at once that such a coupling will always induce some new characteristic form of behavior. Exactly the same addition of new trajectories occurs in a set of dynamic equations, with arbitrary parameters,

$$\frac{dx_1}{dt} = f_1 (x_1 \ldots x_n; a_1, a_2, \ldots)$$

$$\frac{dx_n}{dt} = f_n (x_1 \ldots x_n; a_1, a_2, \ldots)$$

if one of the parameters (inputs) is made some function of (coupled to) one of the variables (outputs). When the new behavior appears in conditions of this generality, one is left puzzled to know to what degree the existence of the feedback is evidence of the existence of self-awareness.

Yet untutored intuition unhesitatingly supports the belief that self-awareness has something to do with feedback. An acquaintance of mine, of good sense but with no scientific prejudices, arrived at San Francisco, which to her had always been a somewhat fabulous place. "I had to pinch myself to see if it was really me," she said. Her phrase can readily be analyzed into technical terms about the setting up of a rarely used feedback so that the communication through the new channel ("feeling the pinch") should be relevant. But relevant to what?—at the present time honesty demands that we admit our deep interest and almost complete ignorance.

Perhaps one essential ingredient in this ignorance is our lack of understanding of how to relate the subjective and introspectional data with the objective and observable-in-others. The question comes to a focus in the simple question: Do animals feel pain? The Greeks held that they did not; we today hold that they do. What the scientist wants to know is not: Do they? but: What is *valid* evidence on the matter? With regard to this question, cybernetics says not merely that it has no answer, but adds that, as it is a science that deals wholly with the observable and demonstrable, it is not likely in future developments to make any contribution at all. It may, however, be able to act as sentinel, warning the would-be solver if he should suggest certain logical non-sequiturs. Thus, the suggestion has often been made (in view of the increasing size and complexity from amoeba to man) that mere size and complexity of organization may be a sufficient basis for the emergence of self-consciousness. Here the cybernetician can utter a warning that size and complexity of organization is measured on a natural scale involving the *quantity of communication* occurring, whether within the system itself, or from the system to the examining anatomist. So on this basis, says the cybernetician, all systems in which the amount of communication exceeds, say, 10^8 bits per second should have self-awareness. Such a level might include the largest general computers and would certainly include such complex dynamic systems as the Steel Industry, the Railways of Britain, the Russian Army, the Amazon Jungle. Those who claim that the complexity of the human brain is sufficient to explain its self-awareness must be prepared either to admit that the systems above have their own "personal" self-awareness, or to give reasons for the denial. The general theory of dynamic systems, the logic of mechanism, knows no reason why they should be excluded.

Summary

The facts given above seem to be those that display most clearly the contribution that cybernetics has to make toward consideration of the question: What is mind? So far as "mind" shows in objective behavior, in how *other* systems behave before an observer, its contribution is decisive and uncompromising. It has developed a complete logic of mechanism, which shows that the basic data in all such questions are *various way of behaving*, technically: sets of transitions. Among the various ways is the subset characteristic of things and substances. It raises objection to the question "What is mind?" on the grounds that the question makes implicit use of the model in which properties are ascribed to the "content" of a "substance." This model is suitable only in certain restricted and specially simple cases. The logic of mechanism, in the analyses given by Sommerhoff and the writer, shows that some of the main phenomena (such as integration and adaptation) are of quite a different type from those ascribable to a "content of a substance." Thus, so far as the objective phenomena are concerned, cybernetics insists that the question stated in noun form should be replaced by one in adverbial form, so that the question posed and its answers should alike be stated in terms of *ways of behaving*.

While cybernetics can speak to some point on the objective aspects of human behavior, it has only one thing to say on the subjective aspects, and that is—that it has nothing to say. It is true that the cybernetician can chat around the topics, perhaps interestingly, but the question is still open to what extent such chat is, or can be, relevant. This generation has largely solved the main problems of the brain so far as its objective behavior is concerned; the nature of its subjective aspects may be left to the next generation, if only to reassure them that there are still major scientific worlds left to conquer!

REFERENCES

Ashby, W. Ross, *Design for a Brain*, Chapman & Hall, London, John Wiley & Sons, New York, 1960 (second edition).
———, *An Introduction to Cybernetics*, Chapman & Hall, London, John Wiley & Sons, New York, 1956.
Sommerhoff, G., *Analytical Biology*, Oxford Univ. Press, London, 1950.
Walter, W. Grey, *The Living Brain*, Duckworth, London, 1953.

HENRY B. VEATCH

Minds: What and Where

in the World Are They?

Should you tell a man to mind his own business, he might well display annoyance, but it is scarcely likely that he would find himself in philosophical perplexity. For that matter, even George Bernard Shaw's purported rejoinder to Isadora Duncan, while it was no doubt calculated to cause perplexity of a sort, could hardly be supposed to have caused what one would normally call philosophical perplexity. Thus, it will be remembered how Miss Duncan was said to have proposed to Shaw that he have a child by her: "For just think what a superb creature it would be, endowed with my body and your mind." To which Shaw is reported to have replied that the idea was an excellent one, were it not for the unpleasant possibility that the child might turn out to have his body and her mind.

No doubt, this does raise a mind-body problem of sorts. And yet, if it be but a question of the intelligibility of terms like "mind" and "body," it is hard to imagine any statement that would be more readily, not to say inescapably, intelligible than this quip of Shaw's. But alas, the poor philosophers! It's as if for them no statement about minds and bodies were ever intelligible—at least not when these philosophers are functioning in their professional and academic capacity as philosophers.

And why not? Everyone knows the reason. It's because modern philosophers have been the unfortunate and unwilling heirs of Descartes' dualism of mind and body. And so far from its being a heritage they could very well renounce, it would seem that the entire course of development of modern science since the seventeenth century has made it practically impossible for the unhappy philosophers to disinherit even themselves. For as science tends to picture it, the world of nature is one in which there is just no place for such things as minds. And no sooner have various philosophers come along, seeking to rehabilitate the claims of minds—usually at the price of setting minds outside the world of nature altogether—than these same minds have a seemingly irresistible method of retaliation: excluded from nature, the worm turns and promptly includes the whole of nature in itself!

Unfortunately, too, as the history of modern philosophy attests only too well, the arguments either way seem at once ineluctable and irrefutable. What, then, is one to do under the circumstances? Adopt the sort of refutation that Dr. Johnson proposed with respect to Bishop Berkeley? After all, so far as our lived world of everyday human experience goes, the mind-body problem just doesn't seem to exist. It presumably did not exist for Shaw and Miss Duncan. And for the rest of us as well, as soon as we put aside various preconceived notions which we tend to prize as a mark of our scientific or philosophic sophistication, it seems perfectly evident that in the world in which we live there certainly are minds as well as bodies; and that this same world, so far from being wholly in the mind or even mind-dependent, has countless features which mark it as being and being what it is, independently of the way in which in your mind or in my mind or in anybody's mind it is taken to be.

Very well, then, why should we not in this present essay aim at an account of human minds, simply disregarding altogether the elaborate and somewhat artificial context of modern natural science? And lest such a program seem obscurantist in character, perhaps we need do no more than remark in passing that just as it is perfectly legitimate to ask whether and how minds can be fitted into the scientific universe, so also it would seem to be equally legitimate to initiate an inquiry into the way in which our human minds fit into the context of what one might call the everyday world of human experience? For that matter there is even a sense in which this everyday world has to be regarded as not merely prior to but even as an irreplaceable support and ultimate point of reference for all of the more or less sophisticated and highly artificial theories which have been propounded by scientists and philosophers in order to explain and interpret this world. Thus as Merleau-Ponty observes:

This first instruction which Husserl gave phenomenology at its beginning—that it be a "descriptive psychology" or a return "to things themselves"—is first of all the disavowal of science. . . . Everything I know of the world, even through science, I know from a point of view which is mine or through an experience of the world without which the symbols of science would be meaningless. The whole universe of science is built upon the lived world [*le monde vécu*]; and if we wish to conceive science itself with rigour, while exactly appreciating its sense and significance, we must first re-awaken this experience of the world, for science is its second impression. Science does not have and will never have the same kind of being that the perceived world has, for the simple reason that science is a determination or an explanation of that world. . . . To return to things themselves is to return to this world as it is *before* knowledge and of which knowledge always *speaks*, and with regard to which all scientific determination is abstract, referential and dependent, just as is geography with regard to the landscape where we first learned what a forest is, or a prairie or a river.[1]

Moreover, we would venture to suggest that such considerations as Merleau-Ponty here offers in support of the ultimacy of the human lived world or *Lebenswelt*, as over against the scientific universe—that these considerations may perhaps be supplemented by considerations of a moral or ethical nature. For it is not only when he is engaged in such everyday activities as eating his dinner, driving his car, or perhaps, *à la* Hume, playing backgammon with his friends, that the physicist, or the paleontologist, or the geneticist, or the archaeologist, whoever he be, and however learned and sophisticated he may be, will nevertheless find that he lives in much the same world as other men; but in addition, when as a moral agent, the modern scientist or scholar occupies himself, not with the objects of his research as such, but simply with himself and with what as a human being he proposes to do and be, then one wonders if he will not discover that his own personal moral situation, with its difficulties and perplexities, will not be startlingly like the moral situation in which, say, Socrates found himself, when he turned away from his cosmological speculations and undertook to try to know himself and to lead an examined life. After all, would anyone suppose that such personal issues as those of ambition, self-deception, discouragement, divided loyalties, conflicting responsibilities, personal integrity, self-respect, etc., are so very different for us in this nuclear age from what they have been for civilized men anywhere and everywhere? And if not, must we not recognize that for an understanding of human beings in the perennial human moral situation in which all men find themselves, the latest advances of science and technology would appear to be largely gratuitous and irrelevant?

With so much, then, by way of explanation and apology, let us pro-

---

1. *Phénoménologie de la perception*, Foreword, an English translation by Alice Koller, n.d., mimeographed, pp. 2, 3, 4.

ceed with our deliberate policy of bracketing all scientific preconceptions about human minds and the world of nature, of limiting ourselves simply to a consideration of what minds are and how they function right within our human *Lebenswelt*. And almost immediately, we are struck by one seemingly obvious and inescapable feature of human existence—i.e., of the existence of rational beings or beings endowed with minds. And that is, that human beings are beings who in some measure or other are capable of knowing what's what and of acting accordingly. Indeed, it is just this capacity which we all of us recognize ourselves as having, simply in virtue of our being rational animals, that originally provided the basis for Socrates' great plea for the examined life, as well as for Aristotle's insistence that the characteristic function, or *ergon*, of man is to live intelligently.[2]

What, then, must our human minds be, if they are to be the sources of, or perhaps to be simply identified with, this human capacity for knowledge and action? To answer this question, we would suggest, first of all, that at least one necessary characteristic of minds must be what, for want of a better term, we shall designate as intentionality. Moreover, to bring out the peculiar import of this notion intentionality in the present context, we venture to quote still another passage from Merleau-Ponty:

The scientific analysis of behavior is defined primarily by opposition to the given data of naïve consciousness. If I am in a dark room and a luminous patch appears on the wall and moves from place to place, I will say that it has "attracted" my attention, that I turned my eyes "toward" it, that in all its movements it "drew" my regard [after it]. Seized from within, my behavior appears as if it were oriented, [and] endowed with an intention and a sense. Science seems to demand that we reject these features as [mere] appearances beneath which it is necessary to discover a reality of a different kind. One will say that the light seen is "only in us." It conceals a vibratory motion, which itself is never given to consciousness. Suppose we call "phenomenal light" the qualitative appearance, "real light" the vibratory motion. Since the real light is never perceived, it could not present itself as an *end* toward which my behavior is oriented. It could only be thought of as a cause which acts on my organism. The phenomenal light was a force of attraction, the real light is a *vis a tergo*.[3]

From this passage, one might gather that there are at least two features of intentionality which deserve special mention. For one thing, there is the feature of what in the traditional terminology of Aristotelianism might be called final causation. Thus, in Merleau-Ponty's ex-

2. *Nicomachaean Ethics*, Book I, Chap. 7, 1098a, 4.
3. *La structure du comportement*, Paris, 1942, p. 4.

ample, my behavior is understood, not as proceeding simply from a *vis a tergo*, but rather as being ordered to, and as tending toward and intending, the light as its goal or objective.

Still, intentionality understood merely in terms of final causation— i.e., merely in terms of one thing's being ordered to something outside of itself and ahead of itself, so to speak—intentionality in this rudimentary sense scarcely does justice to the sort of intentionality that is characteristic of minds. For this one further feature is needed. In addition to *x*'s intending *y*, in the sense of being ordered to *y*, as something outside *x* and as *x*'s goal or object, there is now the further factor of *x*'s being aware of *y*, or knowing *y*. And this feature of awareness or knowing is so nearly *sui generis* that to describe it in terms of other processes and relationships can easily be misleading. Still, we might suggest that any awareness or cognition must not only be an awareness or cognition *of* something other than itself. After all, any instances of a mere tending or intending must be a tending *toward* or an intending *of* something else. But besides this, in any act of awareness, the subject of the awareness must somehow be outside itself, and where the thing known is. Or to put the same point in language that might seem to imply something quite different: the thing known or the thing of which a subject is aware must, despite its being other and elsewhere than the subject, nevertheless be present to the knowing subject.

Unfortunately, any and all such locutions to the effect that the mind, in its intentionality, is already out among the things to be known, or that all things insofar as they can come to be known are capable of being present to the mind or before the mind, or that the mind is able to become all things—all of these ways of putting the matter are misleading, simply because, if taken literally, they seem to suggest that knowing can be understood in terms of an ordinary causal action of a subject upon an object or of an object upon a subject. Thus, to say, for example, that in order to be known objects must be presented to or brought before the mind is to suggest that awareness involves a sort of impressing of objects upon a subject, much as impressions are made upon a photographic plate. But, of course, no matter what or how many impressions are made on a photographic plate, that still in no sense implies that the plate knows what is impressed upon it.

And more generally, mere presence, whether of thing known to knower, or of knower to thing known, still does not constitute knowledge. Rather, in addition to being presented, the thing known must also be disclosed or laid bare or, as Heidegger might say, "uncovered" (*ent-deckt*).[4] Of course, if one wishes, one can perhaps speak of an intentional

4. Cf. *Sein und Zeit*, § 44 (b).

presence, as contrasted with a mere physical presence; and yet such an expression would serve but to point up the *sui generis* character of the cognitive relationship, not explain it.

To be sure, it might seem that such a way of characterizing the intentionality of minds might well implicate us in all sorts of genetic questions as to just when minds make their appearance in the phylogenetic or in the ontogenetic evolution of animals. Or again, there is the question of just where the sort of intentionality characteristic of mere animal behavior ceases and where the sort that is characteristic of human minds begins. And yet we wonder if we may not obviate all such questions by simply remaining faithful to our original project of taking the phenomena of our ordinary everyday lived world, not just as points of departure, but as ultimate points of reference. We could then adopt as our own Heidegger's principle of the centrality and ultimacy of something like *Dasein*; and on such a basis one could very well contend that so far from its being the case that we come to an understanding of *Dasein* from an understanding of lower forms of life, it is rather only in terms of *Dasein*, and by regarding them as privative with respect to *Dasein*, that we come to understand these lower forms of life.[5]

Very well, then, may we not now press on rather more confidently to note certain further salient features of that intentionality which is characteristic of human minds? For example, what about the factor of universality? May we not say that this is a striking feature of human intentionality? Indeed, there would seem to be no way in which we human beings can describe anything or recognize anything for what it is without using universal concepts. Likewise, no inductive evidence is really of significance, save insofar as it enables us to establish a universal or general conclusion. And similarly, any explanation of *why* anything is the way it is, or of what the causes and reasons are for its being as it is—all such explanations can be effected only through the instrument of logical universals.

But at once, we can perhaps see that this device of universality has what might be called a liberating function, so far as the mind's intentionality is concerned. Instead of being riveted to a single, ineffable particular as the object of its intention, the mind, through its very instruments of universal concepts and universal propositions, comes to understand any object of its intention as being of a certain type or kind. It's as if the universal, in virtue of its very unity as a one with respect to many *(unum versus alia)*, had the effect of continually freeing the mind from the single object which it is intending, and carrying it to other similar, but nonetheless different, objects.

5. *Ibid.*, pp. 49-50.

Not only that, but insofar as we human beings use not just universal concepts, but propositions, or, if you will, indicative and declarative sentences, these latter are but so many ways of bringing us to recognize the objects of our intentions as actually being or existing. In this way there is brought about at least an implicit opening up or disclosure to the mind of the act itself of existing, of the fact that things are, of the "that" as contrasted with the "what." Moreover, from this there arises the recognition that while there may be a sense in which things can be said to be *what* they are necessarily, one cannot say *that* they are necessarily. And so once more, it becomes apparent how the mind's intentionality has at once a liberating, as well as a fixating, effect with respect to the objects of its intention.

Nor is the significance of this latter point to be overlooked, once we remind ourselves of what we earlier singled out as being the acknowledged function of our human minds and intelligences, so far as our existence in the lived world is concerned. For as rational beings, we consider that we are able not merely to know what's what, but also to choose and to act freely in the light of such knowledge. Indeed, as we remarked earlier, it is this fact about our human existence that led Aristotle to remark in at least one place that man's *ergon* is not just to exercise his intelligence, but to live intelligently.[6] And in a like spirit it was Socrates who gave over entirely his earlier activities of speculating about the cosmos, in order to devote himself entirely to the business of knowing and, as we might be inclined to add today, of being himself. Accordingly, for an understanding of the mind's intentionality in the context of the lived world, it is important to see how the mind's very intentions have the effect of freeing or liberating us, by carrying us beyond a necessitous immediacy and opening up the otherness of alternatives and the radical contingency of existence.

Moreover, so as to understand human minds in terms of what we may call the mind's intentional functions would seem to forestall any temptation on anyone's part to regard minds as if they were independent substances or to regard human beings as if they were somehow composite of corporeal substance on the one hand and mental substance on the other. No, on the view here presented, "mind" turns out to be but another name for that characteristic power or ability which human beings have of intending objects both cognitively and purposefully.

And yet there is an obvious difficulty that suggests itself at this point. For it may be asked just how one becomes aware of these characteristic intentional functions of our human minds? Just what is the nature of the evidence in support of this contention that human beings

6. *Loc. cit.*

are able to know of things that they are, and know them for what they are, and know why they are? Is it not always through observing ourselves, so to speak, and never through observing others, that we fancy that the things in the world become intentionally present to our minds, or that we grasp them through universal concepts and judge them to be thus and so?

Surely, though, this must have embarrassing consequences, so far as the objectivity of our knowledge of minds goes. Thus, I can observe quite objectively that another man is coughing, or that his blood pressure is mounting, or that there is an obstruction in his digestive tract. But that certain objects have become intentionally present to his mind, this is something which, as it would seem, I can never observe directly at all. Does not this mean, then, that there is no other way for me to know about the minds of other men, save by inference or by a kind of reasoning by analogy from my experience of my own intentional acts.

And with this, the fat is in the fire. Indeed, everyone is familiar with the characteristic behaviorist ploy at this point: these intentional acts of knowing and of acting or choosing on the basis of such knowledge— these are said to be acts that are not only not objectively observable, but in addition are no more than gratuitous and unnecessary fictions. Indeed, one has only to study the evidence derived from the study of animal behavior to convince oneself of this point. As Bertrand Russell observes with his usual sharpness:

> Most people would say that they infer first something about the animal's state of mind—whether it is hungry or thirsty and so on—and thence derive their expectations as to its subsequent conduct. But this detour through the animal's supposed mind is wholly unnecessary. . . . The characteristic mark by which we recognize a series of actions which display hunger is not the animal's mental state, which we cannot observe, but something in its bodily behavior; it is this observable trait in the bodily behavior that I am proposing to call 'hunger,' not some possibly mythical and certainly unknowable ingredient of the animal's mind.[7]

Moreover, having thus eliminated intentionality from animal behavior, it would seem to be but a step, and a very proper one at that, to eliminate it from human behavior as well. Apparently, one can do no more than exclaim *"Facilis descensus Averno,"* and, before one knows it, one will find oneself a behaviorist.

Nor, of course, is there anything wrong with being a behaviorist. In fact, if one accepts the current standards of scientific objectivity, it

7. *The Analysis of Matter,* London and New York, 1921, pp. 62-63.

may be impossible to give a scientific account of human behavior in anything other than behavioristic terms. Indeed, if one were to say with Professor Bergmann, "I believe as a matter of course that the world is Newtonian,"[8] then there may well be no alternative to behaviorism. And yet, as we have already suggested, the standpoint of the present essay is one in which one says, "I believe as a matter of course that the world is the lived world of everyday." From this standpoint the mere fact that the phenomenon of intentionality cannot properly be integrated into the scientific universe does not as such constitute a sufficient reason for behaviorism.

Nor is it entirely a matter of the mere arbitrary choice of standpoint either. For we would wonder whether the behaviorist himself, in the very act of understanding human behavior in the way he does, must not consider that such is the way in which human behavior presents itself to him. He will surely insist that he sees and understands it in this light. But this is tantamount to acknowledging that he thus intends the facts and data before him, and that they are thus intentionally present to him. In other words, considered simply as a human being who has ideas and theories about things, the behaviorist himself, in his very enterprise of confirming and developing his theory of behaviorism, will actually be viewing and understanding the facts and data of behavior in a way which that very theory of his would rule out as being either improper or impossible. It's simply a case of a man's left hand as a scientist not knowing what his right hand as a human being is doing.

Nor would it be difficult to provide still further confirmation of this, if, in addition to considering the behaviorist's own knowledge and awareness of the things which he professes to know and be aware of, we were also to consider the implications of his behavioristic convictions, so far as his own conduct and behavior are concerned. For there is no doubt that as a human being the behaviorist will certainly be impressed by what he believes to be the truth about human behavior. And yet is it not the very criterion of the intentionality of the human mind that human beings are not only capable of having knowledge and beliefs about things, but also of basing their choices and preferences precisely on what they thus consider themselves to know and believe?

Nevertheless, even though it may thus be possible to meet the challenge of what might be called a scientific behaviorism by simply appealing to the lived world as a frame of reference, rather than to the scientific universe, will it be equally easy to dispose of the sort of behaviorism associated with the name of Professor Ryle? For although Ryle's frame of reference is not exactly our ordinary, everyday human lived world, it

8. *Meaning and Existence*, Madison, Wis., 1960, p. 10.

is certainly our ordinary, everyday human language. In fact, in his book on *The Concept of Mind*, he undertakes to establish his behaviorism, not by any appeal to scientific evidence drawn from modern physiology and psychology, but simply by an analysis of the uses of various words and phrases in everyday language.

Not only that, but there is a sense in which Professor Ryle's behaviorism is of a sort that would tend to preserve those very features of man's existence which one has always supposed to be associated with men's minds. For instance, it is a favorite thesis of Professor Ryle's that a behaviorism in no sense entails a mechanism.[9] On the contrary, he insists, it is perfectly possible, simply through the observation of a man's behavior, to tell when the man is reacting purely mechanically to something that one says and when he is reacting intelligently. And similarly, it should be possible to determine when a man is acting voluntarily and when involuntarily; when he is doing what he meant to do and when he is acting heedlessly or inadvertently; or even when he is acting freely and when under compulsion. Indeed, all conduct of the sort we would naturally call intelligent, purposive, deliberate, planned, etc., is recognizable by behavioristic criteria alone and in no wise requires an inference to a mind as being a sort of "ghost in the machine," or even to any mental, paramechanical acts, paralleling ordinary physical acts and processes.

Nor is there any reason why, at least on its positive side, one should not admit almost all of what Professor Ryle insists upon. For certainly human beings will manifest their understanding of things and their purposes with respect to things in intelligent and purposive behavior. Not only that, but one can even acknowledge that so-called inferences to a ghost in the machine do seem in so many instances to be either gratuitous or downright ridiculous. And yet, as we see it, the decisive question is simply this: why does Professor Ryle refuse to recognize that human beings, in virtue of their minds or intelligences or cognitive powers or whatever else they may be called, are capable, if not always, at least upon occasion, of being intentionally beyond themselves and among the things they know and aim at; or correspondingly that the things of the world are capable of being intentionally present to the mind in at least certain instances of human cognition and intention?

Presumably, Professor Ryle's answer to such a question would be that any such intentional presence of things before the mind is never directly observable, but must always be inferred to be taking place, whenever it occurs *in someone else*. Moreover, any inference of this kind necessarily involves the sort of thing that Professor Ryle likes to label a "category

9. *The Concept of Mind*, London, 1949, *passim*, but especially Chap. III, p. 5.

mistake." Now disregarding the problem of category mistakes for the moment, one might immediately ask why Professor Ryle disregards the evidence of such intentional acts taking place in oneself and considers only the evidence of their occurrence in others. Could it be that Professor Ryle fancies that he is making an option in favor of the objective, as over against the subjective, of the outer as opposed to the inner, of the public as contrasted with the merely private?

But already the very use of such hard and fast distinctions, to say nothing of the somewhat arbitrary and absolute exclusion of the one member of each pair in favor of the other, betrays a forsaking of the lived world of everyday experience for the somewhat factitious universe of sheer objectivity. Besides, one wonders whether the category mistake of which Professor Ryle complains is not engendered by the very same arbitrary and artificial sundering of outer from inner, of objective from subjective, of public from private, which Professor Ryle himself would appear to have performed, as it were, a priori and apparently quite unconsciously. For will not an examination of analogous cases of such category mistakes and category jumps reveal that all such category blunders are but the dubious creations of philosophers? Thus, how often have we not heard that all one can observe is "constant conjunction," the "necessary connection" being only "inferred"; or that all one can observe are the properties and accidents, the substance being only "inferred"; or that all one can observe are the facts, the values being only "inferred"; or that all one can observe are the sense data, the material object itself being only "inferred"?

Ironically enough, this last example of such a supposed category blunder is one which Professor Ryle himself is concerned to show is a purely gratuitous blunder.[10] And yet might not one rejoin that what is sauce for the goose is sauce for the gander? For surely, the "inference" from behavior to mind is on all fours with the "inference" from sense data to object. The fact is that in the lived world neither one is properly an inference and neither one involves a category mistake. These are only philosopher's difficulties. Why, then, does Professor Ryle refuse to admit any such thing as an intentional presence of known objects before the knowing mind? Can it be that he has been victimized by the very exclusiveness of such category distinctions as outer and inner, objective and subjective, body and mind—distinctions which Professor Ryle has spent much of his philosophic life inveighing against?

And now having by such means tried to circumvent behaviorism, may we not consider that our job is done? As to what minds are, we have sought to give a rough philosophical account of them in terms of inten-

10. *Ibid.,* Chap. VII.

tionality, and as to where they are, we have attempted to restore them to what would seem to be their natural and rightful place in the real world—perhaps not in the real world if this be understood as being neither more nor less than the artificially constructed universe of modern science, but certainly in the real world if this be understood as simply the inescapable lived world of everyday human existence.

But no, our worries are anything but over. For we have only to face about from the behaviorists and Professor Ryle to find ourselves threatened by a veritable "third wave," this time coming from the contemporary phenomenologists and existentialists. And what is peculiarly embarrassing to us about the threat from this quarter is that the very tactic which we ourselves have employed to get human minds back into the world may well prove to be, in the hands of the phenomenologists, the very means for preventing any such simple integration of human minds or human subjects into any sort of objective, or independently real world order. Thus consider: in the foregoing sections of this paper we urged a return from the universe of science to the lived world of everyday. But in so doing, were we really recommending anything other than a sort of reversion from objectivity into subjectivity? Thus, what else could we mean when we talk about our lived world, or the world in which we exist as human beings, if it be not a world that is ours in the sense that it is relative to us, or at least a world that is a human world in the sense that it is of and for and relative to human subjects? In contrast, when we talk about the scientific universe as not being the world in which we ever do or can live as human beings, could this mean anything other than that such a scientific universe is an objective universe, a universe which is supposed not to be relative to us or to any human subject?

For that matter, when we ask ourselves directly concerning this phenomenon of world, do we not find ourselves forced more or less to agree with Heidegger that world is not a mere sum total of objects in the world? Nor is it, so to speak, just one more object which we find before us, in addition to and on the same order as objects in the world. On the contrary, the objects are what they are in virtue of the world they are in. It's thus that we speak of the world of the eighteenth century, or the world of music, or the child's world, or the world of science, or what not. "World," then, would seem to be nothing more nor less than that entire and total sense that different human beings or human minds or human subjects make of things; it is the total construction that we put upon things, the total complex of meaning that things come to have for us.

And what, then, of these "things" that are thus said to come to have or to take on meaning and significance for this or that, or for these or those, human subject or subjects? Once more, we need only remind ourselves, in this present connection, of that earlier quoted passage from

Merleau-Ponty.[11] More particularly, consider such a statement as "Everything I know of the world, even through science, I know from a point of view which is mine. . . ." Or again, speaking of the lived world or the perceived world, he urges that we must reawaken our primordial experience of this world, for "science is its second expression," "a determination or an explanation of that world."

Now no sooner does one begin to reflect on remarks such as these than one begins to recognize how our earlier injunction about returning to the the actual lived world from out of the artificial universe of science may have a quite different import from that which we sought to attribute to it. For if Merleau-Ponty is right, the lived world to which one returns is not at all a fixed and determinate reality of the sort we tried to make out, and from which one can simply read off, as it were by induction, features of a sort, say, which traditional, common-sense Aristotelians have long been wont to denominate as the four causes, act and potency, form and matter, substance and accident, etc. No, the lived world is one which suggests countless interpretations and explanations and which is patient of an endless variety of meanings and senses. Thus, not only is the scientific universe but "a determination or an explanation" of this world, a "second expression" of it, but so also, presumably, would the common-sense world of everyday, the world which might be said to receive a fairly definitive expression in terms of traditional Aristotelian concepts—this world, too, in its own way would have to be regarded as a "determination," an "explanation," a "second expression," if you like, of the lived world. Or even the world of the neurotic or psychotic personality—the world in which:

. . . for the *melancholiac* the stream of life moves sluggishly, he sees the laborious movement of every change, therefore his movements are heavy and slow; the aspect of the world is colorless, spiritless and faded, therefore he feels tired spent and dull; [or the world in which] for the *maniac* visible life goes lightly, obstacles there are none, his movements are correspondingly quick and light; the world is all life and movement, full of brilliant hues and freshness, that is why he himself feels fresh and alive, he feels so light that in this world, from which all weight has been taken away, he could almost fly, etc.[12]

even such worlds are a "determination," an "explanation," a "second expression," which the sick person brings to his world and which at the same time he finds in it and through which he makes sense of his world and his human situation.

11. *Op. cit.,* p. 3.
12. J. H. Van Den Berg, *The Phenomenological Approach to Psychiatry,* Springfield, Ill., 1955, p. 47.

And where and how does mind[13] fit into this picture? Clearly, it could never be a mere item in the world, as if it were, so to speak, one thing among others. Rather it is that for whom or for which any world is a world; it is that without which there would be no sense, no meaning in the world at all, and hence no world. Once again, let us listen to Merleau-Ponty:

> I am not the result or the intersection of multiple causalities which determine my body or my "psyche"; I cannot think of myself as a part of the world, as the simple object of biology, psychology, and sociology. . . . I am not a "living being" or even a "man" or "a mind," with all the characteristics which zoology, social anatomy or experimental psychology recognize by these products of nature or of history: I am the absolute source. My existence does not come from antecedents, from my physical and social surroundings: it goes toward them and sustains them, because it is I who bring this tradition, which I choose to take up again, into being for myself (and thus make it be in the only sense of the word can have for me), or who bring into being this horizon whose distance from me would collapse (since distance does not belong to it as a property) if I were not there to glance over it.[14]

Alas, we are afraid we can only say we are still unconvinced. For one thing we fear that Shaw's wit at Miss Duncan's expense would lose its point, to say nothing of its bite, were it to turn out that Miss Duncan's mind were no less than an absolute source. And somehow we feel that even so rare a thing as the truth about minds should hardly be purchased at a price so high as this!

Besides, is such a price necessary? For might not one counter Merleau-Ponty's remarks with the straightforward assertion that the lived world just is a world of which we find ourselves to be parts and not absolute sources? Nor does it follow from this that as soon as I recognize myself as being but a part of the world, I immediately reduce myself to "a simple object of biology, psychology, and sociology." No, for the implicit assumption here is that any objective world order must necessarily be the order of the scientific universe, whereas our contention all along has been that the everyday human world in which we human beings find ourselves and in which we must act as moral agents is at once a lived world and an objective world. Nor does this mean that it must be the scientific universe for all that.

Or again, how often does not one find in the contemporary literature of phenomenology the argument advanced that the human subject can

13. Needless to say, in this context the more or less traditional meaning of "mind" must be extended so as to be made synonymous with the self, with the total personality, with consciousness.

14. *Phénoménologie de la perception*, Foreword, *op. cit.*, p. 3.

never be considered as a part of an objective world, simply because the human subject is not itself an object or a substance at all? And the reason given is that a human subject, in virtue of its intentionality, is always projecting itself out beyond itself and ahead of itself; instead of being a mere thing or substance with a fixed and determinate nature, the human being is said rather to be a being who simply is his possibilities, whose essence is his *Existenz*, in Heidegger's sense. And yet are not all the things and substances of our lived world shot through with possibilities, potentialities, and tendencies? And if so, is the intentionality of human consciousness something so radically different as to necessitate its being considered extranatural and so not really a part of the world at all?

Here again, the same sort of misunderstanding would seem to be at work. It's as if intentionality not being able to be integrated into a scientific universe, the conclusion is then drawn that intentionality cannot be a property of objects or a feature of the objective world order at all. And yet we would suggest that intentionality is one of the most obvious and inescapable features of the everyday world in which men live. Why, then, deny its objectivity, merely for the rather arbitrary and preconceived reason that scientific objectivity is the only sort of objectivity there is?

Yes, even the phenomenologists' notion that our lived world is not one of fixed and determinate senses and meanings, but rather one that is always open to new meanings and new interpretations, to new determinations and second expressions, which the free human subject is ever capable of projecting and so of finding in its world—even this notion, we feel, is one the truth of which can be understood and accepted, without one's necessarily being compelled to regard such a subject as being in any sense an absolute source. For why not simply say that human minds or subjects, considered as parts of the world and as completely integrated into this real world, will nevertheless find this world to be practically inexhaustible in the challenges which it offers, alike to human understanding and to human choice? Nor when seen in this light, would it be anything but natural and proper that human beings should be forever discovering new meanings and new possibilities in the real world that confronts them and of which they are themselves a part. At the same time, once human beings are thus recognized as parts of a world order rather than as sources of it, it is clear that they will be but the discoverers of the meanings and possibilities which they uncover in the real world and in no sense the inventors and creators of such sense and meaning. And, likewise, their freedom as human beings will be the freedom, not of beings who are the absolute sources of meaning and value, but rather of beings who, as capable of recognizing the meaning and value that exist in things, can then choose their courses of action accordingly, at once wisely and intelligently.

In short, why not regard human minds after all as being at once our human means of intending a real, objective order of things and at the same time as being themselves parts of such an order—albeit this *rerum natura* be not that of the scientific universe, but simply that of the everyday human lived world?

A Transactional Inquiry Concerning Mind

---

man as a struggler amid illusions,
each man fated to answer for himself:
Which of the faiths and illusions of mankind
must I choose for my own sustaining light
to bring me beyond the present wilderness?

—CARL SANDBURG*

Whatever approach we take for the theory of mind can at best be only a slice of our own life history and our own concern. "No one is a privileged observed," said Poincaré. Mind, like matter, can show itself in a variety of forms, each different from the rest but within limits each as "real" as "true" as the next. As a psychologist and more particularly as a social psychologist, my own primary concern in trying to decide what the abstractions of "mind" refer to is to bracket those aspects or preconditions except for which "mind" would not be what it "is" and would not reflect as it seems to the psychological and social consequences of being human.* In view of the wonders and intricacies that come to mind

---

Some of this discussion is based on previously published material, particularly the first chapter of *The Politics of Despair;*[9] *Perception: A Transactional Approach* written with William H. Ittelson;[12] and "Toward a humanistic psychology."[8]

* From *The People, Yes,* by Carl Sandburg, New York, Harcourt, Brace & World, Inc., 1938, p. 134.

whenever I think of what the word refers to, together with the realization that through the centuries some minds have become famous for contributing to an understanding of what "mind" is, I should like to register here at the outset my own sense of humility as I begin my probing.

I take it for granted, of course, that we are dealing with an organism equipped with particular qualities and ranges of physiological sensitivities and with a particular pattern of neurophysiological organization. I begin with the assumption that the "reality" of mind is to be accounted for as a process in its own appropriate terms. What we describe phenomenologically must obviously be congruent with neurophysiological description. And the reverse is equally true: the awesome and baffling characteristics of "mind" must not be lost sight of or oversimplified because of limitations in our present understanding of the potentialities of matter. The revolution in the physical and biological sciences during the past century has even further dispelled the inadequacy of accounting for mind with "materialist" laws or Cartesian mechanism. The exciting new developments in neurophysiology can, for example, enormously aid us in translating organic necessity and organic consequence into psychological necessity and psychological consequence—and vice versa.

While there is every expectation as time goes on that our understanding of the relationships between mind as we experience it and the naturalistic processes collateral with this experience will continually increase, the gap between what Sir Russell Brain distinguishes as the representative "perceptual world" and the "physical world" will always be there. While such a differentiation is obvious and generally accepted by psychologists, it is worth mentioning here to avoid confusion and to make clear that our discussion is entirely concerned with the "perceptual world" aspect of mind. Discussion of the "physical world" aspect of mind and the apparent relationships between the two worlds must be left to competent neurophysiologists.[1, 2, 6, 15]

Most psychologists today steer clear of the word "mind." If it appears at all in their textbooks, it is generally in discussions of the history of psychology. The word has an old-fashioned sound to most Western psychologists who pride themselves on being "scientific" and tend to be impatient with philosophical discourse.

There is, of course, some justification for this view since this man-made abstraction has all too often been treated as an explanatory concept in a way that has little meaning in terms of its operation. But in avoiding the term and a concern with it, many psychologists have also lost sight of inclusive dimensions the word can refer to and have therefore ended up with explanatory concepts that are just as man-made but that leave a wide gap between scientific accounting, on the one hand, and the nature of human experience on the other. (Psychiatrists, I feel, have sinned far less on this score.) Yet if the abstraction of "mind" *is* to be useful to psychologists, it must be viewed in such a way that its validity can be checked and tested in terms of what it refers to in concrete, real life situations involving as they do a variety of overtones such as anxiety and satisfaction, frustration and accomplishment, joy and sorrow, exhilaration and apathy, loneliness and love.

When I try to get a toe hold on what the word "mind" refers to by starting from my own naive experience (which is, I believe, all anyone can do as a start), I immediately run into two difficulties familiar to nearly all who have pondered the process that enables each separate individual to come in contact with the world, make more or less sense out of what goes on around him, and contribute his bit to the fashioning of an environment within which he can carry out his purposes, some of which he is aware of while others propel him on his way without his knowing exactly how, why, or whither.

The first difficulty is that when we try to capture the meaning of "mind" as a noun, it immediately seems to turn into an active verb. It becomes at once a process, a process in continuous motion, sometimes flowing smoothly like a great river, sometimes unevenly and with the whirlpools, rapids, and falls of a mountain stream. The process somehow changes speed, changes direction, changes focus. There is nothing fixed or static about it. "Mind" seems to lose its "reality" when isolated from the matrix of some ongoing situation, some content.

Yet if the psychologist is to get a grasp on this complicated subject matter so he can take a good look at it and communicate whatever understanding he gathers, he is forced to break up into distinguishable parts what is really an indivisible and functional aggregate; he is forced to consider separately the many variables that together make up "mind" and which are all interdependent and interrelated in such a way that no one of them would function as it does except for all the others. The process of "mind" is, then, an orchestration of many ongoing processes, each of which can be understood and has the meaning it does only when it serves at the appropriate time and in the appropriate phase of the total orchestration.

The second source of difficulty in thinking about "mind" stems from the fact that this conceptual abstraction, like all others, is several steps removed from our primary data, namely, naive experience. In order to bridge the gap between naive experience and conceptual abstractions, the psychologist must consider areas of complexity and abstraction that become progressively further removed from his first order data. We can differentiate at least four different ways in which the process of mind may be viewed.

Mind as Reflected in Ongoing, Naive Experience

This is the level of immediate, "pure" experience as experience—unanalyzed, unconceptualized, unmediated, almost ineffable, and with no concern on the part of the experiencing individual to describe, analyze, conceptualize, or communicate what is going on in his mind. This ongoing, naive experience is what Korzybski called "first order" or "unspeakable" experience.

As has frequently been pointed out, any attempt to describe or analyze experience immediately alters that experience. When we are trying to describe or analyze mind or any aspect of it, we are functionally organized quite differently than when we are participating in the process of living and not describing or analyzing it.

Mind When Described

Verbalization and communication, either retrospectively or simultaneously with the occurrence of some activity of the mind, may be distinguished methodologically from the naive experience mind provides us because of a special form of awareness required to select aspects of the variety of mental processes involved. Some focusing, categorization, and coding are operating in the process of dealing consciously or verbally with any selected phase of the mind's activity. It is as if with any such focusing, awareness is shifted from the full orchestration of the whole to the role of a particular instrument in the orchestra.

It is important for a psychologist using descriptive material of any kind never to lose sight of the fact that reports of mental activity are not to be equated with the mental activity itself. Yet such protocol data still provide the psychologist with some of his most valuable raw material while some of the most penetrating descriptions of experience have been given us by poets, novelists, composers, and religious prophets.

Mind When Analyzed and Conceptualized

Instead of focusing on a selected phenomenon "going on in our minds" as we must if we are trying to describe, we may in the midst of some occasion of living try to "figure out" analytically and conceptually what is going on. We of course do so for some purpose: perhaps we are trying to work through some personal problem, perhaps we are delving into our mental processes in the hope of discovering hunches or clues that will provide us with some hypothesis. Whatever the reason, analysis of any occurrence is a very different operational state of affairs than ongoing purposive behavior itself or than a focus on some aspect of it. It is perhaps what the poet Wordsworth had in mind when he said, "We murder to dissect."

Mind as an Abstraction for Specification

Any attempt to understand the nature of mind is ultimately an attempt to distinguish components, to choose those by means of which we may be able to interpret the significance of any functional aspect of mind, and to describe the variables on which the singularity of any of mind's processes depend. If the abstracting we make can be effectively related to our presuppositions, then we will have an instrument to render communication more accurate and to enable others to understand the abstractions without reference to any particular item of behavior that might illustrate it.

Such abstractions are not affected by individual behavior and are not altered when conceptualized from the point of view of different persons. If they were so affected or altered, they would prove useless; it is their static quality that gives them the utility they have in understanding the significance of concrete behavioral situations. This does not mean, of course, that such abstractions never change. They are, on the other hand, constantly evolving and being modified by scientists and philosophers themselves to increase their usefulness. Any creative individual must test his abstractions by their performance and not by their consistency, realizing that any abstraction is highly tentative. All that we mean by the "static quality" of an abstraction is that an abstraction would be operationally useless if its significance were not somehow "fixed."

It should be emphasized again that when we are dealing with this fourth level of complexity which makes scientific and philosophical communication possible, we are necessarily violating phenomenal data. A full awareness of this fact and of some of the omissions involved in operating in this area may give us some perspective to increase the usefulness of our abstractions.

Mind as Transaction

Much as we might like to do so, we can never somehow isolate mind or reduce it to a "pure" state for investigation. It strikes us as nonsensical even to think of such a thing for the simple reason that the processes of mentation can only be studied as part of the situation in which they operate and except for which they would not be what they are. There seems to be an increasing agreement among psychologists that perceiving—a central aspect of mind's activity—can no longer be thought of in any sense as "mind reacting to" or being "acted on." Mounting evidence from a wide variety of experiments, demonstrations, and field investigations supports the view that mind may be appropriately described as a "transactional" process. The concept "transaction" was used over a decade ago by Dewey and Bentley to differentiate the processes involved in "knowing" from views based on interaction or self-action which have affected so much of psychological theory. While the word "transaction" is hardly inclusive and dynamic enough to encompass the novel and creative aspects that emerge in so many "transactions" of living, it serves as a useful concept in helping us avoid misleading bifurcations that all too easily inject themselves not only into everyday common-sense accounting but into psychological explanation. Such a term keeps us more aware of the fact that there can be no "knowing" without "doing," just as there can be no "person" except for an "environment," nothing "personal" except for what is "social."

The concept of transaction, implying as it does the process of interdependent variables, may also eventually discourage thinking about mind and its operation in terms of "cognition," "cognitive structure," "conation," etc., which are viewed as being "influenced by" other factors such as "set," "intention," "motive," or a host of other forces denoted by psychologists who are often seduced by their own abstractions and discuss mental activity and behavior as though such factors were rather discrete ingredients we can know about separately, that already exist, and that simply get mixed together without transforming and losing their own identities as useful abstractions in the activity that is the stuff of mind. It is the very process of "interaction" that constitutes the event for fruitful inquiry. We must repeat again the danger to psychologists of being caught in the net of their own abstractions without coming to grips with what the abstraction refers to in real life situations.

We can illustrate the problem with reference to Ittelson's analogy of a batter in a baseball game:

It is immediately apparent that the baseball batter does not exist independent of the pitcher. We cannot have a batter without a pitcher. It is true that someone can throw a ball up in the air and hit it with a bat, but his relationship to the batter in a baseball game is very slight. Similarly, there is no pitcher without a batter. The pitcher in the bull-pen is by no means the same as the pitcher in the game. But providing a pitcher for a batter is by no means enough to enable us to define and study our batter. The batter we are interested in does not exist outside of a baseball game so that in order to study

him completely we need not only pitcher, but catcher, fielders, infielders, team-
mates, officials, fans, and the rules of the game. Our batter, as we see him in
this complex transaction, simply does not exist anywhere else independent of
the transaction. The batter is what he is because of the baseball game in which
he participates and, in turn, the baseball game itself is what it is because of
the batter. Each one owes its existence to the fact of active participation with
and through the other. If we change either one, we change the other.[13]

Mind and Externality

An essential feature of the operation of mind is the external orientation, the "objectivization," of some aspects of experience. We attribute
parts of our own experience to events external to ourselves and in whose
independent existence we firmly believe. We experience the things we see,
hear, taste, and touch as existing apart from our minds, outside of ourselves, and as possessing in themselves the characteristics we find in them.

The view that something in some sense goes "into" the organism
has persisted from the time of the Greeks who spoke of the objects
emitting small replicas of themselves which were received by the perceiver, right up to much present-day psychology, with its interest in
"stimulus determination" of perception. This belief is strong in all of
us, and, as we shall point out later, it *must* be strong if we are to be
able to act at all effectively. But the great danger of such a belief when
inquiring into the nature of mind lies in the fact that it gives us the
answer to our problem in advance of our inquiry. For if the objects of
perception exist in their own right as perceived, then all we have to do
is to fit the perception to an already existing object. The error of this
naive view is nicely expressed by Whitehead, whose comment referring
to the physical sciences applies even more forcibly to the world as
perceived: "We must not slip into the fallacy of assuming that we are
comparing a given world with given perceptions of it. The physical
world is in some sense of the term, a deduced concept."[16]

More recently, the same point has been made by two other distinguished British scientist-philosophers. J. Z. Young, the biologist, writes:
"The form we give to this world is a construct of our brains, using
such observations as they have been able to make. Only in that sense
does it exist."[18] And Sir Russell Brain, the neurologist, says, "The scientific account of perception, however, teaches us that the objects which we
perceive outside our brains are not as independent of us as they appear
to be: they have qualities which are generated by our brains and which
have no other existence."[3]

When we perceive, we externalize certain aspects of our experience and thereby create for ourselves our own world of things and people, of sights and sounds, of tastes and touches. "The act of perceiving itself so implies the act of considering-it-real that the latter can be called an attribute of the act of perceiving."[14] The problem then, as rephrased, is the problem of what is done *by* the organism, *by* the mind. To say that the mind externalizes certain aspects of its experience is by no means to answer this question but merely to point out one characteristic of the process. Bridgman writes that

. . . in seeking the precision demanded by scientific use we have thus been led to discard the common sense method of handling our environment in terms of objects with properties, and have substituted for it a point of view that regards a reduction to activities or operations as a safer and better method of analysis. . . . What we are in effect doing in thus preferring the operational attack is to say what we *do* in meeting new physical situations has a greater stability than the situations themselves and that we can go further without revising our operations than we can without revising our picture of the properties of objects. Or, expressed somewhat differently, our methods of handling the external world have greater stability than the external world itself.[4]

Without taking any metaphysical position regarding the existence of a real world, independent of experience, we can nevertheless assert that the world—as experienced—has no meaning and cannot be defined independent of the experience. The world *as we experience it* is the product of perception, not the cause of it. The study of perception just as the study of mind must take the active perceiving individual as its proper point of departure.

Learning Significance

The business of making sense out of what goes on around us involves the fashioning of an environment for ourselves within which we can carry out the process of living. A "happening" thus becomes an "event" for us only when *we* assign it some importance or consequence. And the meanings taken on by the impingements constantly bombarding us through our sense organs have significance and the particular significance they do because of the potential purposive behavior they serve. "Naked sense impressions simply do not occur, and the traditional analysis of our conscious experience into naked sensations as building blocks is palpably bad description."[5]

Just what the significance of any impingement will become, if any significance is attached at all, depends on the way we learn to utilize it in the course of our experience from infancy onward. It is only through experience that the "environment" or the "thereness" around us becomes differentiated into parts as we learn some of the potential significances of the infinite variety of aspects the environment around us has for us. G. H. Lewes observed in 1879 that "the new object presented to sense, or the new idea present to thought, must also be *soluble in old experiences*, be recognized as like these, otherwise it will be unperceived, uncomprehended."

A major function of "mind," then, is to process and sort the consequences of its own activity and its own participation so that patterns of interpretations or assumptions are created and organized to serve as reliable guides for action, bringing the satisfactions an individual seeks.

These assumptions begin to bring some order into disorder by enabling us to predict what will happen in a given situation if we act in a particular way or possibly if we do not act at all. In this process we are trying to improve both the range and the degree of *correspondence* between the meanings and significances we *attribute* to situations and the meanings and significances these situations *turn out to have* for us as we experience the consequences of our action in striving to accomplish our particular purposes. Our actions, of course, will be effective only insofar as the predictions derived from our perceptions correspond to what we actually experience when we do act.

It should be emphasized that the degree of correspondence is inevitably to be judged from the point of view of the participant, from his own unique behavioral center in any occasion of living, and not from the point of view of an outside observer. The word "center" is used here in the dictionary sense of "the point toward which any force, or influence takes its origin; as a storm center." A major contribution a psychologist can make to an understanding of mind is to increase his knowledge of the process by means of which the degree of correspondence between the significances which we *externalize* and those which we *encounter* is achieved. We should perhaps note in passing that the word "correspondence" is not used here in the sense of identity between experience and some outside "reality" but as correspondence between two kinds of experience. Once some aspect of the environment acquires a potential significance of a high order of reliability, then a person can and does think of it as existing apart from himself just as he can and does think of the purposes and values of other people as existing apart from himself. According to our view, all aspects of the environment, whether they are physical or social, exist for us only insofar as they are related to our purposes. If you leave out human significance, you leave out all constancy, all repeatability, all form.

Purposive Activity

As we try to bracket some of the variables except for which "mind" would not be what it is, it becomes increasingly clear that we must include in our consideration the purposive behavior of the organism of which mind is an aspect. Otherwise we isolate mind as a complicated machine engaged in coding, sorting, predicting, generating. For all these processes cannot go on and cannot be evaluated outside the context of what all this elaborate activity is *for* anyway. When we do something, we nearly always do it because of some intent, aim, or purpose of which we may be more or less aware. Generally we are aware of a single purpose or aim; we have a vague sense that "we" are involved in directing the doing because of "our" decision or hunch or bet as to what will be the best thing for us to do under the particular circumstances.

But how, operationally, do we define "best"? What is it, fundamentally, that impels us to action at all and that requires the complex organization we call mind as a guiding and protecting force embedded in the total organism?

For a number of years it has seemed to me that the most general specification we could make concerning the central and overriding motivation permeating all of man's behavior is the desire on the part of human beings to experience greater value satisfactions on the one hand, or, on the other, to ensure for themselves the repetition of those situations or circumstances which have already demonstrated the satisfaction to be derived if one particpates in them. And if we are to account for the higher order processes that distinguish the mind of man which has such characteristics as creative imagination, we must emphasize that the quality of experience human beings seek is far different than that sought by any other type of organism.[*] It is important here to point out the use of the word "value" as a description of the satisfactions characteristic of human beings. For it is man's capacity to experience values and his apparent desire to exercise this capacity that helps us account for the range and novelty, the subtlety and the uniqueness of human experience; that makes it possible for us to appreciate a poem, a symphony, a mathematical formulation, a sunset, an act of heroism or of sacrifice. There seems to be no word more appropriate than "value" to differentiate those affective components of human experience so very

[*] This point of view concerning the nature of human motivation has been elaborated at greater length in *The "Why" of Man's Experience*.[7]

different from the more primitive emotional states involved in the re-flexive activities that accommodate the urges for food, sex, shelter, and protection from bodily harm.

The varieties of situations in which people implicate themselves in their search for value satisfactions are, of course, infinite. The nature of the situations that hold out some possibility for the experiencing of value satisfactions varies, of course, with the life histories, the capacities, and the circumstances of every individual. But however diverse the occasions or the strivings apparently may be, all human activity and all human undertakings seem to me to be geared to the search for participation in situations that would either ensure the repetition of the valueful experiences we have had or enable us to obtain new or "richer" value satisfactions from what we have learned to expect may be potentially available to us.

In emphasizing man's apparently ceaseless search for new value sat-isfactions, we must by no means underemphasize the concern of man to protect and preserve what he has. The bewildering variety of both informal and formal organizations and institutions man has created all appear to be more or less organized social devices to ensure greater value satisfactions through the role they play as protectors of form or provisions for the insurance of flow and development, or both. This would include all of those social devices studied by the modern cultural anthropologist which, somewhat like the unseen forces that hold the nucleus of the atom together, keep individuals from being split off from each other so that together each can play more of a role on his own: family systems, our customs and mores, our use of language and the subtle communications devices provided by many of our manners and codes of behavior, our commerce and industry, our social, political, mili-tary, and religious institutions together with the ideologies behind them.

It is in terms of our attempts to ensure or increase the value satis-factions of living that our minds perceive and fashion the world around us. We see things, people, social occurrences, and old or new ideas in terms of their use or their potential use to us. The whole process of perceiving the world around us is the process of trying to make accurate guesses of the stance, the orientation, or the action we should take in order to carry out our purposes.

From the vast array of happenings going on around us, we select for *attention* those related to our *intention*. We become aware of what we sense is probably important for us to be aware of. In his consideration of "attention" the psychologist must not neglect what Harry Stack Sulli-van referred to as the mind's "selective inattention." In our concern with the creations of mind, we must not forget mind's creative forget-fulness. For both inattention and forgetting often serve a most valuable function, allowing us to focus on what we feel is important to us without cluttering up our minds with the irrelevant. It is an individual's "sensed values," that is, his own feeling of what is "important," "worthwhile," or "satisfying," that are ultimately the impelling aspects of living and that lead him one way or another to any mentation or behavior at all.

So the psychologist's inquiry of "why" mind plays the role it does as this is reflected in what people think and what they do emphasizes again the requirement that the psychologist must always begin his inquiry from the point of view of the individual whose "mind" is operating, is having the experiences, doing the behaving, working out the correspondences. For if we try to record and observe the experience of a person from the point of view of an outside party, we may become insensitive to many aspects of experience *as it is going on*: we may miss completely, for example, the fact that the individual is, probably without being aware of it himself, constantly making choices, weighing probabilities for effective action, wondering about the alternative responsibilities that will be his if he does make a certain decision. The point has been nicely stated by the physicist, Arthur H. Compton:

> When one exercises freedom, by his act of choice he is himself adding a factor not supplied by the physical conditions and is thus himself determining what will occur. That he does so is known only to the person himself. From the outside one can see in his act only the working of physical law. It is the inner knowledge that he is in fact doing what he intends to do that tells the actor himself that he is free.[10]

Or the experimental psychologist may forget that for purposes of experimental procedure it is frequently necessary for him to deduce from some kind of knowledge gained from outside observation the nature of experience the observer would have if he were able to act with its implication that this deduction is only a substitute for potential experience on the part of the perceiving individual.

When we stop to analyze our everyday activities from this point of view, we will find that nearly all of our behavior is characterized by a whole orchestration of purposes going on simultaneously and at different levels. Whatever mind is, it has the amazing capacity to juggle a number of different balls of different colors and sizes.

For example, in nearly every transaction of living one might differentiate the purposeful aspect of the transaction into, first, that involving and ensuring the preservation of physiological and psychological processes; second, that directing action and sensing experience in terms of the accent of purpose; third, that involving the sense of the consequences action will have once it is initiated or completed.

It becomes apparent, then, that the mind of man more than the mind of any other living organism enables man to take an active part in determining what his experience will be, to contribute to the quality and range of the continual flow of diverse events that constitute living.

Varieties of Significance Learned

As we try to accommodate our needs and resolve our urges, we learn through our experience what significances are related to each other and to characteristics of the situation of which we are a part. As experience accumulates, we learn which relationships have high probabilities of occurrence and which only low probabilities of repeating themselves. The mind weights these probabilities in terms of their relevance to the purposes of the experiencing individual as these are involved in the unique situation encountered. Just how a person experiences new occasions will, then, in the long run be determined by the assumptive complex he brings to that occasion.

The process of acquiring assumptions to increase the effectiveness of behavior is guided and channeled by cultural norms. Our perceptions, as we externalize them, are fashioned much more than most of us ever realize by the diverse forms of our particular cultural and subcultural groups. We might almost define culture as the common pattern of learned significances. Modern cultural anthropologists describe experience as "something man projects upon the outside world as he gains it in his culturally determined form."[11] Rapid developments in the field of linguistics demonstrate, as Whorf pointed out, how

We dissect nature along lines laid down by our native languages. The categories and types that we isolate from the world of phenomena we do not find there because they stare every observer in the face; on the contrary, the world is presented in a kaleidoscopic flux of impression which has to be organized by our minds—and this means largely by the linguistic systems in our minds. We cut nature up, organize it into concepts, and ascribe significances as we do, largely because we are parties to an agreement to organize it in this way—an agreement that holds throughout our speech community and is codified in the patterns of our language.[17]

Our own awareness of what goes on in our minds as our assumptions are triggered into operation by the relevance a situation potentially has to our purposes may be a very limited awareness. At other times, awareness may be both extensive and profound. There are obviously great variations according to the nature of the situation, just as there are great variations within and between individuals. But regardless of how restricted or how wide-ranging awareness may be, what we are aware of in our minds comes about through a process in which we take account of many more and many different aspects than we are probably aware of. All complex relationships between externality and impingement, between impingement and excitation, and between excitation and assumption, are taken account of in the perceptual process of the mind insofar as they are available to mind through its experience or physiology.

It may be useful to differentiate at least some of the varieties of assumptions if for no other reason than to show the intricacy of what apparently goes on in the mind as it makes its transition from one situation to another. By comparison, the operations of the most modern electronic computer seem very simple indeed.

1. Assumptions Concerning the Significance of Objects. The objects in the world around us have the meaning they do for us because we attribute to them certain characteristics, sizes, shapes, or properties. We have built up these significances in the course of our dealings with these objects. For example, even though the pattern a piece of writing paper forms on our retina may not be rectangular as we look at it on our desk, we assume that the sheet of paper *is* rectangular; even though the top of a drinking glass may be seen as elliptical when we stop to "look at" it, we still "know" that it is circular. Even though we see only the head of a horse projecting from behind the barn, we will report that we are seeing a horse because we have learned to take for granted that the rest of the horse is there. We assume that things are "wholes." We learn to regard objects as "large" or "small," as "far" or "near," as moving "fast" or "slowly" because of the experiences we have become used to relative to these objects. All of this may be seen most dramatically when we read reports of individuals who have been blind from birth but who in certain rather rare instances can gain their sight after surgery. In summarizing some of these reports, J. Z. Young writes:

The patient on opening his eyes for the first time gets little or no enjoyment; indeed, he finds the experience painful. He reports only a spinning mass of lights and colours. He proves to be quite unable to pick out objects by sight, to recognize what they are, to name them. He has no conception of a space with objects in it, although he knows all about objects and their names by touch.[19]

2. Assumptions Concerning the Significance of People. When a situation in which we are participating or intend to participate involves other people, the assumptions by means of which our action is guided include new and different aspects. For other people have their own purposes which it is up to us to guess and to understand. In the process we must realize that the purposes of other people are just as "real" as any of the physical characteristics of objects. We must predict upon the basis of our assumptions what effect our intended behavior will have on others' purposes, how others will see us, and how their reaction to us in turn will affect our own subsequent action in the endless chain of events in which we are involved. We attribute certain significances to certain individuals because of assumptions we have learned concerning the meaning of the roles they play, their vocations, their place in the status hierarchy, the neighborhood, the nation, the race they represent. All of these personal attributes are often thought of as "fixed" characteristics of people according to the particular purpose any such grouping may serve us. The gestures of a people, their manners, their customs, the way in which they regard and utilize time and space are often cues which are either not understood or misunderstood until a person from another culture learns the standards upon which significance is based.

3. Assumptions Concerning the Significance of Sequential Happenings. Obviously the world of objects and people does not remain passive and static. Things keep changing. There is a ceaseless flow of happenings around us. Day follows night; our life follows certain rhythms; our hunger stops when we eat; the motor of our automobile comes to life when we turn on the starter; the traffic policeman stops us if we disobey his signal. In the course of living, a whole host of sequential significances are built up in us as we carry on in a world that is in continual flux.

In order to make more certain that we can "count on" a particular event to follow another event, man has devised a whole host of artifacts with built-in specifications. Many of the tools, instruments, machines, buildings, power systems, communications devices, and bewildering variety of man-made equipment that characterize modern life have been devised to ensure that certain events or satisfactions will follow each other in directions that are predictable and reliable. Often this standardization is at considerable cost to the richness of experience if one looks at other aspects than efficiency. For example, symbolism with all the aesthetic, intellectual, and spiritual overtones it provides is almost entirely ruled out as man's artifacts become more streamlined and functional. When we look at the combinations of our assumptions concerning people and our assumptions concerning sequential significance, we begin to get some insight into the complexities of understanding each other in a social world which, like the physical world, is constantly changing. For example, the quality of the relationship we have with other people depends in part on our capacity to comprehend simultaneously the sequential significances other people are experiencing in a chain of events, together with the sequential significances we ourselves are experiencing in the same phase of this chain of events. The experiences each of us has in the same phase of the sequence of events may either show how closely we are linked together or how different and far apart we are. For we are able to share the same experience of what is significant in our participation with other people only insofar as we and they experience the same significances simultaneously in a chain of events in which we are all involved. Anyone who has watched an American football game with a foreigner who is seeing the game for the first time has sensed the disparity. Unless the significance of sequential events can be shared by people, then the event as the same "event" simply does not exist. Our allegiances and loyalties to others come about because of the way in which we have learned to share these sequential events and have experienced a particular quality of value satisfaction from joint participation in what we are therefore able to call the "same event."

4. **Assumptions Concerning the Significance of Actions.** Each of us eventually learns, sometimes gradually, sometimes suddenly, what the probable significance of certain of our actions will be. We learn what experience we are likely to have if we initiate a certain chain of behavior. The child learns that a rubber ball will bounce if he throws it on the floor, that the cat will scratch him if he pulls its tail, that he has a better chance of getting the cooperation he desires if he says the right thing in the right way at the right time to his parents or friends. Each individual, according to his purposes, learns through the repeated testing of his own action to become more effective in bringing about the consequences he wants. The rituals, customs, ceremonies, and laws of a culture all ensure a greater repeatability in social affairs by providing more predictable directions, enabling more people to chart their courses of action, and thereby obtain greater satisfaction for each participant.

5. **Assumptions Concerning Temporal Significances.*** Permeating the learning of all varieties of assumptions is its temporal aspect. This is such an integral part of all the processes of mind that we are seldom aware of the variety of assumptions concerning time that we are taking into account. Social psychologists and cultural anthropologists have often pointed out the different meanings and significances of time-measures, the different values placed on units of time, and the effects of technology on the time standards of different groups and their oper-

---

* I am indebted to Dr. F. P. Kilpatrick for discussion of this aspect of our assumptions.

ational definition of "promptness," etc. But the assumptions we build up concerning subjective time become much more complex and subtle when considered from the first person view. For example, the subjective "present," as so often pointed out, is likely to be a span of time more or less unique to every individual and gauged by him in the context of his own life, his age, his circumstances, etc. Similarly with the "past" and the "future."

The subjective time a person may associate with the realization of some value will vary by the "level" or "universality" of the value symbol serving as a standard for personal experience, for example, the differing standards of a Hindu mystic and an American businessman. Different purposes will be implicitly embedded in different temporal dimensions as will assumptions concerning different sequential events and the use and manipulation of different objects. The "timing" of political action by Soviet leaders in terms of their long-range purposes will likely have quite a different baseline than the timing of political action by Western leaders who tend, for example, to give weight to such a factor as the next forthcoming election.

Most of the time for most of us, a variety of these temporal significances are being taken into account simultaneously, being given different priorities in awareness as the pattern of purposes propels the stream of behavior through what we conceptualize as periodic time.

6. **Assumptions Concerning the Significance of Value Standards.** In almost any concrete situation in which we participate, we are faced with alternative choices of action. Whether we are aware of the process or not, we weigh alternative courses of action in terms of the value-significances they are likely to have for us, the relative value-satisfactions we will obtain if we do this or that, or if we do nothing at all. Evaluation among various alternatives is made on the basis of the relative probability that each possible course of action will lead to the desired consequences, will produce the desired results. The process of guessing at the possible value-satisfaction our behavior will bring is enormously complicated since an almost infinite number of subprobabilities relating to each of the above classes of significances must be taken into account. The process involves feelings or overtones that we sometimes sense only vaguely, that are often not bounded by space or time, and that only become real and meaningful as they operate in determining what we will do in the here and now. In this process we may consciously or unconsciously refer to certain abstractions that are embodied in some code of ethics, some political ideology, some religion, and which we have learned to accept as possible guides that we may put to use as possible tests on appropriate occasions. While not real in their own right, these abstractions can become real

for us if they operate effectively in concrete situations. And in this context, they are often indispensable "realities."

This is only a brief list of some of the significances, of some of the varieties of assumptions, constituting part of the active storage facilities the mind apparently provides. Assumptions move in and out in various complicated combinations in fractions of a second. Some of the assumptions endure for a lifetime, others are fleeting. Our differentiation of assumptions into various headings is, of course, quite arbitrary. There is no clear-cut line dividing them. Furthermore, we must emphasize again that these assumptions are by and large interdependent in terms of their operation in a specific occasion of living.

Constancies

The effectiveness of our behavior in terms of carrying out our purposes is dependent upon our ability to act so we can experience the consequences we want to and intend to. This requires some way of knowing what can be "counted on" in the environment to bring about the desired consequences when we do act. For obviously we would not get far in the human venture if we carried on our lives with the continuous and conscious realization that we were acting on the basis of probabilities by assigning significances to the hieroglyphic stimulus patterns around us. If this were the unhappy state of affairs, we would be forever stopping to figure out what objects were, what people were going to do next and what they were really up to, what validity there was anyway to the many abstractions customarily used to guide our own activity. We would be frustrated to the point of near paralysis.

When we do discover from experience what can be "counted on," we can say that our mind has built up "constancies" or, more accurately expressed, "continuities." We begin to attribute certain continued characteristics to an object, a person, a situation, a government, a nation, etc. These provide a sense of surety, the feeling that the same significances will repeat themselves, will prove reliable as we act to carry out our purposeful behavior. The mind transforms the probabilities of assumptions into the certainties of constancies. Every act is based on the assumption that probable events are relatively certain events.

In spite of the long and venerable history the subject of "constancy" has had in the history of experimental pyschology, there has been comparatively little consideration of the *function* of constancy, of what constancy *does* for us. What constancy does is, essentially, to enable us to "size up" the relationship of our own unique position to some object, person, or situation so that we can make a prediction with a fair degree of certainty of what will be the most effective action for us to take at some particular point in time.

And so we create and maintain a whole variety of constancies that provide us the anchoring points for evaluation and the springboards for action. The constancies we attribute to objects in terms of their size, shape, distance from us, and various other "properties" are familiar to every reader of an elementary text in psychology. And we can well add to this list what we might call the "social constancies" we build up and maintain. Psychologically, their function is the same as the function of "object constancy." Here we can refer again to words and symbols with all the intricate relationships between naming and the named that have received so much attention from semanticists; we can refer again to the artifacts man creates in order to increase the range and predictability of his behavior; we can refer again to the mores, customs, loyalties, and laws of a society devised to give greater regularity to social life.

A most important by-product of the constancies we build up is our sense of the constancy of our own self. It is only as we participate in the world around us that we discover our selves. And our own self-significance and self-constancy become increasingly real for us as we participate in the physical and social environment around us and experience the consequences of bringing our assumptions and our constancies to bear on the concrete situations of living.

The mind of the creative individual is a mind that generates new standards: sometimes these are new standards for value inquiry, sometimes new aesthetic forms or models, sometimes new variables for scientific specification, sometimes new social or political organizations, sometimes the creation of new artifacts. The great leaps and developments that constitute so much of the story of man's history have generated in the minds of comparatively few representatives of the human species. Just what accounts for the creative imagination of these gifted individuals is as yet only dimly understood.

Flux and Change

Apparently one of the most basic wants and responsibilities of the human being is the urge to preserve his sense of what is real in a constantly changing world. By acquiring a reliable set of constancies we help ourselves preserve this "reality world" to which we have ourselves contributed so much in its creation. But since the environment around us is in a continual state of change and flux, our problem is not one of merely preserving our "reality world" unchanged but of continuing our reality in an ever-changing, undetermined cosmos. Situations are never exactly alike, and many of the situations we face have elements of novelty and diversity for which we sometimes find ourselves ill-prepared and therefore face with a particular sense of insecurity, doubt, apprehension, or uncertainty. Obstacles are encountered which demonstrate to us in our own experience that our reality system is somehow inadequate. For the consequences of our action turn out not to be what we had predicted they would be: sometimes we are disappointed, shocked, frustrated, surprised, or embittered. And the transition from what we are used to, to something new and different has, of course, been enormously accelerated by technological developments with their unpredictable social and psychological effects.

The process of living, then, involves participation in situations which we do not by any means sail through without experiencing obstructions or problems. Sometimes these are big problems, sometimes they are small; sometimes they are relatively enduring, sometimes they evaporate quickly. Our frustration may come from not knowing *how* to act effectively in order to arrive at some predetermined goal. Or, on the other hand, our frustration may result from a lack of surety as to *what* goal is the proper one for us to pursue anyway.

We can, of course, become aware of the fact that no matter how annoying or upsetting the hitches or problems may be, they are almost inevitable aspects of living in a world where the future is undisclosed and where we, as participants, can play a role in determining that future. Successful actions can only confirm our assumptions, reinforce our constancies. Furthermore, we can become intellectually aware that it is only insofar as we encounter these frustrations, obstacles, surprises, and disappointments that we ourselves "learn" something and that we ourselves have an opportunity to test out new choices, new hunches, new formulations, by experiencing the consequences they lead to in action. If the "now" or the "present" drags on more or less indefinitely and involves no anticipation, no potential foreseeable emergence, we grow despondent, we say "the future is empty" or "there is no future."

Except for activity based on reflexes or habits, nearly all of the transactions of living involve in more or less degree a set of conditions that present a problem for choice or action. Our ability to meet the problem depends upon the adequacy and appropriateness of the patterns of assumption our minds enable us to call forth for the occasion.

We sense sometimes vaguely, sometimes intensely, that what we do involves the choice we make of alternatives and possibilities; the hunch we have that our intended actions will result in the intended consequences with their intended value satisfactions. We have a sense of greater or less surety concerning the probable effectiveness of our choice;

a sense of more or less conflict between alternatives involved in making our choice. And in the process of choosing and carrying out selected behavior resulting from our choice, we have a sense of more or less personal responsibility. We can be intellectually aware that we have no absolute control over future occurrences and that chance is likely to play a greater or lesser role in our behavior. We can become intellectually aware of many of the factors we are taking into account in the process of choosing. We can observe that many of our choices concerned with long-range goals involve the selection of alternatives and possibilities which we feel will in turn lead to further alternatives and possibilities that will make future choices more effective. We sense that our minds, by enabling us to choose, connect the "now" of our experience with the past and future.

We can become intellectually aware that insofar as our behavior is completely reliable, certain, and effective, we will go on to further behavior which will lead us to further desired consequences, but that when we run up against some obstacle, some difficulty, some sense of inadequacy, we become aware of this and must undertake some inquiry. If the difficulty encountered is one of *how* to achieve a predetermined goal, we make use of rational, logical inquiry involving conceptual abstractions. In its most highly developed form we label this "scientific inquiry." On the other hand, if a difficulty involves a choice of goals, a lack of surety with respect to *what* our goals "should" be, then we undertake a different kind of inquiry: instead of indulging in rational and intellectual processes alone, we undertake what we refer to as "mulling things over," "reflecting," "meditating," in which we try to weigh the reliability of different value standards. We can sense that associated with inquiry of the former type is the collection of facts, the accumulation of knowledge, the attainment of skills, the use and development of artifacts, the development of "know-how," the proper use of scientific method, etc. Associated with the latter type of inquiry are the less tangible but equally "real" experiences concerned with the development of faith, the acceptance of things past, the cultivation of charity, the broadening of love, etc.

In any transaction of living there is a multiplicity of alternative possibilities with respect to *what* goals an individual may pursue just as there is a multiplicity of possibilities with respect to *how* he may best realize any intended goal. If we are to maintain our faith in achieving a goal and continue to sense it as "real," then we must be able to foresee or bet on the possibility of some time foreseeing some means to achieve that goal, some sequential steps leading to the desired end. If we cannot sooner or later find means to achieve the goal, then we may abandon it or considerably alter it.

Since psychologists have by and large neglected the form of inquiry involved when we must decide *why* we should do one thing rather than another (or possibly why we should do anything at all), I should like to emphasize here the important function of the mind involved in what I call "value inquiry," the type of inquiry which provides us with a value standard that can serve as a compass, a directive for action. In "value inquiry" we are seeking standards of rightness, wrongness, more right than, goodness, badness, beauty, ugliness, etc., which will serve as signs or cues and indicate to us the nature of the probable consequences we will experience by following a particular course of action. The standards we use and question in "value inquiry" concern our duties, loyalties, and responsibilities. Hence, the value judgments we reach through "value inquiry" involve "conscience," "humility," "ambition," etc.

Since the standards we "mull over" and "contemplate" in value inquiry are not bounded by time and space, we often like to insulate ourselves from the pressures of the here and now as we pursue this inquiry. We do not want to be disturbed. If we seek the companionship and advice of others, it is for the purpose of communion, or in the hope of gaining from them some wisdom. By insulating ourselves from space and time considerations we are able to allow our conscious and subconscious processes of mentation and feeling their widest possible range. Furthermore, some such insulation also allows us to make a more accurate distinction between those feelings and emotions related to our physiological bodily activity and the conditions at the moment of which we are a part and, on the other hand, those overtones of feeling which derive from the standards for value that have become a part of our own reality world and are not dependent on a specific set of conditions or actions in the here and now. It is these value standards that sustain us between one doing and the next. It is these value standards that enable us to weather frustration and deprivation. If we lose such standards or cannot find any, then we say "we are lost."

The value standards each of us uses are the consequences of our action in the past that have been registered and have become a part of our reality world insofar as they have proved to be good bets for further judgment and action. It is important to emphasize that this registration is not of an intellectual nature. It is a chance, a confirmation, or a denial of the weight to be given different assumptions concerning the "worthwhileness," the "goodness," the "rightness," the "decency" of any action. Our value standards thus serve both as our criterion of satisfaction and as our best guide for effective action.

The process involved in "value inquiry" is one of trying to expand the range of the cues we can include. We attempt to increase our value specifications. Hence, if a person accepts as absolute and inviolable any variety of ideology, the cues he uses in his value inquiry will be restricted and the directive for action indicated by his inquiry will lack the reliability it otherwise might have. Similarly, if he is bounded by any particular cultural complex, there is restriction. The reliability of the directives reached through value inquiry is directly related to the adequacy of the cues taken into account.

While rational inquiry is not excluded in the resolution of difficulties on the *why level*, it is of only secondary importance. This extension cannot go on freely, as we have indicated, if an individual is disturbed by impingements from his senses. Apparently the function of our senses is to give us a standpoint in time and space so that we *can* act *after* we have decided *why* we should act. These decisions involving purpose are peculiarly our own, since the value standards that compose so crucial a part of our reality world constitute a complex of value assumptions unique to each of us. These decisions, therefore, involve both responsibility and opportunity. And these interdependent responsibilities and opportunities are highly personal: they are products of our unique biological equipment participating in the culture unique to our own life history. Clarification of purposes in terms of creating value standards that serve as effective and satisfying guides for action can be one of the mind's never-ending processes. And it is such for individuals who themselves surmount the continuing obstacles of frustrations brought about by changing conditions.

Such are some of the aspects of mind that must be taken into consideration as I see them from the vantage point of a psychologist. But as I read over what I have written so far, I am sadly aware of my own inability to capture even remotely the wonder that mind is, especially when I think of such products of mind as the Fifth Symphony, the Sermon on the Mount, the *Brothers Karamazov,* or the calculus. Whatever it is that enables mind to create and to appreciate such marvels seems to elude almost completely the crude nets of any psychological jargon. Perhaps in the distant future minds will have discovered how to reveal themselves in a way that will communicate both what the scientist will then know and what the poet will continue to feel.

REFERENCES

1. Brain, W. Russell, *Mind, Perception and Science,* Oxford Univ. Press, London, 1951.
2. ——, *The Nature of Experience,* Oxford Univ. Press, London, 1959.
3. *Ibid.,* p. 35.
4. Bridgman, P. W., "The operational aspect of meaning," *Synthese,* 1950-51, 8:255-257.

5. ———, "The task before us," *Proceedings of the American Academy of Arts and Sciences,* 1954, 83:98.
6. Brazier, M. A. B. (ed.), *The Central Nervous System and Behavior,* Josiah Macy, Jr., Foundation, New York, 1958.
7. Cantril, H., *The "Why" of Man's Existence,* Macmillan, New York, 1950, Chaps. 2 and 3.
8. ———, "Toward a humanistic psychology," *ETC: A Review of General Semantics,* 1955, 12:278-298.
9. ———, *The Politics of Despair,* Basic Books, New York, 1958.
10. Compton, Arthur H., "Science and man's freedom," *Atlantic Monthly,* October, 1957, 200:73.
11. Hall, E. T., *The Silent Language,* Doubleday, New York, 1959, p. 144.
12. Ittelson, W. H., and Cantril, H., *Perception: A Transactional Approach,* Doubleday, New York, 1954.
13. *Ibid.,* pp. 3 f.
14. Shilder, Paul, *Medical Psychology* (trans. by David Rapaport), International Universities Press, New York, 1953, p. 40.
15. Solomon, H. C., Cobb, Stanley, and Penfield, Wilder (eds.), *The Brain and Human Behavior,* Williams and Wilkins, Baltimore, 1958.
16. Whitehead, A. N., *The Aims of Education,* Mentor Books, New York, 1949, p. 166.
17. Whorf, B. J., "Science and linguistics," *The Technology Review,* 1940, 42.
18. Young, J. Z., *Doubt and Certainty in Science,* Oxford Univ. Press, London, 1951, p. 107.
19. *Ibid.,* p. 61.

J O R D A N   M.   S C H E R

Mind as Participation

For a few days I have been writing. May it go on: My life has some justification. Once more I am able to converse with myself, and not gaze into vacancy. Only in this way can I hope to find improvement.—FRANZ KAFKA

The Problem

"To acquire a knowledge of man, one must first have contact with his companions, only then if he seeks to know, if he seeks to stretch out [his knowledge], can he gain the greatest compass." So said Kant (1798) in his attempt to present an anthropological view of man. This point of view—that man must participate, that he is an inevitable participant in his own local culture and in the internal-external continuum of himself and the world—is the only tenable basic thesis of man as mind. This is not to say, as Plato (1956) does, that one can preceive only the shadow of the real world, nor is it to go so far as does Reichenbach (1951) in his attack upon the transcendental conception of knowledge and his defense of the functional concept of it; but rather, with Russell (1917), we must consider man in the light of a kind of marriage between mysticism and science, between reason and intuition. On the other hand, Bergson's (1907) attempt to pit intellect and intuition one against the other is good advocacy but poor comprehension.

Both views, transigent uncertainty and scientific verifiability, must play their roles in the more complete statement of man as knower, man as actor. Husserl (1960) states in his argument against an "objective" science that "judging is meaning" and further (p. 21) that "by my living, my experiencing, thinking, valuing and acting, I can enter no world other than the one that gets its sense and acceptance or status in and from me, myself." Yet in all of these particulars, Husserl is the gerundive, the participant man, for only as man participates is he. Only as he is in the act of, only as he is an "-ing" being, is his existence verified and made real. This is the position of the existential, or "here-and-now," view of man. In a certain sense, there can be no other.

Whether or not man is associated with a particular cultural frame of reference, his own concrete presence, his teleological or open future, others or himself, the key word is connectedness, or participation, in and of each of these, as the hallmark of his living existence. *Unconnected man, nonparticipant man, is unalive man.*

Yet the nature of man requires closer definition than participation alone, since participation has a *phasic* character as well. It is obvious that man cannot be connected and in this sense cannot be alive at all times. He must from time to time at least, be disconnected, or "out of play." If he is alone, he may be involved in a form of distanced connectedness as was Kafka (1947) as he wrote; but he may also at times be disconnected, or out of play, even in the presence of others. Marcel (1948) has referred to this as "presence." Independently, I also became acutely aware of the significance of what I called *presentness* (Scher, 1958b, 1961a) in the process of ontoanalysis (existential psychotherapy). This phasic quality of availability to the other is crucial in understanding the nature of therapy, especially if therapy involves dealing with patients who are not present, or only partially so, in the course of their alienation. The patient, of course, is not the only one in a therapy situation who may be absent from time to time.

This phasic aspect of participation is not only an element in the therapy situation, but is also an index to a more fundamental aspect of man's nature. By this, I refer to the basic rhythmicity with which man as a being-in-the-world is endowed. *Man as rhythm in the world* (Scher, 1961a) is perhaps the most basic aspect of his participant being. Alienation, the nonparticipant or limited participant state, is the most manifest example of out-of-phase, or dysrhythmic, experience. Alienated man is man out of rhythm with the world, so that he does not participate in proportion that he does not feel the rhythmical surging going on around him.

In the course of recovery from alienation, or nonparticipation, such return is not smooth but stepwise, and may be analogous to the quantum jump concomitant with atomic change of state (Scher, 1955, 1958c). This analogy has several important implications. One is that the openness to participation is certainly not a steady or predictable situation (Scher, 1958c). Secondly, the behavior and feeling state of the individual who comes to fuller participation has certain striking and deceptive features. By this I mean that the moments of change (Scher, 1955) give the outward appearances of greater alienation than the time immediately prior to their onset. Further, the feeling state of the alienated one is equally that of panic, a greater sense of distance, and dysrhythmia. At such times all these are highly deceptive because if the attitude of those around is one of hope, expectancy, and presentness, the alienation will very shortly yield a bit and a new level of fuller participation ensue. Some of the aspects of progressive participation will be outlined further on in the specific instance of schizophrenia, but prior to that, certain cultural and experimental aspects of participation will be discussed.

Isolation—Experimental and Cultural

First, the vast realm of sensory deprivation studies provides certain basic information that man, or man considered as mind, cannot tolerate nonparticipation. In the absence of "sensory flux," consciousness cannot be maintained (Hebb, 1961); but sensory flux alone is not consciousness. Novelty (Vernon, *et al.*, 1961), order and meaning (Freedman, *et al.*, 1961),* differential responsiveness (Lindsley, 1961), amplitude and rate of change (Kubie, 1961)—all help to shape the participating mind. Isolated man, or nonparticipant man, is by these studies almost the antithesis of man as a human entity.

Another area of evidence for the role of participation in the definition of man as mind may be had from studies of the so-called "feeble-minded." What of the individual usually considered to be of no or little mind, such as the retarded? Does he participate, and if so, how? Actually, a good deal of confirmation exists for the position that the participating mind functions relatively well, regardless of the measured intelligence. This functioning, however, depends strongly on the cultural context within which the individual may be found. Nevertheless, even in a

---

* The significance of order and meaning was previously observed during the course of a sleep deprivation study (Scher, 1957d).

culture, like our own, that is essentially unsympathetic toward mental subnormality, only 10 per cent of the 4,200,000 children designated as subnormal will be totally unable to care for their creature needs.

Yet, in certain subcultures, such as the Hutterites (Eaton and Weil, 1955), the number of subnormals is below that of other parts of the population, their adjustment considerably better, and their participant status much clearer than in other areas of the community. This is also true of the Trukese of the South Pacific (Gladwin and Sorason, 1953). Despite this evidence of participation as a salubrious influence, the Trukese seem to preserve a concreteness of response and an absence of the questioning attitude so important and characteristic in Western European culture. Another culture, the Wogoe of New Guinea (Hogbin, 1946), have ruled out the questioning attitude by a complete systematic of detailed mythology that precludes further questioning. What this attitude implies is that a concern for the uncertain, such as we possess, in no way seems to invalidate the role of participation in establishing what has been called "mental health." In fact, the contrary may be true.

Each of these cultural patterns, including the European, contains within it a broad or narrow pattern of some kind of activity and social role for the members. The necessity of participation, even if it remains only the establishment of patterned behavior, like that of Christopher Burney (1952) in his solitary confinement, tends to preserve the intactness of the individual. Burney, to maintain his intellectual and emotional integrity, developed many counting devices and memory stunts to enliven his long loneliness, devices that connected him with the outside world in one way or another.

The Tendency toward Completeness

The individual is, in a sense, never uniquely alone, not even Kafka as he contemplates his work. He is participating in the continuing effort toward self-completion or self-fulfillment that is the essence of participation. *Thus, participation, or movement toward completion, means that the basic unit of man is not one, but two.* On those occasional moments when two comprise a complete set, man pauses for a moment of tranquillity, otherwise unmatched in his experience. Such a moment has been called an "encounter" when it occurs between man and man. This essentially closed and unclosed aspect of man as not one but two has been little developed and understood, especially in Western culture, which is oriented toward individuality and conformity above all else.

For most of us most of the time, the best we can muster is a *tendency* toward this completion. It may take the form of attempted passive union with preset external action that does not involve us, as is found in listening to music, watching sports or television, and the like. The degree of participation here is truly minimal: only when we are personally involved in some external spectacle does it become a more fully empathic experience. By empathic, I mean the extending (Scher, 1960) aspect of participation, whereby one includes or is included in the other. It is an expression of the flexibility of our personal boundaries.

Modulatory Influences (Intercessors)

Other levels of the degree of participation must be considered aside from the passive and the complete (encounter). One phenomenon of the participation process is the modulatory effect of a third party, or a tertiary focus of attention between two parties otherwise engaged. A third person may cause a silence or a modulation of tone or action between the two primary parties of the engagement. This modulation has been called in "intercessor" process (Scher, 1957b).

Tertiary events or persons may be quite significant in the participant action of a primary pair. Such an interpretation would tend to dispute the notion of Goffman (1959) that there can be in any context a "nonperson," that is, a person who does not in some way affect a transaction between two other individuals. In fact, even an inanimate object or animal may well alter the behavior of a primary pair.

The effect of an intercessor can tend either to diminish or to enhance the degree of participation between two others. It is particularly significant and useful to understand this effect in any effort to work with seriously disturbed patients, such as schizophrenics, who can often be induced to participate in the presence of an intercessor in a manner impossible in its absence (Scher, 1957b). The presentation of a slightly deviant or foreign element in a situation has, however, far greater importance than merely as a meaningful agent in the treatment of patients. Actually, the introduction of small to progressively larger variations, producing modulation in the nature of a transaction between two individuals, has important social consequences.

Learning* itself of any kind depends upon the introduction of a third element, an unexpected item or event that produces a shift or modulation in already existent knowledge or experience; otherwise there would be no learning. This introduction of the uncertain or unknown has even more vital interpersonal function, and its absence may block new learn-

---

* Whitehead (1960) has indicated his appreciation of this and the role of rhythmicity also in the learning process.

ing. In a closed, closely prescribed community, such as the Trukese, Wogeo, or Hutterite, deviation of an order to produce new learning tends to be eliminated as the individual develops, even though the very closedness to alien experience produces the security of full participation in the pre-established order of things. Thus, participation in its fuller sense may be an obstruction ultimately to growth itself in the closed community.

The Permutations of Participation

In such a community, contact with the alien has the unique effect of producing immediate suspicion and secondary hostility. It would appear that when the intimate attitude is disturbed between two members of the closed community, the results are not simple exclusion and distancing, as might occur in a Western culture, but immediate, often consuming, hostility, which may lead to the establishment of a vendetta. That is, within such a community, *a single inclusion (intimate) and exclusion (enemy) principle obtains;* there is nothing in between. A parallel will be seen in certain role situations in the more open community, which will be discussed later (in the section titled "Marital Participation").

The presentation of differences, or the new, in the European-American culture, on the other hand, promotes curiosity, ultimate new learning, and even creativity. This is, of course, not always the case, but when it is, it produces essentially new participation, and on a more intricate, unexpected plane. Nonetheless, there is an inherent drawback to this very responsiveness. In fact, in the complex community, the frequency and nature of alien contact may induce a peculiar and potentially disturbing side effect.

This effect might be called the alienation, or "walking schizophrenia," of everyday life. This is the street stranger behavior of common experience. The ordinary pedestrian walks the streets as though in a trance, unless accosted by an acquaintance or friend. It is not really that the pedestrian is out of contact, not that he is really unaware of those who pass. He does not treat others as nonpersons, but as persons he *plays at* not responding to or observing. We are hardly unaware of the magical mutuality of participation, even with strangers on the street, but we choose to pretend it isn't so. The restraint, this refusal to admit relatedness and contact, may be curiously related to certain phenomena of mental illness where pretended nonparticipation is maximized. In fact, such "normal" behavior on our part may well be a precursor of more serious alienation.

I refer here to schizophrenia. It may be that the very training afforded the individual in a society that permits and promotes the frequent presentation of the new also thereby contributes to the development in some of more serious forms of alienation. In the simplest society, all may be intimates within kinship and hierarchical limits. With the progressive complexity of society, there will be intimates and strangers in frequent juxtaposition, the latter of whom may be transmuted into enemies. Such transmutation requires a considerable degree of participation, far more than is required in the simpler societies, where strangers may not have so neutral a status. Only in the most complex and sophisticated society will there appear the class of contacts called "acquaintances" and, again only in such a society, will there arise the stranger who is neither acquaintence nor clearly enemy, that is, the passing pedestrian. Thus, in the more complex society, a whole spectrum of participant roles appear: *intimate, familiar, acquaintance, stranger, street stranger,* and *enemy.* The permutations of participant transaction expand far beyond the intimate-enemy dichotomy of the closed society.

For the individual too long inured to intimates, too long enjoined to intimate participation, sudden propulsion into the world of acquaintances and street strangers has the effect of fostering alienation or withdrawal. It may be that, in the immediate requirement of limiting apparent participation, certain members of the population too long exposed to full contact and intimacy cannot tolerate or learn rapidly enough to comply with the newer expectations. Several responses may develop in this situation, all of them forms of alienation.

Alienation and Schizophrenia

Alienation thus takes many shapes. Among them an overbearing or all-embracing type of behavior may appear that I have called "intromersive" (Scher, *et al.,* 1961) and that may simulate openness. Or the individual may stand in sequestered pause, awaiting action or engagement from the other, as in catatonia. Another compensatory posture may be the pre-emptive one of commandeering subordination on the part of others (imperfectionism). The individual may attempt alienation by caricaturing either participation or the forms of participation. Miming, mocking, and indirection (Scher, 1957c) become modes of experiencing the world or counterfeiting participation. In this way ethics becomes a subtle interplay between alienation and participation. Bertrand Russell (1917) goes so far as to define ethics as a product of what he calls the "gregarious instinct," or in other words, the development in a culture of "a sensitivity to the problem of ingroup mores"

(participation)* and "outgroup judgment" (pretended nonparticipation).* All of the above are seen in serious disorders such as schizophrenia and in so-called normal behavior. It is little wonder that
diagnosis is at times so difficult.

An interesting set of behaviors develops in the process of entry into
and recovery from schizophrenia, defined here as constricted participation expressed primarily through indirection, at least in the closed
community of a psychiatric ward (Scher, 1957a). As alienation deepens
and schizophrenia becomes more clearly the case, the patient moves
closer to the situation of the individual in the more self-contained, less
varied, isolated community. In both schizophrenia and the closed community, there are only the classes of intimate and stranger, the latter
often seen as enemy.

Perhaps the major difference is that, for the schizophrenic, his is
progressively a community of one, intimacy being granted only to himself and all others being seen as enemies or potential enemies. Usually,
the schizophrenic individual does not go out of his way to verify the
animosity he feels extended toward him by the rest of the community.
It is only when he is infringed upon by others that he feels impelled
to react or respond with scorn, hostility, or the other tricks of his trade
(Scher, 1958a). The paranoid is, in a sense, an exception.

Contrary to other modalities of the schizophrenic reaction, which
entail withdrawal or narrowing of the including aspect of the self, the
paranoid is involved with a special extension of self, albeit a nonpartici-
pating one. He includes more territory than the normal or feels included
to a greater extent than the norm. If including more is the process, he
then intrudes upon others in one way or another, often aggressively,
though not necessarily violently. Basically, though, the schizophrenic
process involves the elimination of the various phasic adjustments to
others in the complex community of our culture—intimate, familiar, acquaintance, stranger, street stranger, enemy. This is essentially a problem
of interpersonal distance, size, and territoriality and is a proper problem for ontoanalytic psychiatry. The language and other special usages
of schizophrenia are secondary to the phenomenological issue of size,
boundaries, and distance.

Nonetheless, as would be expected, in a reversal of the phenomenological alteration of the including function, or recovery from schizophrenia, there will develop an unfolding and opening to the other phases
of interhuman contact or participation. This develops in an interesting
fashion, however, and concerns primarily the handling of strange,
familiar, and intimate patterns. Initially, the schizophrenic when most

* My parentheses.

alienated meets those who impinge with distancing mechanisms or hostility, particularly toward those expected to be normally the most intimate, such as parents, siblings, and spouses. Exceptions to this pattern seem to be children, other patients, and sometimes former friends. With the exempted group the schizophrenic will either drop the mask of insanity, though hesitantly, or replace it with a mask of formality and politeness. This "out-of-play behavior" is, of course, not true of those whose alienation has run to great depths or extended for a protracted period of time.

In the process of recovery, however, or better, "return," the reactivation of the phasic relationship patterns shows several curious phenomena. There seems to develop an alternating, or skipping, quality in reconstituting the severed normative relationships. Thus, often intimates remain the last to be accepted in their proffered relationship. In the suite of the successful intrusion of the therapist or surrogate intimate,* the patient may exhibit the least apparent awareness or interest. On the other hand, strangers may evoke a surprisingly successful reaction. By this I mean that the transient doctor, nurse, or visitor becomes the object of excessive and ostentatious pseudo-intimacy (intromersion); there is the appearance of seriously disclosing to the stranger confidences seemingly withheld from the officially designated therapist. This ruse is intended to dissuade or throw off the impinging therapist, but does at least indicate a break in the alienation pattern and the redevelopment of participational flexibility. Such a bit of business passes, especially if the therapist persists despite his seeming rejection. It should be noted that this facet of transaction usually follows on the first tentative steps toward acceptance of the therapist's intrusion. Language behavior of the patient at this time actually reveals very little. In fact, the only indications to the therapist that his efforts are being rewarded are usually in peripheral elements of behavior. For example, it may be noted that there is an increased attention to appearances on the part of the patient: his mood seems lighter and even at times gay; he will show an increasing pliability and less resistance to the requests of ward personnel and a certain readiness, even eagerness, to see the therapist, to whom he may not speak or speak only in clichés.

It is certainly not that he is relieved of covert psychic trauma, since his communication is often either trivial or retains the indirective (Scher, 1957c), abortive, and abstracted quality of schizophrenic speech. The

---

* I shall not elaborate here the details of successful intrusion, which is best reserved for more technical presentation elsewhere. Suffice it to say that this is, of course, not a simple matter, especially with the seriously alienated (Scher, 1957d).

presentation of truly informational speech occurs only at a much later date, when the reconstitution of the relational roles is far more complete. It is a trade deception, or "distortion professionel," to attribute the progressive redevelopment of these phasic role structures to the actual verbal content produced by the patient. It may be that the words of the therapist are of some significance, but the level at which the really meaningful transaction occurs is beyond the region of words, that is, unverbalizable. In the region of feelings, words are only the haziest reflection of the subtle level of transaction between humans. This level of relatedness is immediately felt and immediately communicated. It requires no mediation; if anything, mediation through words or actions obscures and confuses transaction at this level. This subtle and immediate form of communication is actually at once so potent and so embarrassing that little is written of it, and its very existence is usually denied on confrontation in ordinary intercourse; but it is the modality through which the most vital human communication occurs and through which therapy must occur. One might call this the level of immediate interpenetration, or vivacious communication (Scher, 1961e), and it is concerned with the rhythmical nature of man (Scher, 1961b).

As the individual's return progresses, he begins to reconstruct his capacity to deal with familiars in a freer and easier way. To the familiar (ward personnel), he may again appear to relate more easily than to the therapist, against whom he periodically turns and rebels or whom he attempts to shake off. Despite appearances, without the key relationship with the therapist, albeit stormy and limited in verbal content, the reappearance of the other role structures would occur on a more random basis and might not even occur at all. This *Sturm, Drang, und Liebe* exchanged with the therapist is a *sine qua non* of therapy and cannot be evaded if true return is to develop. The therapist should be suspicious if negative reactions do not appear and may well achieve a stalemate rather than progression.

Secondary and transient surrogate intimates may be courted by the patient from among the familiars in the setting, but usually they are as rapidly dissipated as they appear. The cast-off surrogate may not understand the exploratory and experimental process of which he is a part and may become offended at his short tenure and precipitate dispatch. Only much later does that discriminating handling of intimate, familiar, stranger, and so on, take on normal proportions. Perhaps the most difficult aspect of role-structuring for the schizophrenic to develop is that of stranger and street stranger. This is because part of the background of the schizophrenic is a deep feeling of immediate interpenetration or unity with his fellows prior to the onset of flagrant symptoms. Most of us learn to distrust this feeling and to develop a face behind which we hide and survey our fellows for some time before we admit them to intimacy and then only provisionally. This may occur in so complex a society as ours even in the face of factitious intimacy, which characterizes much pseudo intimate participation. The so-called "organization man," outer-directed man, inauthentic man, is the product of this pseudo intimate development. A term for the pseudo intimate that I find descriptive and useful is that of "social zombie."

The alienated or schizophrenic individual usually has failed to perceive and appreciate this very subtle latest invention of civilized man. It is one of the elements that has perturbed him about others and helped to alienate him from people, who, in his words, "are not honest." One mask of the schizophrenic is a peculiar and unique sense of honesty, out of place with that of his fellows, who do not share it and with whom he therefore cannot communicate. He has tried to do so but has been unaccepted as a result and has been pushed farther toward alienation (compare Dostoevski, *The Idiot*). It is really often only his *caricature of normal dishonesty* that he palms off as schizophrenia. It is a mockery he promotes onto the world in response to the mockery he feels coming from it (Scher, 1957a, 1958a, 1957c, 1960). The return is consequently not an easy one.

Marital Participation

The schizophrenic is not the only one who reduces his world to solitary intimacy and external enmity, but the difference is that he has no free areas where the normative structures still persist. The other significant example to which I refer is that of husband and wife. Perhaps this reduction in the span of roles evolving between husband and wife is the reason for the Freudian (Freud, 1924) misinterpretation that love and hate are opposite sides of the same coin. Actually that is not the situation.

Perhaps a better way of understanding the violent shifts between the intimate participants in a marriage is to see them as similar to the relationship matrix of the closed society. In other words, if he is not completely with me, he is against me; that is, there are only two positions, intimate and enemy. Each partner includes the other completely; any indication of nonacceptance, nonapproval, or nonparticipation is considered complete rejection. Each partner sees the other only as an extension of himself, and the self cannot deny the self. A reflection of this primitive all-or-nothing law of relating is to be had in the Biblical injunction, "If thy eye offend thee, pluck it out." Such is the case with marital partners who struggle for intimacy, participation, and, at the same time, individuation. Each must accept the other completely, allow the other his uniqueness, and at once establish a bond of completeness requiring no other. Inherent in each of these are inevitably contradictory elements that can be resolved only by inauthenticity, the hegemony of one over the other, or a state of mutuality and exclusiveness rarely experienced. Thus, the alternative to the accomplishment of such identity in complete love of fullest participation is hate, which may result in armed truce (stranger pattern), open enmity, sometimes of murderous proportions, and in all too many instances, divorce. Otherwise, there is no explanation of intimacy turned to hate without understanding the broader pattern of which this is one detail. This, of course, presumes the existence of the sense of mutual warm interpenetration prior to the marital relationship. Naturally, if one or the other partner has a pre-existing problem of alienation and consequent nonparticipation, then the situation is foredoomed to failure, without enormous effort on either part.

Even without pre-existing alienation, the rapid shift from participant love to participant hate may be a relatively small step. When one partner sees the other as an extension and completion of the self, it may take very insignificant, but persistent, minute elements of regular disapproval or disregard to effect the shift to hate. Like the water of the Chinese water torture, steady but harmless drops will induce serious disaffection. In this way, it is not uncommon for a patient to complain of a spouse, "It's not ever anything very important, but everything I do is wrong, I can't seem to please him (her)." Actually this is a distortion on the part of the patient so complaining.

What is really the case is that one individual (or both) operates according to one of two systems. As each partner is an extension (or inclusion) of the other—inclusion that is externally visible and thereby potentially culpable, that does not conform to the exact dimensions in the mind's eye, is out of focus and therefore condemned. It is common experience in human relationships that we can see the mote in the eye of the other and miss the beam in our own. This is particularly true if the mote and the beam are of the same size, shape, and character. In short, we very often condemn in another merely our own reflection, especially so if that other is, or in our view should be, a completing but more perfect version of ourself. The second circumstance in which we tend to provoke regularly by the water-torture method separation, alienation, and ultimately hate is that alluded to above, in which one or both partners bring into the relationship a condition of pre-existing alienation. Such alienation often takes a peculiar and interesting form, which I have described elsewhere (Scher, *et al.*, 1961) as the *imperfective* mode. This mode of behavior has regularly been confused with so-called perfectionism. The latter term, as far as I am concerned, is a misnomer and an empty category. The only perfectionism I have seen clinically is that variety alluded to above in the problem of condemning the extended or hypostatized self. Certainly there is no perfectionism here but instead a variety of imperfectionism, or seism (Scher, 1961c); that is, the individual condemns, in effect, his own imperfection as seemingly actualized in another. By this means, a value judgment seems to be introduced that one unable to apply to himself transposes to another.

Imperfectionism in Depth

Imperfectionism is a species of alienation. As the relatively normal sees and seeks for completion through participation, the imperfective seems always to be in the process of establishing a state of separateness. He cannot *accept closure,* or the satiety that comes with the moment of completeness or with encounter in fullest participation with the other. Instead, he sets up barriers that seem incomprehensible to his partner or the other party so afflicted. The imperfective literally seeks for the flaw, the defect, actual or ascribed, in any situation, action, or person. No one or nothing can please him. Every experience or statement is greeted with a dependent clause or thought denoting separateness, dissatisfaction, and incompleteness. Characteristically, such people employ what I have described as a "not quite" or "but if" speech pattern; everything is described as all right, but not quite all right. "That is a pretty hat, but not quite the right color, shape, or size."

This is a very common and pervasive pattern in our alienated culture, and it is a response to the all too general fear of participation, closeness, and completion. The pattern may be schematized as A but not a, or A but not a'. Thus, the state of rest ($Aa = Bb$), or the closure of A and B in a moment of encounter, $a = b$, is always foresworn. It is a situation of seeming meeting, but no meeting in some detail. It is a state of *pars sed non totum* (the part but not the whole). What phenomenologically occurs is that the rejection of the part is perceived by the other, if consistent enough, as the rejection of the whole. The person so exposed to this approach, instead of feeling accepted in the main but demurred in detail, feels rejected totally and on a strangely unanswerable pretext. He feels alienated by the alienator and without recourse. What is most frustrating is that somehow the onus of who is rejecting whom is curiously shifted, and the *rejector feels rejected by the rejectee.* Furthermore, no amount of effort seems to unlock the unacceptability of the rejectee by the rejector. The rejectee can never find truly common ground or common cause with the rejector, since none is allowed and all measures taken to find completion and participation by the rejectee are uniformly given the "not quite" treatment.*

Imperfectionism and the Genesis of Schizophrenia

A special case of this imperfective pattern has been given wide currency in the so-called "double-bind" hypothesis (Bateson, *et al.*, 1956). This thesis holds that the rejectee or alienatee is placed in a position of being "damned if I do and damned if I don't" by the individual I have called the rejector or alienator. Although this is a special case of the imperfective mode, I think more has been made of it than need be. As usually described, or at least commonly accepted, the figure employing this approach is often said to be the mother of a schizophrenic individual, at times the father (Lidz and Fleck, 1960), and even, on occasion, a brother, a sister, or the entire family. In fact, there is usually an ascribed unconscious malevolence, and a kind of cat-and-mouse approach may be sensed in the descriptions of such situations. It is almost as though this were the contrivance of a peculiar intentionality on the part of the alienator.

It is my feeling that such a description, if I have accurately interpreted it, is a narrowing and falsification of the situation. It may well be true that one or both parents of a schizophrenic individual may function in a primarily imperfective mode, with the attendant confusion and frustration on the part of a child so exposed; but the imperfective mode is an extremely common one, and undoubtedly imperfectionism begets imperfectionism by reaction or by assimilation. Nonetheless, imperfectionism is certainly *not* a *sine qua non* for the development of so-called schizophrenia.

* Ellis (1962) presented a somewhat irrational program of "rational therapy aimed at severing the dependent, nonclosured clause of imperfectionism." His error is in accenting the so-called faulty logic (or idea) as that which maintains the imperfective posture. Imperfectionism is a phenomenon that precedes ideation as such. It is instead embedded in the matrix of the relation of man to man and is a means by which the *apartheid* of alienation is maintained at a level that seems only moderately unreasonable and naggingly neurotic. Imperfective behavior nonetheless is a potent force for maintaining distance and alienation. What Ellis has suggested therapeutically is only the employment of one particular closure device (Scher, Geisser, and Campaigne, 1961b) to round off the interminably unclosured, imperfective sequence, (Scher, 1962c). Such a sequence arises out of the tendency for incompleting, unterminating ideation to develop in the vacuum of the imperfective variety of nonparticipation. It is not the ideas that are primary, nor do they induce this pathology, although they may help maintain it. Ellis' (1962) approach may also be seen to be a clinical example of what Mowrer (1960) describes under either "nonconfirmation" or "counter-conditioning." Ellis' (1962) approach represents an example of the currently common tendency to seek at the content level to define what can be understood only in terms of the process of transaction.

Quite the contrary, as is obvious, many people not too seriously addicted to the imperfective mode of operation seem to fare relatively well in our alienated society. Schizophrenic behavior, as I have pointed out elsewhere (Scher, 1957a, c, d; 1958a; 1960; 1962a, b), must be considered in quite another context, perhaps a context quite the contrary of that currently held. In fact, a revision of our whole premise of so-called emotional illness and its origin may very well be in order.

When I first began speaking and writing some ten years ago about the ludic, or play, aspect of the situation known as schizophrenia and the decision element in it (Scher, 1950), this suggestion did not find great favor. Since then many of these views have become more widely accepted. Yet, as is not infrequently the case, that which gains the limelight tends to do so in an incomplete and perhaps excessively dramatic form. Mental illness, alienation, schizophrenia is certainly not a myth, as Szasz (1961) grandiosely proclaims, despite the ludic aspect of it, which he seems to has misinterpreted as the entire situation. As I have stated previously (Scher, 1957a; 1962a), schizophrenia has its origin in a quite different situation from that of the "double-bind" (Bateson, *et al.*, 1956) and is a considerably more complex situation than mere impersonation (Szasz, 1961; anonymous, 1961) or ludic behavior (Scher, 1960, 1957a, 1952).

In fact, a much more reasonable thesis of the origin of schizophrenia and one considerably more in line with the growth of the "affluent society" (Galbraith, 1958) must be entertained. To digress for a moment, such postulates as those of Bateson (1956), Jackson (1960), and Bowen (1959) depend essentially on the principle, one way or another, of the rejecting and/or malevolent (unconscious) influences of those around and close to the patient. I believe that quite a contrary hypothesis has been demonstrated and elaborated (Scher, 1957a; 1962a, b). This hypothesis is what I have come to call the sanogenesis (healthful origin), or at least the nonpathogenesis, of so-called emotional illness, and more particularly that process known as schizophrenia. What I mean by this perhaps daring thesis is this: *Emotional illness is the product not of too much pain and trauma, but of too little and too late.* Pain and trauma are normal: they are necessary and vital concomitants of healthy growth and development. To have been spared "the slings and arrows of outrageous fortune, and *by opposing end them*" is to have been spared the possibility of having become fully alive, of having come to normal adulthood, of having come into the possibility of fully participating.

The so-called neurotic is one who has been to a large extent spared from the full force of failure, disappointment, even humiliation. At the conference on the patient and the mental hospital in Boston, in 1955 (Greenblatt, *et al.*, 1957b), I attempted to express this requirement in the treatment of the schizophrenic patient and, *praesertim*, the role of its absence in the origin of such processes. At that time, I expressed this in an epigrammatic form that has had some currency since. The growing child, I felt, needed the "*No* of love as well as the *Yes* of love." This concept of the requirement of proper termination, or halting, of a set of events was entailed in the concept of closure (Scher, *et al.*, 1961). Thus, failure, disappointment, and humiliation are events subsidiary to and subsumed under the general concept of normative closuring. Pain, implied in disappointment and such events, represents the feeling state counterpart of the event of closure. Not all closures, however, are painful and some may even be met with a surprisingly warm and thankful acceptance such as experienced in the "thank you" phenomenon, following a closuring event by a staff member in the structural ward approach to the schizophrenic (Scher, 1958a). In a society such as ours, where failure and pain are reserved more and more for the adult years, the necessary preparation for and apprenticeship in the pain of living tends to be progressively more delayed and avoided.

A thesis such as Freud's (1924), that man tends to seek pleasure and avoid pain, has been distorted into the thesis that man *should* avoid pain and seek pleasure. Certainly pleasure, ease, and comfort are equally vital in normal growth, but they cannot be put forward to define the entire condition of man as there is currently a tendency to do.

Consequently, that child who is *pre-empted* (Scher, 1957a, 1962a) from the simpler and the more complex experiences of normal pain and anxiety will be unprepared to cope with these situations when they arise, as they inevitably do, at a later age. In fact, he will be equally unprepared to cope with pleasure, since he will not know how to evaluate it and savor it in all its fullness nor how to terminate it. It is therefore terminating or closuring gratification, not delaying it, that is the problem. *Thus, paradoxically, it is the sane society, the loving society, that by its excessive urge to spare spares not and by its excessive urge to preserve sanity establishes the very conditions that will tend to destroy it.*

How then, does this lead to alienation, and in some cases, schizophrenia? Who cannot, or dare not, feel great pain cannot by the same token feel great pleasure. He cannot feel great love and certainly cannot feel full participation, which is the greatest love. It is a curiosity that in the Freudian system, aside from genital gratification, there is no clearer description of the fullness and richness of love; nor can it really be put into words, any more than music can be transposed into words. Alienation, however, even of a considerable degree, is still not schizophrenia, although it is certainly a precondition. Where then is the line of demarcation, where does the garden variety of alienation change, if it does, into the more exotic plant of schizophrenia? This shift arises out of a failure to be able to cope with the progressive massing of moments of pain and strain in one deprived of the preliminary experiences of pain and strain in growing up. Alienation is a product of developing in a culture and/or a family that limits through pre-emption the apogeal satisfaction of responsible individual accomplishment and at the same time fails, through such devices as imperfectionism, to give the individual a capacity for self-closure; but these alone are not sufficient grounds for the state of schizophrenia.

It is, as I have outlined (Scher, 1957a), those *sites of major shift* to new responsibilities, new and unfamiliar tasks, with all of their inherent travails, that become the *moments of decision* for or against so-called schizophrenia. This is a decision (Scher, 1960) that is not entered on lightly or merely by way of joke and play. When the perception on the part of the individual is that the pain of existence is too great to bear, the moment of decision arrives. This pain, by the way, is not in itself too great but so appears to an individual uninured to normal pain as noted above. All schizophrenia passes through a phase of depression or the withdrawal of affectual relations with the outside world, prior to the actualization of the commitment to the schizophrenic posture. The person contemplating this departure has already given full consideration to the possibility of suicide and through cowardice or courage has rejected this solution. Many have even tried it, seriously or abortively. It is only in the full congizance that they neither fully want to die nor fully want to live that the schizophrenic mantle becomes the coat of choice.

This, then, is no disease process, although it is an attempted solution to a dis-ease state. Unfortunately, it is no solution, but only a prelude to a more constant and, at times, irreversible state of progressive dis-ease, since pain unopposed tends to amplify and extend itself. This amplification may then become the trap through which greater hopelessness and despair become a way of life. Although schizophrenia may begin as a posture, it certainly does not persist as one, any more than acculturation to any way of life can be indefinitely resisted and played at. This last aspect, that of acculturation, makes the process in its more chronic forms so difficult to cope with. On the other hand, it is the freshness of the decision and the firmness of the resolve that in its earlier phases renders this era of the development of schizophrenia no easily solvable problem either.

Alienation, Participation, and Society

One might well ask how all the normative subtlety, alternation, selectivity, and variety of interpersonal expression and attitude develop. How does the child learn to formulate these shadings of action and response, which may lead to ultimate alienation or joining?

For the newborn, the world is probably a series of flashes, discrete and hazy images and impressions, disregarding temporal and spatial array. Progressively, he views things and people in more form and order, but the infant who smiles is not smiling out of love, care, or even joy initially. On the contrary, he smiles by way of flexing certain facial muscles and later smiles to reinforce the pattern. In fact, it may be that he learns to relate the mother's smile to his own not only through vision but through touch and perhaps largely by accident. He touches her mouth and face and also his own. An important element in the peek-a-boo phenomenon of which Maurer (1961) speaks may well be a manipulation of tactual, visual, and auditory apparatuses as part of the project of the infant to *integrate* these modalities. The infant touches cloth and face, or faces; he employs the sight and darkness, the laughter and prosody, of "Peek a boo, I see you" to become completely himself. So does the infant begin to *synchronize and harmonize perception and action*. He begins to partake of the external rhythms of the world, *but only as a solitary*.

It would be a gross mistake to confuse this kind of activity on the part of the infant as participant in the sense of intimacy. It is exploratory, isolated, much as the conditioned animal reacts to stimuli, but he is not responding at the level of shared feeling or experience. The infant is an outsider, a stranger, to such feelings as love and hate or the other varieties of emotion available to the adult and *ascribed to him* by the adult.

The infant knows not love; he is an animal in the process of conditioning to the world. He is learning the world mechanically and by rote. There is no magic for him, only randomness and a certain *movement toward order* promoted by others through a series of trials and steps, only partially or incompletely reversible. Magic must come much later. It is a crucial mistake on the part of the adult to ascribe the possibility of real intimacy and participation, of which he is perhaps capable, to the infant. The infant, soft and cuddly as he is, is nonetheless an alien, a stranger to the subtle and deep emotions of adulthood. It is no wonder then that the child who loses a parent very early through death, divorce, or separation may never acquire for that parent the depth of feeling the parent later might wish.

Alienation then is *not a superimposed product of an overmechanized society, but is instead the natural state of the infant out of which he may grow to a greater or lesser extent*. Alienation, I must repeat, is the initial and natural state of man. Little wonder that Harlow's (1958) monkeys can come to regard even the wire mesh with equal "affection" as toward a real mother. Thus, nature has endowed man *only* with being a stranger in an alien world and only the *possibility* of achieving greater feeling for his fellows, greater participation with them. It is for this reason that alienation is so pervasive a situation and not merely the superimposition of the acculturating process. Man is born separate and must acquire twoing. He must achieve the movement from the solitary to the participant and only at great price. He must chance the movement from the one to the two-that-is-one in the highest sense. This is the problem of separateness and together*ing* (not "togetherness," a pathetic expression of a static, nonexistent state).

Alienation is, then not an alien state to man but a native one. Its persistence occurs in the *failure to develop* the capacities for the finer shadings of participation and is not a defect of the more complex society that produces out of whole cloth alienated man in an alienated society. Perhaps the greatest influence exerted by a socially automated society such as ours is the narrowing of territory and accelerating of time induced by the geometrically expanding population. It is useless and feeble to inveigh against our culture for producing that to which it is only a party.

It is for this reason that so much of the emphasis on man's alienation and the consequent assaults on our society as causative are of limited meaning. That man remains alienated and does not move toward participation is traceable rather to the tendency for there to be an initial drag retaining him in the simpler solitary state and the failure on his part to overcome it. It is only through heroic efforts that he can shake off the dark of alienation and break through into the dazzling light of participation. It is only through an understanding of this pristine and preconditioning position from which man starts that we can fully appreciate the greatness of his accomplishment in overcoming it and the reason for so many individual failures or limited successes.

Man is born alienated and only through enormous effort accomplishes participation. As early as he could mark off and delimit, he has been involved in separating *meum* from *tuum*, Caesar's from God's; only in his progressive sophistication of feeling and awareness has been able to discover the me *and* thee, the Gaius *and* the Gaia. Thus, prior to the rule of law, prior to the rule of ethics, is the rule of *self apart*. Law helped man with the horizontal process of demarcating and later with that of joining; but ethics evolved out of man's vertical longing, the longing of the inner self searching for its other, its higher self. Ethics discloses the rule of fit and participation. Religion is the combining force, that rule of fullest participation and union, where vertical and horizontal have their crossing and extend in depth.

How much higher can man ascend? How astral is his flight? That man can fly we know, that he can transcend we suspect. "Wheeling and soaring high in the sunlit silence," will he lose the pulse of the earth? Will he, in learning to master, lose his hard-won ability to feel?

Man, hero, who has learned so much, will your wax wings melt? Will you plummet back to earth or never rise from it? The future is open to you, you must decide. To gain the whole Heaven and find no trace of God. To evict Him from His Home and find Him not in Self and Other. To lose the painfully acquired richness of participation. To lose the very Self that fails full-force to meet the other openly, freely. Man you have won the greatest victory. You have won the Hero's laurel. Where go you now?

REFERENCES

Anonymous, "A new theory of schizophrenia," *J. Abn. & Soc. Psychol.*, 1961, 57: 226-236.

Bateson, G., Haley, J., Jackson, D. D., and Weakland, J. H., "Toward a theory of schizophrenia," *Behavioral Sci.*, 1956, 1:251-264.

Bergson, H., *L'évolution creatrice*, Librairies Felix Algan et Guillaume Reunies, Paris, 1907.

Bowen, M., Dysinger, R. H., and Basamia, B., "The role of the father in families with a schizophrenic patient," *Am. J. Psychiat.*, 1959, 115:1017-1020.

Burney, C., *Solitary Confinement*, Coward-McCann, New York, 1952.

Eaton, J. W., and Weil, R. J., *Culture and Mental Disorders: A Comparative Study of the Hutterites and Other Populations.* The Free Press, New York, 1961.

Ellis, A., *Reason and Emotion in Psychotherapy*, Lyle Stuart, New York, 1962.

Freedman, S. J., Grunebaum, H. U., and Greenblatt, M., "Perceptual and cognitive changes in sensory deprivation," in P. Solomon, P. E. Kubsansky, P. H. Leiderman, J. H. Mendelson, R. Trumbull, and D. Wexler (eds.), *Sensory Deprivation*, Harvard University Press, Cambridge, Mass., 1961.

Freud, S., "The economic problem in masochism," in E. Jones (ed.), *Collected Papers*, Hogarth Press Ltd. and the Institute of Psychoanalysis, London, 1924, Vol. II.

Galbraith, J. K., *The Affluent Society*, Houghton, Mifflin, Boston, 1958.

Goffman, E., *The Presentation of Self in Everyday Life*, Doubleday, New York, 1959.

Harlow, H. F., "The nature of love," *Am. Psychologist*, 1958, 13:673-685.

Hebb, D. O., *The Organization of Behavior*, Science Editions, New York, 1961, p. 147.

Hogbin, H. L., "A New Guinea childhood: From weaning till the eighth year in Wogoe," *Oceania*, 1946, 16:275.

Husserl, E., *Cartesian Meditations*, Martinus Nijhoff, The Hague, p. 10.

Jackson, D. D., "A critique of the literature on the genetics of schizophrenia," in D. D. Jackson (ed.), *The Etiology of Schizophrenia*, Basic Books, New York, 1960.

Kafka, F. Cited by Thomas Mann in his introduction to Kafka, F., *The Castle*, New York: Alfred Knopf, Inc. 7th printing, 1947.

Kant, I. *Anthropologie in progmatischer hinsicht*, Friedrich Nicolovius, Konigsberg, 1798, p. 8. (Translated excerpt by J. M. Scher.)

Kubie, L. S., "Theoretical aspects of sensory deprivation," in Solomon, *et al., op. cit.*

Lidz, T., and Fleck, S., "Schizophrenia, human integration and the role of the family," in Jackson, *op. cit.*

Lindsley, D. B., "Common factors in sensory deprivation, sensory distortion and sensory overload," in Solomon, *et al., op. cit.*

Marcel, G., *The Philosophy of Existence,* translated by Manya Harari, Harville Press Ltd., London, 1954, p. 25.

Maurer, A., "The child's knowledge of non-existence," *J. Exist. Psychiat.,* 1961, 6:193.

Mowrer, O. H., *Learning Theory and Behavior,* John Wiley, New York, 1960.

Plato, *The Republic,* translated by W. H. D. Rouse, Mentor Books, New York, 1956, p. 514.

Reichenbach, H., *The Rise of Scientific Philosophy,* University of California Press, Berkeley, Calif., 1951, 253-255.

Russell, B., *Mysticism and Logic,* Doubleday, New York, 1917.

Scher, J. M., "Some considerations on schizophrenia," presented at the Psychiatric Institute, University of Maryland, 1952.

————, "The transitional juncture: Allometric mobilization in recovery from the schizophrenic state," presented at the Staff Conference, Psychiatric Institute, University of Maryland, 1955.

————, "Schizophrenia and task orientation: The structured ward setting," *AMA Arch. Neurol. Psychiat.,* 1957a, 78:531-538.

————, "I. Diffusion of communication and role exchange in the treatment of schizophrenia," in M. Greenblatt, D. Levinson, and R. Williams (eds.), *The Patient and the Mental Hospital,* The Free Press, New York, 1957b, pp. 309-316.

————, "Indirection in schizophrenia: A communicative basis for a theory of schizophrenia," presented at the International Psychiatric Congress. Zurich, Switzerland: September, 1957c.

————, "Perception: Equivalence, avoidance and intrusion in schizophrenia," *AMA Arch. Neurol. Psychiat.,* 1957d, 77:210-217.

————, "The structured ward: Research method and hypothesis in a total treatment setting for schizophrenia," *Amer. J. Orthopsychiat.,* 1958a, 28:291-299.

————, "Presentness and ontoanalysis," presented at the Chicago Ontoanalytic Society, November, 1958b.

————, "Saltation and the open system in schizophrenia," paper read at the Society for General Systems Research in conjunction with the AAAS, Washington, D.C., December, 1958c.

————, "The concept of the self in schizophrenia," presented in an earlier version at the Fourth International Congress of Psychotherapy, Barcelona, September, 1958. Revised and elaborated for the Institute on Chronic Schizophrenia and Hospital Treatment Programs, Osawatomie, Kan., October, 1958. In L. Appleby, J. M. Scher, and J. Cumming (eds.), *Chronic Schizophrenia,* The Free Press, New York, 1960.

————, "Presentness and transaction in the ontoanalytic process," presented at Annual Symposium, The Bradley Center, Columbus, Ga., March 18, 1961a.

————, "The rhythmicity of human transaction," presented at the Symposium for the Third World Congress of Existential Psychiatry, Montreal, June 7, 1961b.

————, "II. Primary gain: The game of illness and the communicative compact in the borderline patient," submitted in July, 1957, published in *Pyschiat. Quart.,* State Hospitals, Utica, N.Y., July, 1961c.

————, "Ontoanalysis: Man as rhythm in the world," presented at the Fourth International Congress for Psychotherapy, Vienna, August, 1961d.

———, "Vivacity, pathology and existence," presented at the Conference on Existential Psychiatry of the American Ontoanalytic Association, New York, December 10, 1961e.

———, "Some comments on intervention in psychotherapy," *Am. J. Psychoanal.,* 22:63-65, 1962a.

———, "Ontoanalysis: The maieutic of existence," presented at the Conference on Existential Psychiatry at the annual meeting of the American Ontoanalytic Association in conjunction with the American Psychiatric Association, Toronto, May 6, 1962b.

Scher, J. M., Geisser, S., and Campaigner, H. M., "The psychotherapeutic transaction: An operational model and system of analysis," presented at the annual meeting of the American Psychiatric Association, San Francisco, May 13, 1958. In *J. Exist. Psychiat.,* Winter–Spring, 1961, 1:4.

Szasz, T., *The Myth of Mental Illness,* Paul B. Hoeber, New York, 1961.

Vernon, J. A., McGill, T. E., Gulick, W. L., and Candland, D. K., "The effect of human isolation upon some perceptual and motor skills," in Solomon, *et al., op. cit.*

Whitehead, A. N., *The Aims of Education,* Mentor Books, New York, 1960, p. 39.

C. A. CAMPBELL

The Mind's Involvement in "Objects":

An Essay in Idealist Epistemology

The present paper calls for a few preliminary observations. I shall make as few of them as possible.

1. I appear in this volume as a representative of the "idealist" tradition; but there have been many brands of idealism, and the cleavages between them are often deep. The standpoint from which I shall be writing is that of the post-Kantian idealism that dominated the philosophy of the English-speaking world in the late decades of the nineteenth century and the first two decades of this. Rightly or wrongly, I am convinced that post-Kantian idealism has still much that is of value to offer to philosophers today and that the main reason why this is not recognized is that what it has to offer is so little known.

2. For (post-Kantian) idealism the theory of *mind*—to which the present volume is devoted—and the theory of *reality* are, in the last resort, one. It would be futile, therefore, within the limits prescribed for this paper, to try to deal with the idealist theory of mind in its full scope. To readers with any knowledge of idealist philosophy the treatment could not but appear intolerably superficial; to the uninitiated it would mean little or nothing. Even on the restricted topic I have elected to write about—the idealist view of the mind's involvement in "objects"—I have found myself obliged to accept the further restriction of eschewing metaphysical argument and adopting an almost exclusively

epistemological approach. Nevertheless, the topic chosen is one so central to idealist thought that it ought to be possible, despite these limitations, to bring out a great deal of what is most important in, and most distinctive of, the idealist theory of mind.

3. Within post-Kantian idealism itself variations are very far from negligible. Hegel is no doubt the prototype: but it is a serious error to suppose that later idealists have been simply Hegel's disciples. There is a strongly individual flavor about the respective versions of idealism offered by outstanding modern representatives of the movement like Green, Bradley, Royce, Bosanquet, and Pringle-Pattison. Perhaps only Bosanquet among them could with any strictness he called an "Hegelian." The differences are less strongly marked, I think, in epistemology than in metaphysics, which is one reason why I have here preferred the epistemological approach. But I shall not deny that there may be occasions in the following pages where what I refer to as "the idealist theory" might with greater accuracy be described as "the version of idealist theory that to me seems the soundest."

Adoption of the epistemological approach entails that I shall be constantly talking in this paper about "cognition": indeed, the paper will in large measure be an exposition and defense of the idealist theory of cognition. Unfortunately, "cognition" (with its derivatives) is one of the less satisfactory words in the philosopher's vocabulary. It carries misleading suggestions that one would fain avoid. Perhaps a brief terminological note on "cognition" at the outset will be the best way of ensuring that in what follows no great harm will come from its use.

The need of a word to do what "cognition" is intended to do is hardly open to question. Almost everyone is agreed that there is a mode of mental activity whose specific aim is truth, and whose instances exhibit very varying degrees of success and failure in the realization of that aim. We want a word to denote this mode, applicable to the whole range of its instances irrespective of considerations of their actual success or failure, their truth or falsity. "Knowing" obviously will not do, since a knowing that is false is a contradiction in terms. The word that has on the whole won most general favor is "cognizing." Yet it must be confessed that if what we are searching for is a word that is neutral as between truth and falsity in its significance, "cognizing," though less conspicuously unsuited to the office than "knowing," still leaves much to be desired.

The trouble is, of course, that "cognition" retains in ordinary usage a good deal of its original etymological significance of actual knowing; so that to speak of "false cognitions" excites a discomfort closely akin to that which we feel toward an expression like "false knowledge." Here before me is an elm tree which I mistakenly think to be an oak. Can my thinking that the tree is an oak properly be described as a *cognizing* that it is an oak? It is hard not to feel that so to describe it comes very near to being an abuse of the English language. You cannot "cognize," one is inclined to say, what is not the case. You can "cognize" that the tree is an elm, since it *is* so, but not that it is an oak.

Could the language of "cognition" in such cases be defended on the ground that, though we are in error in thinking this to be an oak, and though "cognizing" does imply apprehending correctly, we *are* nevertheless correctly apprehending *something*—namely, the false proposition that this is an oak tree? But clearly there is no help to be had in this direction. Instances are easily enough conceivable, no doubt, in which what we are doing is simply apprehending correctly a false proposition. But, of course, that is not at all a proper description of what we are doing when we think that this tree is an oak. The essence of what we are doing is not correctly apprehending a false proposition, but mistakenly thinking that the false proposition is true; and the whole trouble is to see how, without violating ordinary usage of the word, we can call this mistaken thinking a *cognition*.

And yet, are the possible alternatives to "cognition" that might occur to one in any better case? One might perhaps be tempted at first to fall back on "thinking," which is at least free from the particular disability we have noticed in "cognizing." Most people would agree that we can think erroneously as well as think truly. But the term "thinking" has specialized associations that fit it very ill for the generic use proposed. It is sufficient to remind ourselves that we commonly distinguish between, and even contrast, thinking and *perception*. Yet perception is certainly among the most important of the mental acts which we should want our general term to cover. Clearly we cannot conveniently use it to cover a term from which it is commonly, and as a rule rather sharply, distinguished.

Could we do any better with "believing," which shares with "thinking" the advantage that either truth or falsity can be predicted of it? I think we should fare even worse. Whatever ought to be understood by "belief" (and on this philosophers by no means speak with one voice) it is at least common ground that it is not an *act* or *process*. We talk of "belief" in terms of states occasionally, and of dispositions more often, but no one talks of "acts" of belief, or of believing "processes." Yet it is precisely a mode of mental *activity* for which we are seeking an appropriate name. Central among the phenomena to which the name is to be applied are judgments and inferences, which are neither states nor dispositions, but acts or processes. (A judgment or an inference may be, perhaps must be, *accompanied* by a belief, but neither a judgment nor an inference can be regarded as an *instance* of belief.)

On the whole it seems best just to "make do" with "cognition" as probably the least objectionable of the several unsatisfactory candidates. But it will require to be borne in mind throughout what follows that the word is being used as a technical term and not in all respects in conformity with its ordinary usage. Its etymological connection with actual knowing is to be forgotten. It is to be taken as applying indifferently to *all* instances of the mode of mental activity whose specific aim is knowledge or truth, without regard to whether or not that aim is fulfilled.

In deciding how best to expound the idealist theory of cognition, one has to face at the outset a difficulty at which I have already hinted. Acquaintance with even the general character of post-Kantian idealism cannot safely be taken for granted among philosophers today. That this is the situation, in English-speaking countries at any rate, is hardly disputable. Naturally it makes no easier the task of giving an account of a fundamental aspect of idealist philosophy which will be at once brief and intelligible.

On the whole, the problem of presentation this entails will perhaps be best solved if we approach the idealist theory of cognition indirectly, allowing it to emerge as far as possible by way of critical reaction to the kind of views about cognition which are most familiar and most widely approved at the present time. This is not quite so paradoxical a procedure as may appear at first sight. Contemporary theories about cognition have to do in the main with *sensory* cognition; and though these theories do of course incorporate in their superstructure many novel conceptions, their basic premises seem to me very seldom to be substantially different from those of the empiricist thinkers with whom the old-time idealists did battle, and in so doing defined in large measure their own positive epistemology, several generations ago.

Indeed, if an old-time idealist were to return from the shades, he would, I fancy, be somewhat taken aback to find, on so crucial a question as the role of "sense" in sensory cognition, a position commonly adopted today which at least looked as though it lay open to criticisms the same in principle as those by which he fondly supposed he had demolished the "sensation" of the old-time empiricist. He would seek eagerly for evidence in modern empiricist writings that his criticisms had been pondered and answered, not just sidetracked; but I am bound to say that, in my opinion, his search would be largely in vain. It seems to me, therefore, that a restatement of these criticisms, directed specifically to the contemporary situation, may not be altogether without profit, quite apart from its topical usefulness in serving to introduce the idealist's positive theory of cognition which it is our business to expound.

Our procedure, then, will be to consider the analysis of sensory cognition which is typical of present-day theory, explain just where and on what grounds a critic bred in the idealist tradition would find this analysis unacceptable, develop therefrom the main features of the idealist's own theory of cognition, and, finally, exhibit the implications of the idealist theory in respect of "the mind's involvement in objects."

We shall take our start from, and indeed long continue with, sensory cognition in its simplest form; for it is on the correct analysis of this that almost everything turns. I am referring to such cognitions as are popularly described as "the seeing of a color," "the hearing of a sound," and so on. They could also be indicated by saying that they are such cognitions as most philosophers today would regard as instances of the "sensing of sensa." A formal definition is, however, obviously desirable; and it is not too easy to give. The trouble is that a definition of "simple" sensory cognition is very liable to beg questions which ought to be decided only in the light of the subsequent analysis. A definition that avoids question-begging must do so, I fear, at the cost of being cumbrous; and I certainly cannot claim elegance for the attempt which follows. By simple sensory cognition (hereafter, for brevity's sake, I shall drop the prefix "simple" save where misunderstanding might thereby arise), I propose to mean "the unmediated cognition of those *qualia* which are commonly classed as 'sensible' on the ground that experience gives good reason for believing the cognition of them to be in all normal cases specifically conditioned by stimulation of our organs of sense."

We can list as follows the most important issues that are not prejudged by the way the definition is framed:

1. Whether there is—as the title "sensory cognition" tends to suggest that there is—a distinctive cognitive mode of pure "sensing."

2. What sort of "being" belongs to the *qualia* cognized in sensory cognition (hence our adoption of the noncommittal term *qualia*).

3. Whether the *qualia* are objects cognized by *direct inspection* (for though all direct inspection is unmediated cognition, it can by no means be assumed that all unmediated cognition is a matter of direct inspection).

4. Whether there can be sensory cognition in which *nothing besides* what is sensible is cognized; and if there cannot, what is the relation of the "something besides" to the "sensible" in the cognition.

Now to each of these questions, which are of course closely interlocked with one another, most philosophers during the last thirty or forty years have been ready with a pretty definite and confident answer. They maintain that:

1. Pure sensing is a distinctive mode of cognition;

2. The *qualia* cognized by sensing are actually existing entities of some sort;

3. The *qualia* are cognized by sensing as objects of direct inspection; and

4. Sensory cognition of the *qualia* does not essentially involve the cognition of anything besides.

The sensible *qualia,* since it is through sensing and sensing alone that they are supposed to be cognized, these philosophers usually call "sensa," or alternatively "sense-data" (the latter term being especially appropriate to emphasize the virtual passivity of the mind in their apprehension—their aspect of "givenness").

It will be convenient to label the theory which returns the above answers to the above questions the "sense-datum" theory of sensory cognition.

I shall now try to explain why the idealist thinks that none of the sense-datum theory's answers can be accepted. An accurate analysis of what is involved in sensory cognition, it will be argued, is completely destructive of the whole notion of "sensing sense-data."

It matters very little what example we select for special analysis, and we may as well accept the one which is so often invoked by the devotees of sense-data to illustrate their theory, namely, the sensory cognition of "a patch of red." We are supposed to be able, by sensing pure and simple, to cognize a patch of red. *Can* we?

Difficulties arise at once concerning the relation of the "red" to the "patch." Let us suppose for the moment that we sense the red, and (still more difficult to suppose) that we also sense some spatial configuration that can answer to the term "patch." Clearly these two apprehensions—of the red and of the patch—even if they occur simultaneously do not give us the apprehension of a *red patch.* To apprehend a red patch, if the apprehension is to be a *cognition,* we must apprehend the red patch *as* a red patch; and for this to occur, we must apprehend the red as characterizing the patch or the patch as characterized by the red. In other words, cognition of a red patch implies an apprehension of the subject-attribute relationship. But such apprehension is certainly not included in the sensing of the red plus the sensing of the patch; and it seems absurd to suppose that the lack can be made good by some further operations of sensing. No one, so far as I know, has ever suggested that the subject-attribute relationship is the sort of thing that can be a "sensum"—a direct object of "sensing."

In point of fact sense-datum theorists quite often betray understandable symptoms of discomfort about their own choice of "patches" of color to exemplify "sensa." Beginning with talk about "a patch of red" being the sort of thing of which we are directly aware in sensing, they tend later to drop the "patch" and speak of the sensum as though it were just the "red," or (sometimes) "*this* red." And it may be that they would justify their earlier language on the ground that it was intended as no more than a preliminary description which would sufficiently serve its purpose if it drew the reader's attention to the sort of thing that is meant by the term "sensum." It was not ·intended as a precise statement of that which is directly sensed. This, the sensum proper, is just the "red."

But at least equal trouble then threatens the sense-datum theorist from another direction. If all that is present to sense (or to the mind *qua* sensing) is just the "red," then the experience, whatever else it may be, is not a *cognition*. Cognition, we must remind ourselves, is the mode of mental activity whose specific concern is to *know*. As such, it presupposes (just as knowledge does) independently existing objects to be known; and every cognition is an attempt, successful or unsuccessful, to "know" this objective world, i.e., to characterize it correctly. If what is apprehended be not taken as characterizing the objective world or some constituent thereof, then the apprehension is, from the standpoint of actual or possible knowledge, and therefore from the standpoint of *cognition,* as good as *nothing*. Of this it seems to me that anyone can convince himself by simple experiment. Let him contemplate (or try to) just "red," *without* the acceptance of it as in any way or under any conditions characterizing the world which in cognition he is seeking to know. If he contemplates it to the end of time he will still not find it conveying to his mind any information of any sort about anything. To call such an experience a *cognition* would be absurd. Only if, and insofar as, the "red" as experienced is taken as characterizing something in the world which in cognition we are seeking to know, can our experience of it even begin to have a relevance for the business of *cognition*.

Later we shall have occasion to elaborate considerably the point we have just been trying to make. But in principle it seems to me to be sufficiently made already, and I shall take it as at least provisionally established that even the most elementary sensory cognition is "cognitive" at all only if its sensible *quale* is cognized as characterizing something in an independently existing objective world. How far removed this is from the view of the *quale* as a sensum directly apprehended by sensing, I need not stress.

Let us turn now to a different, and perhaps simpler, objection to sensory cognition as the sensing of a sensum.

What of the "red" itself in sensory cognition—quite apart from any relation it may bear to something which it characterizes? It will be agreed, I suppose, that the red, if it is to be anything for *cognition,* must be apprehended *as* red; or at all events as *some* determinate color—for we have to allow for cases where we do genuinely cognize the determinate color to which the name "red" is conventionally affixed but do not yet know the correct name for it, nor even, perhaps, that it *has* an agreed name. But to apprehend it as red, or as some determinate color, involves discriminating it from (and accordingly relating it to) other actual and possible colors in our experience. Now this is precisely the kind of operation which is commonly regarded as distinctive of *thought*, not of *sense*. "Sensing," we are given to understand, consists in the direct apprehension of its so-called "sensum," the "red." If the mind has to go *beyond* the red in order that there should be cognition *of* the red, then it has to go beyond sensing also. The operation involved, as already remarked, is of the kind normally attributed to thought; and there seems no reason why we should not frankly acknowledge that it is thought that is at work here.

The same criticism applies, with double force, if the sensum is supposed to be not just "red," but "*this* red." Just as for "red" to be cognized it must be apprehended "*as*" "red" (or at least as some determinate color), so too for "this" to be cognized it must be apprehended *as* "this." But to be apprehended as "this" implies that it is apprehended as "not-that." The "this" has meaning for us as "this" only insofar as it is distinguished from (and thereby related to) a "that." Accordingly a discriminatory operation of the intelligence is necessarily involved. Not of course, that the meaning of "this" for a cognition ever consists solely in its negative relationships. As a demonstrative adjective prefixed to a *quale* in sensory cognition it signifies at least "the particular *quale* to which I am now attending" (in contradistinction to other *qualia* to which I might be, but am not, now attending). This is, I think, the minimum positive significance it carries in sensory cognition. The point of immediate importance, however, is that, whatever meaning the "this" carries, that meaning presupposes an operation of *thought*.

Can we go on to say that an operation of thought is further involved in sensory cognition in that the sensory *quale* is always cognized as *an exemplification of a universal?*—meaning here by "universal" a character capable of identical exemplification in an indefinite number of instances. Something of the sort is said at times by critics of empiricism, but it seems to me to be going too far. There is a good case for saying that in sensory *recognition* the sensory *quale* is so cognized. But not all sensory *cognitions*, surely, are sensory *recognitions*; although admittedly the great bulk of those that occur in adult life are. Cases to the contrary, however, are not even confined to childhood. There is nothing excessively rare in the experience of coming across a color *x* that to the best of our knowledge we have never seen before nor even learned of indirectly.

We are not on this account debarred from cognizing it as a determinate (though to us, of course, nameless) color. It is true that in adult life, since we have by then gained possession of the general notion of "universals," even a sensory *cognition* may well be, perhaps usually is, a cognition of the *quale* as a universal. But it does not seem plausible to say this of our earliest sensory cognitions. In these it need not enter our heads, so far as I can see, to think of the *quale*-character we cognize as a character belonging to, or capable of belonging to, anything besides that which we here and now cognize as having it. Later on (probably stimulated thereto by subsequent cognitions of what seems to us to be the same character in other things) we may well come to regard a particular *quale*-character (and, generalizing, *any* particular *quale*-character) as something capable of identical exemplification in an indefinite number of instances. Then we do have the notion of it as a universal; and we are likely in future experience to have many cognitions of what we then take to be (identical) exemplifications of this universal. At this later stage, too, looking back, we could say with a certain justification that even our initial apprehension of the *quale* was "the apprehension of a universal." What we should *not* be entitled to say, however, is that it was the apprehension of the *quale as* (or as *exemplifying*) a universal. The initial apprehension is simply of something as having a determinate character.

The point is not one of major importance for the purpose of this essay, and I must not labor it. I have deemed it desirable to touch briefly upon it, however, if only because it behooves anyone who sets out to rebut the extravagant claims often made for sense in sensory cognition to guard himself against the countercharge of making equally extravagant claims on behalf of thought.

From the idealist criticisms of the sense-datum analysis of sensory cognition that have been so far advanced we can perhaps begin to discern the lineaments of the idealist's own positive theory dimly emerging. They should come into much clearer vision, I think, at our next stage, even though what we are to consider there is, formally, not much more than a corollary of what has gone before.

Sensory cognition, we saw, is always the cognition of something as characterized by a sensible *quale;* the cognition, e.g., of x as red. Now is there any difference between cognizing x as red, cognizing x to be red, and mentally affirming (or accepting) the proposition "x is red"? So far as I can see, none whatever. They are three ways of saying the same thing. The third way has superficially a rather different look from the first (even when bridged by the second), but that the difference is only apparent, not real, seems clear enough when we attend closely to that in our experience to which the expressions refer. Nor is there anything in the least surprising about this. It seems even obvious that, if an experience is to be a cognition, it must be of such a kind as to find its appropriate verbal expression in the proposition. Presumably no one would be prepared to call an experience a "cognition" if it were not *informative* (or *mis*informative) in some way about something. It must be an experience which the experiencing subject takes as contributing— it may be only negatively, it may be only indirectly, but contributing in *some* way—to the goal of knowledge which is the specific concern of the cognitive mode of the mind. But an experience which is *informative* about *x* is an experience for which the one proper verbal expression is a *proposition* in which *x* figures as subject and some quality or relationship is predicated of it.

The doctrine that is here being introduced might fairly be described as the lynch-pin of the idealist epistemology; the doctrine, namely, that all cognition, from the most rudimentary to the most advanced, involves *judgment*. It is a doctrine which, at the present time—the small contingent of idealists apart—some philosophers think to to be false, others think to be true but trivial, and the great majority do not pretend to have thought about at all. I hope to show that the case for accepting it is a compelling one, and that, so far from its being trivial, it has implications of first-rate and far-reaching importance.

Let me begin by touching briefly on two matters on which some preliminary clarification seems desirable: first, on the idealist's predilection (which I share) for the term "judgment" where most people would say "proposition"; and, secondly, on the distinction between "affirming" and "accepting" a proposition.

It is well known, and the idealist does not attempt to deny it, that the term "judgment" has a certain ambiguity. It stands indifferently *either* for the mental act of judging *or* for the content judged; either for the affirming or accepting that S is P, or for the proposition that S is P. With some plausibility the critics complain that since we have available to us the perfectly good and (in this respect at least) unequivocal term "proposition" for the content judged, it is perverse of idealists, and an obvious source of confusion, to use for the content judged a term which can equally well direct the mind to the act of judging.

It is a partial, but I should agree not a sufficient, answer to this objection to point out that no real harm is done by using a term which has an inherent ambiguity so long as it is made clear by the user, either by *ad hoc* declaration or by context, in which of the two meanings he is using it. In point of fact it is, I think, very rare indeed for the term "judgment" to occur in any of the standard idealist writings without the context making it clear to any reasonably careful reader which meaning is intended. Still, if "judgment" has even a tendency, which "proposition" has not, to mislead in this way, we ought certainly to prefer "proposition" unless some special advantage can be shown in the former term which outweighs its disadvantage. *Is* there any such special advantage?

I think that there is; although only in those cases where the "universe of discourse" is epistemological or metaphysical rather than (in the traditional sense) logical. The advantage is this. The content judged, the "proposition," is an abstraction. It has no being in itself, but only in relation to a mind which affirms or denies or at least entertains it: and in an epistemological or metaphysical discussion it is vitally important not to forget this. The advantage of using the term "judgment," which, as it were, "looks both ways"—both to what is judged and to the judging— is that it becomes virtually impossible to forget it. To the logician this is a matter of indifference. He has no need to bear in mind that he is talking about abstractions, since none of the questions he raises about them, *qua* logician, will be affected whether he remembers or forgets it. There is nothing to be lost, and there is something to be gained, by *his* preference for "proposition." But if the epistemologist or metaphysician forgets that propositions are abstractions, the danger is very real. He may easily slip, and not seldom has slipped, into thinking of them as actually existing entities with some kind of "reality" of their own. Then the fat is in the fire. All sorts of vexatious problems arise which are in fact pseudo problems. What kind of reality or existence do propositions have, and what, above all, are we to make of *false* propositions? Pseudo problems generated by the hypostatization of abstractions have had a long history in philosophy, but we can at least safeguard ourselves against this danger in the case of "propositions" if, save in strictly logical contexts, we abandon the term in favor of "judgment."[1]

Let us pass to the second matter for preliminary consideration. I have spoken above of judgment as (mentally) affirming *or* accepting a proposition. Idealist usage has generally been to speak of "affirming" (sometimes "asserting") and leave it at that. I believe this usage to be essentially correct, inasmuch as, in my opinion, "accepting" a proposition is just an inexplicit "affirming" of it. But it does seem to me that when judgment is described in terms of "affirming," and it is not made clear that this is intended to cover not only affirming of which we are explicitly conscious, but also affirming the consciousness of which is very far from explicit, then the doctrine "all cognition involves judgment" is apt to provoke avoidable objections that arise from mere

---

1. It is, of course, very well known that the so-called "philosophical logic" in which idealist philosophers have been primarily interested is much closer akin to epistemology, and even to metaphysics, than to what has traditionally been called "logic," which accounts for their preference for the term "judgment" even in works that bear the title "Logic."

misunderstanding. For it is in fact the exception rather than the rule in cognition that there should be an explicit consciousness of affirming. We are explicitly conscious of affirming only in regard to that small sector of the cognized world upon which, for one reason or another, our cognitive interest happens to be focused. In our normal, incurious "taking in" of our familiar physical environment we mentally subscribe to a whole host of propositions about its features, but almost all of them (and it could be *all*) are "taken for granted" or "accepted" rather than explicitly affirmed.

I do not think it is really open to doubt that by far the greater part of our cognitive experience consists in the accepting, or taking for granted, of propositions. But is it also the case that this "accepting" is just implicit "affirming"? It certainly appears so to me. I can find no difference at all between the common cognitive experience of "accepting" a proposition and the much less common one of "affirming" it except that in the former the affirming is something of which we are less clearly conscious. Sometimes circumstances occur which lead us to affirm explicitly a proposition which we had previously been just "accepting." When this happens, no difference of kind that I can discover is detectable between the cognitive attitudes to the proposition in the two experiences—only the difference in degree just alluded to. Whatever we can say that is of any *epistemological* significance about the one, we can equally well say about the other.

In what follows I shall usually conform to traditional idealist usage and speak of judgment "affirming" propositions; but there will be certain contexts in which it will be desirable to mark the inexplicit nature of the affirming by the use of the word "accepting."

Having cleared the ground so far, we may now proceed with the defense and development of the idealist's "judgment theory" of cognition: the theory (as it is in its present skeletal form) that in cognition of any sort whatsoever we are affirming that some subject S is characterized by some predicate *P*. I shall continue to conduct the argument, for the most part, in close connection with the sense-datum theory; for it is in the region of what we may call the "low-level" cognitions of sensory experience that objection to the judgment theory is most naturally taken—almost no one would wish to deny that our high-level, reflective cognitions involve judgment. Moreover, the sense-datum theory, in one form or another, is still deeply entrenched in philosophy, and it constitutes, in my opinion, an outstanding obstacle to philosophical progress. The two rival analyses of sensory cognition clearly stand in the most fundamental opposition to one another. According to the sense-datum analysis, the sensible *qualia* cognized are objects directly apprehended by sense, and actual existents in their own right. According to the idealist analysis, their sole being is as characters predicated of some subject in a judgment. (Not, of course, that the idealist would wish to deny that we can *abstract* this element from its context in the judgment and consider it *per se*. But the crucial point for him is that, as so considered, it *is* an abstraction, and that to lose sight of this fact is productive of a stream of ruinous errors.) The difference between the two analyses is indeed so far reaching that there is scarcely a problem of any philosophic interest about the external world that is not profoundly affected by it. Some problems, of first-rate importance on the sense-datum analysis, simply disappear if the judgment analysis is accepted—the problems, for example, of the ontological status of sense-data and the relation they bear to "material objects," and in particular the problem whether material objects so-called are properly to be interpreted as logical constructions out of sense-data. It ought to be unthinkable, therefore, for a serious philosopher to accept either analysis without a thoroughgoing attempt to appraise fairly the claims of the other.

Let us ask, then, how the judgment theory of cognition would meet the kind of objections most likely to be urged as fatal to it by the votaries of sense-data.

A convenient starting point will be a criticism which has been found convincing by some able philosophers, but to which I must confess I have never been able to attach much weight.

The critic concedes that whenever there is a sensory cognition there may very well be also, and even always, judgment. The "red" of a sensory cognition is, quite possibly, always judged to have some shape and some size and to stand in some kind of spatial relations to other items in our experience at the time. But the fact (if it be a fact) that there is always judgment in sensory cognition, he argues, has no tendency to disprove that there is not always *also* in sensory cognition a "given" which is merely *sensed*—a "sensum." On the contrary, the judgments just mentioned *about* the red presuppose a red which is cognized *otherwise* than through these judgments. And what can this "red" be but our old friend the sensum? Accordingly the judgment theory of cognition, insofar as it aims to replace, and not merely to supplement, the sense-datum theory, must be rejected.

It seems to me that this criticism misses the essential point of the idealist doctrine. Certainly any judgment which is *about* the red presupposes the red as already otherwise cognized. But then *this* judgment —let us call it judgment B—is *not* the judgment which the idealist is referring to when he claims that judgment is involved in sensory cognition. The judgment which the idealist finds essential to sensory cognition is not one *about* a (cognized) red, but one which first *constitutes* this red as a *cognized* red at all. Obviously the *latter* judgment—let us call it judgment A—does not presuppose a red already cognized. No doubt the idealist may be wrong in his argument that judgment A is involved in all sensory cognition. That is fair matter for debate. But since it is judgment A that the idealist is talking about, it seems a mere *ignoratio elenchi* on the critic's part to point out to him that judgment B presupposes an already cognized red. The idealist has no interest in denying this. What *he* is claiming is that the "already cognized red" is constituted by judgment A.

Nevertheless, this criticism can easily be developed into something a good deal more formidable. The idealist must agree that judgments of type B, *about* the cognized red, can and do take place. It is perfectly possible to attend solely to the red in, say, a perceived tomato, and judge it to have certain qualities and relations. Now what we certainly *seem* to ourselves to be doing when we do this is attending to something *given*, to an entity "out there" directly present to our inspection and continuing to present itself to our inspection merely on condition of our continuing to attend to it. Does it really make sense to say, as the idealist account of the matter would seem to imply, that what we are attending to (and judging about) is not this at all, but some character which we are predicating of a subject in another and contemporaneous judgment?

I think it has to be admitted that the idealist account does not have a very plausible look. For the mind which is attending to the cognized red, the only relation which the red seems to have to it is that of being attended to; and it is far from obvious how its appearance of "givenness" can be reconciled with its "really" standing in the very different relationship to the mind of being a predicate in a judgment. The required reconciliation can, I believe, be satisfactorily effected. But it is not a simple matter, and will involve our probing a good deal deeper than we have yet done into the nature of our sensory cognitions.

The first thing that must be made clear is this. In arguing that the intellectual act of judgment is involved in sensory (as in all other) cognition, I have by no means wished to defend the paradox that there is nothing in sensory cognition save an operation of the intelligence. I have not even wished to deny that there may be in sensory cognition something that can, in a legitimate sense, be called a "sensibly given." I have denied only that there can be any meaning in a "sensibly given" which is, as such, an object of *cognition*. That sensory experience cannot as such yield sensory cognition does not entail that sensory experience is not an essential factor in sensory cognition. Indeed it is rather hard to believe that anyone has ever seriously supposed that in sensory cognition the intellect operates without a basis in sensory experience of *some* sort. The difficulty is to attach a clear meaning to this sensory experience, and to interpret in intelligible fashion the function it fulfills in sensory cognition.

The line of argument which has long seemed to myself the most hopeful on this perplexing question is as follows. In all sensory cognition the cognizing mind is aware of a *compulsion* to make the particular judgment it makes, and the compulsion is experienced as one that is not *intellectual* or *logical* in character. Judging in a given sensory situation that this is red, we do not feel free to judge it to be any other color; and yet what compels us to judge it in this way is not, we know, any sort of *intellectual* necessity that it should be red. An "extralogical" compulsion imposed upon the intellect in all sensory cognition must, I think, be accepted as sheer matter of fact. But *why* we feel so compelled, or what it is that does the compelling, is another story. Analysis of sensory cognition from the point of view of the cognizing subject affords, so far as I can see, very little help. The feeling of compulsion is not accompanied by any positive indication of its source. On the other hand, in the light of what we know "from the outside" about the situation which exists when sensory cognition takes place—in particular the excitation of events in the sense organs and sensory areas of the brain—reinforced by what we can reasonably conjecture from the *inside* on the basis of certain "internal" sensations which accompany sensory cognition and which have for us at least the appearance of being located in our sense organs, it does seem a fair enough assumption that the source of the felt compulsion lies in some kind of "sensing." But this "sensing," we know, is not any kind of *cognizing*. If there is such a sensory "experience" at all, it must be of the nature of *immediate* experience, or "feeling." The hypothesis that emerges is that the source of the felt extralogical compulsion in sensory cognition is the existing situation *as immediately experienced in sense*.

This hypothesis, it should be said, does not entail that, given an immediate sensory experience, the appropriate judgment *must* ensue. It is very probable that whether or not this ensues depends upon whether or not certain other conditions are fulfilled, upon whether, e.g., the sensory experience occurs in a mind which is at the time intellectually oriented to what is going on in the outside world. All that the hypothesis entails is that when (or if) immediate sensory experience of a situation occurs, this creates a feeling of compulsion in the mind to judge in a specific way *if it judges at all*; to judge, e.g., that this is *red*, and not that it is black, or white, or green, or any other color.

Now how is all this going to help us to resolve the special difficulty which we acknowledged as confronting the judgment theory—the difficulty that when we attend, for purposes of closer examination, to a sensory *quale* which we have cognized, we seem to ourselves to be so manifestly attending to something that is just "given" to us from without?

The hypothesis just offered to account for the feeling of extralogical compulsion in sensory cognition was confessedly conjectural; but fortunately this does not matter. What matters for the argument now to be deployed is the *fact* of the felt extralogical compulsion, not any particular explanation of the fact. The relevant point is that in sensory cognition the mind feels itself to be subject to compulsion from without, and thus in great measure *passive* in respect to the cognition. The mind cannot be *wholly* passive, for it does perform the intellectual act of judging. But the intellect's role in such judgments is so meager, its activity so formal, that it would not be surprising if it tended to be overlooked altogether. Now this *is*, I think, what actually happens in the type of case we are concerned to understand, where there supervenes upon a sensory cognition a period of attention to the sensible *quale* cognized with a view to making judgments about it. Throughout the duration of the attention, we may assume, the situation which evoked by extralogical compulsion the original cognition of the *quale* remains constant, and continues to evoke an identical cognition—we continue to cognize "the same red." And throughout this period (here is the crux of the matter) our feeling of compulsion from without in respect of our cognizing of the red, coupled with our awareness of ourselves as intellectually active in the different business of attending to and examining the red cognized, causes us to overlook completely the immeasurably slighter intellectual activity involved in the identically persisting judgments which constitute and sustain the red we are attending to *as* an object for our cognition.

Hence, it is that we so confidently regard the cognized red as something just "given" from without, whose only relation to the mind is the purely external one of being attended to and judged about. But we are deceived in so regarding it: and I have tried to show that the origin of the deception is not really mysterious.

We have now seen how the judgment theory would seek to repel the very plausible objections based on the appearance of givenness in the *qualia* cognized in sensory cognition, and, at the same time, that and how it is able to accept in the sensible *qualia* a genuine element of givenness. It is tempting to explore further the implications of this element of givenness, particularly in relation to the question of the incorrigibility often alleged to belong to simple sensory cognition. We cannot afford, however, to follow up even the most seductive bypaths while so much still remains to be observed on the main road.

Our early examination of the sense-datum analysis of sensory cognition from the standpoint of idealist criticism, together with our recent defense of the rival idealist analysis against criticism from the side of sense-datum theory, have contained by implication a good deal of the answer to the question why, and in what sense, "the mind's involvement in 'objects'" is a central tenet of the idealist philosophy. For idealism, as we have seen, the mind's objects in even the most rudimentary sensory cognition are in large measure constituted and sustained by thought. Their qualities and relations, as cognized, have their sole being as elements within judgment, and are in that sense "ideal." On the *higher* levels of sensory cognition—let alone on the level of *non*sensory cognition —the mind's involvement in its objects is certainly not likely to be *less*. But we have still some distance to travel if the idealist position on this matter is to be elucidated even to the extent that can reasonably be expected in the space at our disposal. There is a very relevant topic which has so far been little more than hinted at. Reference was made earlier (with a promise of later development) to "an independently existing objective world" which, it was contended, all cognition postulates. Now if idealism accepts this as a postulate of cognition, it is apparently recognizing, in addition to "objects" which the cognizing mind largely constitutes, "objects" which are entirely independent of the cognizing mind. To objects in this latter meaning the idealist doctrine of "the mind's involvement in its objects" would seem not to apply; and it certainly cannot apply in the sense we have so far given to "the mind's involvement." Evidently there is something here that must be cleared up. Just how, for the idealist theory, is "object" in the one sense related to "object" in the other sense? The answer (to the extent that the limited epistemological approach can give it) necessitates some consideration of the formal analysis offered by idealism of the nature of "judgment," on which we have as yet said nothing; and to this analysis and its implications our remaining pages will best be devoted.

The first point of importance to be noted is a very simple one, namely, that there is a claim to *truth* inherent in the very form of judgment. If we say "S is P," and someone retorts "that's not true," this denial of the *truth* of our judgment we take as a matter of course to be a denial of a claim we are making in our judgment. It is not felt necessary to say expressly "it is true that S is P," simply because it is assumed that everyone accepts this as implied in the form "S is P."

More interesting is the question of what exactly we *mean* when we thus claim "truth" for our judgment.

The notion of "truth" obviously presupposes recognition of the distinction between truth and error. Now this distinction, the idealist would contend, itself presupposes the recognition of another distinction; the distinction between, on the one hand, an objective "order of things" with a permanent determinate nature of its own—a "reality" independent of the judging mind—and, on the other hand, a subjective field of "ideas," in the sense of "ideal *meanings*,"[2] which ideas, according to the manner

2. The reader may be reminded that there are two very different aspects in which "ideas" can be regarded. Every idea has (a) a *psychical existence,* as a state

in which they are brought together in the judgment, may *either* conform to *or* be discrepant with the nature of the independent objective reality. On the basis of the distinction between these two realms, the claim to truth inherent in judging is interpreted by idealists as simply the claim that the complex of related ideas (the "ideal content") which we affirm in our judgment does conform to, or correctly characterize, the nature of the independent objective reality. To this interpretation I can, for my part, see no reasonable alternative.

This leads on, however, to a development of the idealist analysis which seems to have puzzled a good many people—the doctrine that in judgment the ultimate logical subject is always "Reality." Yet the reason for maintaining this seems plain enough when considered in our present context, i.e., in the context of what is implied by the claim to truth inherent in the judgment. If, in seeking and claiming truth, the judging mind is seeking and claiming to characterize correctly the objective reality, then the ultimate subject of judgment, that about which we are making the affirmation, is in a perfectly intelligible sense always "Reality." In further confirmation of this doctrine idealists have been wont to appeal to the significant fact that *any* judgment "S is P" can be reformulated, without change of meaning, as "*Reality is such that S is P.*" No change of meaning is detectable because what the reformulation does is merely to make explicit something that is left implicit in the customary formulation, namely, that the affirmation is "about Reality."

It must be presumed, I think, that the main reason why there is so much suspicion of this doctrine is the appearance it has of doing violence to the ordinary conception of the "subject" of judgment with which the logician traditionally works. According to the doctrine, the *whole* ideal content of the judgment, *including* what is ordinarily distinguished as the "subject," may legitimately be regarded as a predicate affirmed of Reality. Now it can very reasonably be insisted that no analysis of judgment is acceptable that does not find room for the *ordinary* distinction of subject from predicate. Even if it be justifiable to say that the judgment "this tree is a poplar" predicates what is meant by "the poplarity of this tree" (i.e., predicates the ideal content for which this expression stands) of "Reality" as subject, it must surely also be recognized that

or event in someone's mental history; and (b) a *meaning*, as the character or complex of characters which constitutes the "objective content" of the idea. It is, of course, in aspect (b) that ideas are used in judging. Their aspect as mental states is quite irrelevant for the mind *qua* judging. In Bradley's characteristically pithy comment "When I say 'this horse is a mammal' it is surely absurd to suppose that I am harnessing my mental state to the beast between the shafts." (*Appearance and Reality*, seventh impression, p. 164). Idealist writers have usually sought to prevent misunderstanding by speaking of "ideal content" when what is meant is "idea" in aspect (b).

there is a valid sense in which, in the same judgment, "this tree" is subject and "poplarity" is predicated of it.

In point of fact, however, the idealist agrees that this is so, and he makes specific provision for it in his analysis. According to his analysis, it is necessary to distinguish between the *ultimate* and the *immediate* subject of judgment. In all save a few exceptional cases, we are seeking in judgment to characterize not just "Reality in general," but Reality in some specific aspect of it upon which our cognitive interest happens to be focused. The idealist view is that while the ultimate subject is Reality, there is, almost always, an immediate subject which is the specific aspect of Reality to which the mind's attention is at the time directed, and which is, as it were, the "starting point" of the judgment. This immediate subject coincides with what is *ordinarily* called the "subject," e.g., "this tree" in the judgment "this tree is a poplar."

The "immediate subject," it should be carefully noted further, is for the idealist analysis, in an important sense, *both* "ideal" *and* "real." It is "ideal" in the sense that it is always part of the ideal content affirmed of Reality as subject. It is "real" in the sense that it is always *that* part of the ideal content which, on the basis of past cognitive experience, the judging mind *already accepts as correctly characterising Reality*. Precisely on this latter account—because, though "ideal," it is accepted by the judging mind as being, as it were, a valid representation of the "real" so far—it serves in the judgment as the *basis* for the *further* characterization of Reality; i.e., serves as "the immediate subject." A return to our example "this tree is a poplar" may help to make the position clearer. What this judgment essentially does is to affirm that Reality, in the *specific aspect of it accepted as already correctly characterized so far by what we mean by "this tree," is correctly characterized further by what we mean by "poplarity."* The ground for the "further characterization," it may be added (though there is no space to develop the point), is the detection in the immediate subject, "this tree," of those marks—or at least a sufficiency of them—which serve to define "poplarity." And this procedure of establishing, through "ideal identity," fresh links between our "immediate subjects" and other elements in our experienced world, is for idealism typical of the development of human knowledge generally.

Overcondensed though this account of the idealist analysis of the judgment has inevitably been, it should, I think, enable us to see how in principle idealism reconciles the *mind-independence* of "objects," which seems a postulate of all cognition, with the *ideality* of "objects," which is a central tenet of its own philosophy.

The core of the matter is this. The term "object" stands for two distinct, though closely related, notions. We may mean by the mind's "object" that particular part of the presupposed independent reality which in our judging activity at any particular moment we are seeking to know. The object in this *first* sense has, *ex hypothesi*, a nature of its own which our cognizing mind does nothing to constitute. The mind has just *no* involvement in its object when "object" is so understood. But we may also mean by the mind's "object" that same part of the presupposed independent reality *in the character which it bears for our present cognition.* This character which it bears for our present cognition is a complex of ideal meanings which we accept, on the basis of many past judgments and inferences, as characterizing correctly the independent reality so far. In this *second* sense of "object" there would seem to be no question of claiming for the object independence of the cognizing mind. Take such an object as a tree in the character it has for a present cognition (in which character it will probably serve as "immediate subject" for judgments in later cognitions). Even if we were to concede (as of course we do not) that there are certain basic *qualia* here, such as determinate shapes and colors, which are directly "given" to sensory inspection, these would be very far indeed from yielding us what we mean when we take the object to be a *tree*. By a "tree" we mean an entity with a definitive and relatively permanent set of properties, most of which are *not,* on *any* theory of cognition, open to inspection at the moment of cognition. The "invisible" properties are accepted as belonging to what is before us on the basis of past judgments and inferences relating to similar congeries of shapes and colors. Such "interpretation" of the *qualia* has, as a rule, quite early in our lives, been established by custom as a virtually automatic mental response; but it still presupposes a long history of conceptual analysis and synthesis. We cannot indeed say without qualification that the mind "constructs" or "constitutes" its object in this character. That would be to ignore the "given" element in sensory cognition whose importance we have freely acknowledged and even stressed. But it hardly seems to me possible to deny that, in *this* sense of "object," the mind's involvement in its objects is at once profound and pervasive.

The distinction between the two senses of "object" might also be formulated, in relation to the wider perspective of knowledge as a whole, as the distinction between *our* world and *the* world. Our world, the object world in the character it has for our cognition at any given time, is in large measure constituted and sustained by us through judging. But this is compatible with, and indeed is misleading if not supplemented by, the recognition that *our* world is not *the* world. *The* world is the independent reality which *our* world is a more or less successful attempt to characterize correctly. To the extent that the attempt succeeds, to that extent *our* world becomes indistinguishable from *the* world, except in the one all-important respect that it remains inescapably "ideal." In Bosanquet's words "our world as existing for us in the medium of knowledge consists, for us, of a standing affirmation about reality."[3]

But is it not the case, it may reasonably be asked, that *the* world, the objective reality we are seeking to know, even if it be acknowledged by the idealist philosophy to exist independently of the judging mind, is nevertheless for that same philosophy constituted by "mind" in *some* sense—perhaps "Mind" with a capital M? Undoubtedly this is so; for those idealists, at any rate, who (unlike myself, I fear) find the constructive side of Hegel's thought as convincing as its critical side.[4] For them, indeed, the ultimate reality *is* Mind. But to say anything worth saying about this aspect of idealism would require another paper at least as long as the present one, and a concentration upon just those metaphysical considerations which, the reader my recall, I gave notice at the outset I should be obliged to abjure.

Our space has run out, with the writer disturbingly aware of how much remains to be said by way both of clarification and of recommendation of the views he has been trying to present. But perhaps he might be permitted a very brief appendix on a matter that has, in his experience, been a source of much unnecessary confusion in debates about idealism.

One cannot help noticing that when a contemporary philosopher has occasion to refer to idealism, he seems much more often than not to be thinking in terms of *Berkeleyan* idealism. In a way it is natural that this should be so. Certainly there would be no difficulty in explaining it in the light of the climate of philosophical opinion which has overwhelmingly prevailed, and has in consequence determined the general pattern of philosophic education, for something like three decades. Natural or not, however, it is extremely unfortunate. For Berkeleyan idealism and post-Kantian idealism are poles asunder. They are developed along quite different lines from quite different principles, and it is seldom that a criticism of the former brand of idealism has any relevance to the latter brand.

Berkeley, like most present-day philosophers, accepts (and hardly dreams of questioning) the general epistemological premise that cogni-

---

3. *Essentials of Logic*, p. 32.

4. I must frankly confess that—as those who have done me the honor of reading my books will already know—I cannot for my own part regard as valid any of the metaphysical arguments for the identification of reality with Absolute Mind or Spirit. I cannot even accept Bradley's more general asseveration that reality is of the nature of "experience." I suppose I ought, on this account, to disclaim altogether the title of "idealist"; though my strong conviction of the validity and basic importance of the epistemology of idealism makes me reluctant to do so.

tion of the "external" world starts from, and continues to be constantly supported by, direct apprehension of *something*. From the Representationalism current in his time Berkeley takes over the further premise that the "something" is "ideas," and in the main the criticisms offered of Berkeleyan idealism consist in arguing that this further premise is mistaken. The contemporary critic generally (though not invariably) takes the "something" to be sense-data, which need by no means be interpreted as "ideal." But such criticisms do not touch post-Kantian idealism. As we have seen, it is of the very essence of the epistemology professed by the latter to deny the fundamental premise which Berkeley and his "realist" critics share. According to the judgment analysis of cognition, we begin by directly apprehending neither ideas nor sense-data nor physical things nor anything else. We directly apprehend *nothing*. Every cognition, however elementary, is a *judgment*, in which the mind seeks to characterize correctly an objective nature of things, whose independence of the judging mind is necessarily presupposed in the judgment's inherent claim to *truth*. Hence, not only is post-Kantian idealism *opposed* to Berkeleyan idealism, its opposition is actually far more fundamental than the opposition of most of Berkeley's critics. Berkeley and these critics give different answers to the same question; the question, namely, how, if at all, we can justifiably pass from what is directly apprehended to the affirmation of an independently existing reality. For post-Kantian idealism the question itself does not arise. There is no point in asking how we "pass" to an affirmation which, if all cognition involves judgment, is necessarily there from the beginning.

PETER A. BERTOCCI

A Temporalistic View of Personal Mind

I. The Identity of Mental Being

If there were no other ground for believing in "mental being," the fact of cognitive error would force us to postulate its existence. For cognitive error, in any degree, cannot be understood if the knowing process is identified with physiological or chemical-electrical being. Obviously, these assertions need defense, and this will constitute our first point.

Error is a unique kind of occurrence. All forms of it involve the state of affairs in which a statement that was supposed to be true of some other being or event is to some degree not true. Again, very broadly stated, whenever error occurs in any degree, an "entity" (assertion, image, percept, idea, symbol, sign, experience) is found in some degree not to refer correctly to, to present, to represent, or to be identical with, the state of affairs to be known.

But, and here is the crucial consideration, the error exists, or has a "locus," for some being, in relation to something else. This erroneous judgment must have an unusual nature. It must itself be a state of affairs referring to another state of affairs that does not exist as indicated. As such it must enjoy some state of being. If no error were ever made, no question would arise about the kind of being an erroneous assertion has. But the assertion: "That is my book" (when it turns out to be another's) is a state of affairs clearly not identical with or representative of (or in any other way veridical in regard to) the actual situation. And this fact throws the spotlight on what kind of being such assertions involve.

The answer, we suggest, is: Here is a kind of being intended to reflect a state of affairs not itself, a kind of existence whose very nature consists in its being referred beyond itself by a knower. *The judgment as a state of being is not in error. A knower, seeking to use this state of being to get beyond it is in error!*

What can we then say about the nature of the knower? The knower, we suggest, must be the kind of being that can have as part of its being a state of affairs whose very being consists in being referred beyond itself to another state of affairs. The fact, discovered later, that it was referred erroneously, does not change the existence of a judgment, though the error might have led to evil consequences for the existent which "referred" it. To say that the "error" no longer exists is not to say that the being in error no longer exists. *The "being" who is in error thus turns out to be the kind of existent that* (a) *can have its own existence,* (b) *be capable of the state of affairs here called "referring" an attribute to something other than the referring state, and* (c) *go on entertaining that state without (necessary) vital difference to itself.*

This kind of being also, we contend, is unique. No other being "makes" errors. One billiard ball striking another, a cell in interchange with the environment, an electrical current which moves in one direction rather than another, all are affecting and being affected, but they cannot be in error. For error has no meaning in terms of interacting events as such. The erroneous being, however engaged in referring, carries on its own business of existing and interchanging, like all other events. But, different from all others, it is undergoing a kind of activity (the experiencing of images, signs, ideas, or symbols), whose very being consists in designating, without being or affecting, the event presumably referred to. This kind of activity is the kind of activity we call cognitive, and it can exist only in the more comprehensive kind of being we are calling *mind.*

To state our contention crisply: If we had no introspective knowledge of mind, if there were no other shred of evidence for mentality, when we try to indicate how error is possible, we find it reasonable to postulate mind as the kind of being which alone can be in error. To summarize our reasoning: Given the fact of error, there must be a being that exists, in error or not. That being, as part of its existence, *can refer,* by way of one phase of its activity upon which its sheer being does not depend, to something other than itself. It is this kind of being which we call *mind*—though mind will turn out to be more than a cognizing being.

To express our first thesis in another way: Assuming that we could define a human being in purely chemical or physical terms, we might regard him as a unique complex of electrochemical changes. Or, perhaps better, assume that we could say that a human being represents a certain emergent phase of evolution from electrochemical being capable of taking on life with its own self-maintaining processes. We then could say that human beings have encounters and undergo changes which destroy their vitality and reduce them to physicochemical events. But this level of description could never yield an account of cognitive error as human beings are involved in it. For it is one kind of being to be hurt, or to become diseased, and another kind of being to exist in cognitive error, though harm might result from error. Why? Because error as error is a unique kind of event demanding for its explanation another kind of existent, emergent or created, namely, *mind*.

To expand our meaning: The processes involved in physical interchange and biological interaction are not the same processes involved in knowing and in erring. The capacity to be in error leads us to invoke a quality or dimension of Being that has no counterpart in the physical or biological realm, and which we might not have invoked had we never been "in error." This new being can "harbor," "have," "undergo," states of its own being which exist "in" it, whether they are true or false, but whose very being consists in their being referred to a state of affairs beyond themselves.

What we have been saying is a long, roundabout way of reaching a point that could be reached easily if we had begged the question and used the psychological language we purposely avoided. We might have said simply: the unique thing about the knowing situation, forced upon our attention by the fact of error, is that in knowing there is an event which exists as psychic but whose very being consists in its being referred beyond itself by the knowing being. This reference beyond itself makes error (and truth) possible, and it distinguishes the being who can "refer," from every other being we know. One can appreciate H. H. Price's exclamation: "Let us rather take off our hats to any creature which is clever enough to be caught in a trap. It is the capacity of making mistakes, not the incapacity of it, which is the mark of the higher stages of intelligence."[1] It would, on the other hand, make no sense to attribute such intelligence to a certain congery of biological changes or electrical vibrations in the brain, which affect and are affected, but which have no states that "refer."

Before passing on, we wish to call attention to the approach we have been following. We did not start with mind, but *in medias res*. Seeking to understand different types of events, we found that the existence of error could not be possible if all events were physicochemical or "purely"

---

1. H. H. Price, *Thinking and Experience*, Harvard University Press, Cambridge, 1953, p. 87.

biological. We did not ask, with the rationalistic presuppositions of a Descartes, of what kind of being we could be rationalistically certain, though we would not object to a more carefully guarded statement of Descartes' approach. (For doubt is an amazing kind of existence which forces, we believe, the same kind of conclusion error does.) Nor did we start from some unique datum of introspection called a self or mind—although we were no doubt introspecting as well as inspecting, without, we hope, special psychological or metaphysical bias. All we have said is that if we try to understand the human being as a physicochemical, or biochemical, being, we face, in the possibility of error, a state of affairs which simply has no counterpart or definition in terms of the properties given to such events by experts.

It simply makes no sense to talk about hydrogen being in an erroneous relation to oxygen, for the whole of hydrogen's being is what it is without *reference* to anything, in the sense designated by "true" or "false." While it may make sense to say that an animal makes a behavioral mistake in the sense that some action it takes brings harm (or misses its instinctive or unlearned goal), such mistakes are hardly cognitive errors. However, let it be carefully noted, we are not tritely saying merely that a man is a knowing-erring being, but we are urging that the possibility of cognitive erring involves us in saying that the erring being (man or animal) has the quality or kind of being we call mentality in contradistinction to vitality and physicality.

Having thus sustained the contention that error constrains us to believe in mental being, and that the knower is the kind of nonphysical and nonbiological being that can entertain truth and error, we must now add at least another attribute to such a mind, namely noncognitive agency (to speak generally).

C. I. Lewis has told us that knowledge, action, and evaluation are "essentially connected." It is clear that knowing and evaluating, for human beings at least, exist to guide action into a future that, because it is not-yet, can only "exist" for an *anticipating* existent. Lewis brings out the difference in being that knowing involves (though this is not his purpose) when he says:

A creature which did not enter into the process of reality to alter in some part of the future content of it, could apprehend a world only in the sense of intuitive or esthetic contemplation; and such contemplation would not possess the significance of knowledge but only that of enjoying and suffering.

And he adds:

For the cognizing mind, something immediately presented—some item of direct experience—is a sign of something else, not so presented but likely to become realized or capable of being realized in further experience.[2]

We need not commit ourselves to the ensuing theory of knowledge in detail to underscore the central point that knowing and erring involve an *active* being capable of using some of its experience (or undergoing) to refer beyond itself (the enjoyed experience) to another state of affairs. In our own preferred epistemic terminology we should wish to say: A person can experience *objective reference*, which means that he undergoes certain psychological states whose very being consists in being referred beyond themselves by the person to "something" in the past, present, or future.

II. The Unity and Continuity of Mental Being

We have already moved from the possibility of error to the existence of mentality as an active being in commerce with "the world" in both cognitive and noncognitive manner. It is the existence of memorial capacity that brings us face to face with a special set of problems in defining the nature of mind. We need not remind ourselves that empirical perception, imagination, and thought are impossible without remembering. Nor shall we expand on the fact that objective reference obtains in memorial activity. For remembering is a present experience in which a present object is referred "back," correctly or incorrectly. This alone, if our argument has been sound, justifies our conclusion that remembering is mental activity—whatever its connection with the nonmental.

The intriguing problem for a theory of mind stems from the fact that retention is not an experience or activity we directly introspect. It is an inference from recognition and recall. From the direct experience of "againness" that saturates recognition,[3] we infer a past which somehow is linked with the present. But how shall we conceive the nature of mentality whose capacity for retention is not only the basis of empirical knowledge generally but also of its own past? What must mentality be if memorial activity is to be understood? It may help us if we take two steps and ask first: How shall we conceive the nature of any present moment? Second, how shall we conceive of the relation of moment to moment?

First, it seems introspectively clear that any moment of mental exist-

2. C. I. Lewis, *An Analysis of Knowledge and Valuation,* The Open Court Publishing Co., La Salle, Ill., 1945, p. 3.
3. Cf. Price, *op. cit.,* p. 44 f.

ence is never a simple, nontemporal, mathematical point (allowing this description for purpose of contrast). Any mental "present" is a durational complex unity. It is "filled" time, or better it is psychic time which can later be abstractly broken into smaller units of "before" and "after." An *erlebt* moment never is a compound of smaller units for it exists *as a temporal span*, or, to use James' special image, it is a "saddleback" with its own given complexity.

In introspected experience, then, we find nothing more elementary than this Gestalt or *durée*. Whatever other *measures* of time we improvise for different purposes, the segment that is *given* as the present is not a series of instants and is psychically indivisible. We must avoid the picture-thinking responsible for such expressions as "one moment of our experience 'flowing' into the next," or "the present *gradually* emerging from the past." Such pictures might be true if any present were simply the spatial extension of a point being drawn into a longer and longer line. But we cannot spatialize a moment of mental experience, however our words tend to ensnare us into spatial traps. What we actually *experience* is one complex span or moment from which we try analytically to "carve out" some aspects as "past," and some as "future."

Let us, nevertheless, aware of the snares, attempt a closer cross-section view of a moment of our mentality. What we find is a given indivisible complex Gestalt of activities which, after study, we define minimally as sensing, imagining, perceiving, conceiving, feeling-wanting-emoting, willing, and oughting. These activities, as undergone, are phases of the experienced whole that is itself a dynamic span, or *durée*. But our main concern here is to note that within the original, *experiencing-datum*, or *erlebt* moment, a change is felt that we may describe as a thrust into a future "emerging" from a present. This is simply our way of saying that the present is full, or, in Whitehead's word, pregnant.

In this very burgeoning present, however, we detect two aspects: the relatively unchanging, active *structure* of activities (abilities and capacities) and the changing *content* or quality of the total experience. The activities mentioned above need not be accepted in detail, as a basis for granting our basic distinction between the structure of ability-capacity and any specific content or object of these.

We may use a diagram further to suggest our meaning, but it will be inadequate because, drawn in space, it suggests an atomicity not intended. With this qualification, let us represent a mental moment (Figure 1).

One "filled," growing-waning, passing, moment. The whole figure is a complex dynamic unity, the small circles being used to indicate the multiplicity of contents qualifying the activities (arrow-diagonals). The diagonals also symbolize the fact that as felt, any moment is "on the go," "passing," "growing." So far as we know, at this stage of analysis, this moment may be a center of a larger Being, or the conscious development from a Freudian-like unconscious, or of any other being, for that matter. As *experienced* it has temporal span, complexity of activities, and each activity may have *a* qualitative object or content which defines its phase at that moment. The point is that this is the complex, unified Gestalt of activity-structure and content that constitutes one moment of what we are to call the unified person, or personal self. The activities may wax and wane, mature and degenerate, but they are relatively stable from "moment" to "moment," while the qualities or contents given in them at any one moment may change (say: pleasure gives way to pain; "blue" to "yellow," one idea to another, one want

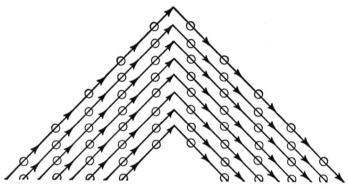

FIGURE 1

to another; but feeling, sensing, conceiving, continue to be qualified as each allows).

Figure 2 may suggest the manner in which the original unity-structure grows in response to its environments and yet maintains its own basic activity-structure. Here, the coiled, expanding, inclusive line is intended to suggest a given structure for mental being, despite the unevenness of development. (The coiled lines are not equidistant.) The arrows suggest the active thrust, and the open end the constant sensitivity to the surrounding world that it "absorbs" according to its own capacity for intake.

These diagrams of a mental present and our discussion thus far may indicate what we regard as the fundamental nature of mental being, generically speaking. First, the unit of mentality as such is an original given, the unity being such that, as Leibniz said, it cannot be *created bit by bit* (though it may change gradually). Thus, for example, the activities of desiring, imagining, conceiving, are not "made up," but they are given in their interpenetrating nature and structure. In the lifetime of a person these may grow into their maturity, and then wane, but the unity of mental being is not a concoction blended in a psychic test tube. For the psychic moment *is* the test tube or matrix; it is what we shall call *the personal self* in one of its moments. And its nature is the original unity of interpenetrating activities without which it would be nothing at all.

Second, mentality at the human level, given its structure, can change in the content of what its activities can grasp and endure, with the result that these structure-activities can develop themselves, as it were, or express themselves, in many different ways.[3] But any specific content of, or object of, the activities cannot be identified with the activities themselves, however they may limit or give specific quality to the life of the

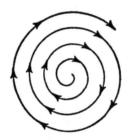

FIGURE 2

person. That is, thinking does not consist of, and is not exhausted in, thoughts, nor sensing in the sense-data experienced, nor desiring in the specific or general objects of want.

Yet at any given moment the matrix of structure-activities and quality-content are the matrix of mental being in a complex unity. More activities may develop (as thinking does in the life of the maturing infant and child), and some may be lost (sensing as vision, for example, when one becomes blind), but the life of any mind at any moment will consist (at least) of the way in which the structure-activities have been able to respond, in accordance with their own natures, actual and potential, to the environment. In a word, the activity-structure of mentality remains the same, and changes may occur in the "capacity" of the activity. But an activity does not become another activity; for example, the activity of thinking does not become the activity of sensing.

3. We shall say that these expressions will constitute the learned *personality* (not *person*), or the unique mode of the person's relatively systematic adjustment to the total environment.

Yet as long as it exists the activity-structure endures through the various contents which it "enjoys." (Much more, of course, should be said at this point about learned dispositions.)

It is this level of complex activity-structure—with its capacities for certain contents and not others—that we call a person, personal mind, or personal self. But crucial to it as mentality is the fact of *unitas multiplex* with enduring capacities and relative flux of content at any moment of its being. So much for the cross-section view of the moment, or the *datum-person*.

More difficult problems face us as we turn to a longitudinal view of mentality, that is to successive or serial moments of experience. For our purposes here, once more, we need not commit ourselves to any final ontology of the datum-self. It may be recreated from moment to moment in the light of its past by a cosmic Person, or it may be a center of an Absolute Being, or it may continually emerge from electrochemical conditions.

Whichever of these, or any other, views may be correct, the data which theorizing must confront is that, as memory indicates, there are *successive* moments, befores and afters, in our conscious experience (to which we are limiting ourselves at the moment). Did the successive moments of consciousness and self-consciousness always follow hard upon each other, as happened during the writing of this last page, the problem of accounting for successive moment that are not identical with each other, would be difficult enough. But the fact is that consciousness may be "lost" for a shorter or longer interval and then "return."

This fact makes the question: "What makes continuity possible?" all the more important for a theory of mind which takes the fact of *memorial continuity* seriously. Whatever my ontological nature is when consciousness and self-consciousness "return" after an interval of deep, "undisturbed" sleep, I immediately recognize my being as memorially continuant with myself as before the intermission. Where "I" have been I do not know, but that "I" am in some sense continuing my prior existence is attested to by the fact of memorial continuity. I cannot deny memorial continuity without presupposing some! For to justify denial of my memorial continuity I would have to depend upon my memories of the past to support the denial!

Once more, then, the existence of memory is one of those ineluctable facts of mental being. Whether there be intermittent consciousness or conscious states without interval, there is no denying that personal experience links its presents with its pasts and, in imagination and thought, anticipates its futures. Thus, if anything is central to all personal experience, it is *both* the unity of any "present" mentality, and also the continuity, cognitively realized, between presents and pasts in remembering. What the ultimate metaphysics of memory is we can decide only after we consider how mentality is related to other existents. Our problem here and now, however, is to consider what we may reasonably say about the nature of personal mind in view of the unity and continuity we find in mentality.

III. The Substantive Self versus the Temporal Self

Space will limit us to the analysis of two theories about the self which have been advanced to explain the unity and continuity of the self. The significant fact for any theory to explain is that, as B. P. Bowne put it, an experience of succession is not a succession of experiences! That is, we cannot say that events are in serial order unless something endures from the beginning to the end of the series. The problem is, then: What is it that abides through the succession of unitary moments we have called the person?

The first view we shall consider has a history extending in western thought back to Plato at least, but the best recent statement is in C. A. Campbell's *On Selfhood and Godhood.*[4] We approach the second view through an analysis of basic contentions in Campbell's theory of selfhood.

Professor Campbell first argues that the activity of knowing "implies a *subject* that is active." He goes on to urge: *"that which is* active in activity cannot possibly be *the activity itself."*[5] We do not contest the first thesis for we too have been arguing that memorial and other cognizing activities are intelligible only as we distinguish, in Campbell's words, "a cognitive subject distinguishable from, though not of course separable from, particular cognitions."[6] But there are reasons for doubting the second statement, the grounds for which we must now study cautiously.

If X is the psychical operation of knowing Y, it cannot be that the *activity of apprehending is Y;* and it cannot be that the activity of apprehending is *"that which apprehends."* "What is 'known' cannot be known *to* the operation of knowing. It can be known only *to* a subject which, while *engaged in* the knowing, is not itself *identical with* the knowing."[7]

Now we should agree that the psychical performance does not exhaust the subject, and that the psychical performance (X) is not the object known (Y). We may definitely affirm (S) subject, (X) psychic

4. Macmillan, New York, 1957.
5. C. A. Campbell, *On Selfhood and Godhood,* p. 70.
6. *Ibid.,* p. 70.
7. *Ibid.,* p. 71.

activity of cognizing, and (*Y*) object known. Thus far, with F. R. Tennant[8] and with A. Bowman[9] giving him strong support, Campbell is on firm ground. Our own analysis would force us to agree that cognition of *any* kind—not merely in remembering—implies a subject conscious of its own identity in its different apprehensions.[10]

Furthermore, Campbell also urges that, unless the abiding subject is conscious of its own identity through a sequence, there would be no basis for asserting that a sequence is a sequence in "my" experience. The prerequisite for remembering, and for cognitive awareness generally is not simply an identical subject, but an identical subject aware of that identity. Once more, so far so good.

But it is the next step, the further interpretation of this unity and identity, that gives pause. "We are led by the argument, apparently, to posit a self which is something 'over and above' its particular experiences; something that *has* rather than *is*, its experiences, since its experiences are all different, while *it* somehow remains the same."[11] Campbell is aware of the avalanche of objections which tumble down against such a substantival view of an "I" over and above its experience, an "I" with which we have no acquaintance but only inferential knowledge.[12] Yet, however stiff the resistance to an "I" that is the same despite its manifestation through differences, Campbell finds alternative views so much more difficult that he retains his own substantival view.

Let us, as Campbell suggests, try to conceive of a self-identifying and self-conscious "I" as any kind of *relationship between* experiences. What happens? The central fact about the subject-mind, its holding a sequence together as *its* sequence, vanishes among the "relations."[13] In the last analysis, Campbell urges, "self-consciousness . . . is a *fact,* a datum from which we have to start.

This means not that the substantival self is a Kantian noumenal self about which we can know nothing. For, and this is crucial, the subject self apprehended in self-consciousness is always "a characterized self"; it is a self characterized by, and "manifesting *itself* in," operations of thinking, desiring, and feeling. Campbell's view accordingly, is that though the self is not *reducible to its* experiences, it does, nevertheless, manifest "its real character (in whole or in part) *in and* through these experiences."[15]

8. *Philosophical Theology,* Volume I.
9. *A Sacramental Universe,* p. 196.
10. See Campbell, *op. cit.,* p. 75.
11. *Ibid.,* p. 77.
12. Cf. *ibid.,* p. 77.
13. *Ibid.,* pp. 78-80.
14. *Ibid.,* p. 81.
15. *Ibid.,* p. 82.

In order that our succeeding discussion be pointed, let us intervene and state where we believe the issue now is. Insofar as Campbell is saying that the self is never a peculiar set of relationships, that it cannot be put together from atomic parts, that it must be conceived as a self-identifying self-consciousness in order to make cognition intelligible, we are in hearty agreement. Insofar as he urges that the self is not reducible to its experiences, we should concur, for we have insisted on distinguishing the more persistent activity-structures from the flux of content.

But Campbell is going further and is holding to a self which, though irreducible to experiences, is nevertheless manifesting itself, in whole or part, in and through its experiences. But ambiguity, at least, and real difficulty occur when we try to see what it can mean to distinguish the self *in any way* from its activities. Why must we use the language of "manifesting itself through" such activities and experiences? Why must we also say: "The self of which we are conscious in self-consciousness *is* a subject *which in some sense has, rather than is, its different experiences, and is identical with itself throughout them?*"[16]

To be sure, Campbell does not articulate the difference between "experiences" as activities in our sense, and as "content" (specific objects of awareness and desire), and we assume it would not make any difference to his essential point, namely, that whether we speak of activities or experiences, the self, though characterized by them, is always more than they and *has* them. Our thesis is to be that the self *is* a continuous unity of its activities which are indeed not reducible to the experienced qualities. And it will be our special burden to give an account of the way in which such a self-identifying agent-knower can be identical from moment to moment and day to day.

Our central difficulty with Campbell's viewpoint may simply involve a lack of insight on our part. But if Campbell holds that the self is not identical with its activities, and if he urges that it is *the same* while all of its experiences change, then no matter how much he says it manifests *itself* through its changing experiences, how can we know that the sameness is manifested? The sameness of the subject must remain other than the changing activities and experiences in which it is supposed to *manifest its* nature in part of whole. To such a charge of self-contradiction and unintelligibility Campbell responds in a way which seems to us adequate in one respect but inadequate in another, so we must look at it carefully.

The charge of self-contradiction, says Campbell, rests on the assumption that sameness totally excludes difference. Sameness as includ-

16. *Ibid.,* pp. 82, 83 (italics mine).

ing difference does indeed involve contradiction on the level of abstract definition, for it is impossible to understand *how* sameness can include difference. If we stay at this logical level, it does indeed become unintelligible to say that any entity *A* includes non-*A*. But at this level, "intelligible" means "capable of being understood" in terms of "how" the one subject remains itself amid the plurality of changing experiences. And Campbell correctly holds that how things are what they are must be accepted rather than dictated by logical demands. Thinking does not make events or the states of affairs it is trying to understand, and *if* this kind of sameness *is* given, thinking misses its function when it denies a given because it cannot tell *how* it appears. Again, so far so good.

Campbell is safe in distinguishing intelligibility in this how-sense, from "meaningfulness" in the sense of being able to point in experience to what the nonintelligible event is. We should want to agree that when in self-consciousness we are aware "that I who now hear the clock strike a second time am the same being who a moment ago also heard the clock strike, even though I must have become different in the interval,"[17] then we are given a datum in terms of which the claim that the self's sameness includes difference is meaningful (though not intelligible by strictly logical norms).

But while the self's sameness in difference may be given and be meaningful, the *theory* of the self Campbell gives, as a self not reducible to the total of activity and experiences cannot escape either the requirements of logic or, as it seems to us, a more adequate "meaningfulness" in terms of actual experience! Sameness, at least as required by memorial continuity, cannot be denied despite inability to explain how, but *a particular theory advanced to explain sameness in plurality* had at least better be questioned if it proposes relationships which defy either the demands of logical consistency or of experience. Indeed, it seems to us that the view that the self *has* rather than *is* its activities and experiences itself rests on logical analysis, and not on experience itself. Only in terms of logic *may* one say that *that which is* active in activity cannot possibly be the activity itself, or that the sameness must to some extent not be the different activities.

It may rather be, as we hope our earlier analysis of a moment of experience showed, that what constitutes a datum-person is the unified activity complex rather than a subject *of* activities and experiences, as Campbell suggests. In a word, even to suggest that the sameness of the subject involves a "that which" that *is* not active but *has* activities is to give a description which might fit abstract logical considerations better than it fits the experienced datum at any moment. If Campbell's

17. *Ibid.,* p. 83.

logic forces him to say that the same self is manifested in its activities (in whole or part), if his logic forces him to say that this self cannot be its activities—any one of them or the whole of them in an original unity—then we may well ask to what *in experience* this theory points.

We agree that any part of an activity-structure cannot be whole activity, but we deny that we have any experienced ground for supposing that there must be something other than activity-unity as experienced to explain the unity. It is the merit of the self-psychology of E. S. Brightman[18] that, in the interest of a radical empiricism, he rejects any shade of a homunculus subject, and simply says that the self is the unity of activities we find in conscious activity and its contents. We shall now put this personalistic self-psychology positively, and then hope to remove some doubts by suggesting an account of the way in which such a self could maintain its identity through difference in successive moments.

IV. The Person and Continuity through Immediate Succession

Whatever else Being refers to, it includes self-conscious being. But wherever there is self-conscious being the following conscious activities are distinguishable: sensing, feeling, desiring, remembering, thinking, willing, oughting. Some may want to expand, some limit further, this list of activities which in a Gestalt of sameness-difference constitute the irreducible, original, unlearned, unity-in-multiplicity designated the person-datum. At any moment some of these activities are more regnant than others (and in infancy all are not yet present). The sameness is never other than, or beyond, what these activities are, though it is not reducible to any one of them, nor even to a composite of them. Rather do these activities define the nature of mentality at the personal level. The sameness is not the sameness of a logical or mathematical equality, but the very sameness that each of us finds in successive moments of *his* experience. To say " *that which* is active in activity cannot be the *activity itself*" would mean in this view only that the activity of the self is not exhausted in any one of its activities (like thinking). The "subject" is the unity-sameness which *is* experienced (without "more-than") in, and only in, these activities at the conscious level.

At any one saddle-backed cross section, or in any one longitudinal moment, as described above, there is also the particular kind and degree of acquired personality-unity which the person-activities have developed to date as a result of maturation and interchange with the environment. We might thus distinguish the *constitutive or ontic person-*

---

18. See Edgar S. Brightman, *Person and Reality*, edited by Peter A. Bertocci, *et al.*, Ronald Press, New York, 1958.

activities from the acquired *psychological personality* with its different degrees of integration; but we must remind ourselves that neither ever exists without the other. In the remainder of this paper we shall be concerned not with the important problem of the continuity of personality but with the central problem of continuity of the ontic person.

Thus, we must now ask: Granted that in any one moment unity in difference is given, how can we account for the fact that successive moments in personal history are experienced *as a succession?* Here, like Campbell, we must simply accept fact of unity in any specious present or moment for what it is. But we need some theory to explain the continuity-in-change we remember from moment to moment. The startling fact is not that sameness endures in the momentary differences, but that sameness in difference is required for any succession to be succession in our experience, be it immediate succession or succession after intervals. We must try, therefore, to suggest a conception of the person which may allow first for successive continuity without intermittence and then for continuity despite intervening time-gaps.

The given activity-structure of the person is in interaction, from conception on, with agencies, events, beings, not identical with himself. We are not asking what conditions or causes the person ontologically, but, given his existence at any one moment and given his memorial nature, how may we conceive the process which enables the initial person to maintain continuity and "self-identity." We repeat that the fact of activity-identity is undeniable in the sense that any attempt to deny it assumes the very memorial identity denied. Yet, just as clearly, one moment of person-datum is not identical with the next.

How then shall we conceive the essential nature of the continuity-giving process? Our first suggestion is that the person-datum "maintains" himself as a persistent activity-pattern from moment to moment by being selective in accordance with what his potential up to that point allows in relation to the potential of the environment. Concretely, I am what I am now because as I enter into each not-yet and constitute it a now, my given activity-nature has been able to accept those elements in my interplay with the not-self which were congruent with my continuance. My activity-identity was evidently "impermeable" to others. My "past" is simply the story of what I have been or of what I have succeeded in facing; it exists for me because it was once *me in a certain moment of being which I have succeeded in transcending without losing my nature as affected in that past.*

However, I must *not* make the mistake of picture-thinking my past, and think of myself in memory reaching back to ten minutes ago. For, after all, ten minutes ago is no more; and myself of yesterday and thirty seconds ago are no more. *I am, now,* pregnant with *my* past, and being affected by what is happening to me as my not-yet future is being born. *My* future at this moment is nonexistent, and "exists" only as that which I shall have been able to "absorb," "digest," or "endure" in such a way that I do not lose my activity-identity. In other words, to go back to an earlier diagram (Figure 2), let us assume that self-being began as the original activities in phase (*a*) below, and continued in successive moments to become (*ab*), and (*abc*) (Figure 3).

Figure 3 must not be taken to mean that (*a*) remains as-is in (*ab*) and (*ab*) remains as-is in (*abc*). Rather, my *now* (*abc*) is all I am, but it is what I now am because of my ultimate constitution and what I have become, selectively, in accordance with the nature of (*a*) and (*ab*). In other words, the interval between states (*a*) and (*abc*) is not a gap. Rather is it the case that every (*ab*) and (*abc*) is what (*a*) was capable of becoming in a given environment, and then actually became because of selective interplay with the environment.

Again: "I" do not "pass" into a future any more than I "pass" out of the past. My being is always a "now" which is said to be older than a "then," or earlier than a "later," only because of differentiations which we call memories and anticipations. "I" do not move through pre-existent time as a ball might roll in space. I *am* my time and the changes which take place "in" me are discriminated as past, present, and future by virtue of my capacity for remembering and organizing my experience, always in *a* present, as involving a past and anticipating a future.

Thus, while all Being is mysterious or unintelligible from the point of view of our ultimate "know-how," there is no real problem about explaining the way in which the same of one moment can be identified at a later stage as "my" self. For I am now able to identify myself with

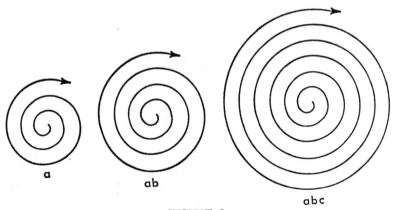

FIGURE 3

Three successive moments, including past (selectively), "open" to present interchanges, as the future is born.

my past because I never moved away from my self, but selected and "absorbed" the world according to my own subjective aim, to use Whitehead's phrase. Some encounters with the non-self could destroy me, but the fact that I now exist indicates that I have been able to keep myself alive in, and through, and despite, some threatening encounters. There is no passage of "time" but only the selective experience of a person who maintains the given unity of activity in the course of interchange with the world.

The person, then, is a successive mental unity of activities that in turn persists beyond any particular content created by his interaction with the environment. A unity in any given moment, he is a unity for which there can be succession because (whatever the how), he is able to "accept" and "reject" the world which beats in upon him, and he is able to do this in accordance with his own original being and his original potential—which actually is discovered as each experience and activity are enjoyed.

But, we remind ourselves, this view of continuity may do well for continuity which is not interrupted by sleep and "sheer" unconsciousness. Does this account of continuity enable us to understand the self-identification that exists despite such intervals in conscious experience as sleep and periods of unconsciousness? *Must our theory of mind not introduce a continuant which persists through the intervals?* This might seem all the more likely in view of the fact that some sort of "work" seems to go on during what we call sleep-time. We refer not so much to the periods of dreaming, in which there is consciousness if not self-consciousness, but to such facts, for example, as our waking up with a solution to the problem that could not be solved the night before. And the very fact that we usually awake refreshed indicates that change has taken place during the intervals.

V. The Person and Continuity through Intermittent Succession

The problem of identity through intermittency calls for a paper in itself. We are not completely satisfied with the account to be suggested. One must be careful not to assume a metaphysics of continuity at this point; he must require that his theory account for the data. Several general observations may be made in a preliminary way.

The problem of identity through intermittency—when not superficially solved—is no greater obstacle for a temporalistic view of mind than for others. In any case, what seems clear is that *mind as consciousness,* which did not create itself originally, does have lapses. That is, every *conscious* activity by which we characterize mind is simply nonexistent during the lapse. Consciousness continues as these activities reoccur, and to say that the mind (as *conscious* mentality of some sort) continues between intervals during which these activities do not occur is to contradict oneself. Once more, to say that I, *defined as a complex of conscious activities,* "continue" when I am no longer exercising these activities, is to assert contradiction. Furthermore, a mind that is unconscious—*meaning nonconscious or nonmental*—is a mind that is not mind in any experienced sense. Reasoned, empirical, theory cannot bridge the gap between intervals of conscious experience by asserting that a *nonconscious or nonmental* mind exists during the intervals.

Such considerations will press heavily against many explanations of the unconscious interval, and perhaps even against the view to be suggested below. But no hypothesis should blur the fact that conscious activity (and self-consciousness) does, so far as each of us knows by direct experience, in fact vanish and return (just as the light of an electric bulb vanishes and returns). Does it actually help, for example, to say that a *nonconscious entity* (like the physiological organism), or even an infinite Mind, remain as the basis of continuity between intervals—or does this simply push the problem a step further? The fact *still* remains that during the interval, no matter how long, there was a lapse in *my* experience as conscious being. A biological continuity is continuity at the biological level and not at the level of person-mind. A parallel line of reasoning would hold if we tried to allow the continuity of God's being to bridge the gap, for His continuity is His, not mine. Better remain with no theory than with one which neglects the very facts to be explained.

Let it, however, be clearly understood that we are not denying interaction—or some other relation—between the biological realm, or the divine, and our minds. But we cannot think that to say that *they continue* across the gap in "my" consciousness explains "my" self-identity through intervals. Whatever other realities may be, and however they are related to my mentality, their existence during my nonexistence cannot in any way substitute as such for my being able to identify myself despite intervals.

It would seem, then, that we must look into the nature of the individual person himself for some explanation of the fact that there is self-identification possible despite intervening gaps. The tentative suggestion we now propose—not halfheartedly yet not sure that it would satisfy all the data—requires that we identify a person not only with conscious–self-conscious activity but also with an activity present wherever consciousness and self-consciousness exist, namely, *telic* or *purposive* activity. So far as we can see, nothing in what we have said about the unity of mentality or the temporalistic person would be gainsaid.

For we are suggesting that mentality at the human level not be *identified only* with conscious–self-conscious phases, but with telic phases of the kind found also at the conscious–self-conscious level. The focus of definition moves in short, from essentially cognitive activities to essentially conative activities of feeling-emoting-desiring (to speak minimally).

Let us expand our meaning briefly. Cognition itself, be it erroneous or correct, involves telic or purposive processes. Remembering, and forgetting, anticipating, solving problems—or learning and thinking generally—take the course they do because, in good part at least, they are affected by desire or interest. To be a mind is to be a kind of being *in want*, active in a present, whose very nature it is to reach for something it has not yet, and for a state of being it is not yet. In this sense, *conor, ergo sum* tells a more complete story of the human being than *cogito, ergo sum*.[19]

We suggest that the telic strivings involved in our feeling-emotive life—in such states as fear, anger, elation, respect, tenderness, wonder, lust—constitute the womb in which memorial and intellective activities arise. Such nonintellective urges and stirrings, let alone the sheer thrust of volition, are the power-reservoir or the dynamo of person. Much in daydreams and night dreams, much in the varied manifestations of rationalizing as opposed to reasoning, and much of what we know about the formation of prejudice, let alone neurotic maladjustments and psychotic diseases, testify to the power that feeling-emotive tendencies and needs have over cognitive functions. Yet, as we have already suggested, there is no way of extirpating this affective-conative life from the rest of "normal" mental functioning. The psychological analysis of attention, remembering-learning, imagining, perceiving, and thinking will quickly come upon the selective work of feeling, emotion, and desire in the processes of cognition. There is a constant interplay of purposive or telic processes and cognitive activities. Indeed, it would be better to say that in the unified complexity of mental life these conative-cognitive processes may be distinguished.

But what we wish now to stress is that telic-conative processes are broader, though still mental, than the cognitive functions and persist in them. We do not appeal to any theory, Freudian or any other, of the unconscious life to substantiate this claim. Indeed, it is the relationships between conative and cognitive factors in our conscious life which must,

19. Incidentally, Descartes, while a rationalist in criterion of truth, did not define *cogito* in intellectualistic terms. Note the sadly neglected passage: "But what then am I? a thing which thinks. What is a thing which thinks? It is a thing which doubts, understands [conceives], affirms, denies, wills, refuses, which also imagines and feels" (Descartes, *Meditations on First Philosophy*, Meditation II). Thus, the place of the affective-emotional and volitional life in the matrix of *cogito* is undeniable even in Descartes.

in the last analysis, provide the model-analogy between conscious and unconscious life generally. It is in the normal life of awareness that we feel the contrast between the changing waves of cognition which focus and "light up" the sea of conation. There is always that relatively clear focus of awareness emerging out of the relatively unclear, felt background of seething.

It may help us to distinguish this broader conative matrix if we can designate three stages or phases of mentality. First, *self-conscious awareness*, in which one is aware of oneself as the focus of cognition. Here one is able to contrast self and not-self. The regnancy of this phase is intermittent. As I write, my awareness is not focused on myself but on what I am saying; and this is true, we might say, for most of our work-a-day awareness.

This first "self-conscious" phase emerges out of the second stage of awareness in which I am so absorbed in my task that self-consciousness all but disappears. This stage of which most of our awareness consists we have called *consciousness*. Self-consciousness, as we have said, lights it up, and brings it into a special focus.

The third dimension of mentality we are now postulating involves telic processes such as are not open to but continuous with their nature as experienced in *consciousness and self-consciousness*. Such telic processes are neither self-conscious nor conscious, in the senses used above, but they are a complex unity of same-difference. They are able to maintain themselves during the intervals when consciousness in the above forms are not experienced. They are never nonexistent, nor "asleep," but they are altered from the individual's birth to death by the processes which they do undergo when they are in the phases of consciousness and unconsciousness.

As we have hinted, a specific account of what these telic processes are would have to be heavily weighted by what is found in consciousness. But in general we may say that, in this phase of mentality, a unity of telic activities is postulated that does not have the "advantage" of having the directive "guidance" and differences which they would enjoy in consciousness and self-consciousness. In ordinary conscious experience both the life of desire and the environment are in relatively directed interaction with each other. In this *sub*conscious, not nonconscious or nonmental, state, the nature of conative tendencies as affected through conscious and self-conscious experiences maintain themselves without conscious "guidance" or "interference."

We are suggesting, in short, that mental life in human beings is polar, that it does not lend itself to clear-cut dichotomy between cognition and conation (or other activities), although we postulate a phase in which telic processes go on without consciousness, without losing their mentality. For these telic processes in a conscious phase are present also, we should say, in conscious mentality.

To comment further: There is the phase of my mental life in which feeling-conation seem to be all there is, and another phase in which awareness of the world dominates, with self-consciousness in almost complete abeyance, but to some extent present. As long as we do not make the mistake of *simply adding cognitive* (and volitional, and moral, and aesthetic abilities) to the telic life of conation, or think of the latter as completely nondirected, and waiting for guidance from without, we shall not make serious mistakes.

It will now be clear that we are defining *the essence of mentality at the human level as the range of telic tendency from unified minimal purposive striving* (in which neither "self"-focus nor "world"-focus is clear) *to self-conscious, purposeful organization of telic tendency.* The word *unconscious* (or *subconscious*) in this view would mean not non-conscious, but that pole of mentality in which there is no articulation of self-experience but only individuality of feeling-emoting capable of maintaining itself as it is modified through interchange. The person, therefore, during the deep-sleep (intermittent) periods does little more than persist, without disturbance by memory or cognitive activity. But he springs into the various degrees of consciousness required for differential activities, be they dreams or somnambulism, or other phenomena. When the person is "awake," his feeling-conative life takes on directions and organization which would be impossible without the capacity to remember and think. But there is never an interval in mentality (as purposive striving of a sort to be better defined) but only in consciousness.

There is much more that needs to be done to show that this theory can account for the various types of activity or "work" which seems to go on through unconscious intervals. In general, we believe that this theory would account for much since it can appeal to many stages of alteration within the development of individuality. In closing we may, for example, indicate how it can be related to the Freudian view of the unconscious.

If the unconscious, in the Freudian sense, refers to that phase of conative experience which the patient cannot himself recall and has difficulty in controlling, no serious problem confronts our theory. This "unconscious" in our theory would be that area of an individual's experience which, owing to conditions in his development, he cannot now recall and control without aid—the psychoanalyst becoming the person who helps him to manipulate his conscious content in a way that will allow such recall and release to take place. But to say that the "laws" of the unconscious are completely different (as Freud sometimes seems to say) from those discoverable in conscious life seems simply to presuppose a rather superficial and conventionalized analysis of conscious experience.

Once we realize that criticism of the inner and outer world begins with the development of memorial and cognitive functions, that the life of feeling-desire is thus expanded and restricted, there seems to be no basic fact about dream life and dream work, about neurosis or psychosis, that is *in principle* impossible to explain. No particular problem of psychosomatic medicine is solved, obviously, by a general theory of mind.

VI. Summary

The existence of mentality as a unique and irreducible kind of being is rendered highly probable by the fact of error. Cognitive error, involving as it does a kind of existent which has been referred to what does not exist as claimed, is incomprehensible in terms of physics, chemistry, or physiology. Mentality is the kind of being which can exist, can experience and refer ideas (images, symbols, and so on) to a state of affairs beyond themselves which may or may not exist as claimed.

Memorial activity, at the basis of all empirical knowledge, presupposes ultimately a complex unified agent which, at the level where logical thought, obligation, and value-choice is possible, we call a person or personal self. This original unity is a Gestalt of interpenetrating activities which endure in their basic structure despite changes in content or expression. This agent-unity of activities, either in a given moment, or in successive moments, is durée.

The theory of a substantive unity of activity beyond, yet manifested within, the activities and their contents, though it preserves unity, creates a serious problem which can be avoided if we think of the person as able to endure selectivity in and through its interchanges with his environments. We have sought to explain continuity despite intermittent consciousness by identifying the person not only with conscious–self-conscious phases of mentality but also with continuant affective-conative activity ranging from the unconscious to the conscious and self-conscious.

Speaking generally, therefore, telic activity at the feeling-conative level, analogous to the quality of feeling-conation found at the conscious level of activity, may be conceived as maintaining its unity, continuity, and individuality despite discontinuity of consciousness. Throughout all levels of personhood there is original unity in telic agency which is able to maintain itself within the limits of its own varied nature and take on new quality and scope as conscious–self-conscious activities illuminate it in relation to its nurturant and challenging environment.

As a person responds selectively in his interplay with the environment, he can develop personality (or personalities, or relatively systematic modes of adjustment) in order to meet the requirements of its own telic-activity-unity and of the environment. But every varied channel of becoming in which a personal self is involved is possible because of the specific pattern of activity-identity that can maintain itself *in* maturing, learning, and action.

EUGEN KAHN

Some Thoughts on the Mind

Accepting the editor's invitation, I wrote him: "I have made up my mind to write a contribution. . . ." It appears to be logical that I ask now: What did I make up? Did I make up the mind that is to be the leitmotiv of this book? Whatever I may come to say about "mind" in the quoted sentence, I wanted to express that I decided to cooperate. "To make up one's mind" is indeed one of several phrases meaning to make, to confirm, and to communicate a decision.

Although this "make up one's mind" is just a manner of speaking, it is pregnant with concepts like decision, confirmation, communication which in one way or another point to "mind" in a sense far wider, yet sharper than the colloquial use of the phrase "make up one's mind" might indicate at first sight. There is still more implied in this phrase. The statement that "I made up my mind" clearly rests on cogitations, on thoughts preceding it. Retrospectively, it is clear to me that I went through some doubts pondering "should I say yes or no," in a manner different from the working of a digital computer.[1] These thoughts did not take place in a vacuum of 100 per cent cool reasoning but were at times more and at times less tinged with emotional factors.

Let me get this straight. I was pleased to be invited, my vanity got a stroke along its back. I couldn't help presuming that my work which

---

1. Walshe writes poignantly: "that while these machines may represent our logical and mathematical concepts symbolically, and facilitate their handling, it is nonsense to speak of their thinking since they require a human intelligence to read off their collocation of symbols."

often, if not mostly, was done in a sort of solitude might have been noticed more than I had assumed.

I shall restrain myself from going into more details here, in particular from assigning every bit of the pertinent experiences its sense and place in some tailor- or ready-made system.

I

In the above remarks, I let the cat out of the bag using two words, namely, sense and experience. They are in my thinking inseparably related in mind. Perhaps it is often more serviceable to say meaning instead of sense.

When I consider terms and concepts of physiological psychology, I see that there the concept mind is not needed; indeed its use may occasionally produce confusion. It would be entertaining to investigate how scientists in their devotion to the facts of natural sciences may go around the concept of mind. This is especially true in psychological schools of the last sixty or seventy years that based their tenets on natural science even when working with experiences of and their meaning for human beings.

Says Hebb, "Mind can only be regarded for scientific purposes as the activity of the brain." This is the physiological-psychological attitude For a person interested in experiencing and in meaning, this observation of Hebb's is clearly superseded by Straus' short statement, "Man is doing the thinking, not the brain."[2] Whatever the activities of the brain and of the sensory organs are, they may be looked at as organs of activation. However, the activation which they induce or mediate would be meaningless, it would not even occur without the person in his situation as the performer. The person in his situation is meaningfully experiencing. It is not sufficient to consider man as an anatomically and physiologically extremely complicated robot. A robot would presumably show effects from whatever "causes" hit it from the outside. It would be equipped with mechanisms comparable to the key, stops, pedals, etc., of a church organ which does not play unless the mechanisms are pushed or pulled. Whatever may be obscured and twisted in this comparison, one aspect, I believe, comes out clearly: the robot and the church organ are played upon by a person to whose situation they belong. They do not receive stimuli to which they would react in the manner of living organisms. The person playing the organ or using the robot (both of which were constructed by persons in situations) is causing changes upon the organ or the robot; these causal changes bring about effects. While one thus looks at organ and robot entirely

2. "Der Mensch denkt, nicht das Gehirn."

mechanistically, the playing upon them by the person in his situation is not mechanic or mechanistic, but it is done and experienced because of meaningful motives.[3]

II

Where do these mental gyrations lead? We decline to identify the mind with the workings of the brain. We realize that such gyrations could not be performed without the brain. We cannot think without brain; changes in our brain are accompanied by undeniable changes in our thinking. If our brain does not do the thinking, if it is done indeed by the person in his situation, is then the person identical with the mind?

It appears to be paradoxical that the same thinker who is made responsible for the splitting of the unity of body-mind has particularly stressed the importance of thinking for being in his sentence *"cogito ergo sum."* It would be unfair to make Descartes responsible for every ideation referring to him and crossing out almost everything as regards the body-mind unison that had been a matter of course before his time.

We may have made our task more complicated than it was before mentioning body-mind when probably we might have said body-soul. However, let us face the issue. Are we going to identify mind and psyche? Do we try to evade major difficulties in ascribing, say, ideation and intellect to mind and see the headland of the psyche in the emotions? Incidentally, where would we stand if we were to re-establish pre-Cartesian unity? In fact, what we understand by person in his situation is at least as comprehensive as the previous unity.

III

There seems to be an approach from the "mental disturbances." *Mens* is the Latin word for mind, and mental is the adjective derived from it. When we consider the disorders of the mind, would we not find out what the mind or, rather, what its definition might be? We are in a predicament. The terms "mental disturbances," "mental disorders," and "mental deterioration" would give hope unless the most competent authorities had not informed us that the mind cannot get sick at all. They teach that in deteriorative and a number of other afflictions, it is the body—often the brain—that falls sick. The symptoms of "mental disease" which we are able to sunder out in such instances are manifestations of the person in his situation suffering from a bodily affliction that directly or indirectly influences the function of the central nervous

3. See footnote 1.

system. This means that the person in a situation has changed or is changing his way of experiencing with the result that the person in his situation is experiencing himself as well as his situation in a manner different from the manner in which he experienced before.

In order to formulate a clinical diagnosis we have to establish certain symptoms. Those symptoms are reliable as symptoms only when they are backed by physical findings. They are, e.g., the speech disturbance in general paresis, the confusion in infectious delirium, the hallucination in toxic psychosis. Without physical findings we may be symptomatologically at sea. We then try to make the best of our observation of the patient's behavior, especially his utterances—trying, as it were, to enter into his world through an understanding of his experiences. Then one deals not with more or less clear-cut symptoms, but with phenomena which may have a variety of relations in and meanings for the sick person's experiencing. This is frequently a rather uncertain field when the patients report vaguely and/or fancifully about present and past experiences.

There is the talk about mental diseases, about mental health, and mental hygiene—the sickness of the mind (that cannot get sick), the health and the hygiene of the mind, but the mind seems to be the more evasive the more it is discussed. Is there perhaps pretension of knowledge instead of insight and critical knowledge? We recollect an observation of Straus': "The 'objective' theory demands that our world of experiencing should be derived from nature as it is conceived in mathematical physics. Physics is considered to be the basic science of psychology. The fact, however, is that we, human beings, construct physics in our world of experiencing. Physics, as we construct it, is possible only in our world of experiencing. Even if the assumption that the world structure as comprehended by physics were the authentic and primary one, for us it is inauthentic and secondary."[4]

The physiological psychologists using physics and mathematics for the framework of their science have produced many an interesting and important result. We deem it impossible to arrive at an understanding of experiencing and of the mind by ways of physical-mathematical methods, even if they become more and more refined. We believe, furthermore, that results produced in this manner have not infrequently been given interpretations which were not—and which could not be—satisfactorily based on the experimental results. Pavlov, in fact, originally a physiologist, is a characteristic example. While one admires the genius

4. Walshe emphasized "for me, the chill physico-mathematical concept of the human mind is a muddy vesture of decay in which I am not willing to be unfolded. It is unworthy of the dignity of man."

of his experiments, one cannot but deplore the insufficiency of his interpretations.[5]

IV

Comparative psychologists, some of whom are a special group of biologists and zoologists, want to come to an understanding of organismic, especially of animal, behavior and to a natural philosophy of their own. They look at the organism as the center of its own activity. For them according to Portmann, whose presentation we follow in some essential points, "the subject has become the object of biology." If there is activity, if there is behavior that can be observed, something must go on within the organism. This is comprehended by the concept of inwardness (*Innerlichkeit*, Portmann) of which in principle every living being is possessed. Closely connected with inwardness, perhaps one of its "aspects," are the "drives." Fortunately, one is eliminating the notion of many special drives and is essaying to reduce the "life impetus" to one "drive," which is better called "tendency"—if only to do away with all the drives that literature has been cursed with. Gehlen[6] considers the tendency of the highest possible unfolding of life fundamental. Without inwardness, one may well say, no activity, no behavior. One must add that inwardness cannot but have the tendency to manifest itself toward the outside; this occurs in the healthy creature, which is not cramped by impediments, through the realization of the tendency of the highest possible unfolding of its life. We need not discuss that life itself is one of the mysteries at which we wonder.

The use of these two notions—inwardness and unfolding tendency—appears to be an oversimplification of extremely complicated "factors and functions." In using these notions one is able to work up to a certain understanding (by interpretation) of what seems to be going on in all creatures, including man. As far as comparative psychology is concerned, comparisons with the human psyche are inevitable. Therein lies the weakness of which the pertinent scientists are fully aware: this is the danger of anthropomorphism or anthropocentrism, even if it is highly critical.

For whichever terminology one decides, it can be said animals have inwardness and tendency to unfold—both are presumably more often not conscious than conscious. There appears to be limits as regards to inwardness and optimal unfolding. These limits are given in the hereditary make-up of the species concerned; the unfolding, however,

5. Straus gave an extensive discussion on Pavlov's work.
6. Quoted from Jores.

depends also on the animals' environment. For instance, alertness and apathy as well as the alternation between them may be due to hereditary *Anlagen* that can optimally be unfolded only under the influence of certain environments.

Our example brought us into the closest neighborhood of the moods. It is assumed that the whole subjective condition (*Verfassung*) of a living being—the "how-where-when" if I may say so—how it "feels" itself in his environment (where!) at a given time (when) reflects the functioning of the organism: it is experienced as "mood" and manifested in a variety of ways—depending on the species and the more or less "fitting" environment. Inwardness and unfolding enter into this particular mood.

Lest the suspicion occur that I want to equate man with other creatures, I point to their inability to say I or you and to their inability to think. On the other hand, the many biological and behavioral features that man has in common with animals are obvious.

The "how-where-when" implies the situation. I prefer to reserve the term for man, since the "situation" seems to stipulate relations of a kind animals are lacking. Yet animals (including the anthropoids or "the more popular and cheaper rat"—Walshe) are living in a web of relations which they have to take as they are and the change of which is for them determined in a limited way. Here again *Analgen* cannot be discussed away:

As Walshe puts it clearly: "They (animals) show determinate ways of acting, as for instance, in courting, mating and nesting and so on. In a true sense of the word they show no originality"—I am tempted to add: nor do they need it. The relations in which human beings live and experience necessarily "overlap" analogous relations in animals. Yet there appear to be considerable differences in the inwardness, in the optimal unfolding and in the "how-where-when." *Si duo idem faciunt, non est idem.* Just here, though, we can learn from our colleagues about the interwovenness of animals' life with animals' environment. In their species-limited way, animals react to environmental "stimuli"; they are "blind and deaf" to stimuli to which according to their limitations they cannot react. In other words, (1) animals react in species-determined and species-limited ways to their environment; (2) they can live (survive) only in environments to whose influences they are "attuned" or "attunable."

Portmann, who would probably not agree to all my preceding remarks, explains that there is a potential structure in all living matter which the organisms develop in their reciprocal relations with their environment. Portmann formulates, "*Alles Lebendige ist vorbereitete Beziehungsweise*"; this signifies that the manner of relationships of any living organism is bound to develop with the development of the organism, of every organism.

Space is limited for animals—despite the facts of their migrations—to and within certain areas of their environment. Lack gave a pertinent description in his classical book on the robin. In their limited areas the relations of animals are "fixed." With taming and domesticating and training animals, their living areas have been narrowed rather than widened. Animal life passes in time, but animals do not know time. Here we bring several quotations from Buytendijk: "Man is not an animal with an upper stratum of mental functions. He is incarnated mind. This signifies that in every behavior mediated by his body (*Leiblichkeit*) the 'dimension of the mind' is involved." "Man does not exist (like the animal) only in and with his world, but also facing his world." Man's living areas are not as limited as those of animals, but they are not limitless. In contrast to animals that remain within the limits of their areas, man is craving beyond his limits. He is ever changing his relations and meanings in and of the world in which he is living and experiencing. "Man participates in the meanings of the situation like animals; but his meanings are realized in activities. In addition man has a knowledge (*Erkenntnis*) of the meanings of the meanings. . . ."[7] I doubt that there are meanings in animal life that are in any sense close to the meanings in human experiencing. Inwardness and the tendency to unfold grow obviously different in animals and humans, however basic and vital they may be considered in all living creatures. Here I restrict myself to calling attention to the reactions of animals, including higher animals, to their environments, and to the receiving and giving in man's experiencing. Not only for practical reasons does it appear commendable to reserve terms like experiencing, situation, and particularly meaning to the human species.[8] If need be, auxiliary words like pre-experiencing, animal-situation, meaning-like could be used in respect to animals.

Animals and man are equipped with sensory organs and are able to act, to behave. Says Buytendijk: "Man's existence depends not solely on sensations and actions, but is realized also in knowledge and achievement!" Buytendijk is aware of the creativity of what he calls the incarnated mind. Referring to Walshe, I should like to say: man shows originality in a true sense of the term. The circumstance that man is

7. I am reminded here of a remark of Jaspers referring to Nietzsche: "Our understanding of the world is interpreting and our understanding of the world of others is interpreting of interpreting."

8. Buytendijk: "To be human is a way of physical being-in-the-world in which in every relation a knowing mind is realizing itself in its achievement." "Language is an achievement," about which Buytendijk observes: "Man is not an animal that can talk. Human language makes evident that man's way of existence is different from that of animals." Despite Buytendijk's emphasis of not dealing with levels, one cannot help to be reminded of Nicolai Hartmann's pertinent observations. What is the great advantage in using the more fashionable word "dimension" instead of the word "level"?

facing his world renders the human stamp to his relations and makes the unfolding of meaningful experiencing unavoidable. Here the indispensability of language[9] and thinking is evident. In this context an experiential feature ought to be mentioned which I propose to call the *choice of meaning.* Even if one would talk about meaning-like phenomena in animals, a choice of meaning could not possibly be considered. I do not deny that whenever dealing with meanings the main difficulty is to break away from one's own meanings and to guard against imputing them to others—men or animals.

V

After paying our compliments to the psychology-minded biologists, it seems fair to express our respect to a philosopher. To Nicolai Hartmann we are likely to be attracted by his description of the very levels one or the other of his fellow philosophers find naive (Heinemann). Hartmann's exposition concerning the mind is one interpretation among others. In his interpretation we can see relations to the thought of the scientists quoted in the preceding section and to our own thinking.

Hartmann does not really "define" the mind but he describes it under various aspects; we shall mention and comment on a few only. "The mind in not floating in the air. We know it only as mental life borne by the psychic existence which is borne by the organic and ultimately by living matter." The mind is specifically human. Every human individual has his own psychic existence (*seeliches Sein*). One may be sad or cheerful with or for another individual, but it is not the other's sadness or the other's cheerfulness. On the other hand, one can think the same thought another individual is thinking.[10] "Consciousness separates men, the mind unites them."

Hartmann describes three kinds of mental existence: the personal, the objective, and the objectivated mind. The personal mind is known to us from ourselves and from other people; it is "inner, spontaneous change, a consistent searching and finding of new constructs (*Gestaltungen*)." The objective mind is the mind of the group (*Zeitgeist*), it is alive like the personal mind. Like the objective mind, the objectivated mind is

9. Buytendijk: "Communication in the animal world refers to moods and changes of moods. This is true also in group and states of animals (*Tierstaaten*)." The same author: "Man is not an animal that is able to talk, but his language is the manifestation of a way of existence (*Seinsweise*) different from that of animals."

10. Hartmann repeatedly stresses this thought. He says, e.g., "Every individual has his psychic existence for himself. . . . Mind unites; consciousness isolates." "The community (*Gemeinsamkeit*) of the mind goes above (*ueberbaut*) the community of the blood . . . consciousness separates men, but mind unites them."

superpersonal, superindividual, but it is not alive. Personal and objective mind make up the "real world of mental life." The objectivated mind is deposited in works (of art, science, religion), from which it may talk to us "like a living mind."

"The personal mind can see itself from within. . . ." "The mind in the world gives meanings to and shapes the world."[11]

For Hartmann the living mind is living only in time; it has no direct relation to space, although it is "spacebound." The living mind never "is" in space, but is living in time, always becoming, developing (Hartmann). The individual mind finds meanings in accordance with the *Zeitgeist* (objective mind), but the individual mind is also giving meanings (*Sinngebung*, Hartmann).

Here I see that specifically human trend which I call the choice of meaning. In a multitude of instances (rational and/or irrational) the meaning of a word, of an idea, of an act, of a production, of a destruction depends on the meaning provided by the *Zeitgeist*. There still are countless instances in which an individual is free to give an actual (or past) experience his own meaning. This is what I want to have understood by the "choice of meaning."

Hartmann distinguishes between purposefulness and purposeful activity.[12] It appears to me that we ought to remain aware of this distinction. Animal behavior, e.g., of the bees (see Frisch), appears to be purposeful *to us;* it certainly is not due to any purposeful activity on the part of the animal. Hartmann writes: "It is fundamentally important for the person that he is capable of purposeful activity." He postulates, indeed, that purposeful activity opens "mindless happening to the real influence of the mind," that on purposeful activity the mind's "power (*Machtstellung*) in the real world is founded." The mind is endowed with superiority since it "is capable of giving a goal to itself (*Zielgebung*)." I hold animals incapable of giving goals to themselves although their actions may appear purposeful to us. Animals are unable, too, to develop any system of values—there are, for the bees, no values in the bees' preferring nectar; there are, for the bears, no values in the bears' being meat eaters. In respect to values Hartmann observes: "It is not the purposeful activity as such but the feeling of values (*Wertgefuehl*) behind it, due to which man decides which purposes he will pursue." One may well assume that the words activity and action have for Hartmann a sense akin to the sense Buyendijk gives to the word "achievement" and that, in this context, I give to the word performance.

11. "*Der Geist der Welt ist . . . Sinngeber und Gestalter der Welt.*"
12. *Zweckmaessigkeit* and *Zwecktaetigkeit*, respectively.

VI

Whatever the world's "real structure" may be, we approach it constructively. Even in our analytic undertakings we are searching for a constructive view of the world which and in which we are experiencing. This constructive view of the world appears to be peculiar to man: in all situations in which he finds himself as a person some constructive attitude can be seen.

There is here a difference between man and other living beings. Many animals, e.g., are building their nests or coves or any other places in which they stay for a shorter or longer span of time. Their buildings as their life span remain unchanged throughout the life of the species. They certainly fulfill their purpose well enough. On the other hand, man made some progress in building his abodes. He clearly demonstrated his ability to construct—progressively to construct his tools, his language, his works in the broadest sense of the word.

There are a goodly number and variety of "performances" which distinguish the human performer from animals. The common denominator of these performances is their actual novelty: they are produced, thanks to man's special ability, to find and to construct new tools, new words, and new ideas; he is also producing works of various kinds—of art, of science, of techniques.

Woven into this production—or ability to produce—are necessarily planning and decision: thinking! Furthermore, communication of the particular kind that human language makes possible. All this might not be feasible without man's ability to *doubt* which is tied up with his desire to look into "things," to take them apart, in order to learn how they are ticking, with the goal afterward to put them together again.

The phrases "to doubt" and "to take apart" point to man's analytic ability *and* to his ability to destroy. Man uses his tools, words, ideas, and works not only for construction and production, but also for destruction. He counteracts his constructive by his destructive ability; in fact, it happens that he is compelled to destroy at least "within limits" when for his survival he secures his food, and with fewer limits when he feels threatened in his property, power, or existence as an individual or as a member of a group. If we were to consider construction and production as characteristics of the mind, we could not deny that destruction can be a characteristic of the mind. This is easy to see and to "admit" when destruction is but the initial step to new construction. However, there is all manner of destruction without any design of reconstruction—even acts of mere destruction need not be outside of the range of the mind.

It goes without saying that in construction as in destruction—in thought as well as in action—we meet the person in a situation with his needs and emotions. We are not sketching a personality blueprint here, but wondering about the mind or about what may be considered mental.

VII

Whatever we want to understand by the mind, it is not to be viewed as an "apparatus" or a special gadget in a complicated machine. The relations to the body and to the brain are undeniable, but they do not help in *understanding* the mind. The methods of the physiologists and objective psychologists despite their otherwise basic importance are not applicable here. Modifying Straus' observation on brain and thinking, we propose: it is not any organ that is experiencing, but it is the human individual, the person in his situation, who is doing the experiencing. The person in his situation cannot do so without his body; he is living and experiencing it, through it and with it.

Experiencing may be said to have two aspects or facets: time and space—the person in his situation is living and experiencing "through" time and "in" space. The concepts time and space are mostly used as though they were two separate entities; in fact, they are one unbreakable entity. We take this entity apart since we are unable to master it in its totality, we do so in our urgent need for interpretation—in our desire to understand or rather to make ourselves understand what for us is not understandable. The same is, in our opinion, true of the concepts becoming and being; they are an unbreakable entity which we "take apart" in order better to fit them into our thinking. If we proceed in this manner it appears inevitable to conceive of particular affinities between the aspects of time and becoming and between the aspects of space and being, respectively. So far, we "divided" the entities time—space, the becoming—being into the workable connections time—becoming and space—being. A third entity we have to consider is inside—outside. We are dealing with the living and experiencing person in his situation and cannot but assume that time and becoming for him is more a matter of evolving and involving inside, while outside for him concerns more closely space and being. We arrive at two chains: time—becoming—inside and space—being—outside.

We have now to consider the possible impact of these chains on our experiencing. We want a sort of formula of experience that would allow us an interpretative tie-up with the two chains. What we understand by the experiential arc lends itself to this purpose. The experiential arc is the frame of every single experience. The arc begins with an impression which mostly is picked up by sensory organs but need not be directly related to them. For instance: I see a table standing on four legs or, preoccupied with the furnishings of my office, I may think of such a table. The impression serves, in general, as the content of the single experience, the arc of which gets underway. In our simplified example, the four-legged table is the impression as well as the content of the experience; it is, as already alluded to, followed by a relation; the relation connects the current experience with preceding experiences; in the example used above, former experiences concerning tables might be related to. Not only things or creatures grasped by the sensory organs but also notions, concepts, ideas can serve and can be related to as impressions and contents. In other words: anything concrete or abstract, anything perceived or thought can be experiential impression and experiential content. The impression and/or the content of any preceding experience can be related to any new experience. Any experience goes or points toward the future; the relation is the connecting link, as it were, between past and present and beyond them to the future, to anticipated experiences. After a relation has been established the experiencing person in his situation gives a meaning to the current experience. The table may mean a handsome working table or a table to put something on or a model of tables or a reading table with books on it or books themselves or any special book or ideas or an idea contained in books. A coloring of regret, disappointment, frustration, satisfaction, etc., may enter retrospectively; or expectation, hope, zeal, joy, etc., may enter prospectively. An emotion may also impression-wise or content-wise start the wheels of another experience rolling. This would signify that emotions may serve as impressions and thus have definite influence on the meaning. After the relation is established and a meaning is given to the current experience, the experience is ready to be expressed. The expression can be any action—motor or verbal, etc.; the expression may also be a word leading to a new impression or content and referring to what had just transpired. Not every single experience is followed by an expression. Any single experience may be interrupted midway and may be expressed later on or never. Expressions may be simple but they may also be on a high level and quite complicated, e.g., in scientific work and in artistic creations.

The complete experiential arc looks like this: impression—relation—meaning—expression.

The relation in its "hookup" with the preceding experiences and in its pointing into the future falls into the becoming of the person in his situation and of his experiencing. The becoming of every person in his situation is full of relations. Our chain time—becoming—inside thus is lengthened by another link; namely, by the experiential relation.

We can experience only in the present. We may look back—retrospect —on experiences of our past, we may expect—anticipate—experiences in our future but the actual experience is always a matter of the present— of the present of the experiencing person in his situation. I have any actual experience at a certain time: *now*, and in a certain place: *here*. In the *now-here* the experiencing person in his situation gives a meaning to his actual experience. Because of the here, the meaning appears to be closely affiliated with being and space. The chain space—being— outside thus is lengthened by another link, namely, by the experiential meaning.

In our attempt to do justice to the interpretation of a variety of "existentials" and to their significance (meanings) and relationships (relations) to experiencing, we "found" the two chains time—becoming —inside—relation and space—being—outside—meaning in which may be seen the permanent flow of relations and "heard" a sort of staccato of meanings. The sensory organs are never working by themselves but they are functioning in the total of ourselves as persons in situations. It is not only the impressions mediated by sensory organs which can play a role in our experiences as already indicated, but emotions can serve as impressions, too. For instance, I may be listening to a speaker and hear him making an error in his report. This error may touch one of my own weak spots. I may become outright angry about the error committed by the speaker, my anger, as it were, pushes back the mere sensation and thus may render to the ensuing experience an emotional tinge.

VIII

We wrote that we "found" these chains. This is in a certain sense correct although we constructed the chains separating as well as linking wherever we deemed it indicated. Thus it is, in the context of our interpretation, possible to perceive in both chains the affinity to the experiential arc. The chain time—becoming—inside—relation represents the forward "motion" of human experiencing. The experiential relations and the chain time—becoming—inside—relation appear to go beyond the physical aspects and physiological functioning of the person in his situation. As far as we are able to judge, animals enjoy neither the wealth of relations nor their utter changeability which we observe and experience in the experiencing person in his situation.

In the context of our interpretation, the chain space—being—outside —meaning represents a certain stability in experiencing. The never-ceasing flow of the other chain would be intolerable, for it would indeed annihilate the person in his situation if there were not certain "points of rest"; in these "cross sections" through the flow of experiencing, the person in his situation has the necessary "leisure" to give meaning—exercising his choice of meaning—to the current experience. The giving of meaning, as interpreted in this context, makes it particularly evident that experiencing is a matter of the *now-here*. In the flow of time, relations never carry the stamp of the present as clearly as meanings do in general. This statement does not imply the notion that meanings are "rigid"; they certainly change and one might imagine that the choice of meaning is one among other features in experiencing that keeps meanings from getting frozen. Yet meanings are less fluent (flowing) than the immediately "time-powered" relations. Meanings are not "time-less"; nothing belonging to or affiliated with experiencing can be timeless. However, meanings can be considered as "brakes"—the more so according to our thinking meaningless experiences would not be experiences at all.

Experiences cannot be "spaceless" either although a multitude of relations do not have any spatial attributes, but they are "space-bound" insofar as the experiencing person in his situation is experiencing in space and time.[13]

Our discussion shows that it is helpful to make separations, but it also demonstrates that, despite all our separating, entities remain entities. The entities time—space, becoming—being, inside—outside remain entities. In addition, it should be conceivable that relation and meaning form an entity although we handle it from two sides.

Turning once more to the experiential arc impression—relation—meaning—expression, we have to point to a fundamental difference between impression and expression on one hand and relation and meaning on the other.

The significance of the sensory organs in respect to impressions and of the motor system as regards expressions is patent. All around ourselves we pick up sensations—we see, we hear, we taste, etc.—which again and again start new experiential arcs. The sensations as they are sensed by us can serve as experiential contents. No doubt that in this connection very often a perception derived from the sensation forms impression as well as content. Here relations are "at work." Despite their connections with former experiences—of the same or of another kind—the relations seem to occur on a "level" different from the sensory level of so many experiences. The meaning which the person in the

---

13. Elsewhere (1959) we discussed the tie-up of change with time—becoming and of perseveration with space—being.

situation gives to the experience following the relation stays on the level experientially reached with the relation. If the expression that ends an actual experience is manifested in some bodily movement it is likely that—it may, perhaps, in the vast majority of instances—the previous level (the level of the impression) is resorted to again. Then, as it were, the game can begin again. In this "game" with which we are dealing here in a simplified and probably abbreviated manner it should be intelligible that outside (sensation—impression) reaches into inside (relation—meaning) and that inside connects with outside (expression—motion). There are experiences, there may be a whole series of experiences in which all "proceedings" remain inside, in which numerous relations and meanings are gone through without any immediate impression from and without any immediate expression into outside. We cannot spare the "immediate" since sooner or later (mostly sooner) the outside makes itself powerfully noticed in experiencing.[14] In other words: as long as we are living and experiencing we do so in our world—as a person in a situation; we may for a span of time retreat into the privacy of our "inner life," yet we must breathe and eat, work and rest, all of which we cannot do exclusively in the inside, but in a more or less well-regulated exchange between outside and inside.

Our notion inside is not identical with Portmann's inwardness, but we hold the two are close relatives. The life in and of our inside—our "inner life" as we just called it—may be thought of as a descendant of the all-over-inwardness which Portmann attributes to flora and fauna. There is likely to be some inwardness left in us, inwardness in the sense of Portmann's notion. But what goes on inside the experiencing human being in his situation has become qualitatively different from the less complicated inwardness of plants and animals. This "inner life" of ours comprehends human thinking, human intelligence—the thought and intellect of a creature that is not immersed into his environment, happily ignorant of time and of space (in our sense), but is faced with his world and even with himself. This creature—Homo sapiens so-called—has possibilities and potentialities entirely foreign to his fellow creatures. He does not have these possibilities and potentialities "because he is human," but having these attributes makes him what we understand by "human."

Approaching the problem from the side of experiencing we conclude that relating and meaning are *mental performances*. As we explicated relating and meaning can be, and perhaps most frequently are, closely merged "between" the functions of our sensory organs and our motor system. Notwithstanding this mergence with our body and its activity,

14. If, e.g., the scholar "lost in thought" refills his pipe or his fountain pen.

and notwithstanding the wonderwork of the brain, relating and meaning are performances which cannot either be explained or understood through the methods of natural science. In these mental performances is manifested what is called "the mind"—the mind of man that renders to him a not always admirable distinction from the animals, if, e.g., the abovementioned destructive liabilities get the upper hand.

The mental performances are not mechanisms, nor is the human mind a supermechanism of the kind of the computing machines. It is the human mind that invented and directs the machines. As Munk recently observed: "Every scientific triumph is, in truth, a triumph of the Mind."

Repeatedly we underlined that we are giving—or trying to give—an *interpretation*. On the ground of this interpretation the mind could be tentatively defined as that existential aspect through which the person in his situation experiences (establishes, maintains, loses) his multifold relations and finds and gives meanings to his experiences. One may ask "why existential aspect?" For the simple reason that our interpretation is built up on becoming and being in time and space. We observed that existence comprehends becoming and being and we took pains— here and elsewhere—to remain aware of the intertwining of becoming— being with time—space.

We refrain here from entering a discussion of the emotions in respect to experiencing. Allusions to it are made above.[15]

Our concepts on human experiencing were first presented in 1936. Later we discussed outside—inside, and more recently time—space and becoming—being. Our opposition against the psychiatric followers of M. Heidegger probably helped us in clarifying our thinking, at least to some degree.[16] In this respect we owe more to Nicolai Hartmann.

It is encouraging to find in works of scientists of the rank of Portmann and Buytendijk concepts which appear to be—at least from the "outside" —similar to our own notions, although they arrived at their formulations through approaches different from ours. The mind seems to make inroads into scientific thinking. At the same time a few philosophers are getting more interested in and accessible to biological concepts.

15. We also refrain from a discussion on the distinction of mind and psyche. But we may be permitted to indicate that what is often understood by psyche, though in man tightly connected with mind, appears to be an "area" into which and within which the kinship between man and animal can be searched and found to a higher or lesser degree according to the attitude of the searcher and of the finder.

16. At his retirement from the presidency of the Royal Institute of Philosophy Lord Samuel observed: "First, that philosophers should endeavour to speak in language understood by all educated people, and not in an esoteric language understood only by themselves. Obscurity of style is a discourtesy to the reader or the listener; and it defeats its own purpose, for it is the purpose of speech to be understood. . . ."

IX

Reviewing what is reported and discussed in these pages, we emphasize once more that we just offer another interpretation. This emphasis is indicated as it happens so often that an interpreter gets so wrapped in his interpretation that he ultimately thinks "it is so." We do not know "how it is," else there would be no need of so many interpretations some of which we amply use.

We start from and again and again take recourse to our body. We deem it feasible to tie up the "how-when-where" with the body. The "how-when-where" in respect to the body—not only in man—may be looked at as the matrix of emotional life in general and of mood (*Stimmung*) in particular. In the frame of human experience it appears to be unsatisfactory—to say the least—to deal with the mental life in the same manner.

Our colleagues in comparative psychology—men of admirable sagacity, wisdom, and patience—came to sketching the difference between man and animal most impressively. They tried to replace the old anthropomorphism with a critical anthropomorphism being aware that they were unable to exorcise anthropomophism completely. Attributing inwardness (Portmann) to animals is a point in question. Notwithstanding inwardness, Buytendijk holds that man is "incarnated mind," that "man does exist not only with and in his world, but he also faces his world." There seems to be in this context nothing else but mind to grasp "the difference between man and animal." The attribute "incarnated" betrays the observer's wonderment which we share.

It appears to me that Hartmann's distinction between *Zweckmaessigkeit* and *Zwecktaetigkeit*[17] throws some light on our problem from an other viewpoint. We, human beings, are able to act purposefully (*zwecktaetig*): We anticipate a goal and strive for it. We see in and into the activities of animals a purposeness of which they are unaware. In this, as in other respects, animals are a priori limited; they are "prepared" only for activities commensurable with their make-up and their manner of reacting to their environment. As we have elaborated, animals have no tendency to go beyond their species limits. Thus they are able —as has been said so often—to live happily in and harmoniously with their environments.

Man has a much wider, if not unlimited scope. However, he does not enjoy the happiness and harmony we anthropomorphistically attribute to

17. See footnote 12.

animals. In the wealth of his experiences, in the countless relations at his disposal and in his ability to give meanings to his experiences, man has the urge to go beyond, to transcend his limits. The desire to transcend is a unique human desire. We remember that the achievement of language is indispensable for the human being in his human situations; this implies the desire to transcend.

In his social-cultural milieu the actual (not the potential) number of the individual's relations is diminished.[18] The milieu has also a considerable impact on the meanings, especially on the choice of meaning in human experiencing. One may well think of Hartmann's objective mind (*Zeitgeist*) here. It may be taken for granted that the experiencing members of the social-cultural group influence the *Zeitgeist* in their turn. The group, to use other words, affects the individual's (the person's in his situation) experiencing as regards kind and "weight" of impressions and expressions and vice versa. What transpires due to the "steering" by relations and meanings is a system of values, indeed a variety of systems of values. Royce, whose basic attitude differs from ours, writes: "We choose, we behave, and we become; and we choose and become in terms of what we value most."

In the choice of meaning, in the accepting of and in the building up of systems of values, again the difference between man and animals becomes poignant. Animals seem to prefer what is useful and to avoid what is dangerous to them. Value systems cannot be ascribed to them. They certainly lack the feeling of value (*Wertgefuehl*) that Hartmann attributes to the "mental creature as moral person."

We are mindful of the fact that Hartmann's system shows—as every system—the weaknesses of systematization. With every systematic statement and/or explication that we make, a part of the freedom is lost which Nature lets us see and feel if we care to see and to feel. Yet for our human ways of experiencing, we need help—crutches like the lame, canes like the blind—to get and to hold to some orientation in a universe that for human beings is so extremely complex.

As far as Hartmann's "Problem of Mental Existence" is concerned, the impossibility of carving up Nature into levels and the mind into slices, is admitted. Nevertheless, Hartmann's ideas are highly valuable when we remain aware of dealing with interpretations. Whether he is "right or wrong," Hartmann has pointed to the ubiquity of the mind in an original manner.

The mind—rather what we call mind—is a way of existence. Dealing with its problems the scientist cannot dispense entirely with philosophical concepts, and the philosopher is well advised to consider the "body"

18. There is here a certain parallel with the tamed, domesticated, trained animal.

without the fear of delivering himself to the devil of any of the materialisms of the past.

We tried to do justice to these points of view in our interpretation. It behooves us, though, modestly to acknowledge Hartmann's observation: "It is natural that the individual sees only what he comprehends, and that he comprehends only what in his opinion concerns him."[19]

REFERENCES

Buytendijk, F. J. J., *Mensch und Tier,* Rowohlt, Hamburg, 1958.

Hartmann, Nicolai, *Das Problem des geistigen Seins,* 2nd Ed., de Gruyter, Berlin, 1949.

Hebb, D. O., *The Organization of Behavior,* Wiley, New York, 1949.

Heinemann, Fritz, "Metaphysik," in *Die Philosophie im XX Jahrhundert,* ed. Fritz Heinemann, Oxford, Ernst Klett Verlag, Stuttgart, 1959.

Jores, Arthur, *Der Mensch und seine Krankheit,* 2nd Ed., Ernst Klett Verlag, Stuttgart, 1959.

Kahn, Eugen, "Über Innen und Aussen," *Schweizer Mon. Schr. f. Psychiatrie und Neutrologie,* 1955.

———, "Weitere Erwaegungen ueber Innen und Aussen, *ibid.,* 1955.

———, "Becoming and Being in Time and Space," *Psychiat. Quart.,* July, 1959.

———, and Louis H. Cohen, "The Way of Experiencing as a Psychiatric Concept," *Psychol. Monogr.,* Vol. XLVII, 1936.

Lack, David, *The Life of the Robin,* Witherby, London, 1944.

Munk, Arthur W., "Philosophers' Conference in Retrospect," *The Hibbert Journal,* January, 1960.

Portmann, Adolf, "Zur Philosophie des Lebendigen," in *Die Philosophie des XX Jahrhunderts,* etc.

Royce, Joseph R., "The Search for Meaning," *Am. Scient.,* Vol. 47, No. 4, December, 1959.

Samuel, Lord, in October, 1959, issue of *Philosophy, The Journal of the Royal Institute of Philosophy.*

Straus, Erwin, *Vom Sinn der Sinne,* 2nd Ed., Springer, Berlin, 1956 (translated into English by Jacob Needleman, The Free Press, New York, 1963).

Walshe, F. M. R., "Thoughts of the Equation of Mind with Brain," the 13th Hughlings Jackson Lecture, *Brain,* March, 1953.

———, "Some Views upon the Nature of the Relationship between Mind and Brain," *J. M. Education,* November, 1959.

19. N. Hartmann: "Es liegt im Wesen der Sache, dass der Einzelne nur sieht, was er begreift, und nur begreift, was ihn seiner Meinung nach angeht."

CHARLES HARTSHORNE

Mind as Memory and Creative Love

Words express contrasts: with what is "mind" to be contrasted? Words are often multivalent, used with a variety of meanings. What are the principal meanings of the word "mind"? Putting the two questions together: What are the principal pairs of contrasting elements of which our word expresses in each case one member?

Mind is often contrasted with matter, the mental or psychical with the physical. This we may call the two-kinds-of substance contrast. We shall ultimately reject this meaning, or reduce it to the distinction between the concrete and the abstract.

Mind as expressed in thinking and reasoning is opposed to instinct, impulse, emotion. In this sense, an infant has very little mind compared to a normal adult. Indeed, it is arguable that an ape has more actual mind than a newborn human infant.

Sometimes a mind is viewed as an actuality, enduring through time, to which various states or activities of thinking, feeling, and perceiving successively belong. But in philosophies of process or becoming, the states or activities are the actualities, and the enduring soul, mind, or self is an abstraction or pattern of relatedness. This will be my view.

For the most part, people are thinking of human beings when they speak of minds; but they may also refer to the animal mind, below man, and some claim to be able to conceive divine mind above man. We shall include these aspects of the subject in our discussion.

In this essay we shall take mind as the process of "minding," in the broad sense of experiencing, with aspects of remembering, perceiving, feeling, anticipating, dreaming, purposing, thinking. We shall not greatly stress the difference between thinking and feeling.

440

The oldest roots, in the Germanic languages, of the word "mind" apparently refer to memory and love. And indeed, if love is generalized as any more-or-less-sympathetic valuation, and if memory is similarly generalized to the fullest extent, then it may be argued that the mental or psychical functions are almost summed up in memory and love.

Psychiatrists seem rather well agreed that mental disease is chiefly incapacity for love—including self-love. Sympathetic valuation and evaluation, the latter being the more conscious, form the indispensable motive of mental functioning. When evaluation is primarily negative or hostile, or still more, when there is extreme apathy or indifference, then mind is sick and in danger of destroying itself.

In order to love, we must have awareness of suitable objects. Such awareness comes to us, it seems, in two forms, memory and perception. By memory I am aware of my own past experiences, and of the decisions I have made and purposes adopted, some of which at a given moment I am, more or less resolutely and consistently, attempting to carry out. By perception I gather what other creatures around me are doing, thinking, and feeling, and evaluate them accordingly. It appears, then, that mind is not merely memory and love, but memory, perception, and love. However, I wish to argue that the first two can be assimilated to one, and that memory is in some respects a better name for this single function than perception.

How do memory and perception differ? Memory gives us ourselves, as in the past; perception seems to give us chiefly other persons and things, though in part also our own bodies, as in the present. Memory is apparently an identity relation primarily; perception, in large part, a relation to others: memory relates present to past time; perception is ostensibly of the present world. Accordingly, to assimilate perception to memory would imply that in perception we are not really aware of a strictly contemporary world, but rather of a past world; and that in whatever sense there is identity between the remembering and the remembered self there can also be in principle, though not necessarily in the same degree, identity between perceived and perceiver.

You may ask, why try to assimilate either way? Why not let memory and perception remain distinct, as they seem plainly to be? The answer is that it is the driving motive of science to find unity in difference. Of course, what we call memory and what we call perception are somehow different; but they may also be somehow similar. And we shall not understand the difference clearly until we also see no less clearly what the similarities may be. And obviously, as we have already seen, memory and perception have at least this in common, that both give us materials for more or less sympathetic evaluation. They give us things to love and hate. Even self-love is mostly a relation to the remembered past, as well as imagined future, states of one's self; but since imagination derives largely from memory and perception, these last are the two primary modes of receptivity, of acquiring materials for evaluation. What we call thinking is the fashion in which human beings tend to carry out their evaluations. The lower animals evaluate, but without thinking, at least in our human sense of the manipulation of words and other symbols. But animals must have memory and perception, or they have nothing to evaluate.

Are there really two absolutely different forms of awareness, memory of one's own past, and perception of others as in the present? The closer we look, the more do we find the seemingly absolute differences turning out to be relative, and matters of degree. First, consider memory. Recalling an incident of one's childhood or youth is not adequately expressed as an experience of identity. How alien and other that remembered past self sometimes seems; and in the repressed memories that psychiatry finds, this otherness is even more startling. You may use the identical word "soul," or self; but an identity that admits relations of sharp antipathy and extreme condescension must have something relative about it, must be admixed with important aspects of nonidentity. We shall take up this point again later.

Turning now to perception, man has discovered that his perceived world is in reality a past world. In looking at the night sky, the time interval may be very vast, far greater than any personal memories of ours can extend over! And any object outside the body, however close, is at least minutely past by the time we perceive it. Accordingly, if "memory" is defined as "experience of the past," then all perception, unless of inner bodily states, and perhaps, as we shall see, even of them, is a form of memory, by this definiton of the word. Moreover, the fact that with near objects the time interval may be extremely small establishes no distinction from personal memory, for (and philosophers have an inveterate tendency to forget this), while the obvious examples of memory cover appreciable time intervals—a minute, a day, a year—less obvious but undeniable examples cover but a fraction of a second. Such immediate, or very short-run, memory is so much with us that we almost fail to notice it consciously, and our philosophies are greatly injured by this oversight. As I begin the latter portion of a long word, my utterance of the first part is already in the past. But I do not experience this latter portion as a fresh start, but rather, as continuation of the earlier portion. We hear a great deal about the mistakes of memory; however, somewhat as vision for close objects is the most reliable, similarly trustworthy is memory for the very short-run past.

Perception then is akin to memory, at least to this extent, that both refer to the past—in the most reliable case, to the near past. What now about the other apparent difference, that perception is typically experience of a not-oneself, in contrast to memory as self-experience? We have already suggested that this sameness of the self is but relative, admitting deep differences in attitudes and beliefs. I can today believe that proposition P is false; and yet a year ago I was firmly convinced of its truth. And as an infant I could not have believed either P or not-P. There is no absolute sense in which the believer in the falsity and the believer in the truth of P, as well as the creature incapable of either belief, are all identical! If one insists upon such an absolute identity, in spite of these profound differences, then how can one refute the Hindu mystic who says that *all* selves whatsoever are but the one supreme Self, Brahma, regardless of differences in content of experience and belief? There seems then to be a profound relativity in the notion of human self-identity through time. Accordingly, personal memory is experience, not of the simply and absolutely identical, but of that which is in some respects identical, and in some respects not. You may say that the former respects are more important or fundamental, but here again the questions arise, how *much* more fundamental, and for what purposes? Is the fertilized egg already, in the most important sense, the individual to be later named John Doe? Is even the nearly mindless, and insofar quite subhuman, even subprimate, newborn infant already John Doe? Relativity can here be escaped only by obstinate verbal-mindedness (which indeed we are all likely to fall into).

What then about perception, as awareness of another, a not-self? Is this otherness meant absolutely? We speak of a sense of identity with another; some mystics—as noted above—speak of identity with all others. Is this absolutely wrong? No more, I suggest, than the talk about personal self-identity is absolutely right. We are not dealing with absolutes here, positive or negative. A person has indeed intimate relations to "his" own past; but he has fairly intimate ones with the past of others, and with that of all the neighboring world, if largely unconscious feelings are taken into account.

I shall cut the argument short here and state my conclusion: all material which comes into "the mind" (and this means, gets itself, more or less sympathetically, evaluated) is from the past rather than the present, above all from the immediate past; and in all cases, what is thus experienced is relatively, but not absolutely, other than oneself. It is both alien and not alien. Normally, there is a great difference of degree: one is very close indeed to one's own personal, especially immediate, past of feeling and thought, and less close to that of other persons. But it is a matter of degree. Thus memory and perception are basically alike.

You may have been thinking that in perception of one's own bodily states there is no time lapse; do we not here have awareness of the strictly present world? This is not a necessary reading of the facts. The twinge I perceive in my tooth need not be going on there exactly *now*, as I perceive it, but may have just *been* going on. By the time it is my experience, the physical occurrence in the tooth has, perhaps, lapsed into the immediate past. Thus even here perception may be akin to memory. There are reasons for taking this suggestion seriously. We arrive at a more attractive scientific generalization if we dismiss the apparent dualism between perception of the sheer present and memory of the past, and adopt instead the view that only the past literally gets itself experienced in its concrete actuality. The present world is given as a prophecy from the perceived past: thus the star we see may well be out there still, because the chances are that it has not ceased to be since the time when it emitted the light by which we see it. With near objects this probability of still existing becomes a virtual certainty, which is all we need pragmatically. Just so for practical purposes we experience, in immediate memory, what we are *now* thinking, for we are aware of what we were in process of thinking an insignificant time before, and we can scarcely be doing anything very different right now.

At this point we can deal with the deceptive argument that there must be an ego which can never be known, a "subject which can never become object." There is always a latest knowing self which has not yet become known, but it is just this self which will become object the next fraction of a second, in immediate memory. Every subject may become known, though it is never true that every subject is known. The latest self does not make itself object, but it will be object for subsequent selves.

To take an analogy: a class of classes can become a member of a class of class of classes, and any class can thus become a member. Similarly, any subject with objects which are previous subjects can become object for a further subject. In this respect the famous notion of the unknowable subject is not so very deep after all. There is no final class of all classes of classes of ... etc., and no final subject.

There is one question we have not yet faced: is it the very things perceived or remembered themselves which get "into the mind," or which we directly enjoy, possess, or evaluate; or is it rather some mental state or representative of the things? I hold that it is the things themselves, at least in the case of things very near in space and time.* Immediately past personal experiences are directly had, enjoyed, or "intuited," in memory; and immediately past bodily states are directly had in perception—which is "nonpersonal" memory. Mistakes of memory, or

* See my article, "The logic of givenness," *Philosophical Quarterly*, 1958, 8:307-316.

of perception, with respect to immediately past and spatially near objects are all mistakes of evaluation of the given, involving, in human beings, some element of verbalization, or other mode of symbolization. By the time we have said or judged what we remember or perceive, we must have run various risks of error, in the fallible process of formulating or interpreting. But something must be there to evaluate, or there cannot even be erroneous evaluation; and the theory that we "experience only our own mental states" is really the contention that we evaluate but our own evaluations of our own evaluations—of what? Or, it is the theory that, not only is all perception "memory," in the sense of having something past for its object, but all perception is merely personal memory. The relativity of self-identity makes this position glaringly arbitrary. If I could not directly perceive "another," and if even my past self is, in a moderate, but still genuine sense such another, then by this logic I could not really experience even my past states. And since no state can experience itself (just as a proposition cannot affirm itself) we should end in Santayana's absolute skepticism, according to which only a timeless essence is directly experienced. How even "animal faith" could then understand what it is about, or what "faith" means, even that great literary genius could not explain to us. And it is all unnecessary. No mistakes of immediate memory and bodily perception are recalcitrant to explanation as mistakes of formulation, verbalization, evaluation. Extremely short-run memory and bodily awareness are not usually even proposed as examples of mistakes, and when they are, inspection will reveal their inconclusiveness. The amputated leg cannot be the seat of a pain, true, but the body, especially the nervous system, very well can be, and doubtless is, that seat. Our locating of the pain "in the leg" is an elaborate interpretation; all that is given is its location "down there," spatially below some other bodily sensations, and even the identification of the direction "down" will probably involve correlation of several senses, and symbolic interpretations of various kinds. It has yet to be shown by careful argument that "direct realism" of bodily awareness is untenable.

What about dreams and illusions? I answer that they, too, may be taken as interpretations of bodily states actually going on. I dream that I am cold; I awake and find that I am and have been cold. I dream that I should go to the bathroom (my bladder is distended); I awake, and that is my physical condition. One may go on and on, especially if less obvious cases are taken into account. For instance, I seem to hear a sound or see a color in sleep. The optical or auditory system is, for all we know, involved in this business, and I hold that some portion of it is taking on the very form which is required for waking perception of similar sounds or colors.

The whole notion of "mere dreams," as though they were but mental states in which no physical object is there for evaluation, is a "mere" dogma, even though a natural one. Upon it rests many a skeptical argument à la Descartes, about the possibility that waking perception is but a series of orderly dreams, in the sense of mere states of the subject's own mind. It is the Cartesian premise which is to be suspected, that dreams could ever be "mere" dreams, i.e., could manufacture their own physical "images." They interpret the images, which themselves may be physical processes actually going on, at least in the nervous system. The skeptic assumes the contrary. But his assumption is worse than arbitrary; it is the unintelligible notion of experience experiencing itself.

A mental state, I conclude, is always an evaluation not of itself but of something else. In personal memory, to be sure, what is evaluated is another, often very similar evaluation, or mental state; however, no mental state has personal memory for its sole content. There is also that impersonal memory which we call "perception," the possession for evaluation of certain just occurrent bodily states.

With perception of things outside the body, there seems no good reason for supposing a direct grasp (unless a very faint and ineffectual one) of the things we see or hear. Primarily, we are experiencing the state of the optical or auditory system, including its cortical part; but in adult life we experience this inner bodily state as sign of something outside the body. So in looking at a photograph of a beloved person we may experience the shape of the light and dark masses on the paper almost as the very shape of the person, though what we literally see is the paper, not the person. And similarly in actual "seeing" itself, what we literally experience, I believe, is our own bodily state; but we evaluate what we experience as equivalent to an external state of affairs. And this for practical purposes it usually is, somewhat as when we see the words of a book, and seem almost to experience the described happenings. Again, perceiving is like reading an ever-changing map of the external world. That we read the map so well as to be scarcely aware of the map itself surprises (or deceives) many philosophers, but it does not, I imagine, surprise psychologists very greatly. It is only what their knowledge of the immense learning process back of it all, beginning even in the womb, would lead them to expect. We must learn habitually to think, not about the map but about the country mapped, or we shall not have long to live in that country. But it may still be true that the map is the chief datum which the thinking interprets.

I wish now to discuss my second main concept, love. Learned men have debated the difference between love as *eros* and love as *agape*, and various other contrasting meanings. I find myself dissatisfied with these discussions. They are largely rhetorical. They do not spring from close analysis of experience, with intellectual freedom as to choice of logical framework. For one thing, they assume self-identity as an absolute, which makes any subtle clarity impossible.

The primary motivation, I suggest, is neither self-love nor love of another self. The enduring self is only a relatively identifiable entity, and it cannot furnish an absolute principle, a strictly universal point of reference. Two thousand years ago the Buddhists made this discovery, and they have scarcely wavered, with all their differences, from this great insight. The absolute principle is sympathy, felt not by a "self" (in that abstract and pseudo-absolute meaning which philosophers tend to give this term) for that very self, nor yet for another such self, but rather by one concrete and momentary self for other concrete and momentary selves, or some aspect or sequence of these. Certain of these other selves constitute, in accordance with the vaguer, more abstract notion of self-identity, "oneself" in past and future states; or, to speak more precisely, they are past and future momentary selves in the same "personally ordered" series, such ordering involving unusually intimate relations of memory, continuity of purpose, and the like. But some of the concrete selves with which we sympathize are outside our own personal sequence. And as the Mahayana Buddhists realized, though perhaps only Whitehead has furnished adequately clear concepts to express the point, the unity of self with self in a single sequence is but a special strand of the relations of unity binding existences together into a cosmos.* I am self-identical in important senses and degrees because I sympathize with my own personal past and future selves more constantly and vividly than with those of anyone else, and because there is a special degree of similarity in the members of my personally ordered sequence. But it remains true that the general ideas of sympathetic evaluation and of similarity are in principle neutral to the difference between one enduring or abstract self and another. Always, in sympathy, there are two or more concrete selves, and the only difference between self-interest and interest in others is in the sort of order and relatedness which the various sympathies establish among those selves.

What then becomes of the contrast selfish-unselfish? I am selfish if I subordinate the future selves or states of others to my own future states, as though other persons were to serve me and not I them. But this does not mean that self-love is a mere identity-relation. If it were, how could there be any comparison between self-love and love-of-others? They would be sheer metaphysical opposites, while all clinical

---

* Perhaps the simplest approach to an understanding of Whitehead's view of the self is to read Chaps. xi and xiii of his *Adventures of Ideas* (1933, 1948); also pp. 271, and Chaps. xx, secs. vi-viii; and *Modes of Thought* (1938), pp. 29-57.

experience shows their kinship and interdependence. On the view I am suggesting, the reason is clear: self-love is not the love of an entity for that very entity—a nonsensical notion; it is the love of one concrete, momentary self for other such selves, but others sequentially connected by peculiarly intimate relationships of similarity, and of actual and potential remembrance; unselfish love is love of a concrete self for others not thus intimately connected with it in a single sequence. In both cases there is nonidentity, but there are also aspects of identity. For if my past and future are like my present, and if my future will recall my present, so in lesser degree are your past and future like my present, and so also, to a lesser extent, may you recall my present. The differences here are all relative. Recognizing this relativity facilitates achieving an intelligent understanding of what the problem of selfishness really is. It is the problem of the scope of sympathies which the present concrete self is able to entertain, its capacity for participatory evaluation. If it cannot get far outside its own personal series, then it will tend to be unsympathetic even toward members of this series. Selfish people notoriously have hate as well as love for themselves, and sometimes they are rather apathetic toward the past and future, whether personal or not.

Suppose then that concrete selves are in good mental health, i.e., able richly to sympathize with future possibilities, both within and without their own sequence, is this the highest form of love? If I serve you, expecting you to serve me in turn, is this not after all a kind of enlightened self-interest, a mere sensible bargain? However, note that if I not merely serve you but also sympathize with you, then I serve you not merely because you may then serve me, but because, sympathetically sharing in your feelings and needs, I want you to prosper. I love you somewhat as you love yourself. And I may even, at times, like the thought of your serving me not so much because that will benefit me as because I realize that, in this service of me, you also will find happiness, since you too are a sympathetic soul, and want to help others, including me. What is selfish about such an attitude? Does not the word begin to lose all meaning when carried so far? However, there is still more to be said.

I am to die, and there will come a time when you cannot serve me, and (for all we know) no one can. Yet if I am really sympathetic, I will want you to be happy after my death, should you survive me. If this is not unselfish, what could the word connote?

There is an old sophism, at this point. If I want you to be happy after my death, then since acting to bring about a desired result gives satisfaction, it is really, it is argued, this satisfaction I am aiming at, even in promoting your welfare after my death—as in purchasing a life-insurance policy, with you the beneficiary. But please note, the satisfaction I take in now acting for your future welfare is the satisfaction of the present concrete self. It is utterly trivial to say that doing what I now want to do is giving me satisfaction; the contrast between "selfish" and "unselfish" concerns, not the location of the present satisfaction of the agent, which naturally could only be in the agent, but the expected locus of the future good which the act aims to bring about. Suppose I am making my will, and expect to die the moment after. My concrete self enjoys its act, of course, or it could not perform it heartily and single-mindedly. But the future objective aimed at is a future benefit to another, to concrete selves in another sequence. To call this attitude selfish is mere abuse of terms. Minding is remembering and anticipating, and both are forms of love, one for the past actual, the other for the future possible experiences and their immanent subjects (which are the experiences as one, and as self-active).

Suppose, however, we knew we were immortal, and could serve each other everlastingly, would we then be unable to escape selfishness? Would we then have to content ourselves with the mutual exchange of benefits as the meaning of our friendship? There is at least one respect in which unselfishness would still be called for. I must be content that the good I contribute to your life shall be, in some part, beyond my comprehension, so that I cannot have the privilege of complete sympathetic participation in this good. I may see, and like seeing, that you are happy in the music I have enabled you to hear, perhaps by furnishing you with the financial means or the leisure, but if I am unmusical, or musical in a different way, I cannot literally enjoy your musical happiness in its concrete qualities. I must be content to produce for you a good in which I have only a limited and imperfect share. An omniscient being alone could participate fully in the good of others.

Putting together the two points just made, we may say that as mortal, and incurably more or less ignorant creatures, we must either be selfish or be content to do good to others without hope of fully sharing in that good. While we survive, and remain in close communication, we may indeed share to a considerable extent, but never fully.

The foregoing suggests a contrast. Suppose an immortal and all-knowing individual whose sympathetic evaluations were infallible and all-embracing. Such an individual could not do good to others without fully sharing in that good. He would not merely know that, but exactly how, they were happy. Unlike Moses, he could not send others into a promised land which he was himself debarred by death from entering; unlike any of us, he could not be in the position of helping others to a good partly incomprehensible to himself. The omniscient and everlasting, if such there be, must always reap any crop which he is able to sow, and must fully assimilate the crop to the last nourishing grain. For adequate knowledge of a good is possession of it. In this sense, the omniscient and everlasting cannot be capable of "unselfishness" if that is to mean "willingness to cause a good result whose value can never be its own." However, to call such a being selfish is, once more, a highly misleading use of terms. For what is it to be unselfish if not to take pleasure, to find satisfaction, in the welfare of others? A concrete agent could not act without enjoying value in the action, for that is what it is to act deliberately. To will (and therefore take satisfaction in the projected achievement of) the good of others is what we mean by "unselfishness"; and it is no less that because the good of others may also later become ours by virtue of our sympathetic participation, so far as we are capable of this. Those incapable of any such sharing in the joys of others are precisely the significantly selfish persons. To argue that a perfect and immortal capacity for sharing would mean complete selfishness is a silly use of terms, contradictory of the normal function of this word.

In the light of the foregoing, the history of human thought is an amazing business. Multitudes, and—it almost seems—the overwhelming majority, of philosophers and theologians in all lands have tried to conceive the supreme mind or mode of reality not by maximizing sympathetic evaluation or participation in the good of others but by minimizing it. They have said that the supreme or divine reality derives no value whatever from our happiness, being completely "independent" in all respects from us and our weal and woe. At the same time, Christian, Mohammedan, and Jewish thinkers and many others as well, have held that the divine is to be conceived by analogy with love, or as benevolent as well as beneficent. But a moment's reflection should convince us that whether or not a completely independent reality could be "beneficent," a cause of good, it could not sensibly be termed benevolent. It could not will good; for what is will but the bringing about of some result the intention to produce which pleases the agent, and the actual achievement of which tends to give him further satisfaction?

Moreover, if we deny that God thus derives value from the good he does to us, we not only deprive the idea of deity of any coherent meaning, we also imply that the only sympathetic sharing that exists is the mortal, fragmentary, imperfect sort which we possess. "Perfect participation" logically requires immortality and infallible knowledge.

Thus this form of theological tradition makes no real use of the principle of love as sympathetic evaluation, and it fails to see that (as I have argued in various writings) the ideal inherent in such love furnishes a conception of deity which is more significant and coherent than the usual one.

We shall return to the question of superhuman mind. But first let us consider subhuman forms of mind. They are inferior forms of sympathetic valuation whose materials, like ours, come from memory, including the impersonal kind we call perception. It is (I hope) agreed among naturalists that there is no absolute distinction between social and nonsocial animals, since all, in some degree and fashion, are social. This means that sympathetic valuation (if not the more conscious or rational form we call *e*valuation) may always have some role to play. As for memory, learning has been detected even in one-celled creatures. Is this the lower limit? In the most general sense, memory is the way in which the past is possessed by present experience and thereby colors and influences that experience. But an experience not influenced by the past would be totally exempt from the principle of causality. The suggestion is close at hand, though few philosophers have seen this, that causality is memory, at least so far as effects are experiences. Experience is influenced by what it remembers of the past, and it is, some of us think, the idea of memory which explains influence, not vice versa. As Hume showed, influence is an utter mystery if we try to conceive it in terms of mere insentient matter. But Hume never discussed at all the theory that effects are always experiences, on some level, and experiences possessing the immediate past in memory and therefore colored and influenced by it. This theory, highly developed by Whitehead, but foreshadowed by Peirce, Bergson, and others, has yet to be soberly evaluated in intellectual fashion. It is either ignored, or cavalierly and often emotively rejected. I am not impressed by this method of criticism. For no alternative theory of positive causal influence has been proposed. Influence is either taken as an arbitrary "constant conjunction," or else as memory; there is no additional possibility that has been made at all clear.

The implication of what has just been said is that the duality of mind and matter is not ultimate, and this not because materialism is correct, but because psychicalism is. It is psychical conceptions of memory and sympathetic evaluation, not mere insentient matter, which can explain the coherence of the world. Physicists today generally concede that the notion of matter is not an ultimate explanatory conception. The notion amounts to this, that something or other is extended in space-time (or better, something or other is going on in space-time) of which we know through science certain geometrical patterns, certain forms of relationship. But what it is that is patterned or related, physicists do not pretend to know, though many physicists, biologists, and philosophers suspect that it is mind in various forms, mostly nonhuman.

Here we must notice the Cartesian dogma that mind is "inextended," a dogma still enunciated today. On the contrary, if mind is essentially sympathetic and social, then extension and space are easily explained, without resort to mere matter. For space is just the way in which we can have "neighbors" and social relations. With time alone, without space, there would be but one sequence of experiences, one enduring or abstract self. Space is the way in which diverse sequences can have members inheriting from outside their own sequences. It is (ask any physicist) the way in which there can be multiple intersecting lines of inheritance among events, rather than a single line of influence. The notion of "matter" throws no light on how this is possible, but is a mere name for the possibility. But "mind" does throw light on it, for the combination of personal and nonpersonal memory ("perception") is all that is needed. And both are traits of mind.

The human mind is indeed not spatial in just the way a table is; but neither is the table, much less beams of light, in just the way atoms are. Extendedness has long since become so subtle and flexible a concept in science that it is trifling to deny any and every form of extendedness to mind merely because the human mind cannot be bumped into or seen. It is also hard to see electrons, or to bump into light. And the fact that the human mind is very peculiar in its mode of extendedness does not show that mind generically has this peculiarity, any more than the oddities of human walking or running show that all spontaneous locomotion must be in this special form. Here is a question of willingness or ability to generalize. Science and philosophy are nothing without this willingness and ability. Materialism, dualism, are forms of the refusal or failure to generalize.

Our account of mind on the higher or vertebrate level can now be completed in striking ways, and this is further confirmation of our psychicalistic view. If "matter" is a form of mind, then the constituents of our bodies, such as cells and molecules, must consist of processes of remembering and of sympathetic valuation. What then can be our relation to these processes? It must be that of participation. Hurt my cells and almost immediately you hurt me, because intimate and continuous sympathy with my body is precisely what distinguishes my sequence of selves from all others. It is part of what makes my body mine and no one else's. That I depend upon the states of my body obviously follows; for the more intimate our sympathies with something, the more it can influence us.

That we can control our bodies is the other side of the relation of sympathy between us and our cells or other constituents. They must have primitive sympathetic valuations of our thoughts and feelings. But human experiences being richer, more intense, our influence over each cell is by far more powerful than its influence over us. In this sense each of us is king over his bodily kingdom. And so is any vertebrate animal mind over its organic constituents.

We may here consider the issue of behaviorism, or of the observability of mind. One's own actual mindings or experiencings are given in memory, most directly in immediate memory, a tenth of a second or less afterward. Introspection, as has often been said, is simply retrospection. So far there is no great difficulty. But what about other mind, and about one's own mind as intersubjectively observable? A science must deal with all things in intersubjective terms. (Please note, however, that this very way of talking assumes that there are subjects.) Nevertheless, it would be surprising indeed if all things were equally accessible to all subjects. Insofar as this is not the case, there may be a domain of especially accessible objects peculiar to each subject. We have earlier, in effect, indicated that in fact each human subject has two such domains: his own past experiences as remembered by him, especially just afterward, and certain neural changes in his own body. Because of the latter, the physician asks us what pains we feel. The neural changes are not absolutely inaccessible to the observation of others, but they are relatively so, and this relative "privacy" can in no state of science be more than relatively diminished; it can not be absolutely abolished. The privacy of personal memory can perhaps be relatively but again not absolutely overcome through telepathy, supposing this at all possible, or through indirect reasoning from past observations or records of behavior. Since the mind is king over the bodily kingdom, and since its experiences are constantly given their sensory content by neural changes, inference is obviously going to be possible from behavior to experiences and vice versa.

There is no sound reason for doubting that (to put it dangerously oversimply) two people who act alike in similar circumstances have in substantial degree similar experiences. Psychology can take care to frame its hypotheses so that they have behavioral implications which public observation can test, and conceivably falsify. To go beyond this, and actually define "experience" as identical with behavior is to gain no reduction of the aspects of real privacy involved in our lack of memory for other peoples' experiences as such, and our lack of direct sensitivity to their inner bodily changes. Though the test of theories is in the public observable consequences, it does not follow that what we seek to know by such tests are merely facts of behavior.* He who says these are the only facts involved is either "telling lies" (as an eminent logician once

* One of the earliest clear (and it is quite clear) statements of behaviorism as a method was given in 1902 by C. S. Peirce, an "objective idealist" or panpsychist! See his *Collected Papers*, Vol. VII (Harvard University Press, 1958), p. 237.

said in this connection) about the nonexistence of things we do experience, or else he is forbidding science to deal with a certain class of facts. Neither procedure commends itself. The facts must indeed be dealt with by means of observations of behavior, but all the facts of mind should be open to psychology. And the last thing which is scientific is to deny facts because they seem inconvenient.

If the human mind is not the body, does the mind "have" the body, or the body the mind? Which is the attribute or part, and which the whole? I hold that Plato was right here: the "soul" contains the body, rather than the body the soul. We can if we wish say that the body has the mind as a function or attribute, provided we mean: if and only if there is a certain kind of body in a certain condition in a certain region of space, then a certain kind of minding is going on in that region. But it remains a misleading way of talking. This is so for two reasons.

1. The human mind is given retrospectively as including within itself sensory content which can only be understood as certain aspects of the bodily process directly given or enjoyed: this means that a state of minding is a *whole* of which certain bodily functions are merely constituents. This whole is not the body.

2. There are no positive explanations, at least such as make sense to certain of us, in either scientific or philosophical literature, of the mind-body relation except those of the "panpsychic" type which we have sketched above. In this account the brain cells do in a fashion possess human experiences, but only in this fashion: they have their own experiences which (very dimly or inadequately) participate in the human experiences, feel their feelings. Thus, it is as themselves mind, on lower levels, not as mere matter, that the bodily processes can intelligibly be viewed as possessing (some faint realizations of) the human mind. Otherwise, there is merely a question of the two being together in space, in some unexplained way dependent upon one another.

Materialists are forever confusing two concepts, that of "extended reality" (which mind itself is) and that of "extended reality devoid of mind," i.e., "mere matter." Then they argue that, since extended reality is intersubjectively observable (a concept, by the way, incurably mental, with all that one may say about cameras as observers), matter must be independent of mind, which is best viewed as a complication of "matter." This is an unconscious sophistical trick. Matter as devoid of mind is as unobservable as anything could be, for no observed property entails the sheer absence of minding. "Extended reality" is all that is plainly given, and the question of its self-sufficiency, apart from mind as such, human or otherwise, is precisely what has to be shown. Materialists only play another little trick when they argue that mind as given is dependent upon body, hence upon matter. For since there is, as we have seen, a psychic theory of the constituents of body, all that is shown is this: a human or higher animal mind, e.g., depends upon certain lower levels of extended reality. The question whether these lower levels are or could be made up of mere matter devoid of mind is independent, logically, of the valid premise from which the materialist is arguing. Moreover, the theory of mind as love or participation explains the dependence of mind upon mind, on various levels, in principle, perfectly!

It is mind as such, not matter as such, which is observable. In retrospection mind is observed directly by each of us, and more plainly than anything else can be observed (for consider how obscure the physicists have discovered the nature of inorganic and protoplasmic extended reality to be). Mind is also, for all that has been shown to the contrary, directly observed by each of us in sensation, taken as participation in cellular feelings. Less directly, but intersubjectively, it is observed in external perception, if we accept the only coherent positive theory available as to what matter is (rather than what it is not), beyond the obviously abstract properties of spatiotemporal structure which physical science discloses, properties logically incapable of being a complete description of anything concrete.

Defenders of the idea of mind need not, then, be on the defensive. The whole history of knowledge indicates that, as Russell once said, "matter" is anything so far as we have not yet come to understand it, or perhaps never can understand it. Positive insight the term does not furnish.

Of course, those who cannot see that minding is spatiotemporal will not easily give up the concept of mere matter, since spatiotemporal structures are the most distinctly knowable features of the empirical world. But, as we have seen, observational or logical grounds for the Cartesian dogma, "mind is inextended," are lacking. The extendedness of mind is its social-sympathetic structure, whereby each experience has multiple inheritance from other experiences, some of which are mutually independent of each other.

We may now expand our earlier discussion of selfishness and love. A higher animal cannot be merely selfish, for it consists essentially of sympathy for its bodily constituents. Thus, not only does each concrete self sympathize with past and future members of the same sequence; but in animals it also sympathizes with members of some of the sequences making up the body. Selfishness is simply a narrow, often ridiculously narrow, scope of unselfishness. We get rid of the absolute dichotomy, egoism-altruism, and retain—all we need for any practical purpose—the important relative distinction between adequate and inadequate sympathies. Moreover, all the higher animals at least have sympathies not only beyond their own futures but beyond that of their bodily constituents; much more so man.

Our conception of motivation is still highly incomplete. If each concrete, momentary self sympathizes, not with itself, but with other selves in or out of its own principal sequence, then the final objective is not "self-realization," but contribution to the future fulfillment of others. It is devotion, not self-seeking. True, in this devotion, the concrete or actual self does achieve its own satisfaction or enjoyment. But it *is* this good, rather than seeks it as something beyond its own present actuality. The adequate good beyond the present can only be some future good potentially recipient of our present selves as contributions to its own actuality. I call this view, *contributionism*. We offer ourselves for the sympathetic appropriation or remembrance of the future. But now, what is the ultimate future, in this reference? Is it merely that of man, or even of vertebrate animals? All individual organic sequences are finite, and the species themselves will presumably terminate sometime. And besides, posterity inherits only extremely partially and accidentally from each of us as we are at given moments.

We face a dilemma then. Either there is no adequate objective for our devotion, no appropriate recipient for our contributions, or there must be an immortal sequence which can never terminate, and which sympathetically enjoys, not fragmentarily and accidentally, but fully and inevitably, all our experiences in their most intimate qualities and values, in short, an everlasting and infallible form of sympathetic evaluation. This is one aspect of what I think religion intuitively meant by "God," although theologians often did strange things in spinning out theories of this meaning. God, for believers, is or should be the final and uniquely adequate referent of our life's contributions. How distressing then to find theologians denying that God is capable of receiving any additions to his value! In that case he must totally lack the one essential value of perfectly adequate sympathy. This indeed we could not contribute; but by virtue of the divine possession of it, we cannot fail to contribute all that we are to the richness of the divine experience.

You will perhaps have already inferred that, according to our theory, there must in God be an analogue to memory, since personal and impersonal memory is the sole way in which evaluation has something to evaluate. You will have been correct; this is the implication. The divine life "inherits" our lives, as we do those of our bodily constituents, and God could be said to remember us, but with imperishable and adequate retention. And the divine also inherits his own past by the "eminent" form of personal memory. If you ask me, How can the supreme mind have a past and future? I reply: since the potentialities of value are absolutely infinite, no actuality could exhaust them. Those who think to exalt deity by considering him "perfect" once for all have significantly been forced to admit that what God creates is not all that he might create, and is not, in spite of Leibniz, the greatest possible creation. (For even Leibniz could not explain what that could mean.) So the allegedly "complete" deity must face a world which could have been or could be greater. But then, as possessing that world, he is not complete or greatest possible, after all; for he could possess more greatly. The only remedy for this paradox is to admit that since the divine creative power is inexhaustible, it is never exhausted, and hence goes on forever producing more value for its own sympathetic appropriation. Thus, there is a sort of future and past even for God. So much for superhuman mind.

I have said virtually nothing so far about mind as thinking in the sense of employing symbols. (It has been my suspicion that others in this volume will say much about this topic.) The chief difference between us and other vertebrates is, of course, this, that their ability to use signs is almost infinitesimal compared to ours. We evaluate through language, and other more or less elaborate patterns of symbols; the other animals evaluate at most through very primitive and simple sign patterns. I have found through my own study of animal behavior, especially that of songbirds, that the animal limitation can be expressed in roughly quantitative terms.* A bird can grasp and accurately reproduce a musical or verbal pattern, provided it takes but a second or two, or at the utmost twenty seconds, though rarely so much as four seconds. Beyond this, there is little definiteness. A bird which sings for minutes with only brief pauses is stringing together in largely random order a number of short phrases. It is not following any definite over-all pattern. And it cannot do so! Now suppose such a creature were to try to talk with understanding. It must then speak in very brief sentences indeed, as parrots always do, and it could have little awareness, in the second or third sentence, of what the first sentence contained. How much could be communicated under these restrictions? Thus, the ability for symbolic behavior which sets man apart is somehow intimately connected with the unique scope of his memory or temporal attention span.

Musical analysis of bird song in comparison to human music shows that the basic difference is not that we can sense relations of harmony, melody, rhythm, and the birds cannot. What is indicated is rather that birds sense musical relations quite well, but only in extremely simple examples each of which can be exhibited in a few seconds. Any musical device which requires many seconds and many elements is beyond them;

---

* See my essay, "The relation of bird song to music," *Ibis*, 1958, 100:421-45. Also, "The monotony-threshold in singing birds," *Auk*, 1956, 73:176-192.

but whatever can be done quickly and simply is not. True, each species is narrowly limited in what it can do, but for every simple musical device, there are species which can and do employ it.

Is such a difference one of degree or of kind? But perhaps this distinction itself is one of degree? Given a vast degree of difference, it can for some purposes be taken as absolute. A human musician grasps patterns occupying thousands of seconds, not just two or three, and tens of thousands of notes, not just dozens. Considering how the possibilities of variety mount in such an increase in the number of elements, the difference cannot be expressed as a ratio of a thousand to one, but of at least hundreds of millions to one. Indeed, to get a full idea of the difference in symbolic possibilities between birds, or even apes, and man we should have to use astronomical numbers. So may we not say that this is a difference of degree so great that it amounts, for most purposes, to one of kind?

Mind exists on a vast variety of levels, and, as we have seen, the idea of mere matter has no absolute validity. Hence all our dealings with nature can involve sympathy. Love in some conscious or merely intuitive form can be the entire motivation of the mind. That we seem able to employ objects as mere means is in large part explicable through the fact that our senses generally fail to discern the dynamic individuals but give us blurred masses of individuals only. A stone cannot be sympathized with because it is but a dense swarm of molecules or atoms, and these we know only abstractly, through physics. When one adds that a man can use his horse essentially as means, although we all suppose that a horse has its form of mind, there is no further mystery about our use of inanimate material things without any conscious sympathy. Besides, on our theory of perception, only one's own body is directly experienced, the others being known by a kind of inference become automatic in infancy and childhood. Mind then is all concrete existence, except for masses, aggregates, whose analysis into individuals escapes us. These alone are simply mindless, and then only for our ignorance, or only as groups, not in their constituents.

Mind, we may say, is reality itself, so far as it is concrete and understood. What is left over is the abstract, either abstract in itself, like numbers or the ideal of virtue, or abstract merely for our knowledge, like the physical world, as disclosed, and also profoundly hidden, by natural science. And these dichotomies of abstract and concrete, and of more and less understood or disclosed, are wholly contained within the idea of mind. Mind, then, explains absolutely everything, except for this, that to the human mind, its own and all other forms of mind—therefore all reality—are more or less mysterious and impenetrable. Nothing is added to this mystery of mind by saying, "There is also the mystery of matter." The first mystery, in its ample infinity, swallows up the second without remainder. Or so it seems to some of us.

Looking back upon this essay one may note at least two great omissions. The first is that, although we have said a good deal about love, we have ignored hate. Psychiatrists have shown, I think, what has long been an open secret, that hate is secondary and derivative from love. But it can be a very powerful derivative. Without some element of sympathy there is no human consciousness at all, no understanding of another, no use of language, no anything human. However, if other people are seen primarily as sources of pain and frustration, rather than of joy and fulfillment, then hate, negative valuation of the human other, is the result. The terrible thing is that once this has happened, it tends to go on happening through generations. Intensely hating parents are bound, by a law less exact but as certain as Newton's or Einstein's, to produce some hatred in their infant offspring. In this sense "original sin" or inherited perversity is a fact, and science has shown it to be such. (That this was not Augustine's view of original sin is not the only instance in which Augustine chose darkness rather than light among the views open to him.) The infant may hate because it has been hated; later on it will act wickedly because it has been wickedly treated, unless it becomes the recipient of some very remarkable form of love which produces a miracle of transformation, like that brought about by the generosity of the bishop in *Les Misérables*. (I owe this example to the psychiatrist Dr. Bernard Holland.)

The second omission in our discussion so far is that I have said nothing about the freedom or creativity of mind. Determinists mistakenly identify the freedom of action with its mere lack of constraint or compulsion. But we have another word for that, "voluntary." We need both terms, for there are two ideas here. I shall try to sketch—I can here do no more—the meaning of freedom in the sense of creativity. Mind, being essentially memory, is bound to be influenced by the past, for to be aware of the past is to be influenced by it. Thus one has in the idea of mind a clue to "causal efficacy." But one also has a clue to the limits of causality. The datum of memory comes from the past. But the past did not remember itself; the memory is an addition to the datum. Every experience is insofar a creation, and the idea that the unique unitary quality of an experience might be derivable from antecedent events and causal laws could only occur to those who have never clearly grasped what this must mean. The new experience is an additional datum, a new premise for the logic of events, not a mere conclusion of this logic. Or rather, this logic is not the logic of necessity, but of creativity. Its "conclusions" are made, not deduced. The data from the past are materials employed in their creation, but though materials influence, they do not dictate, their own use. This would be an incoherent notion. To that extent determinism is an absurdity.

In addition, since nearly all agree that the laws and past history of nature are logically arbitrary, contingent, we need some notion of the transition from the logically possible to the arbitrary factual world. Either this transition is a mystery back of the beyond, behind the world, or it occurs everywhere, and expresses a universal category. This is what the philosophy of mind as creative process affirms. All events are free acts, influenced but not absolutely determined by their causal antecedents.* Thus, the arbitrariness of the world creeps into it everywhere and at all times, rather than being given in one huge dose. Either way, wholesale or retail (or both), it is mind and not matter which explicates positively the idea of the "transition." Contingency is simply freedom, creation; and this is an aspect of mind as such.

Obviously man, with his symbolic behavior, is much more free than the animals, which merely select among tiny details, according to a life plan fixed in rather definite outlines by instinct. Man chooses between whole classes and kinds of actions, between "designs for living," ideals, universals. Thus his freedom is momentous. It changes the face of the earth beyond any readily assignable limit.

All freedom is dangerous. This is a simple matter of logic. No laws and no providence can guarantee the exact outcome of the interaction between even two free individuals. X chooses goal a, Y chooses goal b. What ensues is some compromise combination of ab that neither chose. If they are wholly pleased by the outcome, this is good luck, but it could not be guaranteed. Bring providence in, and you have added a third goal, c, which has a certain pre-eminent attractiveness so that subsequent goal-setting will be universally influenced in unique degree by c. But in principle, influence cannot degenerate into sheer determination. Creativity is always involved on both sides. Thus, we get rid of the theological nightmare of benevolent despotism, selecting not only every good, but equally every evil, in the world. This view was always illogical; for it attributed eminent freedom or creative power to One, and did not attribute (as would have been logical) inferior freedom or creativity to the many, but rather fake, phony, or merely apparent freedom. We think we select; God eternally has selected for us, such thinkers said or implied.

One penalty for the long flirtation with this strange doctrine is that the necessarily dangerous character of human life as free was disguised or evaded. Utopianisms are one of the consequences. All freedom is dangerous, the greater the freedom the greater the danger. No provi-

---

* See my article, "Freedom requires indeterminism and universal causality," *J. Philos.*, 1958, 55:793-811.

dence and no planning could make it otherwise, for the necessity is logical. The justification of the risks of freedom is in its opportunities. But the truth, if I am not mistaken, is that great opportunities with small risks are a logical impossibility. This is quite apart from the question whether a being other than God and able to choose in good faith and good will must not also be able to choose in bad faith and with ill will. Even with the best intentions all around, freedom cannot be made harmless. In partially creating their own characters and specific objectives, men only by good luck escape conflict. Wickedness adds a grievous complication; danger there would be in any case.

With all its difficulties psychology (in the broadest sense) has an unrivaled advantage: it is the only science which can study a part of nature, not simply in the external way made possible through vision and touch, but in the intimate way of direct participation in its qualities, as we study our emotions, sensations, memories, hopes, fears, and thoughts. It is quite sound to make the most of the external observation of man, as a moving object; but to reject the internal observation of man, as sentient and thinking, is to throw away a unique privilege. Here alone we experience the quality of an individual, what it is in itself, rather than simply its spatiotemporal relationships. All the rest of nature is either unknown in individual quality (what is it like not to see but to be a frog, a molecule, a particle?) or it is known (in the modest way possible for man) by analogy with ourselves. Moreover, we have discovered that the impression of sheer nonanalogy between ourselves and, say a piece of chalk is an illusion of the senses. We are active, the chalk is inert—for the senses, not for our scientific knowledge! We are organisms, the chalk is mere homogeneous stuff—for our senses, not for our knowledge, which finds that just as half a man is not a man at all (in contrast to half a large piece of chalk, which is simply a smaller piece of chalk) just so half a molecule of the chalk is not a molecule of a similar kind, but something radically different. We are self-active, more or less unpredictable; the chalk does what it is expected to do—for our senses, and in its gross macroscopic characters, not for our knowledge, and in its minute constituents, which are likewise unpredictable. The schema "stimulus-response" scarcely applies to chalk, but in nuclear physics its inapplicability is not so obvious.

Scientist friends tell me that microphysiology is not visibly nearer to the mechanistic dream of seeing organization—say in the living cell, with its myriads of simultaneous but coordinated activities—as a mere consequence of chemicophysical laws, than in the days of Loeb. But there is another dream: that the really universal factors are psychological. The cell perhaps acts coherently because there is a dominant feeling influencing its molecules, and influenced by them. No mysterious Drieschean "entelechy," but a primitive and to us strange version of the sort of thing we find in ourselves, feeling, with some slight sense of the immediate past, and of desire for the immediate future. The pretty picture of an all-sufficing mechanism is fading, the sole alternative which could possibly rival it is the more beautiful picture of a psychicalism which has learned the two deepest lessons of recent psychology, that creative love is the law of mind, its basic principle of health, and that harmony in the midst of tension and uncertainty is the intrinsic reward of love. The universe is unintelligible, or it is a realm of experiences on countless levels and of unimaginably many specific kinds, on all levels experiences with freedom and social relatedness to other experiences. These relations are sometimes "democratic," as in a colony of cells, say an embryo, or a man in deep sleep; sometimes monarchical, as in the waking vertebrate animal relative to its cells, or perhaps a cell relative to its molecules, where a sequence of experiences on a greatly superior level tends to dominate over numerous sequences of inferior experiences (constituting cells, molecules). Thus, the alleged "influence of the whole on its parts" —as it stands a logical conundrum, not a scientific theory—becomes simply the influence of the dominant experiences, in which what goes on in the parts is perpetually, though incompletely summed up (as a man's sense of well-being or of suffering sums up much of the goings on in his nervous system), this summing up being then reacted to by the parts, which are also social in character.

Mind as social offers the coherent alternative to materialism. Psychology therefore holds the key to the synthesis of the sciences, not physics or biology. (It can use the key, however, only when it has thoroughly rid itself of the relics of Newtonianism—determinism and materialism—from which physics has been busily purifying itself, beginning with Maxwell and Gibbs.) In th end, physical analogies will explain mind, or psychical analogies will explain matter.

Let us not forget that it is biology, with its principle of evolution, which has furnished the grand framework of all natural knowledge; will it not be psychology, with its principles of love, creativity, and the striving for harmony, which will furnish the explanation of evolution? The higher levels of existence exhibit the universal characteristics in greater degree, hence in more readily discernible form (very small values of a variable may make the variable itself imperceptible to us); the highest planetary creatures, ourselves, are also the only ones we can study in all the ways in which we can study anything. Here is the sole possible window (admittedly at best translucent, not transparent) opening upon the intimate nature of things. Are we likely always to keep shutters on that window?

To summarize:

1. The content of minding comes to it through memory, in the broad sense of "intuition of past experience."

2. Memory is always a form of participation or sympathy.

3. The subject participating is always, strictly speaking, unique to the given momentary experience (the Buddhistic factor), so that in a sense even "self-love" is love for other selves, past or future.

4. The mind-body relation is another instance of this love, but this too is, and in even greater degree, a one-many relation, since mind-events in interesting lines inherit from one another, and hence are spatial as well as temporal.

5. All inheritance needs to be summed up, if there is to be any meaning, in an immortal and infallibly sympathetic evaluation, which defines the supreme level of mind.

6. Minding is always creative or free, but in widely different degrees; the supremely free minding orders, without in detail determining, the inferior instances of freedom.

7. Freedom is in principle dangerous, and yet, since mind and concrete reality in general coincide, this danger is the price of existence itself and of all opportunity for good. In any heaven or Utopia there must be need for courage and loyalty in the midst of risks, difficulties, and opportunities.

E R R O L   E.   H A R R I S

Mind and Mechanical Models

I

Progress toward a definition of mind is the same as advance toward knowledge of what the mind is, how it acts, and how it is distinguished from what is not mind. Definition is the demarkation of the *definiendum* and its distinction from other things. In a book such as this, we are not simply concerned to define a term or the use of a word; if we were, we should not need to seek contributions from physiologists, psychiatrists, and psychologists and should do well enough simply to consult the lexicographer. It is as an entity, as some element in or sphere of reality, that we seek to know the mind, and as such we think of it (rightly or wrongly) as a possible object of study for some of the natural sciences. In this enterprise the function of the philosopher, though some might wish to restrict it simply to the examination and clarification of the use of words, is, in my view, more properly that of reflecting upon the results of the relevant sciences, viewing them as contributing to a single systematic conception, and, by removing from them the abstraction necessarily imposed upon each by the limitation of its viewpoint to one special field, constructing from them, in conjunction with our everyday notions derived from common experience, an idea of the mind that will throw light at once on their divergence and on their mutual agreement. This is no mean or easy task and cannot be adequately fulfilled within the limits of one chapter. All I can essay here is to list those characteristics usually held to distinguish mind, as such, from what is other than mind, to give a brief account of the more important of them, to consider how far the widespread attempts currently being made to understand the mind in terms of mechanical models can help us, and, if they do not, what alternative is available to us.

It is perhaps remarkable that though the construction of a mechanical model, which Lord Kelvin revered as the ideal of explanation in physics, has long since been abandoned by physicists, it has in recent years been proposed with considerable enthusiasm as appropriate in the biological and psychological sciences. The range of investigations within which value has been claimed for mechanical models as a source of illumination is quite impressive; though no longer viable in physics, appeals have been made to them in genetics, in evolutionary biology, in neurophysiology, in psychiatry, and in psychology. How far mechanical analogies assist research in these various disciplines, I am not qualified to judge, and it is for the specialists to decide. My concern, in this chapter, will be to consider whether the philosopher seeking to clarify the concept of mind can derive any profit from such mechanical analogies and to ask whether the analogies have always been legitimately drawn and to what extent odd and unnoticed metaphors might not tend to mislead.

It would be well to begin by considering what in this connection no reasonable person ought to deny. First, it seems clear that, whatever the mind may be, its activity is, at least in part, manifested through that of the body, and the body is a material entity the constitution and activity of which is physicochemical; to which, therefore, physicochemical laws must be applicable and in the movement of which mechanical principles must be involved. It does not, of course, follow that these laws and principles are limited to those we have as yet discovered; that, when discovered, they will be found to be the same as, or even similar to, those which govern the movement of nonliving bodies; or that they are in principle discoverable. If anybody is competent to pronounce authoritatively on these matters I am not. What is indubitable is that the living body *qua* physicochemical is subject to physicochemical laws of some kind and that, so far as it is a machine, as in some measure it undoubtedly is, some mechanical principles will be exemplified in its movements. There seems to be no a priori reason to assume that these laws and principles are in their essential nature undiscoverable. But it is probable from the evidence already adduced by scientists that they will not be the same as now seem to be applicable to nonliving bodies. Perhaps in pursuing their researches, physicists and chemists will be forced to modify their conception of physicochemical laws in such a way that living activity hitherto inexplicable by them (or at all) may come to be so explicable. All this I should be prepared to admit at the outset.

It would follow that mechanical models of various kinds might very well prove useful and suggestive to the cytologist, the geneticist, and the physiologist, but it would not necessarily follow that they would assist the psychologist studying animal and human behavior if it should prove to be the case that patterns of such behavior are not ultimately reducible to patterns of mechanical activity. Nor does it follow in any way that they would help to understand the activities of the mind if only because it is seldom clear what that activity is, as it is clear that the activity of a body is chemical and physical activity.

Leaving to biologists and physiologists to demonstrate the ways in which mechanical models have elucidated the workings of the body, as well, on the other side, as the extent to which suggested analogies (as seems sometimes to have happened) have proved misleading, I shall confine myself to questions about the mind and in doing so I shall be compelled, however ill-equipped, to draw somewhat upon the preserves of the psychologist which no philosophical consideration of the nature of mind can altogether avoid.

What I have so far stated will at least clear away one preliminary obstacle to discussion. It has been asserted that the way in which we normally use the words "mind" and "machine" is such as to exclude the application of the latter term to whatever it is the former connotes. Dr. W. Mays[1] quotes the *Oxford English Dictionary* as defining a machine as "a combination of parts moving mechanically as contrasted with a being having life, consciousness and will." Hence, what is a machine by definition is neither a living thing nor mind and vice versa. On the other hand, Professor A. M. Turing (against whom Mays is arguing) forecasts that our use of words will have changed by the end of the century to such an extent that nobody will feel outraged by the suggestion that machines think. Dr. Mays is not so obtuse as to believe that current usage settles the question once and for all, but sees that the facts which have prompted that usage are the important consideration. The issue is not simply verbal. If mental activity manifests itself even partly in physical (as we must surely confess) then the question is legitimate whether mental activity may not be at least analogous to mechanical.

II

The suggestion that this is the case is strengthened by those who allege that mental activity is nothing but bodily movement. This is the position of some forms of behaviorism and a view which has derived some encouragement from Professor Gilbert Ryle, who, though he repudiates behaviorism as anything more than a method advocated for psy-

---

1. "Can machines think?" *Philosophy*, 1952, XXVII:148-162.

chological research and rejects mechanism as a "bogey," does insist that all our linguistic forms which refer to mental activities denote only the actual occurrence of overt behavior, or dispositions to such behavior and denies the existence of any occult, unobservable, inner mental states or processes. This attitude invites engineers and mechanics, whose contemporary ingenity in devising automatic self-regulating machines is prodigious, to compare the work of the mind to the working of their machines. The overt behavior, in which (according to Ryle and others) mental activity consists, is performed by a physical body in physical space and time, as is the operation of a machine. It is not surprising, therefore, to find Turing,[2] D. M. Mackay,[3] and F. H. George[4] claiming that as soon as we can specify the behavior typical of any given mental activity it becomes possible to describe the mechanism that has to be built to perform it. This, however, is taken as evidence that machines can think, remember, learn, make decisions, and even enjoy themselves, which it is not in the least. For it has by no means been established that everything involved in these states and activities can be precisely specified as overt bodily behavior. It is simply assumed that it must be because it is alleged that there is no other legitimate way of describing the supposedly mental.

Some behaviorists are tempted to deny the existence of consciousness altogether. But this denial can, of course, only be applicable to other people, and never to oneself. For even without the asseverations of Saint Augustine and Descartes, each one of us knows that he is conscious. And not all behaviorists go to this extreme. Many support their position by methodological considerations and insist merely that reports of conscious states are inadmissible as scientific evidence which must be restricted to publicly observable facts. Others support their view by philosophical argument like Professor Turing's contention that to appeal to consciousness is to commit oneself to solipsism,[5] as the only consciousness of which we can be assured is our own.[6] But if all our states of awareness are to rank as unobservables it is the behavorist who is committed to solipsism. For what is observed is perceived and can be perceived only by a conscious subject in whom that perception is a conscious state, private and exclusive. That the same object may be perceived by others in no way detracts from the private character of the

2. *Mind*, 1953, LIX:438.
3. *British Journal for the Philosophy of Science*, 1951, II.
4. *Philosophy*, 1957, XXXII, p. 169.
5. *Op. cit.*, p. 446.
6. It is to be noticed that this view differs from that of Professor Ryle, who denies that we can know our own mental processes in any way more reliably than those of others.

perception in each case. If nothing private is to be accepted as scientific evidence, then no report of any observation made by others is admissible as it is the report of a private experience of perception and each scientist will be caught inescapably within the circle of his own observations which will be incommunicable. "One could . . . describe these feelings to the world," says Professor Turing, "but no-one would be justified in taking any notice," and perceptual experiences are no different from feelings in this respect. In such a predicament public fact ceases to have any meaning and science becomes impossible.

It would seem then that the distinctions so commonly favored both by philosophers and scientists between public fact and private experience cannot be sustained. Fact is public only inasmuch as the private experience of it can be communicated, and private experience can be communicated only so far as it can be expressed in a form experienceable by others. Objective knowledge therefore is dependent upon intersubjectivity, and any attempt either to deny or to disregard the relevant deliverances of consciousness must be fatal to science. This is not subjective idealism for, from the dependence upon intersubjectivity of objective knowledge, it does not follow that nothing exists except subjective experience. What is implied is rather the contrary.

The scientist's demand for observable data does not involve a refusal to credit the contents of consciousness—quite the reverse. It is a demand for palpable evidence, and this consists in what is experienced and of the reports of such experience, which are not only legitimate but all that is publicly available. What is rejected as insufficient is the single or aberrant report lacking corroboration by, support from, and systematic connection with, other reports. If we remember this we need not be misled at the outset by behavioristic demands to distort our understanding of the facts by excluding from consideration what may prove to be the most relevant part of the evidence.

III

Rejection of extreme behaviorism, however, though it makes the relevance of mechanical models less plausible, does not dispose of it altogether. For conscious activities are in one aspect behavioral, and the claims made by the advocates of machines at least deserve some examination.

As I said earlier, language cannot be made the sole deciding factor in any question of the mind-like performance of artifacts. It is futile so to define our terms as to make analogies between minds and machines impossible. But the enthusiasm of some writers does lead them to use language so incautiously as to cloud the issue, and removal of confusions from this source is desirable. Mechanical devices are constantly described in anthropomorphic terms, sometimes consciously to draw attention to certain similarities of behavior but often quite inadvertently, revealing unwarranted tendencies on the part of an author to beg the question at issue. Even when the terminology is consciously metaphorical it may cover up an essential discrepancy which ought not to be overlooked between mind and machine. Let us inspect a few examples. Several may be found in Mr. W. Sluckin's instructive little book *Minds and Machines,* where the mechanical device is said to take cognizance of information,[7] to respond to signals, clues, stimuli, to display what amounts to discriminatory responses, search for environmental optima,[8] and so forth. Yet when Mr. Sluckin turns to describe the behavior of living organisms his language is loaded in the opposite direction. Now the physiological processes are all mechanisms, though it is confessed that what they are precisely and how they work is not, in all cases, fully known.[9] He writes of emotional mechanisms as homeostatic emergency responses,[10] and of purposive behavior in general as more or less complex exemplification of negative feedback. Learning again is a homeostatic mechanism and problem-solving a self-regulatory mechanism.[11] Clearly, if we speak in this way we create too easily the impression that there is just no difference between organisms and machines. Yet we rely on the common belief that there is an important difference by using "mental" terminology to describe mechanical processes in order to create the impression.

Let us examine more closely some of these ways of speaking. "To take cognizance of information" is to be consciously aware of something which, having a symbolic form, can be interpreted and given intelligible significance. But nobody would wish to suggest that any artifact yet constructed or in principle imaginable really is conscious of anything; and the symbols of any code, though they are processed and transformed in its operation, have no significance to the machine, but only for the person operating it, who alone can interpret them. "Signals" are signals only to one who knows what they signify; "clues," to be so-called, must suggest lines of inquiry and involve a recognition of their relevance to a specific problem. Such words can be used legitimately

7. P. 62.
8. P. 63.
9. P. 99.
10. P. 103.
11. Pp. 145-146.

only in relation to a conscious intelligence, and to speak of a machine's responding to signals and following clues is tacitly to assume what remains to be demonstrated.

Again, consider the language used by Professor Turing, who claims[12] that a machine could play what he calls "the imitation game," in which it is said to try to imitate a human being in giving answers to questions. This should mean that the machine makes a deliberate effort to do this whereas clearly the effort, if any, is made by the man who programs it. Professor Turing says that the machine can deliberately introduce errors into its working (explaining that he does not mean mechanical malfunctioning but wrong answers to proffered questions). But where does the deliberation enter in? Clearly, if deliberately programmed by its operator to produce wrong answers at prescribed times, it will do this. Or if some random element is introduced into its construction, the wrong answers may occur with a determinate statistical frequency. But to the machine they are neither right nor wrong answers—only to the questioner who can interpret them—nor does the machine in any sense consider whether or when it would be best to produce them, as the word deliberation would imply. If Turing, as he professes, wishes to exclude all elements of consciousness from his descriptions, he should not use such words.

Again, he discusses the questions whether machines can be designed that would be cleverer than humans; or, if some humans will not be cleverer than any possible machine. The relevant question, however, is whether machines can rightly be described as "clever" at all, except by metonymy from the skill of their designers.

Turing argues that consciousness is only inferrible from overt behavior and that the machine's performance in a viva-voce examination would be no worse than that of a human being. But frankly I do not understand how this is supposed to be effected. Could the machine really be made to answer questions intelligently about the poetic propriety of similes in a Shakesperian sonnet, as in Turing's example? In what sort of code could this examination be conducted? Can one program a machine with rules of poetic propriety? Are there any? The machine is supposed to be able to answer correctly the question why we should not substitute summer for winter in: "Shall I compare thee to a summer's day?" But suppose instead I were to ask: "Why not substitute 'mulberry bush' for 'prickly pear' in 'here we go round the prickly pear'?" Could the machine answer that and what would be right? Any attempt to answer such questions according to stereotyped rules would at once reveal the difference between man and machine to any compe-

12. *Mind*, 1950, LIX.

tent examiner. Is any good scientific purpose served by making extravagant claims?

Dr. Mays has rightly taken Turing to task for his animistic use of words in reference to the machine, and particularly in referring to its "mimicry" of human behavior. This is a common way of speaking among the advocates of the powers of artifacts. But, as Mays points out, "mimicry" refers to a purposive effort on the part of one person to imitate the behavior of another, which may be either unconscious or deliberate. But the purpose in the case of the machine is only that of the designer who makes it so that it will behave, as nearly as he can devise, like a human being. The machine itself does not observe human behavior and then make efforts to behave similarly. For this reason it would be better to use a word more neutral than mimicry to describe the similarity of the behavior. "Simulation" is perhaps less objectionable.

And here a special caveat is necessary. What ought to rank as imitation or simulation of living behavior? How much similarity, and of what kind, is sufficient to draw significant analogies, and how much are we entitled to conclude from it? Our answer should be based upon precise analysis of the working of the machine and not just on the superficial external similarities of behavior.

IV

Perhaps the most general and universal characteristic commonly attributed to mind is the purposiveness of its activity. This is the most general, since it applies to all animals including men and the lower species alike and is attributed to them even by those who hesitate to acknowledge other commonly recognized mental attributes. It has been argued, however, that purposive behavior of all kinds is in principle the same and can be reduced to simple forms which are possible for machines and of which living examples can be regarded as complex elaborations. The development and study in recent years of servo-mechanisms and the principle of negative feedback have given rise to the view that a complete account of purposive behavior can be rendered in terms of these ideas. First, it is maintained that purposive activity is always goal seeking; next, that the attainment of the goal is always the establishment or restoration of some state of equilibrium; and third, that the intervening process is one guided by feedback of information to the source of control concerning the discrepancy between the present state of affairs and the goal-state. Examples are ranged by allegedly continuous gradation from homeostatic physiological processes, like the maintenance of body temperature in mammals, or of the sugar content of the blood, through the movement of eyes and limbs in directed activity, to trial-and-error learning and ultimately to problem-solving in theory and practice.

It would be foolish to deny that homeostatic processes and the neural and muscular mechanisms involved in the regulation and coordination of bodily movements are in many cases spectacular examples of the operation of negative feedback and of servo-mechanisms in the organism, but we should tread circumspectly in proceeding further. We need not contest the idea that, in purposive action, some tension or disequilibrium, in the state of the organism is involved which is relieved when the purpose is achieved; nor that the striving is directed by an awareness (for can "feedback of information" here mean anything else?) of the discrepancy between the actual and the desired condition. But when we so describe it, do we not implicitly admit that purpose is a great deal more than a complex of feedback mechanisms? It would have to be a conscious process of desire and cognition.

But an objector may protest that we are moving too fast. Desire, he will say, is nothing but tension and disequilibrium, and no conscious awareness need be assumed in feedback, since "information" here is to be understood in its technical and not its "ordinary" meaning. This, however, will not do. Disequilibrium may be resolved in one of two ways. By increasing the weight of one pan of the balance, or by decreasing the other. Both are not equally relevant. Hunger causes disequilibrium in the organism, which may be removed either by eating or by dying. death is not a goal-state (even though it is an end in itself). The physico-chemical disequilibrium involved would not be a disequilibrium, if it were not a factor in a system of organic functioning. What physico-chemical reason is there, apart from the maintenance of the life of the organism, why a reduction of the sugar content in the blood should be counteracted? It is only within the organic structure and functioning of the animal that such disequilibrium creates tension. And what sort of tension is this? Not a physical or a chemical disequilibrium merely, which might be redressed in either of two ways. It must be a *felt* tension, an unease, a distress; something impossible without at least inchoate consciousness. Apart from this there would be no drive in the desired direction. The essential point is: that of the two possible directions one must be desired—it must be preferable; it must be better for some purpose; it must have value in some sense. Tension and disequilibrium in any relevant sense, therefore, presuppose purpose. They may not be substituted for it.

The correct assessment of the position would seem to be that feedback mechanisms are not sufficient to explain purposive behavior, but that an understanding of purposive behavior and evaluation might very well help to explain the utilization by the organism of feedback mechanisms. Their presence and operation constitute rather a symptom of purpose than an explanation of it, just as the presence of a thermostat is a sign that a constant temperature of a specified degree is required for some purpose. This fact is often tacitly admitted by writers who refer to the state of equilibrium, or steady state, as the optimal condition. Optimal is an evaluative term and evokes the question: Optimal for what?

It is perhaps tempting to answer this by saying that the steady state in question is optimal (in some way) for survival, but this is only to beg the question in a new way. What is it that must survive? Not just any physicochemical activity—that will survive whatever the circumstances. Yet it would be sheer tautology to say that the special sort of physicochemical reaction constituting the steady state is that whose survival the condition optimally subserves. If sense is to be made at all of the notion of survival-value, what survives must be of some value for reasons other than its mere ability to persist through time. It is value that gives importance to survival, not survival that gives value to a steady-state; and our question—Optimal for what?—can therefore be answered only by an appeal to axiology and not, without stultification, by reference to a steady state and negative feedback.

Further, either the element of information fed back in purposive activity must be conscious or the feedback mechanism must be reduced to an entirely subsidiary role. In the working of a governor on a steam engine, the speed of the engine is fed back to the source of energy by purely mechanical means. No knowledge of the engine's speed is here involved. Energy derived from the output of the machine, as it increases, simply shifts part of the mechanism so as to reduce the intake. In a thermostat a similar process is effected electrically. The automatic aiming of an antiaircraft gun, directed by radar, is more complicated involving intricate servo-mechanisms and a predictor. The regulation and coordination of muscular activity when a boy throws a stone at a bird[13] undoubtedly operates on similar principles, but in this case a new and somewhat mysterious element is involved in the feedback, namely, the visual image. It is not simply the image on the retina which is required; the bird must be *seen*, and this involves cortical activity as well. But just what cortical activity and just how it mediates in the process, we are as yet ignorant. The aiming apparatus of the gun can give and has given suggestive analogies for the understanding of the physiological process, but we cannot wholly assimilate the two, because while the

13. I borrow the example from A. Tustin, *British Journal of Psychology*, 1953, XLIV.

radar reading might be analogous to the retinal image we can find no precise analogue to the conscious experience of seeing.

Professor Tustin has suggested[14] that this is paralleled by the predictor, and certainly it does perform a similar function. Moreover, the predictor, in some coded fashion, reproduces within itself relevant features of the external situation in similar mathematical relations. Something of the sort may go on in the brain for all we can tell; but seeing a bird is no more just having some sort of reproduction of the bird in the cortex than having a picture of it on the retina. It is being apprised of the fact that the bird is at a determinate distance away from the human body in the external world. It is being aware of the spatial relation between the bird and the body (including the brain, whatever its contents), and to this no analogy with the predictor is in any way adequate. To allege that it is simply poses the age-old epistemological problem of how the mind can know anything other than its own ideas—how it can know the relation between these ideas and the objects, which are not in the mind and to which the ideas are nevertheless supposed to correspond.

Could we escape this difficulty, as some may hope, by ignoring altogether the occurrence of consciousness and by treating the whole action simply on the level of physiology? I hardly think we can, without abandoning our endeavor to understand the nature of the mind. The boy throwing the stone cannot ignore the occurrence of consciousness if he wishes to hit his mark, and without it the physiological process would either not occur at all or would be totally different. We should seem unwise, therefore, to discount it altogether. The information fed back in this case therefore must, at least in part, be consciously apprehended.

When we come to still more complicated forms of purposive behavior, like the pursuit of food or the effort to escape from danger, the indispensable evaluative function of conscious apprehension becomes obvious. True it is that a state of tension is created, but only if the situation is perceived as menacing, or the object appetizing. This involves considerable interpretative and evaluative mental activity. The discrepancy between a dangerous situation and one of safety, between an edible morsel and an inedible one, must also be appreciated mentally before any relevant information about it can be fed back to the locomotory centers. And consciously appreciated information is significant knowledge, which is precisely *not* the sense attached to the word in communication engineering. In defining the unit of quantity of information as a "binary digit," the communication engineer deliberately abstracts from

14. *Op. cit.*, p. 27.

meaning and significance. For him, the actual purport of the symbols transmitted is irrelevant, all he is concerned with is the frequency and probability of their occurrence in the communication system. "It should be clearly understood," writes Professor M. Richardson, "that this technical definition of quantity of information ignores completely whether or not the information has meaning or significance and whether or not it is of any human value."[15] This being the case we should not look to information theory for light upon the nature and source of meaning, significance, or value. Yet the appreciation in some way of meaning, significance, and value is indispensable to purpose, and I cannot see, therefore, how the mechanical analogies so far considered, even with the help of information theory, are likely to advance us much in our efforts to understand either psychologically or philosophically the nature of purposive action.

D. M. Mackay, however, has given the mechanical model for what he calls valuational feedback.[16] consisting of a sloping runway tapering to a knife-edge down which balls run and drop off randomly into the right-hand pan of either of two beam-balances placed one on each side. On the left of the runway a target is then set in the form of a funnel leading the balls into the left-hand pan of the left side balance. The discrepancy between the position of the balance on the left and that on the right of the runway now "evaluates" the "success" of the balls in hitting the target. By linking the left-hand pan of the left side balance with the runway so that its descent causes the axis of the apparatus to tilt to the left, the probability of success is correspondingly increased. This is valuational feedback.

Again, however, words are being used in special senses. "Value" here is used as the mathematician uses it, in phrases like the "value of π," to mean numerical assessment. The descent of balls into the funnel has no value in any other sense—they could equally suitably fall anywhere else. Again, "success" in hitting the target is a misnomer, because the balls do not try to hit it or the apparatus to make them. Consequently, what we have here is certainly feedback, but it is indicative of purpose only insofar as it reveals the effort of the designer to increase the probability of the descent of balls into the funnel which has value for him only so far as he is concerned to make his mechanism work in a special way.

Our discussion has brought to light the fact that purposive activity as a character of mind is closely connected with consciousness and evaluation, which the effort to explain it away in mechanical terms presup-

15. *Fundamentals of Mathematics* (New York, 1958), p. 173.
16. *Vide* "Mentality in machines" in *Proceedings of the Aristotelian Society,* supplementary volume XXVI, pp. 71, 72.

poses and yet overlooks. The desire to give a mechanistic account of purpose is often associated with the distaste for teleological explanation in science. Such explanation proceeds by analogy from the deliberate purposive activity of which we are ourselves conscious, and if this could in turn be mechanically accounted for, the basis of teleology would have been destroyed. I have argued elsewhere[17] that this opposition to teleological explanation is the consequence of a misconception of teleological process as a linear series of events, the course of which is mysteriously determined by the last event of the series before it has occurred. No such conception of causation is tenable, and there are no such processes. Purposive activity as we know it is by no means of this kind, but is an activity directed by the awareness of an order of life constructed by ourselves in the course of our experience in the effort to satisfy ourselves as total personalities. Purpose proves to be a systematically organized form of activity directed to the maintenance of a structure of satisfactions which have value for us by reference to the totality of this structure. It is the awareness of an order of life of this kind determining the value of alternative courses of action which makes possible the exercise of deliberate choice.[18]

Purpose, therefore, in its most developed form, involves consciousness of self as a person seeking a total satisfaction which is attainable only through the ordering of life by choices implying principles of value, and any account of the mind which omits these features will be seriously at fault. But the most developed form implies stages of less complete development as its precursors, and this fact gives rise to the difficult questions: At what point in the scale of development may we justifiably exclude mind, and just where does mind, in the full sense, appear?

V

Deliberate choice and activities of ordering, however, involve judgment and thinking, and these are usually included among the distinguishing characteristics of at least the human mind. Yet to the activity of thinking, also, machines are said to provide at least an analogue, and some have even suggested that our own thinking may be only another case of mechanical operations occurring within the brain. But exactly what sort of activity thinking is taken to be is seldom made clear, for

17. Errol E. Harris, "Teleology and teleological explanation," *Journal of Philosophy*, 1959.
18. Cf. *ibid.*, and A. Macbeath, *Experiments in Living* (London, 1952), pp. 48-49.

"thought," like many other words, is used in various senses and refers to several different kinds of process. Sometimes it means ratiocination and argument, sometimes judgment; at other times we use the word to refer to imagination and memory, wondering and wishing, and sometimes (like Descartes)simply to being conscious. All these are activities we normally attribute to minds, but they are very diverse, and no precise result is likely to come of our lumping them all together under a single name. However that may be, many of them, in one way or another, have been attributed to artifacts.

Suggestions are not lacking that digital computers can produce behavior indistinguishable from thinking. By increasing their storage capacity, it has been said, memory and imagination can be stimulated, and, by the inclusion of random elements, free will, originality, and "independence of opinion."[19] It seems to me that all these claims are rather rash, but I cannot here deal with all of them, nor with any of them at great length.

As to memory I shall limit myself to the remark that "storage" is not enough to justify the comparison nor even the capacity to reproduce stored information at appropriate times. This is possible, I presume, only so far as the machine has been suitably programmed and so is dependent upon the thinking of the programmer. Be that as it may (and I shall return to it presently in another connection), true memory involves not only retention and recall of experience, but also recognition that the centrally reproduced experience (be it image or what not) is an identifiable past experience. As Russell has pointed out, it involves a feeling of familiarity and, more important, a judgment placing the remembered event in a definite context of past time. This judgment is not, of course, always true, but that is because, being a judgment, it is susceptible either of truth or falsehood. The mere recurrence of a past image is not. Storage and reproduction in a machine lack this element of judgment as does (in fact) every other operation carried out by machines.

If, however, we confine the term "thought" to formal processes of deduction, attention is directed to the prodigious feats of calculation performed by computers which not only simulate but surpass the capabilities of men. Computers, it is alleged, not merely think, but think better than we do ourselves. Here, however, two points seem to have been overlooked, the first of which may be brought out by reference to the doctrine of the Idealist, Bernard Bosanquet, who found no difficulty in attributing thought to machines. He maintained that thought was the

19. Cf. D. M. MacKay, "The mind-like behaviour of artifacts," *British Journal for the Philosophy of Science*, 1951, II.

construction and elaboration of ordered connections between the elements of a system. This view, though it gives a wider meaning to the word "thought" than many contemporary philosophers would wish to tolerate, is not wholly incompatible with much that has recently been written about deductive and inductive logic and is in harmony with much of the teaching at least of the Gestalt psychologists. But if we adopt it, we should have to confess that thought might not be an exclusive or distinguishing characteristic of mind, at least as we normally understand that term. For many processes which construct and elaborate systematic structures occur at the physical and biological levels of existence where we should ordinarily hesitate to admit the presence of mind. Bosanquet, of course, was not troubled by this difficulty because he regarded mind as ubiquitous and for the very reason that he discerned the activity of thought, in the sense defined, in every sphere. He considered mechanical systems to be quite compatible with thought and capable of manifesting it, and he argued this at some length in his Gifford Lectures. But he has been criticized for emptying the word "mind" of its meaning by making it universally applicable; and we may observe in passing that others may be similarly emptying the word "machine" of its meaning by attempting to demonstrate the universal applicability of mechanical principles. For, if thought is a system and thinking the process of systematization, we could as justly refuse to consider it exclusively a property of mind as assert that, on account of its presence, machines displayed the characteristic of mind. Nevertheless, thinking is an activity of the mind, and what seems to be required is some criterion for distinguishing between such processes of organization as are and such as are not possible without mental functioning.

The second point overlooked by those who attribute to machines the ability to think is that calculating is by no means identical with thinking, and the work of a computer is essentially calculation. That some calculation is done by thinking I shall not dispute, but the greater part is not. In calculating we use rules of thumb for nine-tenths of the time which involve no thinking. When we have difficulty in remembering past steps, or combining operations mentally, which we soon do unless we have exceptional abilities, we have to write down our "working" in order to progress. This writing down requires a notation without which calculation beyond the most elementary stages is impossible. The facility and versatility of the process depends upon the structure of the notation and are increased to the extent that it renders thinking less necessary. Much greater effort of thought is required to do arithmetic, for instance, with Roman numerals than with Arabic, because the decimal notation reduces the amount of thinking needed and replaces much of it by the merely mechanical substitution of symbols. In effect, therefore, a notation is a machine, operating according to certain rules which give us our results automatically so long as we work with it correctly. An abacus does the same in a somewhat more primitive fashion.

This is the character of every kind of calculus. It is notional mechanism, composed of symbols, translatable in set ways, according to prescribed rules, and such that if the rules are applied, certain results can be mechanically obtained from certain data. It does not matter whether the calculus is numerical, algebraical, or what is currently termed "logical." It is a mechanical system working in the manner described, which has been designed to enable us to reach certain results with a minimum of thinking.

The operation of calculi in writing is a relatively laborious process, and it is a simple matter to devise machines to operate them for us. The abacus has already been mentioned; the pedometer and the cyclometer are other simple examples. Slightly more complex are hand-operated and electrically operated calculating machines. The digital computer is only a vastly more complicated and more rapidly acting mechanism of the same kind. They are all counting devices of varying complexity, sometimes based on different types of notation or numerical scales, but not differing essentially in principle. That machines have been similarly constructed to operate logical calculi involves nothing more remarkable or more mysterious.

The essential point to observe, however, is that all such machines are designed to relieve the mind of onerous, dull, mechanical operations, in order to release it for thinking. What they do for us is essentially *not* thinking but what, if we have to do it for ourselves, obstructs thinking. "Calculating machines," says Professor Richardson, "not only relieve the mind of the burden of performing fatiguing and uninteresting calculations but also have the additional virtue of being less likely to make a mistake than any human being. Thus it is sometimes advantageous not to think. But it should not be forgotten that only by thinking can one invent, repair, reconstruct or even understand the machine."[20] This has also been pointed out by Mays, who maintains that computers are only highly developed forms of calculi, which are themselves devices for relieving us of mechanical manipulation of symbols,[21] and no thinking, he insists, is involved without the interpretation of the symbols. That sometimes the calculus is a logical calculus makes no difference. "Logic," in this sense, Mays asserts, is not thinking[22] and thinking is not its concern.[23]

20. *Op. cit.*, p. 167.
21. *Vide British Journal of the Philosophy of Science*, II, p. 249.
22. *Ibid.*
23. *Philosophy*, 1952, XXVII, pp. 158-159.

It is only in the invention and construction of computers in their programing, in the coding of information fed into them, and the decoding and interpreting of the formulas that emerge from them that thinking is involved, not in their working. The most elegant and conclusive statement of this point which I know has been written by Professor Michael Polanyi.[24] Every formal calculus, he argues, implies unformalized (semantic) operations for its use and logical completion. These include (1) knowing the meaning of the undefined terms; (2) understanding what is stated in the axioms, and (3) acknowledging that the manipulation of symbols according to formal rules demonstrates an implication. If the calculus is applied to some practical or scientific problem then not only must the axioms be understood, they must in their reference to this problem be believed. These unformalized and unformalizable operations are in Polanyi's words "functions of the mind which understands and correctly operates the system." Thus, a formal deductive system is an instrument, which implies the existence of a mind to use it, and without which it is logically (in the true sense of "logic") incomplete, as a tool is logically incomplete without the hand that uses it. The mind that uses it, however, as Polanyi states, needs no such further completion. Thinking properly refers to the unformalized operations to which the formal or mechanical system is in some sense antithetical. It follows that machines do not think.

VI

Speculation as to whether they could usually issues, therefore, in speculation whether a machine could be designed capable of programing another machine or whether one could be programed to construct another like itself. We should ask further whether a machine could be designed to encode its own input and decode its own output. There are some writers who would answer such questions affirmatively. But if we do, shall we not have a regress on our hands. That a machine could be constructed by another machine implies that the first must have been programed in such a way as to be capable of this; if this again were done by a machine, that one must have been similarly programed. At some point we *must* come back to a mind such as the one Polanyi asserts to be logically complete. But there are others who allege that this mind is itself a machine, though of a kind the mechanics of which we have not yet discovered. Professor J. J. C. Smart, for instance, boldly asserts that he believes human beings to be nothing but very complex

24. *Vide British Journal of the Philosophy of Science*, II, pp. 312-315.

machines and he takes Ryle to task for referring to mechanism as a bogey.[25] The fact that artifacts cannot sign a document, he maintains, is purely accidental. They could do this, and with responsibility, if they belonged to a society of machines that had evolved social rules about such matters. Unfortunately (or fortunately), this condition is just what cannot be fulfilled because communication proper—that is, interpretation of the symbolic medium—without which no society is feasible, involves those informal mental activities mentioned by Polanyi as being excluded from the formal operation which is all that machines can cope with. Responsibility, likewise, and the acceptance of moral rules are products of this informal functioning of mind.

F. H. George,[26] draws attention to the fact that human organisms are, like artifacts, also constructed, but by a different sort of process, the biological process; and he hints that the construction of one machine by another would be no different in principle from animal procreation. If this suggestion is taken seriously we must believe that each living "machine" is constructed and programed by a process at least analogous to that by which our own artifacts are constructed and programed. If it is possible to conceive a machine capable of constructing and programing another which is more complex and more efficient than itself, we could hold that such a process of reproduction of machines might be evolutionary. But nowhere in the series, however far back, could we presume a machine to come into existence out of disorganized parts, without the intervention of an already constructed and programed machine. Thus, the regress would have to be infinite, and the mind demanded by Polanyi would never be reached, yet always inevitably required for what he called logical completion.

This, it seems to me, is nothing more nor less than St. Thomas Aquinas' argument for the existence of God in a new form. Just as for St. Thomas the regress of causes cannot be infinite because the infinite regress never provides an *adequate* cause, so the regress of programing cannot be infinite, because it provides no programmer who is logically complete and independent in Polanyi's sense. The ultimate implication, therefore, should be a final, undesigned designer. Whether this conclusion would be welcome to our modern advocates of artifacts I cannot say, but perhaps the most interesting philosophical implication of their position is that it does provide grounds for the revival of one form of the cosmological argument for the existence of God.

I am myself inclined to adopt a somewhat different position, and I

25. *The Philosophical Quarterly*, IX, 1959.
26. *Philosophy*, XXXII, 1957.

find a more suggestive clue to the nature of mind in what actually looks like a mistake shared by W. R. Ashby and J. B. S. Haldane. Ashby contends that evolution could be effected by a machine which included in its make-up a part that could extract design or "information" from randomly occurring events. A Geiger counter, or a magnet picking particles of iron from a stream of indiscriminate material, would be an example. He maintains that natural selection does this and he calls it "Darwinian machinery."[27]

Haldane, endorsing this opinon, describes natural selection as "a method for conversion of noise into message."[28] W. E. Hick, however, points out that it is theoretically impossible to extract information, in the sense of regularity or order, from a random process by applying a predetermined rule, and it could not therefore be mechanically effected. "If there is one thing you cannot do with noise," he writes, "it is to get anything that could be called a message out of it." If Hick is right, Ashby and Haldane must be wrong. Yet life and mind do seem to involve some active principle which somehow produces order and system out of material which is less organized. At least they are definitely capable of preventing order from degenerating into disorder and of maintaining the entropy of a system at a relatively low level. Shroedinger has made this point with great effect.

"In biology," he writes, "we are faced with an entirely different situation. A single group of atoms existing in only one copy produces orderly events, marvelously tuned in with each other and with the environment according to the most subtle laws. . . . It needs no poetic imagination but only clear and sober scientific reflection to recognize that we are here faced with events whose regular and lawful unfolding is guided by a 'mechanism' entirely different from the probability 'mechanism' of physics. . . . Whether we find it astonishing or whether we find it quite plausible, that a small but highly organized group of atoms be capable of acting in this manner, the situation is unprecedented, it is unknown anywhere else except in living matter."[29]

If evolution could be regarded as a process in which the unprecedented capacity for maintaining organization is increased, and more complex, more highly differentiated, and yet more intricately united systems of structure and functioning are produced, it might not be strictly accurate, but nevertheless very suggestive, to call it a process of converting noise into message. Mind might then be viewed as a very highly developed phase of this process at which a very high degree of

27. *British Journal of the Philosophy of Science*, III, pp. 52-53.
28. *Ibid.*, p. 190.
29. *What Is Life?* Cambridge University Press, London, 1944, pp. 79-80.

organization of behavior is achieved by the mediation of consciousness and the activity of thinking. How organisms are able thus to maintain order and system at any level in the process is at best only partially known. How the transition occurs from that level at which consciousness is undetectable to that at which it is recognizably present is as yet completely mysterious.

The appeal to greater and greater degrees of complexity is not, I am aware, very helpful. Professor Tustin justly protests, "This is no approach to explanation. A machine, however complex . . . cannot legitimately be endowed with new properties because we call it a machine. . . . The whole may show phenomena not shown by the parts . . . but this is no contribution to removing the complete lack of any idea at all of how this particular whole [the brain] could conceivably produce *these* particular phenomena [consciousness]."[30] With this I am wholly in agreement. Nevertheless, there seem to be good grounds for regarding consciousness and thinking as principles of organization and synthesis; and if similar principles can be recognized as operative at lower levels of evolution, and in activities which subserve those of consciousness on the levels where it occurs, the temptation to postulate an unbridgeable gap between life and mind would at least be diminished. This would suggest that the direction of research should be toward trying to discover how more unified complex wholes are brought into existence from the less highly organized, whether in some sense noise may not, after all, be converted into message.

VII

Perhaps it would be best to maintain that only where there is consciousness should mind be acknowledged. When we talk of thinking do we not normally mean conscious thinking? Appealing though this suggestion may be, it cannot be accepted without qualification. Of course, thinking is often consciously performed, but we cannot exclude from the realm of the mind those processes, often on a very high grade, which take place below the level of consciousness. Great thinkers have confessed that when faced by a difficult problem, they have succeeded best when, after thinking intensely about it for some time, they have neglected it entirely for a period. On attending to it afresh, the solution has been found, or at least in the interval some progress toward one has been made. This indicates that high-grade thinking must meanwhile have been going on unconsciously. Psychologists, especially psychoan-

30. *Op. cit.*, p. 35.

alysts, give ample testimony to the occurrence of unconscious processes which we could not refuse, without straining the use of language, to call mental processes. Nevertheless, I think we need have no hesitation in saying that, although not all mental processes are conscious, all conscious processes are mental, and this takes us a step nearer to our goal, since we may now say that wherever consciousness is found, there, without doubt, we have mind. The suggestion that a conscious act might somehow occur apart from any mind, though it has been made, is one which I must confess I find unintelligible.

Our position so far, then, is that whatever is conscious is (or has) a mind, though it must not be taken to follow that mind may not exist where consciousness is absent. A full understanding of mind would thus require a careful investigation of the nature of consciousness. We should, I think, be safe in stating by way of definition that being conscious is being cognizant of something—without cognition no consciousness—and that, for anything to be cognized, attention must be devoted to it—without attention no cognition. All these conditions are matters of degree but they vary concomitantly.

Next let us consider what is the object of consciousness. Commonly it is held to be the things of the material world, upon which consciousness is taken to play like some sort of light, illuminating the surrounding environment of the conscious organism. This conception I believe to be mistaken, and in adopting it we are misled by metaphors. The immediate objects of consciousness are not material things but feelings. Different philosophers recognize this in different ways, but there is a large measure of agreement between them. Empiricists have maintained that the immediate objects of consciousness are not things but sensa, of one sort or another, and these in the last resort are feelings. Spinoza declared that the object of the human mind was the human body and nothing else[31]—and our awareness of the body comes to us as feeling. Hegel asserts that the primary manifestation of mind is the feeling of bodily changes,[32] and Collingwood maintains that feeling is the proper object of consciousness.[33] These are only outstanding examples and not an exhaustive list of concurrent views. Whether feeling itself is conscious is a difficult question. I have recently maintained[34] that an unconscious sensation is a contradiction in terms, and there may well be a sense of the words in which this is true; but I now think that there must also be some sense in which it is not true, for to be conscious of something we

31. *Ethics* II, prop. XIII.
32. *Encyclopädie*, 403.
33. *New Leviathan*, 4.19.
34. "Some reflections on the nature of consciousness" in *Proceedings of the Twelfth International Congress of Philosophy*.

must cognize it, and to be cognizant of it we must pay some attention to it, but there are feelings to which we do not pay attention and those away from which we transfer our attention in attending to others; and so far as we do not attend to them we are unaware of them, yet they cannot for that reason cease to be feelings and merely spring into being as such when attention is directed upon them. They must exist as feelings before they can be cognized. To this extent the empiricist view is justified that what becomes an object of consciousness must be the same when it is not cognized as when it is. *Qua* feeling it is the same, but *qua* object it is not (as we shall presently explain). This also explains how unconscious processes may still be regarded as mental. They are those mental processes, so far beyond the focus of attention that they are not cognized, but we may now say that their mentality consists in their being felt even though no heed may be paid to them.

It may further prove to be the case (as we have seen reason to believe) that the activity involved in cognition is a sharpened and heightened degree of an isomorphic activity occurring at a lower level which is also involved in feeling. Becoming aware of a feeling may be no more than feeling it more acutely (not necessarily more intensely, but with greater precision and in more significant relation to other experiences).

Feeling, however, is not something which occurs in isolation but is a product of interaction between an organism and its environment. One may say that it is the taking account of its surroundings by an organism. Biologically, feeling as it emerges into consciousness may be seen as the means by which the organism assimilates and gains control over an ever-widening range of environment. The worm can react to and control little more than what comes into immediate contact with its skin. The mole can smell and hear the approaching enemy and flee. The bird sees its prey afar off, hears the crackle of twigs as man approaches, and can react to a far wider expanse of surrounding influences. Man adds to all this the capacity to infer from what is present to what lies beyond his immediate purview, and can besides invent and construct instruments to extend the reach of his senses over the whole surface of the earth and to the distant galaxies of outer space. Consciousness, thus, whatever else we may say of it, is a process of assimilation by the organism of the world in which it lives so that its most distant parts come under its surveillance and, in a significant way, become part of its own being. In other words, consciousness, so viewed, is a process of unification or concentration of a varied and complex universe around a single center.

But, in its primitive form, feeling is a confused manifold which cannot be cognized as such because it has no definition—it is not, as such, a definite object. What transforms this vague feeling into a definite datum for awareness is the reflexive, selective act of attention which distinguishes some element, or quality, from its contrasting background and constitutes it, as a *Gestalt,* an object of consciousness. Less than this is not a possible object. It is generally agreed by psychologists and epistemologists alike that a purely simple and uniform field, without limit or contrast, cannot be cognized. Thus, the act of attention is the activity of distinction and interrelation, of apprehending as a single complex unity an articulated structure of distinguishable (but not necessarily separable) parts. Consciousness is thus an activity of analysis and synthesis in one—a "two-edged discursus"[35]—that activity of judgment for which C. A. Campbell (pp. 376-397 of this volume) contends as the essential condition of cognition. It is not a kind of lambent illumination which reveals ready-made objects to some mysterious passive spectator (called "the mind"), but the activity of selecting, distinguishing, and relating elements within a felt manifold which it transforms by continuous stages of elaboration into a world of related objects. It is a systematic experience developed by the continuous activity of judging in which the present judgment (the focus of present attention) is the point of expansion and growth.

This activity is itself the mind. The unification which the conscious process of judging effects of a multiplicity of felt objects into a single world order is the correlative of the unity of the cognizant subject. Without that, as Kant saw, there could be no synthesizing apprehension of the manifold of feeling. As the object becomes more articulately one, so the awareness of self on the part of the active subject becomes more precise and definite. The process is a single process at once subjective and objective and the awareness of self is no more or less than the awareness of one's own membership, as a person, in an experienced world. Solipsism is nonsense, for without the world cognized as a totality, there is no self, and without the self no intelligible world. Accordingly, consciousness is always at least implicitly self-consciousness, and the communication of our awareness (of our feelings) is always a form of self-expression.

A full description of the self would reveal it as an incredibly complex yet inextricably unified diversity of conscious activity. But there are other wholes, unified on similar principles, which are continuous with it and from which its activity can be seen to emerge. The active assimilation of its world which is characteristic of the living organism is recognizable at different levels. At its simplest it takes the form of nutrition, respiration, and metabolism, by means of which the organism transforms substances in its environment into its own substance and

35. Cf. H. H. Joachim, *Logical Studies* (Oxford, 1948).

sheds its own substance into its surroundings. It constitutes a focus of activity maintaining itself by utilizing the materials of its immediate environment for the purpose of self-maintenance.

In the activity of lowly organisms, it is hardly possible to distinguish between what is more suitably termed physiological activity and what may be called behavior. The absorption and digestion of nutritive material would normally be classed as the first; but should one regard the wafting of cilia in a protozoan like *Stentor*, which brings the food into the creature's grasp, as behavior or as part of the ingestive process? *Stentor* attaches itself to a hard surface by its narrow base and propels the water in which it lives into the orifice of its vase-like body in order to procure its food. The polyp *Obelia*, similarly, is joined at one end to the hollow knob in the stem of living tissue which connects the group of polyps together into one colony, and at the other end has a funnel-shaped mouth fringed with tentacles. These tentacles are dotted with stinging capsules, which shoot out barbed and poisonous filaments when the trigger hairs which activate them brush against the minute creatures which the polyp devours. Once it has been paralyzed by the stings, the prey is grasped by the tentacles and crammed into the waiting mouth. This whole process, an elaboration of the simpler wafting of cilia, is all continuous with that of ingestion, yet is obviously more active and behavior-like.

But *Obelia* also produces a free-swimming medusa, like a miniature jelly-fish with a mouth and tentacles that catch prey like those of the sedentary form, but which is capable of locomotion as well. Here, however, locomotion does not serve as a means of hunting so much as of reproduction and diffusion, for the medusae are sexual forms.

Some types of *Coelentrates*, like sea-dahlias, though sedentary, capture prey by active sucking and grasping movements. Worms, next in the scale, seek food by locomotion, and the myriad species of *Arthropoda* and *Molluscs* hunt it down, like the cuttlefish with its tentacles and suckers, its crafty stalking and flashing attack, a recognizable development of the activity of lowlier life forms.

Here, then, we have a continuous evolution of means and methods of seeking nutriment in which what starts as no more than a physiological process becomes continuously elaborated until it is unmistakably behavioral.

Such practical activity clearly involves sentience; as Aristotle saw, sensitivity and living movement are interdependent. Further, behavior of this sort involves dispositions—tendencies to perform special cycles of activity to accomplish specific purposes. And as these develop and become more complicated, they become less rigid and more widely variable to adapt to changing circumstances, although always so as to remain relevant to the purpose to be served. The more elaborate and delicate such appropriate variation becomes, the more nearly it approaches what we recognize as intelligent action, and the degree of its relevant variation is directly proportional to the degree of consciousness involved. Dispositional behavior and consciousness are therefore directly related.

The sensitive apprehension of its surroundings by the organism, which enables it to absorb and control its environment, is thus at the same time overt movement and behavior; and this active character is reflected in consciousness as the directive and selective operation of attention which is inseparable from the outward activities. Further, as feeling, sensory and affective, is the basis of consciousness, mental activity is always emotive as well as cognitive and conative. These are not three separate or separable species of functioning but three inseparable aspects of a single conscious activity. Psychologists like Wertheimer and Koffka have stressed this threefold wholeness of mental functioning, and more recently two philosophers, John Macmurray and Stewart Hampshire, have drawn attention to it afresh by their insistence on the unity of thought and action.[36]

The hallmark of mind, therefore, is consciousness, involving these three aspects and arising out of sentience, which, in all probability, is itself a development of less highly organized biological processes. Consciousness is an activity of synthesizing and systematizing, operating through judgment at once purposive, interpretative, and evaluative. It unifies the variety of the felt environment into the system of a coherent world. In other words, it is a process of organization. This is how it has been described, of late, by J. O. Wisdom:[37] "The mind," he writes, "should be conceived as processes or as *a functioning* rather than as a state. . . . The form of the functioning . . . is *organization*." This, again, is precisely how Bosanquet conceived the nature of thought. But we are now in a better position to distinguish those processes of organization which are mental from those which are not. They are more or less self-conscious processes, operating upon feeling as their object and purposive or evaluative in character so far as they are directed to the maintenance of a systematic order of life and conduct felt to be satisfactory as a whole.

That such processes occur at different and continuously developing levels within the biological world is undeniable, and the line which separates the conscious from the unconscious, the mental from the nonmental,

---

36. *Vide* Koffka, *Principles of Gestalt Psychology*, Chap. VIII; John Macmurray, *The Self as Agent;* and Stewart Hampshire, *Thought and Action.*
37. "Some main mind-body problems," *Proc. Arist. Soc.*, 1959-1960, LX.

cannot be exactly drawn—certainly not with our present knowledge of these matters and probably not at all. But it should now be clear why the mechanical model fails as a clue to the nature of the mind. In the machine there is nothing which can represent or approximate to sentience and nothing which corresponds to consciousness. Although machines do effect processes of organization, although their activities are systematic and their functioning dependent upon structural interrelation of parts and operations, the medium in which they work is not consciousness, their objects are not feelings, and they have no means of *self*-expression for the communication of emotion or the avowal of *self*-awareness. These are the products of mental activity, and of that alone and where they are not actually or potentially present in some degree there is no mind.

I R V I N G   J O H N   G O O D

The Mind-Body Problem,

or Could an Android Feel Pain?

"Truth is stranger than science fiction."
"When I argue with an atheist, I am a devil's advocate for God."
"The more important a thing, the less you can say about it."

I. Introduction

The mind-body problem is that of the relationship between mind and body, whether they both exist, what they mean, whether they interact, and if so how. A complete solution should tell us what can have minds: is it only humans, as Descartes suggested (presumably he was not a vegetarian); or just some people; or just me; or should we include animals, plants, organic compounds, inanimate matter, homing missiles, robots, and the inhabitants of other worlds? Does a man's mind begin prenatally, does it end posthumously, and is it a matter of degree, reaching a maximum at the age of sixteen? Is there a "ghost in the machine," to use Ryle's derogatory expression, and does it also have a more tenuous ghost inside it, and so ad infinitum?

Many modern philosophers think the ghost has been exorcised, and

---

This article is dedicated to the Ratio Club.

All quotations in this paper, not otherwise ascribed, are due to my friend K. Caj Doog, and are gratefully acknowledged. He claims to make incorrect statements in order to be stimulating.

that the mind-body problem is a pseudo problem. They believe that the only meaningful propositions about mind are expressible in terms of behavior. This belief may seem to leave us with no justification for kindness, even to people, apart from the fear of reprisals and of psychological damage to ourselves. But the exorcising of the ghost encourages an objective approach to psychology, and discourages the reliance on introspection, which has been so often misleading. One writer[1] even goes so far as to say that the problem of consciousness "can have no bearing upon the framing and testing of hypotheses in psychology." Taken literally this would imply that a psychologist will perform experiments without reference to whether they cause pain.

Perhaps the current attitude of most psychologists may be summarized by saying that they do not deny the existence of other peoples' subjective experiences, and regarded them as relevant to what experiments are ethical, but irrelevant to scientific explanation. I shall describe this attitude as "scientific methodism." As Hebb says,[2] "A philosophical parallelism or idealism . . . is quite consistent with the scientific method, but interactionism seems not to be." It certainly seems that Descarte's two-way interactionism is sterile in the present state of explanatory psychology. But one-way interactionism, in the direction body-to-mind, seems to be required for the justification of ethics.

The last section of Wittgenstein's beautiful but obscure *Tractatus*[3] consists of a single sentence, "Whereof one cannot speak, thereof one must be silent." Likewise, Ryle, in his brilliant and lucid treatise,[4] says, "Overt intelligent performances are not clues to the workings of minds; they are those workings." Both these statements are in the spirit of scientific methodism, but the latter ignores the past and future findings of neurophysiology, and is therefore incorrect.

I am left with an uneasy feeling. Subjective experiences in other people are permitted to influence our experiments, via our ethics, but not to influence our explanations. For reasons known to God and Freud we must be kind to animals as well as to people. But why stop at animals; should there be a Society for the Prevention of Cruelty to Androids? If science can give us no help with this question we must turn to metaphysics for the answer. Thus the mind-body problem is still with us: it is only a so-called pseudo problem, it is a quasi-pseudo problem.

Part of overt behavior is the use of language. The complete scientific methodist must explain not merely what physiological events correspond to pain, but why I should say, "I have an incommunicable subjective experience of pain." The explanation must be in terms of physiology, chemistry, physics, and probability. If he tries to explain his own behavior he may need to bring in utility or purpose in order to avoid some sort of Godel paradox. If he questions each of his questions, he would be reduced to inactivity.

II. Metaphysicality

"The metaphysics and science fiction of to-day may be the science of tomorrow."*

To discuss metaphysics is for me so presumptuous that I may as well be hanged for a goat, and introduce a personal note.

In a philosophical symposium held in Oxford in 1954 I mentioned from the floor a notion, based on some science fiction, namely, that the universe may be continually branching out into myriads of universes, and that this could be the origin of the probabilities that occur in quantum mechanics. A well-known logical positivist who was present asserted his pecking rights and dismissed my remarks as nonsense. The idea has since been used in a serious scientific paper.[5] This bears out the above quotation. Atomic energy and space travel were discussed by H. G. Wells long before the highest authorities thought it worthwhile to describe them as impracticable. In my opinion, in which I am not alone, science fiction can be stimulating for speculative philosophy or metaphysics, and both scientific and speculative philosophy can be stimulating for science. They can encourage open-mindedness. Speculative philosophy can also have the opposite effect, and most science fiction is trash, like most other fiction. But if you keep your feet on the ground most of the time it makes a change to have your head in the clouds occasionally.

By a metaphysical hypothesis I mean, to put it roughly, one whose log-odds cannot be changed much by any conceivable argument, experiment, or observation.[6] Odds means $p/(1-p)$, where p is here a subjective or logical probability, and log-odds can take any value between minus and plus infinity. In particular, a refutable hypothesis is never metaphysical, so that this definition includes Popper's rule of demarcation between metaphysics and science.[7] What I wish to emphasize is that there is a continuous gradation between very scientific and very metaphysical statements, and no precise *line* of demarcation.

The change in the log-odds is sometimes called the "weight of evidence,"[8] and seems a more appropriate measure than the change in the probability itself. (Consider, for example, a change in the probability from 0.000001 to 0.001 and from 0.500001 to 0.501. In fact, the weight of evidence for a hypothesis H, provided by an event E, is equal to the logarithm of the likelihood ratio corresponding to H and its negation,

---

* Doog attributes this remark to his friend Frankenstein.

so that it is mathematically independent of the initial probability of H.) The reciprocal of the maximum possible change of the log-odds would be a possible measure of the "metaphysicality" of the hypothesis, to coin a natural but ugly term. A more refined measure would be the mathematical expectation of this crude measure, that is, the weighted average with weights equal to the intuitive probabilities that various experiments or observations are conceivable.

The metaphysicality of a hypothesis may well depend on whether it is true. For example, the hypothesis that people maintain awareness after death is not metaphysical if true, but is metaphysical if false. Perhaps another mathematical expectation should be taken, according to the estimated probability of the truth of the hypothesis. According to this definition there is plenty of room for differences of opinion concerning the magnitude of a metaphysicality.

The estimated metaphysicality of a hypothesis can change with changes in technology. Until recently it might have been regarded as metaphysical to conjecture that the other side of the moon is populated by animals hundreds of miles high that occasionally sling a surreptitious flying saucer at the earth. This hypothesis has now been refuted and was therefore not metaphysical. It used to be safe to maintain the even more farfetched theory that the earth rested on an elephant standing on a tortoise: it cost nothing to accept it when it was unverifiable, and it comforted people who suffered from a fear of falling.

If telepathy could be greatly improved by the aid of drugs we may be able to get evidence about the rate of decay of disembodied minds, if they do decay. It is clear that applied metaphysics would involve psychical research. All decisive results may be transferred to the science faculty. Hypnotism is a classical example.

If a billion dollars are spent on research, I do not know how much should be allotted to pure and applied metaphysics. But I should like to mention that in the choice of problems for research, the utility of a solution is important, not just the probability of reaching a solution. We call research presumptuous if it deals with problems whose solutions would have high utility, and if at the same time we think the research man is overestimating the probabilities of success. But we may underestimate the probabilities because success would be revolutionary, and because the research man is junior to us.

One feature of a metaphysical system is that it may cease to be metaphysical when suitably enlarged. As an example, consider any purely axiomatic mathematical structure that gives relationships between undefined terms. Such a structure is absolutely metaphysical, according to the above definition, since, by design, no physical observation could be relevant to its truth. Non-Euclidean geometry, developed axiomatically, is an example. But add a few rules of application, and the picture can be entirely changed. Other examples can be so readily culled from theology that I shall not cull them. A third example is Freudian psychology. Popper maintains,[9] rightly I think, that any imaginable behavior could be explained along Freudian lines, so that the theory is irrefutable. In order that the theory should merit the appellation "scientific," it would be necessary to convert it into a statistical theory. If this program could be carried through it would be a great advance in psychology. Until that is done the theory should be classified as important metaphysics (or metapsychology).

Even the propositions of the scientific methodist are to some extent metaphysical, some more than others. There are hypotheses that explain many phenomena, and others that at best explain them away. The conjecture that man had evolved from more primitive forms of life (which the scientific methodist should always have regarded as obvious) was perhaps in the explaining-away category before the time of Darwin and Wallace.

The scientific methodist is more ready to believe in the possibility of androids than most of his opponents. But some cyberneticians are religious and are not involved in any inconsistency on that account.

Most of us are unsympathetic to other people's metaphysics. Perhaps some readers will say, "Why bother to consider whether an android could feel pain? First build one, then I'll be interested." My answer is twofold: First, I think androids will be built sooner or later, and, second, I think that attempts to answer the question may help us to clarify the meaning of mind and consciousness, even if my own attempts fail to do so.

I once asked Turing whether he thought a machine could be conscious. He replied that he would say so if he would otherwise be punished. This was good scientific methodism; the implication was that the question was not answerable on its own terms. And the question may even seem to be unimportant, until we remember that pain and pleasure are aspects of consciousness. If it is not important to reduce pain and increase pleasure, then nothing is.

III. Thought, Mentality, and Consciousness

"I suffer, therefore I am."*
"I think I think, therefore I think."

When a scientific methodist produces a nonmetaphysical definition or theory of consciousness, he may be whistling in the dark in order to blow away his suspicion that the ghost is there after all. *Thinking*

---

* This remark was anticipated, for example, in *Nightmares*, by Bertrand Russell. Therefore, Doog suffers.

seems more appropriately defined in operational terms, and it may be possible also to give an adequate operational definition of mind.

I cannot define the word "consciousness" standing alone, but if I say I have consciousness I mean that I have conscious experiences, which I cannot describe properly. I can give you instructions for having experiences that you would report in similar words to those I would use, but I do not know how similar your subjective experiences are to mine, nor even how to say what I mean by this comparison. And yet this comparison is the essence of the matter. The comparison may not be completely metaphysical since it is conceivable that a telepathy-inducing drug, or artificial neuronic connections, could make our joint minds operate in a fully integrated manner. The joint mind may then judge that its sensation of whiteness is indistinguishable from the sensations that you and I had previously had. The experiment could not possibly be decisive, but it may appreciably add to the estimated log-odds.

Another experiment, easier to carry out, but giving less evidence, is to ask people with split personalities whether each of their personalities has the same sensation of whiteness. I do not know whether they would ever be able to remember each of their personalities simultaneously with adequate clarity.

If this comparison of sensations of whiteness seems unimportant, what about pain? Why should I avoid giving pain to you, if I do not believe that your feelings of pain resemble my own? The scientific methodist might answer that what is responsible is my upbringing, habit, fear of reprisals; and so far there is no scientific evidence to prove him wrong. Meanwhile I believe you can have subjective feelings of pain, and you know I am right.

It would wrong you to give you pain not because it would make you yell, and retaliate, and not merely because I should have feelings of remorse, but because it would give you a subjective painful experience.

Some Speculations Concerning Consciousness

Since we are apparently material systems it is puzzling to know where consciousness comes from. Is it a thin substance that gets inside certain types of communication system, or is it simply a property of all matter? At school I once suggested that even the smallest particle of inorganic matter has a microscopic measure of consciousness, say 10^{-100} doogs, which is greatly amplified in organized systems. My schoolmates regarded this suggestion as highly risible, stupid, unbalanced, and contemptible. A similar fate befell Spinoza for similar remarks.

Much later I suggested to Turing that information-handling machines made of small components, preferably of high chemical complexity, would be more likely to be conscious than those made of large components, especially cogwheels. He did not think much of this idea. Here I was largely anticipated by Lotka,[10] who, however, did not mention the information-handling aspect. He proposed that matter, in the transition from one chemical form to another, has consciousness.

L. S. Penrose (private communication) suggested that perhaps the the passage of eons of time might be conducive to the presence of consciousness. On this theory, an exact copy of a man would at best be a zombie, because it would have no ancestry.

Soon after the war, I suggested to L. Rosenfeld (and I expect many others have suggested it) that the wave function of quantum mechanics was so mysterious that one might as well attribute consciousness to it and perhaps try to use it to explain telepathy (if telepathy is possible). Where better to find "neutral stuff"? He pointed out that if this were so it would not be the first time that a scientific formalism invented for one application had been found to have others. I am told that A. N. Whitehead identified mind with electromagnetic radiation, but I am sure this is a grossly misleading oversimplification of his views. These theories of neutral monism are closer to Spinoza's views than the theory that consciousness is a property of particulate matter. Spinoza is also attributed with the notion of psychophysical parallelism.[11]

In another conversation Turing made the following conjecture. Let us suppose (he said) that a man is gradually dismembered, with the "boundary conditions" somehow being maintained. For example, at one stage we might have just a brain with its input artificially stimulated so that the mind is unaware that the body has been removed. Imagine that this process is continued even beyond the surface of the brain. Then (he felt) there would be a minimum size, of the order of a cubic inch, of original brain tissue, beyond which there would be no consciousness. Turing described this conjecture as a "matter of faith," having no connection with science.

But it seems possible, in this imaginary experiment, that the consciousness would gradually transfer itself to the apparatus; more exactly that the total amount of consciousness would remain constant, and would in the end be associated with the machinery. This conjecture is not intended to imply that consciousness has spatial position, rather that it may be a feature of very complicated information-handling systems.

The identification of consciousness with the operation of certain types of communication system has various consequences. We seem obliged to attribute more consciousness to two communication systems than to either separately, in fact it is natural to assume additivity. If the two systems, apart from their own operation, are in communication, then this will perhaps increase the amount of consciousness still further. The extra consciousness may reasonably be identified with the rate of transmission of information from one system to the other. This seems to be equatable to a rate of flow of negative entropy,[12] but it is not clear how to produce a rigorous definition of the entropy. In particular it is not clear whether the interneural entropy is more important than the intraneural; and, within the neuron, whether the intermolecular entropy is more important than the intramolecular; and so on, down to elementary particles or beyond. (There may be a different kind of consciousness at each level, each metaphysical to the others.) Without stopping to clear up these important questions, let us proceed with the discussion in an intuitive and possibly self-contradictory manner. If one system gives misleading information to another one, then it is conveying negative information (lies), and the total amount of consciousness is perhaps decreased. If two systems are in very close communication, such as two people having perfect telepathy, we might be tempted to regard them as a single system. We should then perhaps have a single consciousness greater than the sum of the two taken separately. It seems better to talk about amounts of consciousness than to try to count them. For example, the amount of consciousness associated with a man may be, say twenty times that of a chimpanzee.

In an ordinary society of men the total consciousness may not have position in space, but it does have a sort of combinatorial topology, like a set of spheres with interconnecting tubes, where each sphere represents the consciousness of one man. These tubes can appear and disappear according as communication is taking place at any given moment Thus, consciousness is a varying pattern of communication of great complexity. Each sphere has its own fine structure, and more communication goes on within them than between them. In order to decrease the complexity of the description of a communication network we may sum the flow of information over each given channel for a certain period of time. This comes to much the same thing as working with expected values, but not precisely the same since few systems are "ergodic." We must, however, distinguish between unconscious and conscious flow of information. Conscious flow might be identified with information flow having some sort of novelty.

The above view on consciousness is hardly consistent with the idea that we each have a separate spirit that exists after the body is destroyed. But it is consistent with a different religious idea: that we are all sense organs of a universal consciousness. As the Buddhists say, "Separateness is an illusion."

Also consistent with this point of view is the conjecture by J. McArthy (presumably a scientific methodist) that ". . . the division in man between conscious and unconscious thought occurs at the boundary between stimulus-response heuristics which do not have to be reasoned about, but only obeyed, and the others which have to serve as premises in deductions."[13] (The word "heuristics" here may I think be replaced by "neural impulses.") I have myself made a similar distinction, "Logic is a conscious process, whereas immediate recognition is performed without any conscious reasoning. You can recognize a man's face without being able to draw it. The main difficulty in acquiring a new skill seems to be the transfer of conscious understanding partially to the unconscious. On the other hand, the difficulty of designing automata is in expressing in conscious terms what is unconscious."[14]

Hebb[15] says, " 'Consciousness' is equivalent to 'complex thought processes', and hence is not present in animals whose behavior is at a reflexive, sense-dominated level (on the other hand, verbal behavior is not a necessary requirement)." "Normally one feature of consciousness is . . . memory for the immediate past." (This would imply that mathematical activity requires plenty of consciousness.) "Conscious processes are primarily neural activity."

There is certainly nothing in these quotations that would exclude consciousness as a property of some machines, especially some future ones.

Let us briefly consider some scientific methodist definitions of mind.

"The ability to learn, that is, to respond differently to a situation because of past response to the situation, is what distinguishes those living creatures which common sense endows with minds. This is the practical descriptive use of the term 'mind.' "[16]

"*Mind* and *mental* refer to the processes inside the head that determine the higher levels of organization in behavior."[17] (Note that the word "organization" could do with further clarification here, possibly in terms of entropy or of potential flow of information, or of novelty.)

The quotation from Ryle's book, given in Part I above, is also relevant.

Once again there is nothing here that would prevent an android from having a mind.

Thought, too, can very well be ascribed to future machines. This is obvious if thought is defined merely as a mediating process between overt stimulus and overt response, but again it is a question of degree. The interesting question is whether the mediating processes of a machine could be in all respects as efficacious as those of a human being. In a well-known article,[18] Turing pointed out that many definitions of thinking could be proposed, and that in order to discuss whether a machine could think a fairly precise definition should be selected. He chose to say that a machine could think if it could successfully pretend to be a human being in the answering of questions put to it on an electromatic typewriter in another room. He felt that anyone who would not accept this definition must have decided tautologically that a machine cannot think. He considered a general-purpose computer with 1,000,000,000 binary digits of storage, and working at a speed of 500 elementary instructions per second, and guestimated that it could be programed to think (in the above sense) by means of an expenditure of about 3,000 man-years of programing. He also speculated on methods of decreasing the programing effort. He was mainly concerned with the disposal of counterarguments, and in this I think he was successful. He was explaining away rather than explaining how the program could be organized. As H. L. Gelernter said (private communication), he eliminated the negative but did not accentuate the positive.

Thought and mind then could readily be ascribed to an android, and consciousness too if this is defined in a restricted manner. Some questions that remain, in order to resolve the mind-body problem for androids are:

1. What is an android?
2. Could an android be constructed?
3. Could an android feel pleasure or pain?
4. Would it be wrong to inflict pain on an android, or to transfer its communication system to another android?

IV. The Structure of an Android

"Everything is complicated, even mathematics."

"Instinct and suggestion are the parents of the imagination, and the grandparents of the deed."

An android is an automaton that looks and behaves like a human being and is not constructed by the normal processes of procreation, even allowing for incubation. This definition does not specify how great the resemblance must be and what methods of observation are permitted. It will not cry "Oil, oil! I am dying of thirst." In one science-fiction story the only difference between an android and a person was in ancestry and in the fact that androids were stamped round the navel "Made in Birmingham" or "Fabriquée en Paris."

From a philosophical angle a robot would serve our purposes equally well, but in practice it may be better to build androids in order that neo-Luddites should not be encouraged to maltreat them with a clear conscience. The construction of physical apparatus as sensitive as an eye or ear, and of the same size, would be exceedingly difficult, but this anthology is more concerned with mind than with senses. Therefore, it is hardly incumbent on me to say anything more about the external appearance, sense organs, motor and speech organs, sex life, exhalations, and excretions of an android. Let us just imagine that all these problems have either been solved or shelved as barely relevant. I do this in order that the reader should regard the android as a friend and not as something the Martians had just brought in. We are really concerned much more with the android's internal communication system. But let us begin with a human.

Figure 1 is supposed to represent the communication system of a human being. The connecting links mean "has an effect on." This diagram assumes some animism, and the question will arise whether it could be removed by a scientific methodist. If so, then the construction of an android would be possible in principle if not in practice.

Annotation of the Block Diagram

1. The dotted line encloses the internal functions of the mind.
2. Some of the effects may be inhibitory as well as facilitatory.
3. The senses include, for example, sight, hearing, smelling, taste, touch, sense of temperature, and peripheral pain centers.
4. Amplification centers are omitted.
5. There may be overlapping of blocks, or even inclusion. For example, it is possible that the glands should be included in the emotion block. (Incidentally at least some of the glands evolved from neurons.)
6. The diagram probably contains glaring errors and omissions, but the omission of "volition" is deliberate, since I believe that activity is controlled by glands and imagination. Compare the Coué-Badouin remark,

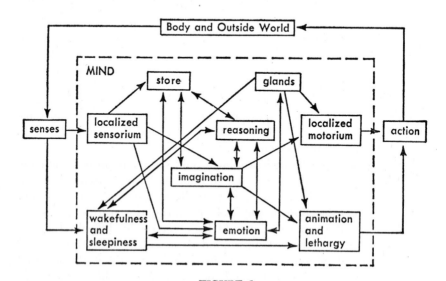

FIGURE 1

Block diagram of a man's communication system.

"When the Will and the Imagination come into conflict the Imagination always wins."[19]

7. The store includes learning, retention, recall, and built-in propensities. Another name for it would be memory, but this would be ambiguous.

8. Other blocks could be placed inside the one illustrated, and new connections made; for example, learning → retention → recall could be placed in store. The "learning" sub-block would be connected both ways to imagination, reasoning, emotion, and glands.

9. Wakefulness and sleepiness should perhaps be represented by two separate blocks, mutually inhibiting. Animation is distinct from wakefulness, witness somnambulism.

10. Reasoning includes logic, mathematics, and probability judgments when these are explicit. Implicit (unconscious) probability judgments should perhaps be classified as part of the store. Intuition involves memory, probability judgment, and imagination, and is often colored by emotion.

11. Some additional sub-blocks would belong to more than one of the main blocks. For example, love, hate, hope, fear, and awe, would all come both in imagination and emotion. Determination involves imagination, emotion, and wakefulness. Attention, interest, and curiosity, involve wakefulness, imagination, emotion, and reasoning.

12. The effect of imagination is to change the propensities (physical probabilities) in the blocks to which it is connected.

13. Wakefulness increases the activities of reasoning, animation, and emotion, but does not increase the activity of all parts of the imagination. In sleep, some parts of the imagination may have free rein, especially those parts that rationalize sensory input.

14. Pain and pleasure are classified primarily under emotion. Therefore, at least a part of consciousness comes in this block. The effect of learning on imagination is exemplified by Hebb's suggestion that pain is to a large extent an acquired motivation.[20]

15. Unconscious activities may occur in all blocks shown, but presumably emerge from the store. Conscious processes take place in reasoning, imagination, and emotion.

16. Autosuggestion and decisions come mainly under imagination, but can be largely formulated (not directly exercised) by reasoning and emotion. For example, your emotions may be divided about getting out of bed on a cold morning. Your reasoning says it is better to get up, and you imagine yourself doing so. This gives you a post-hypnotic suggestion, and a little later you find yourself obeying it.

17. The effect of the localized sensorium on emotion is primarily to the pain and pleasure sub-blocks.

18. There are many other familiar attributes of the mind to which I have made no reference.

19. The block diagram would probably be highly misleading if it were thought that all the blocks correspond to distinct neurophysiological groupings. The store, reasoning, imagination, and emotion may correspond to neurons all over the cortex and elsewhere.

20. Drugs can affect the same boxes as glands. But ingestion, digestion, and injection are omitted from the diagram.

When a machine is being designed one often starts with a block diagram, then breaks up the blocks into sub-blocks, and so on, until parts are reached that can be represented by existing pieces of equipment (Analogous procedure is useful in any organizing job.) To do this with our block diagram would be exceedingly difficult to say the least. One of the difficulties is one of definition, to say what is meant by emotion in mechanistic terms. But for most of the blocks the difficulty would be one of sheer complexity. Let us then start off on another tack.

For the internal workings of an android we might use either a general-purpose computer built of sub-miniature components or a device containing partially random (or partially random-looking) networks, mimicking the structure of the nervous system to some extent. One advantage of the second scheme is that it permits a great deal of parallel working, and so may be much more efficient, although future general-purpose computers may also involve a lot of parallel working. My own guess is that a synthesis of these two schemes will ultimately form the most intelligent machines.[21] [The measurement of the general intelligence of a machine should be expressed by at least two parameters, speed and depth. The same is true of humans: Poincaré (the great man, not the statesman) and Turing apparently did not have high I.Q.'s; the I.Q. depends on speed, but depth beyond a certain level may be opposed to speed in the human.]

An advantage of general-purpose computers is that they already exist, but at present they would be too large to incorporate in an android other than a giant. They can in any event be used for preliminary experiments, even for testing out models containing partially random networks.[22] Programs that can be very easily changed ("heuristic" programs[23]) will be essential in future experiments, although, as far as I know, heuristic programing has not yet been married to the random-network approach. I believe this will be one of the next important developments in the construction of learning programs.

General-purpose computers are especially useful for formalized processes. So far they have not been very useful for spotting analogies and for the recognition of complicated patterns, although they have been used fairly effectively for checkers, chess, and logic, and work is proceeding on geometry.[24]

Several writers have emphasized the random-network approach, among whom Rosenblatt has perhaps recently done the most work.[25] This work is largely inspired by a theory of physiological psychology, known as the cell-assembly theory, which was apparently inaugurated by Lashley and Hebb, and modified by Milner.[26] I shall summarize enough of this theory to give some impression of it, with some modification and oversimplification. (I have introduced the modifications in order to avoid a mere paraphrase of existing literature.) The intention is to make some sort of case that androids should depend on partially random networks. I begin with a brief description of neural activity.

The number of neurons in the brain exceeds the human population of the earth. The estimate of about $\frac{1}{2} \times 10^{10}$ for the cerebral cortex[27] has not been greatly changed since 1899. We could imagine the neurons of the cortex identified by binary numbers of about thirty-two digits each, according to their ancestry. (This notation[14a] extends naturally to the prenatal development; thus, 0. could represent a cell from which most of the brain or most of the cortex developed; 0.0 and 0.1 the cells parental to the left and right hemispheres, and so on.) Each neuron is capable of "firing" in an all-or-none manner, the effect being to transmit electrochemical impulses to several other neurons. A neuron has a restricted vocabulary: all it can say is "hi," and this signal can be interpreted as a weak or strong yea or nay according to the nature and strength of the synaptic junction at each of the receiving neurons. Some theories concerning the combinatorial and probabilistic nature of the connections can be conveniently expressed in terms of the binary notation just mentioned, and so could be simulated by means of a computer program. For example, the activity of a neuron may tend to inhibit those neurons whose binary symbols disagree only in the last three digits, i.e., the "sibling," "cousin," and cousin's cousins. The notation may also be convenient for formulating theories of prenatal growth of the cortex. A neuron will fire if it has recently received enough yeas and not too many nays (facilitatory and inhibitory impulses), and also if it has not been spoken to for some time. After firing, a neuron is "exhausted" (the refractory period) and then gradually recovers its propensity to fire; i.e., its threshold or limen for firing goes up to infinity and then decreases to an asymptotic value. The threshold remains at infinity for the order of a millisecond (the absolute refractory period). The form of the recovery curve, together with the combinatorial nature of the connections, and the strengths and "signs" of the synaptic junctions will determine what kinds of circuits could reverberate. Knowledge on these matters is far from complete. Learning processes presumably involve long-term temporal variations of the strengths of the synaptic junctions. Short-term memory, of the order of seconds, is thought to involve short-term reverberations, which are possible owing to closed loops of connections.

The number of synapses is far greater even than the number of neurons, so that the number of potential circuits must exceed Eddington's number for the number of particles in the universe; an analogy is the number of pieces of sculpture latent in a block of stone.[28] The "sculpturing" may be achieved by the strengthening or weakening of the synaptic junctions. Physiological psychologists try to explain behavior in terms of such processes or similar ones. The size of circuit relevant to any act of behavior or perception might be small or large.[29] Emphasis on very large circuits has been, for example, made by Lashley[30] and Hebb, and I adopt this emphasis. Ashby[31] has conjectured further that the precise nature of a neuron may be irrelevant to psychology, and that what needs study is very large communication systems in the abstract. Bertalanffy has made a similar conjecture.[32] It should be remembered, however, as a corrective that a small brain tumor can have a large effect on behavior. But it is definitely wrong to assume a one-one correspondence between ideas and neurons.

A cell assembly is by definition a group of neurons, mainly in the cortex, and I suppose mainly in the association cortex (which seems to consist largely of random connections), having many closed circuits containing synaptic connections. An assembly becomes activated if an adequate proportion of its neurons fire, and once activated it tends to remain so for the order of half a second. The probability of becoming active is determined by the connections between the neurons, the strengths of these connections, the current activity of the whole nervous system, and the sensory input. A single neuron can be a component of many distinct assemblies not all usually active simultaneously. (Compare superimposed coding or "Zatocoding" in information retrieval.) An assembly is assumed to have some connection from a simple sensory input such as a patch of color, so that the perception of an object must correspond to the simultaneous activity of several assemblies. The outputs of the assemblies active at one moment may facilitate other assemblies as well as parts of the motorium. More precisely an assembly fractionates and also recruits neurons, and so changes (in, say, half a second) into parts of other assemblies. A not very good analogy may be drawn with the changing shape of clouds.

Let us consider how sequences of assemblies may proceed after a concept has been learned. If a sufficient number of assemblies corresponding to properties of, say, a cow are active, then they will activate an assembly that represents a cow, and this will increase the propensity for the word "cow" to be uttered. This process may be compared with John Wisdom's well-known analysis of the meaning of the word "cow."[33]

I shall next describe a probabilistic version of Wisdom's cow,[34] since it seems likely to correspond more closely to what happens, and also suggests a physical embodiment of implicit psychological probabilities.

It is not part of the Hebb-Milner theory to assume that an assembly can have a variable rate of firing. They assume that it is either active or inactive, or primed for activity. But, in the sensorium, the frequency of firing of neurons is known to be correlated with intensity of sensation. It is, therefore, plausible to conjecture that frequency of firing, summed over all neurons within an assembly, corresponds to an implicit psychological probability estimate. Likewise the clarity of perception of a cow would depend on the frequency, F, of firings within the "cow assembly." F, will be some function, $F(f_1, f_2, \ldots)$, of the frequencies $f_1, f_2, \ldots$ of other assemblies; mostly "lower-level" ones (i.e., more closely connected to the sensorium), especially in early life. This discussion could be extended to more abstract matters, such as the probability that it will rain tomorrow. We have machinery for estimating probabilities, even though each experience in life may be unique.[35] At a much higher level of sophistication, there are, for some of us, explicit subjective probabilities and utilities, verbally estimated, and subjected to tests of consistency by means of theories of subjective probability and of rational behavior.[36]

It may similarly be conjectured that we have neural representations of all our concepts, however vague and difficult to express in words. The problems of philosophical linguistic analysis might be greatly advanced if brains could be observed in detailed operation! A new discipline called "physiological philosophy" could be imagined.

In order to explain why activity does not spread out and activate nearly all neurons at the same time, it was conjectured by Milner[37] (with some support from earlier physiological observations by Lorente de Nó) that most neurons tend to inhibit others near them (analogous to rivalry in social affairs). He explains, however, how pairs of assemblies might become associated and even merge into a single assembly (associative learning).

Most, but not all, assemblies must be formed postnatally. The newborn baby's brain is almost a blank sheet. The early bold strokes drawn on it are liable to have a lasting influence on the picture that develops later, especially if they conflict with the prenatal patterns. Early assemblies are the basis for later ones, and for high-order abstractions. Habits are organized assemblies, not easy to change until perhaps senile decay sets in.

If an assembly, A, helps to activate another one, B, then the neurons in B will at first be "fresher" (have lower thresholds for firing) than those in A. Therefore, A is likely to break up before B does, and this will tend to enable "mediating activity" (thought, etc.) to proceed in an orderly manner, in the absence of appreciable sensory input. (But sensory input is usually an important part of the whole process.) After an assembly has just been extinguished, many of its neurons will have received subthreshold activation without having fired. Milner calls them "primed" neurons, and I have already referred to them. A primed neuron may be regarded as the opposite of a refractory one. Therefore, in virtue of "temporal summation" for neurons, parts of a recently extinguished assembly will be primed, so that it will be easily reactivated within the next few seconds. This is an explanation of short-term memory, different from that of reverberatory circuits; but an activated assembly itself must reverberate. Milner assumes that the effect of priming dies away after a few seconds. But I think it would be useful to assume that the time constant can vary greatly from neuron to neuron since this may help to explain our sense of duration, and also medium-term memory. Here, as elsewhere, other explanations are possible, such as the gradual extinction of small reverberating circuits within assemblies.

The problem of explaining motivation in scientific terms, or even of explaining it away, does not appear to have been satisfactorily solved. One may conjecture that motivation depends in the long term on the existence of potentially active assemblies, and in the short term on the propensity of primed neurons to fire (pleasure-seeking), but more details are needed. Certainly motivation is not a human prerogative: chimpanzees have been trained to hoard poker chips that could be exchanged for food in a vending machine.[38] (It would be interesting to train them to gamble!) So Descartes would have been forced to concede that a machine can be motivated, since he regarded a chimpanzee as a machine.

In a primitive sense a homing missile is motivated. (That old bore Doog asks whether it feels pleasure when it hits the target and explodes.) Here the motivation is built in. But motivations can also be acquired by a machine. For example, a computer could be programmed to have various probabilities of choosing between various subroutines, the probabilities being selected in terms of past successes in achieving a built-in goal, G. The goal G (such as winning a simple game) can be regarded as a primary motivation, and the probabilities of the subroutines as learned. There would be no difficulty in principle in making G itself a learned motivation, so that the machine could acquire second-order, third-order, . . . motivations. What is not clear is how the problem of motivation is answered by the theory of cell assemblies. Milner discusses the problem, but he does not claim much.

If a man behaves as if he had a certain goal, then we say he has the goal, although he may vehemently deny it. The scientific methodist must believe that the existence of the goal involves some characteristics of the assemblies; the question is to find out what those characteristics are. This part of the theory is like the theory of evolution, before the time of Darwin. It is a program for research rather than an explanation.

Motivations can be antagonistic, as when a man tries to solve a puzzle, and continually mutters that it is a waste of time. The man is in a state of inner conflict. Hebb[39] speculates that at least some pleasure consists in the resolution of conflicts, and some pain with their presence. We may perhaps express the notion of conflict in terms of primed neurons. While the conflict lasts there will be many primed neurons waiting for release, belonging to assemblies, that do not, as a set, tend to produce integrated behavior. They may lead to contradictory muscular activity, such as a nervous tic. But when the puzzle is resolved, both motivations will be satisfied, and the nervous tic will tend to disappear. (Apparently we attack puzzles because of the anticipated pleasure of solving them or for masochistic reasons.) This speculation is consistent with the theory that consciousness is a feature of some complicated communication systems, and does not seem at first sight to necessitate an intraneural or chemical theory.

Hebb speculates[40] that pain may correspond to disorganized activity in the cortex, and suggests mechanisms by which the peripheral pain fibers may produce this disorganization. Such a theory can explain away the fact that pain is often associated with jerky overt behavior, but it remains a mystery why a gain of entropy should be subjectively painful.

Another way of saying that the activity is disorganized is that it forms an ugly pattern. But we shall still need an observing ghost in the machine, or else a universal consciousness, in order that this ugliness should be appreciated. We might suppose that the neurons are in telepathic communication, and that the total telepathic field can appreciate beauty and ugliness. One retort to such conjectures is that if conduction by fibers is inadequate to explain subjective pain, why should a field theory serve any better? Why multiply hypotheses to so little purpose?

There is another approach to the problem of defining organization in the cortex, apart from negentropy. Most neurons belong to several different well-established assemblies, though normally not more than one of these assemblies (containing a particular neuron) will be active at any given moment. Therefore, most neurons will at most times be receiving no instructions or else *strong* instructions to fire or not to fire, for this is what is meant by a well-established assembly. But during disorganized activity of the cortex there will be an unusually large number of neurons receiving contradictory or overintense instructions. (This could perhaps be taken as the definition of disorganized activity.) We may conjecture that this causes intraneural pain, and that this pain summates over all the neurons that are suffering. This theory forces the problem down into the neurons, and does not explain why pain should summate. We might conjecture that the neurons do not themselves suffer, but instead produce chemicals that somehow cause suffering, either in themselves or by action on the glands. But somewhere the jump to the metaphysical must be made.

Another speculation, consistent with the above, is that the firing of a primed neuron gives a little pleasure, and of a lot a lot. From the total pleasure one might subtract the total pain, though a simple one-dimensional measure seems inappropriate. These speculations, suitably elaborated, may be capable of explaining the pleasure and pain that we can derive from good and bad poetry and music. I hardly need say that the elaboration would have to be extensive.

In order to explain why pleasure and pain should summate, we seem to be driven to a field theory, telepathic or otherwise, though I have never heard an allegation of one man's receiving another's pain telepathically. The only alternative theories seem to imply that a clockwork machine could feel real metaphysical pain, or else that the Young Man of Deal was right. I think a field theory is almost forced upon us, involving at least one-way interactionism.

Somewhat related to these speculations is Hebb's comment that there appears to be an optimal level of arousal for the cortex as a whole, so that we tend to avoid monotony as well as pain.[41] He also mentions the difficulty of reconciling this fact with the pleasure of falling asleep. Perhaps I may be permitted some more speculations on this question.

There must be some mechanism that prevents too many neurons being active at the same time. A part of such a mechanism may be the inhibition by one cell assembly of most of those around it. This is the main point of Milner's modification of the cell-assembly theory. Important though this idea is I shall not try here to summarize Milner's arguments. I think an extra confirmation of it is that an itch can often be removed by scratching *round* the center of irritation. (I presume that an itch corresponds to a cell assembly or, more likely, to a *cycle* of assemblies.)

Milner draws an analogy with an atomic reactor. (Turing also drew this analogy but for a different reason.[18a]) The activation of the neurons may be regarded as a pseudorandom branching process, in which the expected number of neurons next activated is obtained from the current number by means of a "multiplication factor." If this were less than one, the brain would be of subcritical size, and would be a bad thinking machine. The multiplication factor is too unlikely to be exactly equal to one. It therefore exceeds one, and so the process is in danger of blowing up. A negative feedback device is required to prevent this explosion. Milner's suggestion seems to achieve this.

Another form of negative feedback may be conjectured. Suppose that a certain proportion of neurons are connected to, and a certain proportion connected from, the general wakefulness (arousal) center. This would provide a positive feedback loop and would help to explain why once awake there is a tendency to remain awake. There is also thought to be a sleep center, and suppressor areas. These, when aroused, will have a similar tendency to inhibit the cortex. The thresholds of the neurons in these centers will presumably vary from one to another. When an unusually large amount of the cortex becomes active it will tend to be damped down via the stimulation of these inhibitory centers. A wide range of parameters would be possible in order that this negative feedback device should be stable. If the parameters were disturbed, there would be a tendency to fall asleep too often or too seldom. The frequency of the feedback would be large when the subject was thinking vigorously. (Strictly, the suppressor areas are thought to operate by really being facilitatory centers that can switch themselves off,[42] but in the present context this is a technical detail.)

This is one of several hypotheses that would explain some of the rhythms of the electroencephalogram.[43] It amounts to saying that some of the EEG is caused by the "uranium rods being pushed in and out." The frequencies that should occur would depend on the localities of the sleep and suppressor areas.

A mechanism of this type may be necessary in order to synchronize the transition from simultaneous set of assemblies to the next set. Without this mechanism our visual perception and our thinking might be dreamlike, and our speech tumble over itself. Perhaps stammering is associated with special EEG characteristics, but the theory is not yet rigorous enough to deduce what these characteristics would be.

Sleep may be partially dependent on chemical action. Fatigue products and certain glandular secretions could tend to increase the thresholds of all neurons, and thus bring the multiplication factor below one. Or the glandular secretions could be the direct cause, the glands themselves being affected by the fatigue products. Both here and in the preceding paragraph the multiplication factor must be defined, allowing for the activity of the arousal center. If the sensory input is decreased, as by closing the eyes, the activity of the arousal center is decreased, and the probability of sleep is increased.

The explanation of why sleep has a degree of self-perpetuation would be that the positive feedback loop, cortex → arousal center → cortex, had been switched off. Meanwhile some of the sleep-producing neurons could be stimulating one another (for I have not assumed that they all have high thresholds).

Suppose that a sleeping person is given some additional sensory input, say by being prodded. A branching sequence of assemblies will occur (a dream), leading to some motor activity, and to an increased propensity to wakefulness. We may suppose that the sleep center has provoked the glands to inhibit the emotions (see block diagram). *By definition* the emotions have strong connections to the arousal center (wakefulness), or are a part of it. Therefore this center is not stimulated as much as if the person were already awake. Therefore, it may fail to bring the multiplication factor above unity. In this case the sequence of active assemblies ultimately becomes extinguished, and the person returns to dreamless sleep.

When we become tired for any reason, a conflict develops between the mechanisms that produce sleep, and those that keep us awake. To go to sleep resolves the conflict, and is therefore pleasurable. It is like making a decision.

To be bored is to have little to stimulate the arousal center. This provokes a tendency to sleep; but if there are other things to keep us awake, such as the disapproving expression of the android who is talking to us, then we are in a state of conflict, and therefore of displeasure.

Insomnia would be caused by a propensity of certain assemblies to activate or deactivate certain glands, and a propensity of these assemblies to be activated.

The function of sleep, as distinct from its mechanism, is unknown, but is not a "dark mystery," since there are several plausible conjectures in the literature.

The above explanations are all somewhat *ad hoc,* like those of Freud. They need to be made more quantitative and put to more experimental tests. Physiological psychology can become fully scientific only if it becomes somewhat mathematical. The parameters assumed should be consistent with the experimental quantitative facts.[44]

A mathematical theory of waves of activity in the nervous system has been started by Beurle,[45] and a mathematical theory for cell assemblies by Rosenblatt.[46] Although Rosenblatt's results are so far largely disputable, I am convinced that he is right in regarding the general approach as important: a mixture of mathematical theory and stimulation experiments, using general-purpose and special-purpose equipment.

As an example of a simple mathematical argument, let us consider the phenomenon of "habituation." This is the disappearance of responsiveness to accustomed stimulation. Ashby[47] says that habituation cannot be explained by fatigue, and gives the reason that habituation occurs later when the stimulus is greater. But it seems to me that fatigue can be regarded as an explanation provided that a further small assumption is made. For let the frequency of input pulses to an active assembly (or group of assemblies) be f, and suppose that the frequency required, after time t, in order to keep the assembly active can be expressed as a function $g(t, f)$. (This must be an increasing function of both t and *f*. It must also depend on the current activity of other assemblies, but I shall ignore this dependence here.) Then the assembly will become extinguished after time u, where $g(u, f) = f$. All that is required is that the solution of this equation, as an equation for u, should be an increasing function of f. If, for example, $g(t, f) = kt^b f^a$, then $ku^b = f^{1-a}$, and all is well if $a < 1$ and $b > 0$. In fact, we should expect $a < 1$ anyway, since the greater the input frequency into an active assembly, the greater the proportion of "wasted" input impulses. Now, I believe that Ashby's explanation, without reference to fatigue, may be a better one, but the above simple argument demonstrates quickly the potential merit of mathematical expression.

Many of the above speculations may be physiologically incorrect. But for the design of an android it would be adequate if they were self-consistent and not too uneconomical. The only ways of checking this would be by mathematics or engineering, both of which would force greater rigor of formulation. Both methods would be complicated, so that both are necessary in order to supplement the other. It is not part of the definition of an android that its internal construction should be similar to that of a human.

Owing to the costs of printing I shall not give blueprints for the construction of an android, but I should like to mention some of the features that would be desirable.

In the first place it seems important that androids should serve men. I think the best chance of achieving this aim is to make androids highly suggestible and to educate them carefully. Suggestion (the extreme form of which is hypnotism) has always been an essential ingredient for the stability of social organizations.

A man is hypnotized when his imagination is dominated by a small part of his sensory input. It may be conjectured, by an extension of the cell-assembly theory, that what we have here is the dominance of the cortex by a very large assembly, a group of assemblies if you like, or an "aggregate." Now it is a rough law of nature that the bigger a thing is, other things being equal, the larger its time constants are likely to be. We may assume that an aggregate has a time constant more like half an hour than half a second, except under conflict. A closed cycle of assemblies may have an indefinitely long survival time. A propensity for dominating aggregates to form may be postulated for other applications, for example, to explain the determination of an athlete, and any other obsessional behavior. It is a natural postulate: just as neurons form assemblies, so assemblies form aggregates.

A sufficiently well-integrated aggregate may strongly inhibit others; in fact the phenomenon of hypnotism apparently shows that it can do so. Perhaps the rhythm of hypnotic suggestion leads to a closed cycle of activated assemblies. Perhaps a propensity for the simultaneous activation of conflicting aggregates is the physical basis of neurosis, just as the conflict of assemblies causes pain in Hebb's theory. Unconscious autosuggestion is probably essential for the well-integrated personality.

I believe that a developed theory of groups of assemblies will be important in psychology, just as that of clumps of clumps should be important in a theory of information retrieval.[48] In fact, there is more than an analogy here. For although clumps are static, in a very flexible system of information retrieval they would need to be dynamic and would be more like assemblies.

The next desideratum is that either androids should be truthful, or else that their falsehoods should be easily detected by means of a lie detector. It is not important that this apparatus should be the same as the type used on humans (which Z. M. T. Tarkowski has described as a "physiological toy"). It is not necessary to regard the manifestations that operate the lie detector as part of the "overt behavior."

It might be suggested that we are now ready to find out whether an android could feel subjective pain. We ask it. In virtue of the definition of an android the answer given would be "yes." We might then hope to detect that this was a lie by means of the lie detector. Unfortunately, the answer might be truthful, but mean something like "there are situations that I try to avoid, and when I fail I show all the overt indications that you do when you say you are in pain; and furthermore certain internal events occur that I am unable to verbalize and that I describe as unpleasant." If we then ask, "But do you *feel* pain?" the android might reply, "Whereof one cannot speak, thereof one must be silent."

A possible escape from this impasse would be if we could analyze the physical basis of pain in animals and humans. It would help if we could convince ourselves that human pain depends on the action of complex chemical compounds. If the android did not contain such compounds, especially it it were made of clockwork, then I think we should more readily believe that it did not experience real (i.e., metaphysical) pain. If the innards of an android were very different from our own, though complicated, it may "really" enjoy having the manifestations of overt pain. It may be a masochist without behaving like one. Or it may be in a permanent state of delight or misery under all circumstances. If so, one would expect the behavior of the android to give it away, if one reverted to two-way interactionism. (It may also have experiences unimaginable to us.) One trouble with one-way interactionism is that it implies that the most important questions can never be resolved by science. Even telepathy between passive ghosts in machines could never lead to overt behavior. In particular, it could not lead to the verbal guessing of Zener cards, nor to any other verbal behavior. Such "telepathy" would surely have no meaning.

Perhaps the most plausible form of one-way interactionism is that real metaphysical pain originates inside the neurons or glands, or in small clouds of chemicals, and is an effect but not a cause of physical events. It is the terminus of a causal chain. The physical aspects of pain serve a biological function, but the metaphysical aspects serve none. Either they have no function, or the devil put them there for his own ends, or they constitute the punishment that we ghosts are enduring for misdeeds performed in heaven before we were born. We are undergoing terms of imprisonment in bodies. It is preordained that we shall not believe this, in order that the punishment should be effective.

Psychophysical parallelism leads to even more surprising conclusions. It is impossible unless we assume that the physical and psychic worlds are both absolutely deterministic down to the last place of decimals. For otherwise ghosts and bodies would diverge and part company. And how would we know if they *did* part company?!

Neutral monism leads to much the same conclusion as one-way interactionism, that real pain is an effect but not a cause.

Perhaps two-way interactionism is correct after all, but we are not yet ready to make scientific use of it. We could equate the "ghost in the machine" with the wave function, but physiological psychology has not yet emerged from the prequantum stage.

It is often said that we cannot feel another person's pain. Is the problem for androids all that different? We considered one conceivable approach to the problem of comparing subjective human experiences. It was to get into two-way telepathic communication. We could try the same thing with androids. Perhaps, by the time we are clever or foolish enough to construct an android we shall also have discovered methods of automatic telepathy. We may have to submerge our individualities in order to unify the world. If androids are incapable of telepathy, the 10^{19} human neurons should hold their own.

Suppose that scientific methodism is false; that an android could not be properly motivated unless it could feel real metaphysical pain. We might then find that it was impossible (apart from being expensive) to construct a giant android with clockwork innards, but that we could construct one with the help of organic compounds or with "neurons" consisting of unicellular animalcules. (We may be able to mutate existing ones into an appropriate form.) We should then have obtained a little evidence that motivation in androids is necessarily chemical or biochemical. It would be some evidence that chemical androids could feel "real pain." The question whether they could feel real pain is therefore not absolutely metaphysical. But it is metaphysical enough so that we should probably after all fall back on common sense and accept androids at their lie-detector value. Whether this would encourage or discourage us to be kind to them is another matter. It may be easier to hate something if it is conscious. Aggressiveness is the best defence mechanism.

A further problem that arises out of the construction of androids is whether we should construct one far more intelligent than ourselves, a *deus ex machina,* and appoint it president of the United Nations or of the United Planets Organization. For all we know there may be a limitation; if the number of cells were too large, their organization may be very difficult. This is one of several explanations that can be proposed for why genius and neurosis are so closely correlated,[49] and also why human brains are not larger. Even if there is a limitation in size, at least an electronic brain could operate thousands of times as fast as a human one.

This problem, too, I shall leave aside.

MARCH, 1960

Afterthoughts

Many philosophers take it for granted that real metaphysical pain (r.m.p.) is not located in space. But it is located in time, and time and space are aspects of the same thing, namely, space-time. Therefore, I believe r.m.p. is located in space, though not necessarily, or even plausibly, at a geometrical point.

I do not myself believe that r.m.p. is located in individual neurons. It seems to me more reasonable to assume that it is located in a gland, or in an assembly of neurons, or in what may be called an "autotelepathic field." Whatever it is that experiences r.m.p. may be regarded as a ghost in the machine. It is affected by bodily events, and r.m.p. would have no function unless the ghost could react back on the body. So I believe in two-way interactionism. But the ghost may not exist without the matter: physics is more complicated than was once thought.

It may be noticed that, if pain is located in individual neurons, then experiments on individual neurons would be unethical.

In physical theory, fields are assumed to be generated by mechanisms only at the molecular, atomic, or subatomic levels. Therefore, I do not believe that a giant android made of cogwheels could feel r.m.p. But I suspect that one built of organic compounds could do so. If we were clever enough to build an android, it might be supposed that we could predict its behavior on the assumption that no ghost was present, and then show that the prediction was falsified. This would suggest that the android had acquired a ghost. Unfortunately this argument breaks down, since our prediction may very well be empirical, and not based simply on physics and chemistry. Andropsychology would not be simply andro-neurophysiology.

Two chemical androids, built to precisely the same specifications, would not necessarily behave in identical manners, even if they had been placed in identical environments from the moment of manufacture. For their behavior would depend on quantum effects. So, even if their behaviors turned out to be quite different, we should not be able to deduce that they had ghosts with different characters. This is a pity, since it would have shown that the ghosts were there. Those ghosts are hard to pin down scientifically: they have a ghostly nature.

NOVEMBER, 1960

REFERENCES

1. Page 209 of (1a), W. Sluckin, *Mind and Machines*, Penguin, London and Tonbridge, 1954.
2. Page xiv of (2a), D. O. Hebb, *The Organization of Behavior*, Wiley, New York, Chapman and Hall, London, 1949.
3. (3a), Ludwig Wittgenstein, *Tractatus Logico-Philosophicus*, Routledge and Kegan Paul, London, 1922.
4. Page 58 of (4a), Gilbert Ryle, *The Concept of Mind*, Hutchinson, London, 1949.
5. (5a), Hugh Everett, III, "Relative-state formulation of quantum mechanics," *Rev. Mod. Physics*, 1957, 29:454-462; followed by an enthusiastic assessment by John A. Wheeler, pp. 463-465.
6. (6a), I. J. Good, "Kinds of probability," *Science*, 1959, 129:443-447. See also Chapter 6 of (7a). The possibility that an argument can change a probability is discussed on page 49 of (8a).
7. (7a), Karl R. Popper, *The Logic of Scientific Discovery*, Hutchinson, London, 1959. Popper discusses degrees of testability, but dislikes nonphysical (intuitive) probability.
8. Chapter 6 of (8a), I. J. Good, *Probability and the Weighing of Evidence*, Griffin, London, Hafner, New York, 1950. Or see (8b), "The paradox of confirmation," *Brit. J. Sci.* (1960 or 1961); or (8c), "Weight of evidence, corroboration, explanatory power, information, and the utility of experiments," *J. Roy. Stat. Soc.*, ser. B, forthcoming.
9. (9a), Karl R. Popper, "Philosophy of science: a personal report," in *British Philosophy in the Mid-Century*, 1957, ed. by C. A. Mace, especially page 157.
10. Chapter 29 of (10a), Alfred J. Lotka, *Elements of Mathematical Biology*, Dover, New York, Constable, London, 1956; originally published in 1925 with the title *Elements of Physical Biology*. More precisely Lotka conjectures that ". . . the conscious state may be in some way correlated to that transitional state through which matter must pass on its way from one stable molecular configuration to another," and he gives a reference to (10b), Schönbein, *Jl. f. prakt. Chemie*, 40:152. This suggestion is quite similar to the one in my text concerning the wave function, though Lotka could not have had this interpretation in mind, since Schrödinger's original paper did not appear until January, 1926.
11. Ledger Wood gives a reference to (11a), B. Spinoza, *Ethics*, Book II, prop. 7 schol. and props. 11 and 12; on page 225 of (11b), *The Dictionary of Philosophy*, ed. by Dagobert D. Runes, Vision Press and Peter Owen, London, 1951.

12. For some relevant remarks and many earlier references, see pages 162-165 and 206-208 of (12a), *Symposium on Information Theory*, Ministry of Supply, London, 1950, reprinted in *Trans. I.R.E.*, February, 1953; and also (12b), Herman R. Branson, "A definition of information from the thermodynamics of irreversible processes," in *Information Theory in Biology*, ed. by H. Quastler, University of Illinois, Urbana, 1953.

13. Page 84 of (13a), *Mechanisation of Thought Processes*, National Physical Laboratory, Symposium No. 10, H.M. Stationery Office, London, 1959.

14. Page 7 of (14a), I. J. Good, "Speculations on perceptrons and other automata," *I.B.M. Res. Center, Guest Lecture, RC-115*, 1959, p. 19.

15. Page 203 of (15a), Donald Olding Hebb, *A Textbook of Psychology*, Saunders, Philadelphia and London, 1958.

16. Page 3 of (16a), E. R. Guthrie, *The Psychology of Learning*, Harper, New York, 1952; quoted on page 2 of (16b), Ernest R. Hilgard, *Theories of Learning*, 2nd ed., Methuen, London, 1958.

17. Page 3 of (15a).

18. (18a), A. M. Turing, "Computing machinery and intelligence," *Mind*, 1950, 59:443-460; reprinted as "Can a machine think?" in *The World of Mathematics*, Vol. 4, Simon and Schuster, New York, 1956, pp. 2099-2123.

19. See, for example, (19a), C. Badouin, *Suggestion and Auto-Suggestion*, trans. from French by C. Paul, 1924. For a discussion that goes part of the way to giving a mechanistic interpretation of imagination (the "prosensory input") see (19b), J. S. Hayes, W. M. S. Russell, Claire Hayes, and Anita Kohsen, "The mechanism of an instinctive control system: a hypothesis," *Behaviour*, 1953, 6:85-119. This work was based largely on (19c), N. Tinbergen, *A Study of Instinct*, Oxford, 1951.

20. Page 169 of (15a).

21. (21a), I. J. Good, "Could a machine make probability judgments?" *Computers and Automation*, 1959, 8:14-16, and 24-26.

22. (22a), B. G. Farley and W. A. Clark, "Simulation of self-organising systems by digital computers," *Trans. IRE, Symp. on Infn. Th.*, Sept., 1954, pp. 76-84. (22b), N. Rochester, J. M. Holland, L. H. Haibt, and W. L. Duda, "Tests on a cell assembly theory of the action of the brain, using a large digital computer," *IRE Trans.* IT-2, 1956, pp. 80-93. (22c), Frank Rosenblatt, "Perceptron simulation experiments," Cornell Aeronautical Lab. Inc., Report No. VG-1196-G3. The results so far are not yet very exciting, otherwise everybody would know about them.

23. See the following paper and the references contained in it: (23a), Marvin L. Minsky, "Some methods of artificial intelligence and heuristic programming," on pages 3-27 of (13a). This paper contains many useful ideas. I should think that important advances will be made with heuristic programing quite soon.

24. See, for example, the following papers and references given in them: (24a), A. L. Samuel, "Some studies in machine learning, using the game of checkers," *IBM J. Res. and Dev.*, 1959, 3:210-229. (24b), A. Newell, "The chess machine," *Proc. 1955 Western Joint Computer Conf.*, IRE (1955). (24c), Hao Wang, "Towards mechanical mathematics," *IBM J. Res. and Dev.* 1960, 4:2-22. Wang's first program on the IBM 704 found proofs in 37 minutes for the whole list of over 200 theorems in the first five chapters of the *Principia Mathematica* of Whitehead and Russell. (These theorems are concerned only with simple logic, and not with real mathematics.)

25. See (22c) and references given there. In the statement in my text I am referring specifically to the cell-assembly theory. Several previous writers have been concerned with random networks with a somewhat different emphasis, but in a decidedly mathematical manner; for example, N. Rashevsky, and H. D. Landahl, in books and in the *Bull. Math. Biophysics,* and (25a), W. R. Ashby, *Design for a Brain* (Chapman and Hall, 1952). In spite of Norbert Wiener's very great influence in cybernetics, I believe he has not done much work on random networks. See also note 22. Many other references can be traced in *Math. Rev.* under the index heading "Biology." See also (25b), *Automata Studies* (ed. by C. E. Shannon and J. McCarthy, Princeton, 1956). There is further unpublished work by V. Serebriakoff.

26. (26a), P. M. Milner, "The cell assembly, Mark II," *Psych. Rev.,* 1957, 64:242-252. (26b), K. S. Lashley, "In search of the engram," *Symp. Soc. Expl. Biology,* 1950, 4:454-482. Also (2a), which is the most detailed treatment.

27. Page 35 of (27a), D. A. Scholl, *The Organization of the Cerebral Cortex,* Methuen, London, Wiley, New York, 1956.

28. See (28a), I. J. Good, "How much science can you have at your fingertips?" *IBM J. Res. Dev.,* 1958, 2:282-288, for a discussion of the possible number of dynamic and static states of the brain. A much greater estimate was made by W. Grey Walter because he assumed that each pair of neurons is connected by two paths each of which may be either active or not active. In a lecture in 1959 he explained that these connections might be through a field and not by fibers. But then they would be very far from statistically independent, so that his estimate is an extravagant upper bound.

29. For example (29a), N. Rashevsky, "A reinterpretation of the mathematical biophysics of the central nervous system in the light of neurophysiological findings," *Bull. Math. Biophysics,* 1945, 7:151-160.

30. See (26b).

31. See (25a). Ashby's point of view resembles that of (31a), F. A. Hayek, *The Sensory Order,* Routledge and Kegan Paul, London, Chicago University Press, 1952.

32. See, for example (32a), Ludwig von Bertalanffy, "General system theory," *General Systems,* 1956, 1:1-10, where many other references will be found.

33. John Wisdom, lectures.

34. Discussion in Area 6 of the International Conference on Scientific Information, Washington, D.C., 1958. In the forthcoming Proceedings of this conference this discussion will be abbreviated. See also I. J. Good, "A causal calculus," *Brit. J. Phil. Sc.* 12: (Feb. 1961); and "Speculations concerning information retrieval," IBM Research Center, Yorktown Heights, N. Y., RC-78, Dec. 10, 1958.

35. If this were not so, we should more often feel, "This has happened before." The problem of estimating the probability of an event that has never occurred is of interest because without such an estimate we should never know when to be surprised. Some contributions to the solution of this problem are made in (35a), I. J. Good, "On the estimation of small frequencies in contingency tables," *J. Roy. Stat. Soc. ser. B,* 1956, 18:113-124; and (35b), "On the population frequencies of species, and the estimation of population parameters," *Biometrika,* 1953, 40:237-264.

36. See, for example (8a); (36a), I. J. Good, "Rational decisions," *J. Roy. Stat. Soc., ser. B,* 1952, 14:107-114; or (36b), "Mathematical tools," Chapter 3 of *Uncertainty and Business Decisions,* 2nd Ed., University Press. Liverpool,

1957. (36c), Leonard J. Savage, *The Foundations of Statistics*, Wiley, New York, Chapman and Hall, London, 1954.

37. (26a).
38. Pages 133-134 of (15a) and reference there.
39. Page 39 of (2a).
40. Page 185 of (2a).
41. Page 174 of (15a).
42. Pages 213-214 of (2a), which contains a reference to McCulloch.
43. For references to some other theories of the EEG see (43a), Mary A. B. Brazier, *The Electrical Activity of the Nervous System*, Pitman, London, 1951.
44. For a summary of present knowledge of experimental quantitative facts, see (27a).
45. (45a), R. L. Beurle, "Properties of a mass of cells capable of regenerating pulses," *Phil. Trans. Roy. Soc. B*, 1957, 240:55-94.
46. See, for example, (22c).
47. (47a), W. Ross Ashby, "The mechanism of habituation," on pages 93-113 of (13a), with discussion on pages 115-118.
48. See the Area 6 discussion mentioned in Note 34 (which may be pruned). Also (28a), and some work by A. F. Parker-Rhodes and R. M. Needham at the Cambridge Language Research Unit (not yet published).
49. There were no exceptions in the sample studied by (49a), E. Kretschmer, *Psychology of Men of Genius*, trans. by R. B. Cattell, 1931.

D O N A L D   D .   G L A D

"Mind" as an Organismic Integration

Is it a bauble to tease some weary moment? A conversation piece forever fresh because unfinished? And how can the question *What is mind?* be satisfied? In order to consider the question at all in any but an aesthetic sense, we must provide a context. Let us consider the question in terms of constructiveness and satisfaction in living: How may the concept of *mind* enhance understanding of constructive human living? Man's awareness of his integrative processes is present in most activities. Sometimes he experiences thinking as "hardwork," other times it moves smoothly, effortlessly, and induces a sense of pleasure. Or betimes an ecstasy of awareness comes when a subliminal chain reaction blazes into discovery.

It will be noted that *feelings, motives,* and *activities* were included in these illustrations of *mind.* This must be so, in our time, since man is no longer a "thinking machine," but has accepted the motivational-affective aspects of himself as well as the "rational man."

To limit discourse, I shall consider *mind* and its cognates as those aspects of organismic functioning which involve an integrative sense— an awareness of organization. The question will be: In what ways does the human organism arrange and experience a sense of integration? Since there are innumerable ways of approaching such a question, I have chosen to examine some cardinal aspects of several personality theories in such a way that they "fit" an organismic conception of mind. No attempt to be exhaustive or even completely systematic is intended; the purpose is rather to illustrate the feasibility of an organismic integra-

The author is indebted to Virginia B. Glad, Robert H. Barnes, and Stephen Werbel, for constructive criticism in the completion of this essay.

tion of other theoretical systems. Hopefully some useful questions may arise from this form of inquiry.

In a psychotherapy group a young man dejectedly reviewed his failure to pursue his education, his distress at his wife's lack of respect, and his doubts about whether his own life was worthwhile. To evoke a different level of awareness I interrupted with, "If you were an animal, what kind of an animal would you like to be?"

Flushing and fidgeting he replied, "A dove."

"What is a dove like?" I asked.

"Oh, it's gentle, loving, takes good care of its young."

"Like your mother?" I wondered.

"Of course like my mother. I couldn't be like my father, he was mean and drunk! I couldn't stand to be around him! And I'm ashamed of myself when I'm like him. I want to be kind and gentle—good to people, I don't want to be like him! But my wife gives me no respect. She never makes me feel like a man. I fixed her a birthday dinner and brought her the nicest presents, and all she did was say, 'Thank you.'"

"He's just like me," said a woman in the group. "I want to be a scientist like my grandfather. I don't like being a woman."

"Did no one ever love you except your grandfather?" I asked gently.

"The rest just took advantage of me and beat me down."

Little *meaning* of these two patients can be developed from such sparse details; yet, they are suggestive of a failure of a *sense of integration* in two people who, years ago, might have been described as "having lost their minds." In an age which takes for granted that *mind* is a rubric to describe a part aspect of a human-process-in-the-world, it is possible to help such people "find their minds again." This can be accomplished by helping them to develop a sense of adequacy, integration, and skillfulness in living. The experiences of these two patients had been that they were not valued as they were. Their physical characteristics—for instance, male and female—were inappropriate to the demands of parents who wanted something different than their children were able to provide. The young man's mother had wanted a girl. The young woman's mother had wanted a boy. These patients were unable to satisfy such distorted demands and learned to devaluate themselves because of their inability to fulfill their parents' needs. Both are working at the problem of re-evaluation and reintegration. The young man is considering the advantages and skills of masculinity. The young woman is at least flirting with the valuable aspects of womanliness. Their new forms of self-integration are becoming consistent with their organismic structures.

An adequate sense of integration—a well-functioning *mind*—is one that conforms to, or is an appropriate expression of, the structure and function of the organism in its world. When Coleridge was unable to harness his horse because the collar was the wrong shape for slipping over the horse's head, it was no indignity for a philosopher-poet to be helped by a scullery maid. The maid knew the shapes of horses and turned the collar upside down to make it horse-head-shaped. Coleridge's integration was different, but equally adequate to that of the scullery maid, for she had never fed on honey dew nor drunk the milk of paradise. She knew of cow's milk and of horse's heads. It seems appropriate and no denigration of De Quincey's plowman that he should dream of oxen. Oxen were essential to the plowman's *modus vivendi*. They were only remotely consequential to De Quincey's needs.

The human *mind* serves the biosocial function of producing human order and meaning in the world. At times the *mind* seeks nourishment—fulfillment in art, religion, science, or less subtle gourmanderie. At other times the mind seeks relief like a fulfilled skylark pouring out its profuse artistry. Yet science, however filling, has rarely satisfied man's hunger, nor has art, however ecstatic, quite soothed his passion. Like great religions and other value systems, science and art are human conveniences which to some degree have ennobled, fed, and relieved man-in-the-world. My intention in examining an organismic conception of *mind* has a similar purpose of convenience. To draw together some understandings from several theories of personality and examine their potential integration of man-in-the-world. While we may attempt to consider this organismic formulation for its value in enhancing a sense of "meaningfulness" of life, such a search can be rewarded only by an assertion, e.g., "It is meaningful" or "It is not meaningful." Meaningfulness may be simply an affective response to a perceived state of affairs, or phrased in different terms, "I like it," or "I don't like it."

An Interpersonality Integration

The term *interpersonality* is indended to convey a human-being-in-the-world who in some fashion accomplishes a sense of adequacy. The term implies a being who manages himself in some integrative relationship to the world. Of the many possible ways of experiencing, the *interpersonality* selects some relatively, useful and satisfying *form* or *sense* or *model* of the meaning of his self-world relationship. An infinite variety of plausible ways of experiencing are intended by *interpersonality*. I shall attempt to illustrate a few only which may be drawn into some constructive relationship to the question, "What is mind?"*

* In addition to my own works, *Operational Values in Psychotherapy*[3] and *Beauty and Creative Thinking*,[2] I have drawn extensively upon F. S. Perls's, organismic-psychoanalytic volume, *Ego, Hunger and Aggression*[7] and upon May's volume *Existence*.[6] It appears plausible that any point of departure (or obversely, nucleus of

Mind as a function of the human-being-in-the-world may be expressed phenomenologically in at least three different ways.

1. The emergence of "mind" or the experience of awareness, as well as the conscious presence of "reality," is a function of organismic tension systems of some kind, be they tensions of deficiency or surplus quality.

2. The emergence of "mind" or awareness occurs in a figure-ground relationship. That is, in the presence of organismic tension systems or disequilibriums, conscious awareness emerges and phenomenal reality is evoked.

3. When the organismic disequilibriums are relieved, awareness withdraws and phenomenal reality recedes.

These propositions* suggest that the organization of experience is dependent upon resonance between the world and the organismic processes of equilibrium-disequilibrium: the waxing and waning of organic tension systems. They provide the organic nucleus of organization about which many apparently divergent concepts may be economically ordered.

They provide a nuclear organization about which we will be able to integrate concepts from psychoanalysis, interpersonal psychiatry, dynamic relationship therapy, client-centered therapy, and existential phenomenology in such a way as to provide useful understanding of each. The following illustration is suggestive of the many meanings of dreams: Kekulé fancied atoms before his eyes, snakelike, whirling and twisting in many forms, until finally one of the snakes put its tail in its mouth, forming a circle. This dream phenomenon provided Kekulé with the solution to a problem over which he had long struggled. It is plausible to examine the tension-release value of this dream from the points of view of several theories of personality, as a beginning point for considering ways in which the "meaning of mind" may be conceived. The snake in this dream might, in Jungian terms, be close to the notion of a healing symbol and, of course, be consistent with Jung's conception of the circle as symbolizing the most constructive functions of mankind. In Freudian terms, a similar comfort meaning might be construed in a different way as a masturbatory symbol. In classical Gestalt terms the snake with its tail in its mouth would be consistent with the notion of *pragnanz,* or the good Gestalt. In Lewinian, field theoretical terms, Kekulé's dream could be described as having produced closure or as having relieved a quasi need. Each of these forms of conceptualization is consistent with Perls's proposal that an organismic imbalance evokes a perceptual Gestalt which modifies a tension system.

---

meaning) could be selected to generate and encompass other points of view. I have elected in this essay the personal preference of integrating in the phenomenological-existential framework.

* Modified from Perls.[7]

To expand the good-Gestalt analogy, an inflated beach ball provides a metaphor consistent with an organic integration of other personality concepts. If this beach ball be provided with a pinprick in its skin as an excretory process, it is in constant need for replenishment of supplies. Let us also provide an available source of supplies, namely, someone who is willing to refill it with air or gas upon appropriate occasions.* Such a beach ball when optimally inflated is a good Gestalt. It is alive, responsive to touch. From those aspects of the world less firm than itself it requires accommodation and they are molded by it. Nicely rounded indentions form in the sand as the beach ball bounces across. The parts of the world less resilient than itself send the ball bounding away to regain its roundness. It is comfortably alive and plays upon the beach.

But if the ball becomes overfilled, it reacts abruptly, excretes hurriedly, and is in danger of rupture into nonexistence. There is tension, agitation, and what might be described as existential anxiety—it is in danger of bursting to pieces. If it is underfilled, deflated, its liveliness is gone, it becomes torpid, dull, and lacking in zest. Its existence is inadequate. It has the quality of a guilty person and may decay from lack of use.

The experience of the beach ball is immediate and total, yet its present behavior has functional relevance to its past. How adequately was it constructed in the first place? What injuries has it suffered? How has it been repaired? What excesses of tumescence have damaged its resiliency? What periods of flaccidity have engendered decay? All of these historical aspects of the present determine the ball's responsiveness. They are important to its present functioning, they determine how it will respond right now. In this sense, the psychoanalytic conception of historical causality is accounted for. If there has been excessive attention to the intake valve by overuse, a bulge on the surface may appear and make the ball less dependable in its behavior as well as more likely to rupture at that point. If the excretory sphincter has been abused, distortion and rupture are likely at that point. If the ball has been excessively filled and agitated in general, the whole ego boundary may be in danger of collapse. However, the beach ball has properties other than these historical scars or strengths. It behaves in apparently purposeful ways to defend and maintain its good Gestalt qualities—its existence.

If it is only lightly touched or caressed, it remains gently in the hands of the player. But if it is pushed upon it will angrily spring away expres-

---

* In the interests of simplicity the obvious automation and servo-mechanism addenda to the beach-ball analogy will not be elaborated although their *mental* appropriateness is apparent. Rapaport[8] has recently developed these automation analogies in cybernetic and information theory terms.

sing its displeasure with a hiss, then bouncing lightly back from an adjoining wall or seeking another playmate it will renew its search for gaiety.

If gently thrown from one player to another it will float easily in a friendly way and enjoyable concourse between two people will occur.

If thrown too sharply it will hiss its irritation as it bounces away from the other person. If thrown to a person who is not informed of its coming (however pleasant the intention) the unsuspecting recipient is likely to experience an attack.

With my bouncing beach ball I have illustrated many of the aspects of psychoanalysis, interpersonal psychiatry, Rankian relationship theory, and existential phenomenology.

To humanize the beach ball, we may consider its most likely analogy to the "meaning of mind." A sense of awareness seems most plausible when something is happening. And, of course, the beach ball is never completely at rest. Lying on the beach at night it will contract slightly with coolness. Warming in the morning sun it will regain some fullness. The beach ball's skin will vary slightly at different points depending upon the differential exposure to sun, wind, dew, and sand. A moderate sense of awareness or "mind" then would be constantly present. To characterize the meaning of mind in personality theoretical terms we may examine the ball analogy for its power to integrate the several conceptual forms.

The organismic picture of emergence of mind is seen in the shifting tension systems of the beach ball. When inflated to an optimal degree there is an easy interaction with the environment. If the ball is deflated it expresses or "experiences" a need for fullness, a sense of dejection. If the ball is overfilled it "experiences" tension, agitation, a need for emptiness. If it is oversensitive and overactive it "seeks" release of tension. When either surplus or deficiency is relieved, a relaxed ease and smoothness returns to the ball. To represent simultaneous surplus and deficiency systems, a more complex, compartmentalized ball would be required but can readily be conceived. For example, two inner compartments would be sufficient to account for an empty stomach and a distended seminal vesicle operating at the same time.

Phenomenology and Existence

It is apparent that the organismic-Gestalt concepts conveyed by the beach ball to this point provide a reasonable vehicle for basic phenomenological-existential concepts. An overfilled ball has the quality of existential anxiety—the danger of disruption into nonexistence. It may be ruptured easily—a soft mound of sand may be too hard for its thin-stretched skin. We have a picture of an overly sensitive, agitated excitable person, or one who is bursting with ideas but unable to put them to use—a college freshman with more answers than there are questions.

If we provide three compartments in the existential ball—the *umwelt*, the *mitwelt*, and *eigenwelt*—we have the possibility of being overfilled in the physical *umwelt* world, underfilled in the social *mitwelt* world, and overfilled in the self *eigenwelt* world. Such an existential ball would be most erratic in its behavior, taking out its physical need-gratification in an egocentric way and failing to respond to social requirements. Any variety of psychopathology could be constructed on this model. Any variety of adequacy could be represented by the same analogy. To take a simple illustration, the model of existential guilt is emptiness, and an underfilled ball has the quality of an existentially guilty person. This life has not been filled, it has not been lived fully, it is desolate and dejected. It cannot bounce effectively, it conforms itself to the shape of the sand. It has little existence of its own. The dejected young man in group therapy fits this picture very well. No one had fed him with a sense of manhood. No one had loved or filled him as he might appropriately be.

Again, the appropriateness of the analogy is enhanced by at least three compartments in the ball. Perhaps the young man has been overfilled in his feminine *mitwelt*, underfilled in his masculine *eigenwelt*, and optimally filled in his *umwelt*, but the disorganized structure this results in makes it difficult for him to function in an integrated way.

It is feasible to pursue this analogy into all the meanings of existence, but let us shift to other theories long enough to see how they shape the organismic beach ball. Most immediately, Rogers'[9] self-concept theory seems easily assimilated in the eigenwelt aspect of existential theory. We may touch it briefly by noting that Rogers seems to propose a relatively optimal fullness, an emphasis of integration wherein the "mind," rather than the organism, is the nucleus of meaning. There is little turgidity or emptiness in the self-concept ball. It is perhaps best expressed in the minor ambivalences characteristic of a person whom the spears and arrows of outrageous fortune have cleanly missed or lightly scratched. This person's dysfunctioning is minimal and requires only minor relief to return to the quality of a good Gestalt.

Creative Relationship and Loneliness

An excessively filled ball held tightly by a woman who constantly keeps it filled and controlled suggests the Rankian concept of the need to retreat from the world and release supplies in loneliness. Such an angry breaking away implies the loss of the source of supplies with an attendant fear of emptiness, desolation, and despair. In this metaphor the dependency upon the environmental supplies alternating with the need for release provides some order and meaning in the characteristics of many artists who fluctuate between their need for people and their demand for isolation. The analogy coincides with the oral supplies tendency in Rank's conception of creative productivity and is consistent with the psychoanalytic oral-fixation of analysis of creative artists developed by Bergler.[1] Goethe's story of visiting Schiller and being unable to stay because of the odor of putrid apples exuding from a cupboard is redolent of the oral surfeit quality leading to creative production. Houseman speaks of poetry secreted from the pit of his stomach when out on a lonely walk. A schizophrenic patient expressing his affection and distrust for his female therapist with, "You sound as though you're completely loving and good—like a bountiful river always flowing," suggests the surplus threat. The release of excessive oral supplies, then, is one plausible source of "mind" in the Rankian theory. The ambivalent concern over emptiness and fullness is well represented by Keats's "When I have fears that I shall cease to be before my pen has gleaned this teeming brain."

A hunger for roundness, or a sense of emptiness is another organismic aspect of the Rankian notion. Thompson wrote that "Singing is sweet, but be sure of this, Lips only sing when they cannot kiss." Phenomenal reality emerges in the presence of organismic struggles as well as surplus. In the absence of adequacy the organism struggles for completion or closure. The hungry man dreams of or produces food. But hunger for food is frequently equivalent to hunger for affection. The unloved infant is likely to attach his feeling of rejection to the unfeeding, or unloving mother, and to experience a chronic sense of emptiness which will mean both unfed and unloved. This hunger for love can be reduced in many ways. Food fantasy, as in Rorschach Test "Ice Cream" (symbolizing both the love hunger and the unloving breast), is one organismic fantasy response to such emptiness. Another, more effective kind of reaction to emptiness is expressed in the interpersonal psychiatric conception of "mind," as the translation of love-hunger into effective interpersonal skills.

Interpersonal Psychiatry and Social Creativeness

A major locus of disturbance in the interpersonal psychiatric conception of "mind" is the distress of hunger, emptiness, and uncaressedness—an unfilled void seeking a supply. The organism relates for the purpose of being filled. The effective translation of love hunger into interpersonal skill becomes a basis for satisfying the need and producing adequate socialization. Much experience in the psychotherapy of schizophrenics is consistent with this concept. I remember a schizophrenic girl who reviewed her starved childhood, asking over and over, "How can I give love to my children when my mother didn't give any to me." My treatment of this patient included as much understanding affection as the psychotherapeutic relation allows. Perhaps one hour that I stood by her bedside holding her hand while she was being tortured with intravenous injections following an operation was as important a part of her therapy as anything I was able to provide. Later, I was able to teach her something about interpersonal skills. I told her to stop biting her children. I encouraged her to go to church, visit the library, learn to play bridge. She became a much more adequate person. She turned her love-hunger into socialized activity and gave up much of her destructive fantasy. The fantasy became unnecessary when she learned how to gain affection by interpersonal skill. The bouncing beach ball is playful and gay when it is adequately filled. It is able to give and perhaps to have a sense of gaiety and skill in affection.

An American Indian who wanted water to farm his bit of thirsty desert was given honor, a thirty-foot monument in Washington, D.C., and was vaunted as the hero who planted the victory flag at Iwo Jima. He wanted water to farm his sand. The story goes that he finally drowned, face down, in two inches of water. Apparently nations as well as mothers may fail to fill the emptiness of unwanted sons.

Yet the hunger of Mahatma Gandhi's India has produced much human understanding and affection. The emptiness of Socrates may have provoked his search for the fullness of ideas among his disciples. The hungry and thirsty Mormons, made so by "divine" prohibitions against meat and drink, are excessively productive of social activities, inquiring minds, and excellence in basketball, where they manage to take this full, round symbol away from less hungry competitors.

The satisfaction of hunger in a complex society, commonly requires a human relationship—a dependence upon a mothering person. Hence, the seeking for supplies requires the development of interpersonal skills.

Psychoanalysis and Object Relationships

In contrast to the unfilled, seeking quality of interpersonal therapy, psychoanalysis expresses the intensity and anxiety of being overfilled with a seminal surplus. The organism is seeking relief from vesicular tension and is inhibited or interfered with in the search. In the beach-ball analogy there is a patch over the pinprick hole so that the surplus cannot be reduced or if it does burst through, a rupture is likely to occur. It is also of interest in this analogy that a favorable relationship to an appropriate "human object" provides the most satisfactory condition for release. That the psychoanalytic conception of *mind* has physicalistic, object relationship qualities is an inherent necessity when examined in the organismic setting. Seminal surplus is truly attached to and withdrawn from other objects. H. S. Sullivan was never more libido-theoretical and object-oriented than when he joked about going to the lavatory to "express my opinion." The phenomenal realities which emerge in the presence of excretory tensions are quite appropriate as places to empty oneself—objective aspects of the world where libidinal cathexes can be made—be such objects human or otherwise.

An Organismic Integration

The selection of nuclear concepts from Rankian relationship theory, interpersonal psychiatric theory, and psychoanalytic theory has made possible a relatively simple integration in terms of organismic-Gestalt concepts. The meaning of "mind" in each of these separate theories can be economically conceived as the selective awareness and structuring of the world in response to the interplay of the many organismic disequilibriums and their behavioral or symbolic resolutions. Each theory—in the simplified form presented here—can be seen as an organization of meaning arising from a particular focus of tension. Rankian theory arises from and accounts for the surfeit and release of oral supplies. Interpersonal theory arises from and accounts for the deficiency in and search for oral supplies. Psychoanalytic theory arises from and accounts for the surplus of seminal resources. The several aspects of "mind" inherent in these theories can be integrated in the organismic proposition.

How any particular person thinks would be similarly construed. The sense of integration achieved would depend upon the degree to which he had developed effective management of his own most tensional systems. The degree to which he might broaden his ability to think effectively would be a function of the amount of effort required to keep his tensional systems in equilibrium. "Slave to the Wheel of Labor, What to him are Plato and the swing of Pleiades?"

The interpersonality proposition is that the nuclei of meaning arising from these relative foci of organic tension systems may be expanded to include effective integration in the several possible directions. A broader, more effective integration for the hungry interpersonal man is likely to ensue upon his achieving sufficient skill in getting affectional supplies that his awareness can expand in other directions. An increased scope of awareness and satisfaction for the Rankian is likely to follow his management of relationships in such a way that mothering persons will not surfeit him. More breadth of understanding and satisfaction for the psychoanalytic man should result from skill in releasing inhibited erotic surpluses.

The question of a "complete man" in the phenomenological, existential sense is answered somewhat negatively in these terms, for people who have had severe difficulties in living. "Completeness potential" seems limited to a personality whose imbalances in the process of development have been relatively moderate. In any event, such a "whole personality" would be unlikely to experience effectively the meaning of disturbance and distress in other lives which have been severely crippled by the vicissitudes of organismic surplus and deficiency.

The Assertion of Existence

Existential theory proposes that the human-being-in-the-world should assume awareness of himself, decide upon his responsibility for his own being, and assert, at least to himself, the intention to be in control of his own being. To a degree our analysis thus far has examined the potential limitations of existence, the potential interferences with the experience of being-in-the-world in a skillful way. It is proposed that limitations on the scope of potential awareness and the ability to assume a responsibility for one's being is a clear function of the vicissitudes of development, the surpluses and deficiencies which have defined the capacity of the organism to experience. How in this examination is it possible to consider the assertion of self in the world. Man is a helpless and fragile beach ball who cannot enlarge existence by himself without the help of other men who can see and help to remedy his distortions. The distortions that need remedy, however, are defined in our examination. The potential expansion of self is a function of the reduction of sources of limitation: aiding the socially hungry to develop skill in being fed; aiding the sexually inhibited to develop skill in relieving their surpluses; aiding the orally bursting to develop skill in avoiding overcontrol. With such additions to skill in managing sources of distortion and tension the potential enlargement of the self and the assertion of personal responsibility for existence becomes possible. The relief of *mitwelt* hungers should be accomplished by helping an individual to supplant his anxiety-aborting security operations with socially skilled techniques for relating comfortably. The relief of *umwelt* sexual surpluses should be accomplished by changing damming-up ego defenses to ego skills in releasing such excess tensions. The relief of *umwelt* excesses of feeding should be accomplished by aiding the individual to moderate his dependency upon the ambivalent sources of control. Such shifts in capacity to manage limitations of experience should increase the ability to experience self-in-the-world in a more integrated form.

Returning to the meaning of mind in this context, the conception developed leads to an understanding of data of mental processes which are plausibly integrated in this form.

Some illustrative material may be drawn from Lewin's field theoretical point of view. Lewin[5] predicted on the basis of the quasi need-concept (a hungry organismic question) that interrupted tasks would be remembered better than completed tasks. Zeigarnik (see Lewin[5]) demonstrated the empirical validity of this proposition. On a similar premise, which might be restated as "half a loaf is better than none," Mary Henle[4] found that similar tasks have more potentiality for substituting and relieving quasi needs than do dissimilar tasks. Rosenzweig[10] found that tasks defined as intelligence items were reversed in recall—those that were completed being remembered and those that were incomplete being forgotten. Such a reversal may suggest that when hunger constitutes a threat to one's sense of being loved, one will deny that he is hungry. Rosenzweig, essentially, set up two opposing quasi needs, the one having to do with the need to continue an activity, the other having to do with the need to maintain a sense of integration. The sense of integration was more potent than the need to continue.

In a sense the foregoing studies suggest the mind is an implicit decision process or an implicit assertion of integrated existence. The three studies say in relative degrees, "I am he who manages myself in the world." Zeigarnik's study asserts, "I am one who will continue my functioning." Henle's data propose, "I am one who will accept a symbolic substitute." Rosenzweig's experiment proposes, "I am one who must think well of myself." The alienation value of language is illustrated in the intelligence test definition of Rosenzweig's experimental situation. It provides a false sense of completion and satisfaction and produces distortion. A continuation of the hunger for completion and a denial of that hunger restricts the potential sense of being in the world. The decision to define themselves statistically in terms of intellectual success rather than actively in terms of pursuing an interesting activity was based upon implicit decisions about the future. These students of Rosenzweig made the decision to define themselves as intellectually adequate and thereby determined the meaning of the experience which they had undergone. Zeigarnik's subjects, being-in-the-real-world, defined themselves as interacting with the living experience and remembered what happened in terms of those things they were interested in continuing to carry to completion.

From the examination of these studies the proposal that present decisions determine past experiences is strongly suggested. Furthermore, the nature of one's relationship to the world in the future, the degree of being-in-the-world or being alienated from it, is a function of one's present decisions. The assertion of the quality of existence then determines the meaning of future experience. Further, we might infer that Rosenzweig's subjects would be more likely to experience existential guilt: The distress over failing to be, the feeling of emptiness even though it was not allowed in awareness. Zeigarnik's students and to a lesser extent perhaps Henle's would be more likely to experience existential anxiety from the lack of discharge, but would presumably continue the process of movement toward balance and harmony—toward a good Gestalt.

Furthermore, Rosenzweig's experiment reduced the opportunity for a meaningful encounter of the experimenter with the subjects. The experimenter used words to distort the meaning of the world. The subjects responded with memories which distorted the meaning of themselves. There could be little encounter under these conditions. Zeigarnik's approach was more existential, presenting the experiment in an open and direct form. The relationship of the experimenter, the research design, and the subjects was a relatively valid relationship. Zeigarnik's subjects experienced themselves in the world without subject-object relationship. They became involved in the process. Rosenzweig's subjects experienced themselves as objects and alienated themselves from the reality.

The Mind as a Decision Process

The discourse has suggested the definition of mind as the experience of decision making in the process of managing disequilibriums. Furthermore, it has been proposed that, to the degree that tensions are severe, they produce limitations upon the breadth of mental functioning. To the degree that mental activity fails to produce skill in reducing sources of organismic tension, mental processes distort meanings and alienate man from his world. Effective, integrative thinking is a function of awareness of potential surpluses and deficiencies which can be experienced in a sufficiently moderate form that they allow for a breadth of awareness to arise. A capacity to experience to some degree (but not to the degree of trauma) a sense of insufficiency, a sense of surplus in any area of organism-in-the-world, and to develop skill in manipulating symbolically and thereafter operationally seems essential to the expansion of mind.

REFERENCES

1. Bergler, E., *The Writer and Psychoanalysis*, Doubleday, New York, 1950.
2. Glad, D. D., *Beauty and Creative Thinking*, unpublished M.A. thesis, University of Utah, 1943.
3. ———, *Operational Values in Psychotherapy*, Oxford University Press, New York, 1959.
4. Henle, Mary, "An experimental investigation of dynamic and structural determinants of substitution," *Cont. Psychol. Theor.*, 1942, 2: No. 3.
5. Lewin, K., *Field Theory in Social Science*, Harper, New York, 1951 (Dorwin Cartwright, ed.).
6. May, R., Angel, E., and Ellenberger, H. F. (eds.), *Existence: A New Dimension in Psychiatry and Psychology*, Basic Books, New York, 1958.
7. Perls, F. S., *Ego, Hunger and Aggression: A Revision of Freud's Theory and Method*, Knox, Durban, South Africa, 1944.
8. Rapaport, A., "Mathematics and Cybernetics," Chapter 87, in Silvano, A. (ed.), *American Handbook of Psychiatry*, Vol. II, Basic Books, New York, 1959.
9. Rogers, C. R., *Client-Centered Therapy*, Houghton-Mifflin, Boston, 1951.
10. Rosenzweig, S., "An outline of frustration theory," in J. McV. Hunt (ed.), *Personality and the Behavior Disorders*, Vol. I, Ronald, New York, 1944.

PART THREE

Mind as Method

Of Elephants & Men

CLAIRE RUSSELL

W. M. S. RUSSELL

Raw Materials for a Definition of Mind

Ten minutes since my heart said "white"—
It now says "black."
It then said "left"—it now says "right"—
Hearts often tack....
In sailing o'er life's ocean wide
No doubt the heart should be your guide;
But it is awkward when you find
A heart that does not know its mind!

—W. S. GILBERT, *Ruddigore*

Introduction

A request for a useful and workable definition of "mind" might well give anyone pause. "I think," wrote Craik (1943), "that the number of ideas behind apparently simple and isolable concepts . . . is almost infinite. If this unknown background of thought and experience and physiological make-up produces concepts and at the same time conceals their origin it is highly unlikely that a few words will clear the confusion and indicate the true nature of the concept." The concept of mind has become the scene of stupendous confusion, and we may apply Craik's remarks to it with particular aptness and force.

535

Fortunately, the difficulty has been apparent to those responsible for planning this book. We are asked, not to define "mind," but merely to contribute to a movement "toward a definition." This mandate not only absolves us from any pretensions to completeness, but also permits a certain freedom of conjecture and the airing of imprecise hunches. In seeking to define other concepts relevant to behavioral science, we have usually proceeded by thinking around the subject and marshaling as many relevant considerations as possible. We shall employ this strategy here, and merely present some of the raw materials which any useful definition will have to exploit. For brevity, we shall present in dogmatic form what are often hypotheses or even speculations. Most of the ideas will be found (with more documentation) in earlier publications of ours. To save reiterated reference, we list these at the outset and assume them in what follows: (Russell and Russell, 1957, 1958, 1959, 1961; Russell, 1952, 1954, 1956, 1957, 1958, 1959a, 1959b, 1960; Russell and Burch, 1959; Russell, *et al.*, 1954; Chance and Russell, 1959; Hayes, Russell, *et al.*, 1953).

Automatic and Evolutionary Machines:
Specialization and Progress

"The best thinkers, men like Russell or Carnap, have joined William James in maintaining that patterns of relations are all that can be called 'mind'" (von Bonin, 1950). This is all very well as a starting point, but does not take us very far. It would, in fact, be difficult to find a better definition of "matter." But before we cavil, it is wise to remember Craik's (1943) warnings against overprecise definition too early in the game. "Pattern" is a concept on which most of us fall back in the end, and the meaningful and precise discussion of patterns is obviously the next step in science. It is obvious that pattern has something to do with the cybernetic concept of information; no less obvious, that amount of information is only one aspect of patterns. The concept of message (e.g., Shannon and Weaver, 1949) brings us a little closer, and at once permits discussion in terms of *specific* sets. For the present, however, let us simply regard patterns as things with a definite amount of information and a definite message structure, things which can appear, persist, disappear, and above all *vary*. As convenient examples we may think of organisms, nucleoproteins, activities in a cluster of neuron somata and meshing processes, or cultural characteristics in a society. (If the wording is clumsy, we have at least resisted the temptation to speak of patterns as examples of patterns!).

Evolutionary (Darwinian) processes are extremely widespread, and organic evolution was only the first such system to be discovered. They exist whenever patterns are repeatedly generated, possessing varying properties of self-perpetuation. The shape of a whole system of this kind is determined less by what appears than by what persists, and initially improbable events can soon become the rule (cf. Pringle, 1951; Fisher, 1954). The relative claims of the varying candidates for survival, or persistence, are determined by their environment, and hence subject to change. Such a system can be thought of as a source of effectively random variety, or noise, and a filter, the environment, which imposes a continually changing shape on the whole system. The often transient world of the physicist's subatomic particles, no less than the vicissitudes of stars and galaxies, appears well suited to this sort of analysis; and we may have to reckon with the possibility that matter as we know it now may be the end product of an unimaginably long selection process; nor can we expect constancy from the parameters of selection. The less viable particles of today may be the matter of tomorrow.

Anything that behaves, that observably does things, may conveniently be called a machine; anything, in short, with an output. For convenience, we restrict the term to that set of machines which also has an input of information, which governs its output. Such an open system, linked by input and output with an environment (cf. Ashby, 1956; Bertalanffy, 1956), may have input-output relations of greater or less complexity (information content). Correspondingly, it may have a more or less varied behavior. The survival of the machine depends on its capacity to match the variety of challenge presented by the environment.

Such machines may be of two kinds—automatic and evolutionary. An automatic machine is made up of a small number of parts, and its input-output switching relations are fixed, though they may include corrective feedback circuits. An evolutionary machine is made up of a large number of parts; its input-output relations *change* in accordance with its performance in the environment. As long as all or most of the parts are in communication, the machine fully retains its evolutionary character. Patterns of connection between the parts, and hence of input-output relations, endlessly appear, persist, and disappear; those combinations that persist at any time are those generating the most adaptive output for the current environment. If such a machine functions for a long time in a uniform and constant environment, the same combinations are persistently selected, and may begin to harden into permanent components. If this process of *specialization* goes to completion, communication between the original parts is drastically reduced and canalized, *isolation* between them becomes permanent, and the machine reduces to a fully automatic one with few parts and fixed input-output relations. Evolutionary character may thus be totally lost.

As long as a machine remains evolutionary, it constantly becomes more complex, and its behavior more varied. Therefore, of two machines which have specialized to complete automaticity, that one will be the more complex (and successful in the environment) which has been evolutionary for the longest time. In organic evolution itself, this principle underlies the phenomenon of successive ecological replacement.

Specialization may be averted contingently by the provision of a series of environmental changes which never tax the machine's powers too severely, but never permit any combinations of parts to remain stable too long. (This principle may be traced back to Hippocrates.) But a machine may also be intrinsically *progressive*. If it is equipped with an integrated self-scanning device, which can continually break up old combinations, release new variance, and maintain communication between parts, the machine may remain evolutionary for a virtually unlimited period. Such a device implies a centralized control of the evolutionary process within the machine. By such means, a machine may continue indefinitely to increase in complexity and in variability of output.

Isolation and Automaticity: The Instinct System
in Lower Animals

The relationship betweeen isolation and automaticity is most clearly seen, and has been established with certainty, in the instinct systems of lower animals. A simple and critical example is that of male mating behavior in frogs and toads. Once the animals are assembled at a breeding site, mating consists largely of a simple two-stage behavior sequence. The first stage is highly unselective: a male will clasp any other animal, ovulating female, nonovulating female, or male. The second stage is selective: a male will continue to clasp an ovulating female, but will unclasp from any other partner. In nature, a male will swim away after unclasping, and is statistically unlikely to encounter the same partner again. But if a pair of animals is kept in a small aquarium, a male will repeat the process with the same unsuitable partner (nonovulating female or male), so that a series of clasping spells are observed. In such conditions, male clawed frogs have been shown to be incapable of accepting the unsuitability of the partner. For up to twelve hours, they continue to provide spells of clasping, and the length of these spells does not decrease. Similar absence of modification has been shown in repeated tests over periods of weeks, with controls periodically "rewarded" with ovulating females. Nor do repeatedly frustrated males ever modify the orientation of their initial clasp on the body of the female. In short, their input-output relations are completely fixed.

This automaticity stems from the complete isolation between the two mechanisms of clasping and unclasping which make up the two-stage behavior. Since it proved possible to measure both in the same balanced-design experiments, analyses of variance could be made on both stages under identical conditions, and these showed that some factors affect clasping but not unclasping, others unclasping but not clasping. This result would only be possible on the asumption of complete functional isolation between the two mechanisms, for which it provides critical evidence. It was as if there were two frogs in one skin, separately motivated and competing for control of the output. Translated into time, the observation can be described as follows. When a frog is in a clasping mood, it has no access to any inputs that occurred when it was in an unclasping mood. Picturesquely put, the frog approaching an unsuitable partner for the second or twentieth time cannot remember the rebuff it sustained previously.

This particular mechanism is fully automatic. The instinct system of lower vertebrates does, of course, have evolutionary properties, specially notable in birds and teleost fishes. However, as appears, especially from the experiments of Diebschlag (1941), the system is designed for specialization. Parts of it are automatic from the outset, and the rest becomes increasingly so through the specialization process called *conditioning*. This is associated with a steady splitting of the animal's behavior into smaller and smaller sequences governed by moods or submoods in each of which only a small selection of the animal's sensory, motor, and integrative apparatus is available for use. Paraphrasing Von Uexkull, we may speak of such an animal as a "republic of drives"— crude, bloc mechanisms which interact in accordance with simple rules. These constitute what has been called the *determination* system of behavior control. Each has access to an isolated network of *adjustment* mechanisms, but adjustment capacities (e.g., motor skills) acquired in one mood are inaccessible in another, and as the specialization process continues the animal approximates more and more to a set of wholly isolated subanimals. The nearer this process comes to completion, the more fully automatic the animal becomes.

The most obvious symptom of specialization is the relative irreversibility of the conditioning processes. "Unlearning" and "relearning" are extremely difficult for birds and teleosts. Greater flexibility is seen in the young of bird species, associated with the kind of behavior called play. Neotenously, many mammals and a few birds have retained some of this flexibility after sexual maturity. Such exploratory, adaptable species achieve a correspondingly wide ecological range, the reward of a reluctance to commit themselves too readily to special policies, seen in the gradual and fluctuating decline of errors in conditioning experiments (in contrast to most birds, which rapidly achieve a complete elimination of "errors," like "good" totalitarian party members).

The brains of birds and teleosts, dominated by massive structures with isolated islands of cells, are well suited to a process of specialization tending to complex but automatic behavior. The cerebral cortex offers greater opportunity for developing a progressive system. Spread out on a sheet of cortex, neuron groups are readily switched and reswitched into any desired patterns of intercommunication. We might thus envisage a gradual fusing or pooling of adjustment mechanisms into a computing apparatus available to the animal as a whole. Recent neurological work suggests that the interlinking of all parts of the cortex is achieved less by transcortical connections than by to-and-fro circuits between cortex and Penfield's "centrencephalon" in the brain stem (cf., e.g., Penfield and Rasmussen, 1952; Penfield, 1958; Gastaut, 1958; Adrian, et al., 1954—especially Fessard, Lashley, Penfield; similar principles may apply to the two hemispheres in placental mammals—Fessard in Adrian, et al., p. 207; but see J. R. Russell and Reitan, 1955). Full integration and progressiveness comes with the development of the intelligence system in man, to which we now turn.

The Intelligence Factors in Man

"Early attempts at isolation and measurement of intelligence, whether conceived as one or several variables, contributed valuable advances in method, especially statistical method (notably the development of factor analysis) but failed signally to isolate a factor or factors with any clear biological significance. Thus, the well-known Stanford-Binet I.Q., despite its widespread adoption, is virtually unaffected by 'chronic intermittent exposure to relatively high-grade anoxia' [Halstead] or by removal of both frontal lobes or unilateral removal of any other brain lobe [Hebb], and, in general, notably fails to accord, except possibly at its limits, with observations on the individual's behavior in everyday life" (Russell and Russell, 1957).

The first successful approach to intelligence measurement was made by Halstead (1947, 1951), undoubtedly because he started both from biological considerations and from an appreciation of the work of Freud. His four factors, significantly associated with the neocortex, reflect a progressive evolutionary machine in action. Noncommitally described by him as the A, C, D, and P factors, we have called them, for mnemonic purposes, abstraction, integration, specific expression, and the exploratory drive. Abstraction is the recognition of similarities and dissimilarities, and hence permits discrimination between a potentially unlimited number of slightly different environmental situations. Integration is the evolutionary growth of recorded experience through free intercommunication between all records and computations. Specific expression is self-descriptive; its defect appears, for instance, in agnosias and apraxias of specific nature and focal organization. The exploratory drive, whether exercised as overt exploration in an environment or imaginative trial and error with Craikian models in the brain, is a means for suspending immediate stereotyped action to permit inputs to be classified by abstraction and collated by integration with messages from other sources.

Intelligence as a whole is the exact opposite of conditioning. "In intelligence, an earlier experience permits increased variability of response to a situation reminiscent of it, while under conditioning the earlier experience reduces this variability, and determines a unique response" (Russell and Russell, 1959). The one is progressive, the other specializing.

One further useful distinction may be made between two kinds of exploration. We have distinguished correlative exploration, which builds up a general environmental map or Weltanschauung, and executive exploration, which develops strategies of action. The two may be directly compared with fundamental and applied scientific research, and, as in the sociological context, should fruitfully work together but may in fact be ungeared, with harmful results. This particular division has just been supported in an interesting study by Pribram (1959), who speaks of "differentiative" and "intentional" thought, and provides experimental evidence for their distribution to different parts of the cortex.

Consciousness and Attention

"There is no such entity as consciousness; . . . we are from moment to moment differently conscious" (Hughlings Jackson, cited by Fessard in Adrian, *et al.*, 1954). "All progress in this field has been achieved not by obsessional worry about what 'consciousness' is (or, for the more fashionable philosophers, 'means'), but by treating it as a *variable* and examining its different *states*" (Russell and Burch, 1959). Even on the crudest criteria, it is obvious that the number and variety of states are considerable. "No fewer than seven stages of anaesthesia can be distinguished in terms of the human electroencephalogram" (*ibid.*).

Before attempting any classifications in this area, it is useful to consider in some detail the mechanism of *attention,* and what can go wrong with it. We have seen that animal behavior in time is an oscillation of moods. In our brains there are far more control units, and we must conceive of a flashing series of momentary mood transitions. The integrated intelligence system links these together by the mechanism of attention, which scans these transitions. Our general impression of continuous awareness seems to cover a series of time-quanta of attention. The notion of a stream of consciousness is steadily being replaced by that of a volley of consciousness (cf. Lashley in Adrian, et al., 1954). Fessard (ibid.) proposes a model based on step-functions (cf. Ashby, 1952) in assemblies of short-axon neurons with negligible intrinsic impulse conduction; McLardy (1959) bases a more elaborate model on his remarkable anatomical observations in the rhinencephalon and temporal cortex, which gives the same general property of quantal processes. Such models fit in with copious psychological experiments, e.g., with tachistoscopes, and raise the important possibility, to which we shall return, of the attention mechanism "missing a beat" and permitting unscanned, unscreened activity in the brain. Above all, the process of attention is thus related to the well-known property of flicker fusion frequency in vision—our capacity to discriminate individual light flashes of greater or less frequency. The higher the fusion frequency of attention, on this analogy, the less the chance of "missing a beat," and hence the more complete and continuous control of behavior by the intelligence system. The relationship is more than an analogy. In considering visual flicker fusion frequency we must attach considerable importance to the retina, at least in fishes, to judge from the remarkable study by Svaetichin (1956) of fish cones. But comparable information about mammals is lacking, and other retinal properties of lower vertebrates seem to have become centralized in mammals, after loss of the peripheral mechanisms in the nocturnal phase of mammalian evolution. In man, certainly, central nervous variation plays a major part in determining visual fusion frequency (Simonson and Brozek, 1952). Above all, Halstead (1947) has produced unequivocal evidence for a positive correlation between visual fusion frequency and the exploratory drive itself. The cortical electrical rhythms seem to come into this picture, in ways which are not yet clear (Halstead, ibid.; Walter, in Adrian, et al.). They further draw attention to a second quantal process of concentration, of appreciably longer time base (Adrian, et al.—Walter's paper, and Rioch's comment on p. 373), related to the length of time we can "hold" a uniform content unchanged in our attention. Some people can create and hold visual afterimages in this way.

We can attend to a great variety of inputs. We can attend to immediate input from extero- and proprio- and interoreceptors, to memories apparently stored in temporal cortex, to all kinds of imaginative computation, and to the pattern of activity in our brains which constitutes, at any given moment, our mood. This includes the activity of the cruder mechanisms at the base of the brain, which we can use, on a sort of vernier principle, as rough and ready indicators of need, frustration, or danger. In social terms, we can thus be aware of our own feelings, and of the feelings of others, instantly resynthesized from our observations of their behavior. By the same token, any or all of these kinds of input may *escape* our attention.

It is becoming clear that the mechanism of attention involves a screening or selection of inputs at all stages from the ultimate brain analyzers to the peripheral receptors themselves (e.g., Granit, 1955; Hagbarth, 1959). This selection process is a subtle one. As Halstead has put it, attention is like the tuning eye of a radio receiver, and we can tune for high fidelity reproduction of a large assembly of inputs, or for discriminative concentration on a smaller selection. We can focus to a point, or explore the widest reaches of imagination.

It is not yet clear how we can maximize both range and sharpness of focus together. In this connection, the observations of Horn and Blundell are of great interest (Horn and Blundell, 1959; Horn, 1960, and personal communication). These authors studied electrical activity in the cat's visual cortex evoked by light flashes. They found that this response was significantly *reduced* if the cat was attending to (another) visual input—e.g., if it was observing a mouse behind a transparent screen, or searching visually for the source of a sound. But if the cat was attending only to auditory input (and *not* searching visually for its source), the cortical response was unaffected. This observation disposes of the naive view that attention simply means censoring out the inputs which are not being attended to.

The authors give a convincing explanation of this result. They suggest that when attending to a particular set of inputs the animal employs sharpening devices (entailing reduced activity in parts of the pathway) to get fine discrimination. Meanwhile inputs from other modalities are monitored with special *sensitivity*, and a corresponding loss of detail. (That sensitivity and discrimination are often mutually opposing requirements is a commonplace of sensory physiology. This attention model is strikingly analogous to the primate duplex retina itself, made up of a cone-rich *area centralis* for precise reception of a limited field, a peripheral rod-rich zone for cruder but highly sensitive vision, and a fixation reflex to focus interesting events, signaled in a warning way from the periphery, on the discriminative area. We may reasonably suppose mammalian attention to function in a rather similar way, with a sensitive "background" and a detail-rich focus). Horn has discussed the postulated sharpening mechanisms in detail. The sharpening principle is, of course, well known in sensory physiology (e.g., Whitfield, 1956), but Horn raises some interesting new possibilities.

This compromise mechanism must be liable to certain disadvantages. It is clear from many kinds of evidence that conditioning occurs specially readily in response to inputs on the fringe of attention, where we are paying the price for increased sensitivity by a certain loss of clarity, and hence control. Our attention mechanism, unlike the retinal one, is probably not based on a relatively fixed receptor and synaptic organization, and there seems no reason why we should not learn to improve it; this is a vital problem for research. We cannot be too well equipped against "hidden persuaders" (Packard, 1957).

It is sometimes rashly assumed (e.g., Prechtl, 1956) that the mammalian attention mechanism and those underlying mood changes in lower vertebrates (with the accompanying restriction of reactivity to particular sets of inputs—cf. Tinbergen, 1951) are identical, so that we can freely relate the results of mammalian physiologists and lower vertebrate ethologists. There are, however, indications that the mechanisms may be rather different, even if both employ similar basic principles of centrifugal control and tuning. The remarkable experiments of Von Holst (1950) show that a fish that is watching or hunting prey by vision, and so becomes, in his phrase, "all eyes," is actually *more sensitive* to light stimulation in general. His result is unequivocal, and precisely contradicts that of Horn and Blundell on the cat. We may well suppose that the mammalian attention mechanism is the product of a long and eventful evolution, and this may encourage the hope of improving our own.

Dissociation, Rationalization, and Repression

The intelligence system, linking successive moods in time by the attention mechanism, provides the human individual with a continuous *personality*. This connecting thread must be slender in nonhuman higher mammals and negligible in other species. The maintenance of a personality depends on free access by the attention to any kind of current or recorded input. It has been obvious since Freud (and in some ways before him) that none of us has a completely integrated personality in this sense. It was the master stroke of Freud to emphasize accessibility. Both common sense (typified by the story of the centipede who "lay distracted in the ditch" when asked "which leg goes after which") and a great deal of experimental evidence (cf. Leeper, 1951) agree in stressing the advantage of delegating the control of skilled performance to mechanisms which are not continuously attended to, and the fact that this delegation constantly occurs. Granit (1955), discussing the tabulation by Loewenstein and Sand of the responses of labyrinth receptors, makes a feeling comment: "The way it [the Loewenstein-Sand table] resolves space into a number of permutations makes one feel grateful for having the appropriate compensatory movements in the muscles wholly performed by automatic reflex adjustments!" Building computers is only an exosomatic (Lotka, 1925) extension of the principle. But all such delegations should be reversible, and it should be possible to scan and readjust them wherever necessary. As long as this is so, they are not unconscious in Freud's sense. Halstead, who has collected instances of famous musicians giving technically flawless performances while their consciousness was impaired, makes the interesting observation that "the creative artist never regards such performances as works of art." Presumably it is just that facility for general supervision and occasional slight modification of a practiced and largely delegated performance that marks the presence of full artistic attention. And of course the function of all art, as Edith Sitwell said of poetry, is to "heighten consciousness." As long as such performances are subject to just this sort of attention, there is no question of impairment of personality.

But this continuity is, in practice, never perfectly attained. One basic obstacle is the process of *rationalization*. This occurs when the exploratory drive is aroused but blocked from full expression, and may be described, by extrapolation from observations on animal behavior, as a "vacuum inactivity" of the exploratory drive itself. Exploration should continue until a problem has been solved and a strategy formed. Rationalization occurs when a piece of automatic behavior is performed, and a false process of thinking computes this behavior to be the rational solution of the real problem. It is rather like cooking the books. Rationalizations (and the moralizations which are their further degradation) are maintained only at the cost of dissociation. For they entail the setting up of false memories, false inferences, false reports about feelings, which would be exposed as such if brought into relation with true observations. In this way, as can be documented in detail, a personality may be split into isolated blocs of mechanism, which we may call *fantasies*. Further fragmentation among these mechanisms proceeds apace in just the same way as in bird conditioning. Fantasies behave exactly like lower animal instinctive mechanisms, and may compete among themselves. In this way there occurs a full reversion to instinctive function, though the *content* of the system may be quite different, and much more variable between individuals. In fact, of course, the intelligence system takes a long time to develop, and the initial damage is done during this early period, so that no complete personality is ever formed. The adult human individual is a blend of intelligent and instinctive function and may make secondary attempts to reintegrate his personality by means of what we call a *defense* system—a more or less elaborate Weltanschauung in which false and true information are more or less convincingly reconciled. This must be distinguished on the one hand from true integration, which entails the discarding as false of every scrap of fantasy, and on the other hand from that fusion of entirely unrealistic fantasies which makes up the coherent pseudo personality of a Hitler, nourished only by the contingent "fitness of the environment" which (for a time) makes the nightmare seem to come true.

Dissociation is, of course, maintained only if the scope of attention is restricted at any given moment. There are conditions under which attention is depressed in a rather general way. Thus, one of Halstead's subjects, exposed to anoxia while responding to silhouettes of aircraft, "repeatedly denied ability to 'see' the briefly exposed form, yet . . . made perfect discriminations throughout" (Halstead, 1947). Here inputs were arriving from the periphery and being coded into output, without the attention mechanism ever being able to "catch" them. But of course, the screening of events from attention is usually much more specific.

Some idea of the time constants of attention and dissociation can be obtained from the elegant experiments of Benton (1950). . . . He used a tachistoscope, . . . a common device . . . by means of which a word or other pattern can be presented to the subject's view for very short periods. When the machine is set at certain rates, it takes a number of repeated presentations before the subject can recognize any complex pattern, and this number, with other features, can be scored. Benton presented, in each test, two four-letter words, in different colors, but with their letters interspersed. The subject was to recognize the two words. Of many interesting things Benton observed, the most important is this. He would choose two words of which one might be neutral or agreeable, but the other in some way unpleasant. But the two words, if combined as a phrase, were chosen for their effectiveness in evoking extremely stressful childhood experiences. . . . It was found that when the neutral word was presented with another neutral word, to make an innocuous phrase . . ., it was recognized more rapidly (that is, after fewer presentations in the machine) than when presented in the disturbing combination. . . . In Freudian terms, . . . when the disturbing pair was presented, both words were unconsciously recognized, the phrase was unconsciously recognized and interpreted, the phrase was unconsciously linked with repressed material, and steps were taken to prevent or at least delay recognition (in some cases the subject simply gave up . . .), all before the subject was aware of recognizing even one of the two words (for the unpleasant one was recognized even later). In more dynamic terms, we may suppose that at one of the very brief presentations the phrase keyed in, in releasing stimulus fashion, to some block of isolated material. The attention was not able to catch this mood, so the observation was dissociated from the attentive phase. Processes were then set going which actually deflected the attention from the sensory inputs from the machine. . . . The observation shows us that while an isolated mechanism has control of a mood it may take advantage of this, not only to produce overt behaviour, but also to set up specific obstacles to the scanning process of attention for an appreciable time to come. This . . . is one form of the mechanism Freud called resistance" (Russell and Russell, 1961).

Dissociation may take many forms, which have barely begun to be charted. At one extreme, a very short period of experience may be singled out for isolation. A beautiful instance is cited from E. Miller by Klüver (1958). A certain epileptic patient, just before each convulsive attack, used to see the white letters I E L D S on a blue background. It turned out that when the patient was seven years old he was traveling in a train when a man in the carriage made a homosexual assault on him. "The train was passing London Fields station at the time, and the window frame obstructed all but the letters I E L D S as the frightening experience took place" (Klüver). It is easy to estimate the very short time span involved in this dissociated experience.

At another extreme, a personality may be divided into two or more phases so compact, coherent, and separate as to impose the definition of multiple (or split) personality. Many examples have been studied since the classical observations of Morton Prince. This may be regarded as the extreme form of *hysterical* dissociation. In general, this involves a number of separate phases, each of which may control behavior over an appreciable period, and in each of which the attention is restricted to a particular sample of inputs, differing between phases. Hysterical dissociation is readily illustrated by the commonplace experience of mislaying an object, by putting it away in one mood and looking for it in another. Here there is an obvious reminiscence of the frog in clasping mood "forgetting" what he did in unclasping mood; and, indeed, hysterical dissociation strikingly resembles the instinctive dissociation of lower animals, and can be analyzed along much the same lines. A rather different arrangement is the *schizoid* dissociation. Here the real and fantasy worlds alternate with so rapid a flicker as to appear simultaneous to the attention. For an observant schizoid, the experience may be rather like that of an epileptic during a "psychic" attack or a subject whose temporal cortex is being stimulated electrically. (For copious examples, see Penfield and Rasmussen, 1952, who write as follows about a woman whose attack included visions of a childhood scene in which she was frightened by someone approaching from behind: "During the attack she was conscious of her actual environment and called those present by name; yet she also saw herself as a little girl with such distinctness that she was filled with terror lest she should be struck or smothered from behind. She seemed to be thinking with two minds.") Most of the time, of course, the schizoid state is much less dramatically twofold than this. On account of the continuous real picture, the predominantly schizoid individual is more continuously realistic than the hysteric, and makes, for instance, a good pilot (a profession where moment-to-moment realism is literally vital). The presence of the continuous fantasy picture, however, makes it necessary for the schizoid to dissociate reports about his or her own emotions, since the fantasies would otherwise be in constant danger of erupting into action. Besides the hysteric and the schizoid (who make up most of mankind), there are those who, like Hitler, abandon the real world altogether and act upon it only by a ceaseless endeavor to make it corroborate their fantasies. Such people we have described as basic cynics. Their mode of action in an environment can readily be reproduced, in simpler form, in experiments on birds.

When we have grasped that dissociation is basic, Freud's "structural" view of the mind ceases to be altogether satisfactory, though, of course, he himself regarded it as both picturesque and provisional, and provided most of the really important concepts. In certain hypnotic states, the material of what we should call the conscious personality may be just as completely repressed (i.e., inaccessible to attention) as the contents of a session including instructions for post-hypnotic amnesia (a technique to be deplored from the therapeutic point of view) are repressed in the more normal "waking" state. Repression cuts both ways, and dissociation is more fundamental. But it is convenient "to single out, in a given individual, the organized system that controls his behavior *for most of the time,* and to call this his personality. We can then refer to material available in other, more transient moods, and not in the periods when the personality is in control, as repressed" (Russell and Russell, 1961). Behavior planned and executed under full control by the personality, and continuously attended to, may be described as *conscious.* (The term may also be extended by courtesy to any material which we *could* scan if we wanted to—one of the shades of meaning underlying Freud's concept of "pre-conscious.") Fantasies, motives, and moods may be called *unconscious* if they elude our attention just long enough to issue in such transient (but often serious) acts as Freudian slips of the tongue, pen, or typewriter. Fantasies which dominate our behavior over substantial periods may be described as *pro-conscious* (the prefix is used in the sense of "instead of"). The whole of the behavior of a Hitler is proconscious, and such leisurely and deliberate irrationality is the most dangerous of human aberrations. In general, a fantasy will be proconscious (and hence unhesitatingly and deliberately translated into systematic action, or "acted out") if it can be rationalized or moralized in a manner acceptable to the actor—whch in its turn will be greatly influenced by the climate of fantasy in his society. An Aztec or a Carthaginian, unless outstandingly intelligent, would hardly need any personally manufactured rationalization for human sacrifice.

The result of rationalization and dissociation is an increasingly instinctive system operating in uneasy discord with what remains of an intelligent personality. The greater the disturbances of attention, the greater the proliferation of instinctive fantasies, since conditioning takes place (and can only take place) if the conditioning factors are excluded from attentive scrutiny. (Something analogous can be discerned in bird behavior.) We do not claim even temporary finality for our conscious-unconscious-proconscious classification. It is clear, however, that any definition of mind will have to rest on some sort of classification in terms of what inputs are available for action, attention, and other effects.

Instinct and Intelligence in Human Society

It is evident from all this that human behavior is determined jointly and interactively by two quite different systems—intelligence and (acquired) instinct. It must be admitted that the behavior of large groups of people is instinctive to a disturbing degree. But we must not be too surprised to find intelligence manifesting itself at the sociological level. Attendance at a (British) County Court jury recently gave one of us a homely but impressive demonstration of just how intelligently a heterogeneous group of twelve people, assembled for a short period, can behave as a sociological unit. Still, for many purposes of mass survey and analysis, we can expect fairly reliable predictions if we consider only instinctive action and interaction, and at least we can isolate them first and see what residues remain. What is certainly inappropriate, and perhaps responsible for much confusion in present-day sociology and economics, is to mix up the two concepts into an ill-defined notion of "rational self-interest." In so doing, we fail to apply in this context the remarkable results of lower animal ethologists on animal instinctive systems, results attained by and prompting the development of sophisticated methods and criteria which do not yet seem to have found their way into the human social sciences.

This matter is relevant to any attempt at a definition of mind helpful to the sociologist, and may be illustrated by discussion of a single article, which draws attention to some of the drawbacks of present economic theory. "The transitivity of preferences," writes Davis in the article concerned (1958), "is a question of central importance to both psychology and economics." He begins his paper on the subject by drawing attention to a common assumption of economic theory, namely, that man is "rational." He analyzes this assumption into two parts: that man can rank or order preferences, and that man can choose to maximize something. He concerns himself with the first of these, and divides it further into two parts, as follows:

1. It is assumed that man can show a preference or an indifference between two different states.

2. It is assumed that such preferences are *transitive*. That is, if $A > B$ (i.e., A is preferred to B) and $B > C$, then $A > C$. The contrary condition to transitivity is the occurrence of *circular triads* ($A > B$ and $B > C$ and $C > A$).

Transitivity seems a common-sense assumption, but circular triad phenomena are not unknown in natural systems; they occur, for instance, in the dominance rank orders of cattle (Schein and Fohrman, 1955). The present problem concerns the relations between central nervous mechanisms within the individual, but (by analogy) we cannot assume transitivity of preferences *a priori*, and the issue is rightly referred to experiment. Davis reviews a number of earlier reports, on the strength of which circular triads have been claimed to occur. In criticizing these, he notes that "a certain amount of intransitivity in data can be explained as a result of random choice between indifferent objects." Hence, he concludes, a theory of transitivity would only be challenged by the observation of *stable* circular triads, remaining unchanged in the same subjects on two different occasions. Davis shows that this criterion was not met by the earlier observations, and reports the results of two experiments of his own.

In the first of these, he used, as stimuli, verbal descriptions of girls. Each girl was described by three adjectives, referring to her looks, charm, and wealth, respectively (e.g., "pretty, average charm, wealthy"). The nine "girls" were made up combinatorially from different "doses" of these three qualities, and presented in pairs to the male subjects, who were asked to indicate which of each pair they would rather marry. Each "girl" was compared in this way with every other, and the preference between each pair recorded. The experiment was repeated with the same subjects and stimuli six weeks later. The results showed a very large number of transitive preferences which were stable (i.e., identical on both occasions), and very few stable circular triads with preferences in the same direction (sixteen out of 3,948 reactions). The results of statistical analysis were consistent with the assumption that these sixteen stable circular triads were the result of random choice. A slight discrepancy between statistical tests could be explained on the assumption that choice between some of the nine stimuli was random, while choice between others was biased. Davis concluded that his subjects were sometimes choosing at random between indifferent stimuli, and sometimes expressing significant preferences; in the latter case, the preferences were transitive.

A second, less exhaustive experiment, employed as stimuli descriptions of possible bets, differing in respect of stake, odds and probability of winning. The results conformed with those of the first experiment, in that the few stable circular triads in the same direction could be explained as the result of random choice between indifferent stimuli.

It is clear from the work of Davis and his predecessors that in this sort of observation stable transitive preferences occur *statistically*, and not with absolute regularity. We may inquire whether further experimental control might not remove this residual variance. Mead, for instance, (1953), found that hoarding only occurred in a proportion of individuals in a group of rats; but by persistent juggling with environmental variables he finally induced every one of the recalcitrant rats to hoard. In such contexts, randomness is usually a name for our ignorance of the effective variables. Apparently stable circular triads do not occur systematically in this sort of study. It remains to consider why they ever occur at all. We might suppose that environmental situations are ranked in human brains somewhat in the manner of moves in machines designed to play chess, which may sometimes be faced by a choice between "indifferent" moves (i.e., moves of identical score and hence rank), and settle the problem by tossing a coin. Davis seems to assume something of the sort. But the human brain is an evolutionary machine, and in the original context of organic evolution the occurrence of complete indifference or identity in selective advantage between two genetic alleles must be vanishingly rare, mainly because of the interactive complexity of the individual organism and of populations of these (cf. Fisher, 1954; Sheppard, 1954). This latter property may be taken for granted in the human brain. It is notoriously difficult, if not impossible, for the human brain to generate series random with respect to any particular course of events. This is why we use tables of random numbers, and it also underlies Freud's analysis of the psychopathology of everyday life.

We may then assume that, while intransitivity is not an important systematic property of such choices, many still unknown variables must be effective in experiments of this type. If these are to be tracked down, the question of method becomes important, and very important guidance here can be drawn from the work of ethologists (especially Tinbergen). The term "rational," as used by Davis and those he cites, seems nearer in sense to the usage of mathematicians than of psychologists. It appears to mean "systematic from the *observer's* view-point." The three components of this "rationality" which he distinguishes are distinct preferences, transitivity of preference, and capacity for maximization. Any of these could be shown by a very simple machine; it would be slightly more trouble to construct an intransitive machine than a transitive one. The possession of these three properties certainly does not imply rationality (in the sense of intelligence) in the behavior of the individual *observed.* The occurrence of distinct and stable preferences is almost the commonest characteristic of lower animal instinctive behavior, and these preferences seem usually to be transitive. Maximization is a familiar property of physiological mechanisms and of the behavior of the simplest organisms. The behavior of the subjects in such experiments is certainly instinctive, and indeed this is dictated by the nature of the tests. Intelligent decisions about marriage are formed in response to the vast complex of variables making up the individual personality of a potential partner, and they are not made, or even influenced, by the combinatorial possibilities of a set of three crude stimuli each varying through a few dose levels—a system of very small information content by the standards of the human brain. Such tests, like some personality questionnaires, cannot be answered intelligently at all; they can, of course, be answered by intelligent individuals who deliberately allow their instinctive reactions free play in order to observe them. The mechanisms studied here are therefore certainly instinctive, and can be studied by the methods used by ethologists on lower animals.

The only serious difference lies in the greater degree of abstraction implied in the use of language (in both input and output), and this does not affect the methodological issue. The subject's reaction (a verbal statement) is an intention movement. In the "girl" experiment, for instance, the results tell us something about the subject's attitudes, but do not imply unconditional prediction about his complete reaction (i.e., his marriage), which will also (intelligence apart) be affected by the then current environmental situation. Animal intention movements are perfectly analogous. The stimuli (girls, bets) may be regarded as *sets* of *key stimulus* factors, exactly comparable to the models used by animal ethologists (see especially Tinbergen, 1948, 1951; Tinbergen and Perdeck, 1950). In studies of the begging reactions of herring gull chicks, models of the parent's head may be used, which differ in respect of elongation, color contrast, and color composition. A set of such models, each presenting a different combination of "dosage" of the three key factors, would be perfectly analogous to the set of stimuli used by Davis.

The reaction scored by Davis and his predecessors is a *choice.* Each *pair* of stimuli is presented concurrently, and the subject can react to one or the other by displaying his intention movement of marriage or gambling. There are at least *four* factors which may operate to produce irregularities in an experiment of this kind.

First, there is the simple fact of change of mood with dissociation. In two different moods, preferences may simply be reversed. This reversal alone, when choice tests are made between pairs at a time, could generate circular triads. The objection is met in part by Davis through his repetition of the experiment weeks later. But mood changes can be very rapid and may be induced (all unknown to the subject) as soon as the stimulus is presented—as in Benton's experiments, where the instinctive, mood-changing effect of a phrase of two words was apparent long before conscious recognition of its components, and where the same word could have different stimulus properties in different combinations with other words. A given pair of stimuli could evoke the same mood at each replicate of the experiment, and the stimulus pairs might differ in this respect.

Second, one of the most important generalizations of ethology is Seitz's *Reizsummenregel*. This rule states that, in releasing a reaction, when internal factors are constant, a certain level of external stimulation must be reached through the presentation of key stimuli; this level can be reached by intensifying *any* of these interchangeably. If two key stimuli A and B are involved, each of which can vary continuously, the same result can be obtained with a high dose of A and a low dose of B as with a low dose of A and a high dose of B. There are, indeed, reasons for supposing the relationship to be multiplicative rather than additive, so that the product is the determining factor. This does not affect the main principle, that of interchangeability of the component key stimuli. But if the relation is indeed interactive, the distortions introduced become more serious: differences in wealth between "girls" *too* deficient in beauty would become negligible, and *vice versa*. In the experiments of Davis, the three key stimuli making up a "girl" or "bet" were varied independently. As a result, some of the combinations may have been so nearly equal in rank (by summation of their components) that the subject's mood became the overriding factor. Despite the alternative argument of the last paragraph, this mood could very well be different in the two replicates. A choice test could never isolate this possible source of apparently random reaction, which could entail the occurrence of some circular triads.

Third, some doses of some components may have had *inhibitory* effects on the reaction, also well known from animals. These may or may not have overridden the simultaneous excitatory effects of other components. Katisha (in *The Mikado*) was doubtless wealthy, but this variable played little part in determining the behavior of Koko or Nankipoo. Similar arguments apply in the gambling context. Gibbon, in his autobiography, put a cogent point about irrelevance of probability values in some situations. "If a public lottery were drawn for the choice of an immediate victim, and if our name were inscribed on one of the ten thousand tickets, should we be perfectly easy?" Death is not the only repulsive association in the century of depressions and recessions.

Fourth, and most telling of all, it is well known in lower animal instinctive mechanisms that the stimuli *releasing* a given reaction may be *different* from those which *direct* it (Tinbergen, 1942, 1948, 1951). As a dramatic illustration, Tinbergen cites the case of some herring gull chicks reacting to the alarm signals of their mother, who had been disturbed by his own movements in his hide nearby. The reaction released in the chicks was quite appropriate—they went to cover. But in this situation the directing stimuli were inadequate, and the chicks took refuge in Tinbergen's hide! More directly relevant is the case where a reaction is released by one set of stimuli, and directed by another. Normally the relevant object in nature will provide both sets of stimuli, but this condition is not met in lavishly combinatorial experiments (cf. also Larrson, 1956). There is ample evidence for this principle in animals, and it would be most valuable to determine its presence or absence in human instinctive mechanisms. In a choice test, this mechanism can cause hopeless confusion, since one of the simultaneously presented stimulus sets may have a greater releasing effect than the other, while the ranks may be reversed in respect of directing or orienting influence. The two effects are confounded when the subject makes a simple choice reaction; his act may have been released by one of the sets, and directed to the other. When this difficulty was encountered in ethology, Tinbergen met it by employing *successive* tests. Instead of being presented in pairs, different models were presented in succession. The time lapse introduced complications of its own (mood change, conditioning effects, delayed actions, etc.) all of which could be overcome by proper experimental design. Models could now be compared in respect of their releasing effects, by scoring the relative frequency or intensity of the reactions they released when each was presented alone. When a choice test gave apparently random choice between two models, it often turned out that in successive tests one model released far more reactions than the other. By *combining* choice and succession tests, all the sources of irregularity we have listed can be effectively isolated and studied. (It is to be noted that they *could* have been acting to mask stable intransitive preferences, though Davis' results in detail make this highly unlikely.)

The use of successive tests would require slight changes in the method of scoring reactions. We have worked out the fundamentals of this problem in the animal context. There are two obvious classes of solution. Each single test or trial now consists of presenting one "girl" or "bet" alone, and a number of such tests are made with the various combinations in a properly randomized and balanced order. At each presentation the subject may be asked to allot a score (say out of ten) to the stimulus he is shown, reflecting the extent of his readiness to make such a marriage or gamble. (This is essentially the device used in personality studies.) Alternatively, the subject may simply be asked to react with "yes" or "no" to each stimulus. Frequencies may then be obtained either by repeated presentation, in the course of the experiment, of each stimulus, or by counting the "yeses" in a population of subjects, on parliamentary lines. The two techniques are precisely those used in animal ethology. Certainly the replicate procedure of Davis should be incorporated in any such program.

The transitivity question, which we have used purely as an example, would of course only be one of very many possible subjects of experiments of this kind, which are urgently needed in order to establish how far the animal generalizations apply to human instinctive mechanisms, and what new principles await our discovery. Certainly such an experimental approach seems called for as the complement of field studies in sociology and economy. Our digression seemed warranted in the present context; any approach to the problem of defining "mind" will sooner or later require information of the kind which such experiments might furnish.

And while we are discussing mind as the economist sees it, a word about money. In his incredibly rich book (1943), Craik let fall a casual sentence well worthy of the economist's attention, and curiously pertinent in this discussion. He was talking about "implication"—"a kind of artificial causation in which symbols connected by rules represent events connected by causal interaction." "Language," he wrote, "in which sounds or written symbols represent things and actions, is one example of such a system; money, which represents labor, is another." Now it is natural to discuss all the Freudian phenomena of repression, rationalization, and dissociation in terms of a symbolism gone wrong, in which the relation between the two sets of rules has broken down in one way or another. But if we take Craik seriously (as we are always well advised to do), then it follows that the vagaries of finance may fruitfully be treated in much the same terms as those we use to discuss psychopathology in the individual brain. Concepts like repression, dissociation, and secondary elaboration may turn out to be most productive in exploring the behavior of money, which certainly departs as grossly from the world of goods and services it purports to symbolize as the fantasies of the human individual do from the environment they are misrepresenting. The study of finance as an instinctive mechanism offers rich possibilities, and might even bear fruit in a sort of economo-therapy for the body economic. "No lie you can speak or act," wrote Thomas Carlyle, "but it will come, after longer or shorter circulation, like a Bill drawn on Nature's Reality, and be presented there for payment,—with the answer, *No effects*." Bankruptcy would be a good starting point for such a study. Or we could examine the bullion freights from newly conquered Mexico and Peru, which ruined Spain and nearly ruined Europe, as a kind of sociological delusion of grandeur. But we leave to others the precise development of this essay in general systems theory.

Psychosomatics, Dreams, and the Repression of Intelligence

Returning to the individual human brain, it will pay us to examine three special forms of dissociation. The first of these is the "mind-body" dissociation, important in the present context as a salient feature of that "background . . . which produces concepts and at the same time conceals their origin."

Perhaps the major achievement of vertebrate anatomy and physiology in the present century has been the steady establishment and documentation of the principle that nothing occurring in our bodies is either beyond control by or without repercussions on our brains, including the cortex and the centrencephalon. The bizarre and pointless feats of the Eastern mystics, which startled our ancestors, seem anything but surprising now that we know of the elaborate circuits linking the brain with every part and process of the body, and the drastic effects on the variance of physiological responses produced by seemingly trivial changes in the *behavioral* environment or, more generally, in the mood of the responding organism. What does now seem surprising is the remarkable degree to which we *lack* intelligent control of our bodily processes. This is, of course, a clear instance of dissociation, whereby most of these processes, adequately signaled in our brains, are inaccessible to the attention of the conscious personality, and hence to intelligent control. How the dissociation arises is a long story, which we have discussed elsewhere at length. At the moment, we need only consider its effects on our thinking.

The most obvious and important effect is, of course, the fantasy by which we rationalize our helplessness—the fantasy that "mind" and "body" are two separate *things* (rather than, for instance, one system and a set of relationships abstracted from it). This fantasy has repeatedly taken shape as a philosophical doctrine, the most influential being the dualism of Descartes. ("No doubt the same factors which compelled him to rationalize in this way *permitted* him to make his really valuable scientific invention of Cartesian co-ordinates"—Russell and Burch, 1959.) One of the special consequences was an attempt to deny lower animals the privilege of variable states of consciousness, as "bodies" without "minds." Another, later, consequence was the deplorable word "psychosomatics" itself. (Deplorable, because it clashes with the traditional sense of "somatic" current long before in physiology. "The proper term for the matter in hand would be the unattractive hybrid "ethoviscerals"—Russell and Burch.) For it gradually became inexorably obvious that brain and viscera *are* linked, and that *instinctive,* uncontrolled psychosomatic interactions are continual and universal. Having separated "mind" and "body," it became necessary to link them together again, and the return of the repressed is fossilized in the technical term which covers at least half modern medicine. Endless arguments about how "mind" can control "body" are with us even today, when the facts stare us in the face. Even in Descartes' time, of course, it was already clear that we have some control over our somatic (*sensu stricto*) if not our visceral activities, and as everyone knows the theorist even supplied a mind-body hookup in the pineal organ. Before we take a single step "toward a definition of mind," we must certainly take account of this dissociation, rampant in all of us, and give a wide berth to the shoal of red herrings in this sea of confusion. Nor shall we ever learn to control our viscera as long as we regard such control as a form of magic.

This type of dissociation has to be considered mainly as an obstacle to our thinking about mind. The second special case, on the other hand, is a source of more raw material. It is the special case of the dream. In the instinct system of animals, it is easy to see the role of dreaming. In sleep the claims of other needs and minor emergencies have to be disregarded. Under the conditions regulating competition between instinctive drives, this can only be achieved by a sort of licensed vacuum activity or inactivity. Those movements which are not actually incompatible with sleep may occur as vacuum activities (the most obvious being male "nocturnal emission," observed in cats as well as man); in some instances it can be shown that these activities depress the corresponding drive, as of course they should. Vacuum inactivity, however, must predominate. Both mechanisms involve hallucinations, which presumably appear for the animal as rather primitive dreams. For organisms with so little continuous personality, they raise few special problems. The mechanism we have postulated for an animal instinct system requires that a goal, a gratification, and a hallucination are functionally identical at some points in the central nervous network, and indirect corroboration comes from studies with human children (cf. the work of Perky, cited in Leeper, 1951).

In man, naturally enough, dreams are enormously complex, and raise enormously complex problems. That they are always dissociated in a highly specific mode from the conscious personality is obvious, and the scope and limitations of dream recall naturally conform to those for other moods, although always with this specific character, elusive and subtle, but manifestly different in quality from the daydream or hallucination or delusion or proconscious masturbation fantasy. Our knowledge of the raw material of dreams has been enormously advanced by the studies of Penfield and his associates on the temporal cortex of epileptics. Our knowledge of the composition of dreams has hardly advanced a step since the "Traumdeutung," which Freud rightly regarded as his masterpiece, and which any would-be definer of mind must read again and again. Insofar as there are points of contact between the two studies, the stimulation results never seem to contradict Freud. Given the elaborate paraphernalia of human rationalization, much of the dream process, on Freud's analysis, corresponds to the simple picture we have constructed for animals; much, but not all. There are residues. One, which continued to nag at Freud to the end, is the repetitive anxiety dream. But even this, we may surmise, is not likely to take us outside the magic circle of instinctive function. The other important residue points straight to our third and final dissociation problem. We have said that motor activity must be restricted during sleep. But that is no barrier to the activity of the exploratory drive, which can function without any immediate motor products. There thus arises the vital problem of *intelligent* dreaming.

That dreams often contain true inferences or predictions, however disguised, is evident to anyone who has analyzed many. By far the most spectacular examples are those concerned with scientific discovery or technological invention. Well known are Kekulé's dozing dream of the snakelike rows of atoms, one of which seized its own tail, thus suggesting the structure of the benzene ring, and Otto Loewi's nocturnal inspiration, which gave birth to the study of chemical transmitters. (Many less familiar revelations are listed in the excellent book of Beveridge, 1957). A story we have been unable to trace in the literature, but which certainly rings true, is that of Elias Howe, inventor of an early sewing machine. Howe, it is related, experimented in vain for a long period, because he always placed the eye of the needle at its blunt end, as in an ordinary sewing needle. He spent all his resources, and was on the point of ruin, when he had his dream. He dreamed he was employed by a barbarian king, who had thrown him into prison and sworn to impale him next day, unless he produced his invention by them. Howe spent a terrible night in his prison cell, and was still baffled when dawn came. He was being led off to execution by armed guards, when he noticed that their spears had holes near the points. He woke up, tried out a needle with its eye at the point, and completed his invention. Whether this story is true or not, it is certainly *ben trovato,* and concentrates many of the features of the undoubtedly authentic cases.

The case of Loewi merits a little further discussion. Loewi woke one night with a brilliant inspiration, which he jotted down. All next day at his laboratory "in the presence of familiar apparatus he tried to remember the idea and to decipher the note, but in vain. By bedtime he had been unable to recall anything, but during the night to his great joy he again awoke with the same flash of insight. This time he carefully recorded it before going to sleep again" (Beveridge). Next day he carried out the experiment he had dreamed up, and proved at once that the vagus nerve releases a chemical transmitter.

The idea of repressing instinctive function (with the inevitable return of the repressed) is familiar enough since Freud. But the idea of repressing intelligent function is still startling. In his structural formulations, Freud sometimes pictured the ego as partly submerged, but he did not follow this up systematically himself, and when his successors pursued the idea of unconscious ego processes their ego began to look less and less like the intelligence system. That extremely elaborate computational devices are prostituted to rationalizing purposes was indeed obvious early in Freud's work. But what we are now considering is something quite different—the dissociation from the main conscious personality of genuinely intelligent processes.

The difference between repression of instinct and repression of intelligence may be illustrated by a hypothetical example, representative of many situations encountered in the consulting room or more generally in everyday life. A man is due to attend an important business meeting, but he never gets there, owing to some such lapse as forgetting the date or mislaying a ticket or missing a train or plane in some "accidental" way. Any such incident is open to two quite different interpretations, far from easy to decide between without independent additional information. The first is that it would be wholly useful and desirable to attend the meeting, and make some arrangement or agreement when there. The man, however, has an irrational resistance to doing this, which he represses and does not attend to. As a result, by Freud's familiar return of the repressed, the irrational motive catches him unawares and brings about the accident that prevents his attendance, wholly to his detriment. The second interpretation is quite different. The man has accurately and intelligently assessed the people he will be dealing with, and rightly suspects that any agreement he may make with such people will only cause him damage; they might, to take a simple case, be swindlers. If he attended to this true inference from their behavior and conversation, he would consciously extricate himself from the relationship, and never undertake to go to the meeting at all. But he may repress his own intelligent observation. If so, this, too, may return, and create the "accident" which saves him in spite of himself, though in a clumsy manner which may be disadvantageous in other ways.

Incidents where the second explanation applies are by no means uncommon. Shakespeare, as usual, provides a splendid example. When Hamlet is about to leave for England with Rosencrantz and Guildenstern, he is in no doubt about their reliability and his own prospects. "There's letters seal'd: and my two school-fellows,—Whom I will trust as I will adders fang'd," etc. (Act III, Scene iv). In the same soliloquy, he even outlines a strategy—that of hoisting the enginer with his own petar. By the time he is on shipboard, he has repressed all this, and goes to his cabin to sleep. But the repressed intelligent observation is still at work. In his heart (as he tells Horatio in Act V) "there was a kind of fighting, that would not let me sleep . . . our indiscretion sometimes serves us well, when our deep plots do pall: and that should learn us there's a divinity that shapes our ends, rough-hew them how we will." Restless with insomnia, he has a vague impulse to look at the letter. He opens it, finds the order for his assassination, and proceeds to carry out the strategy he had formed in Denmark—without remembering this at all. To him it seems like a new and strange inspiration: "ere I could make a prologue to my brains, they had begun the play,—I sat me down; devised a new commission; wrote it fair" and so on. Anyone who has noticed him or herself having this sort of experience will recognize the perfect accuracy of the poet's description. The "divinity" is, of course, our own intelligence. This sort of behavior is specially common in a particular class of the personality type we have called "idealistic," to which Hamlet conforms in all other ways. The chief feature is a readiness to repress (either instantaneously or after first voicing them) accurate observations about the *hostile* intentions of others.

The point is of the greatest practical importance, for the artist and the scientist are specially prone to this kind of dissociation. A glance at Beveridge's book (1957; cf. also Kubie, in Adrian *et al.*, 1954), or the briefest reminiscence of one's own scientific work, is enough to show how extraordinarily little control we have over our own creative thinking. Beveridge has collected the views of various scientists on techniques of "tricking" or "coaxing" our inspirations into appearing for our inspection. Loewi, on these views, was doomed to failure until he had completely relaxed—and also ceased to *try* to remember. The same rather defeatist prescription appears in the Freudian technique of free association. *Faute de mieux*, it may be wise to fall back on such techniques, and undoubtedly a frantic or obsessional attempt to think or recall is always futile. There must, however, be a more rational way of removing this kind of dissociation, which must have constantly retarded the progress of science and art, and which is bound to be most intense in the science of behavior. In the present context we need only notice the important principle that dissociation occurs within the intelligence system itself.

Science Fiction?

The notion of repressing intelligence, and the implication that it should be possible to make intelligence enormously more efficient by overcoming the difficulty, leads inevitably to conjecture about the creative abilities this could release. In any approach to a definition of mind, we cannot indulge an ostrich attitude to what are called "paranormal" faculties. Despite its respectably classical (if hybrid) etymology, "paranormal" is still to a surprising extent a dirty word among scientists. It is therefore useful to preface any discussion of these faculties by a cautionary tale (for which see Griffin, 1958).

In 1793, when the great Spallanzani was already sixty-four, he noticed that a captive owl, when it flew too near to the candle and blew it out, crashed into the wall and any other obstacle, and lost all power to orient its flight. Spallanzani decided to try the experiment with other nocturnal animals, and at once discovered that bats could avoid obstacles perfectly in pitch darkness. In the next few years he and the Swiss surgeon Jurine had established that blind bats can fly perfectly and even catch as many insects as their comrades, that deaf bats are hopelessly disoriented, that this disorientation also occurs when the mouth is covered, but *not* when everything has been done to upset the sense of touch. At the end of his life Spallanzani was still baffled by his own results, which of course seemed fantastic in the eighteenth century (and long after), but he realized that the facts could not be explained away. "Can it then be said that . . . their ears rather than their eyes serve to direct them in flight? . . . I say only that deaf bats fly badly and hurtle against obstacles in the dark and in the light, that blinded bats avoid obstacles in either light or dark." The greatest experimenter then living had thus provided all the clues to a solution of the problem. But the scientific hierarchs of the time, and above all their pope, the anatomist Cuvier, because they could not understand the results, any more than Spallanzani could, simply dismissed them. "To us," pontificated Cuvier, who knew of the Italian's experiments with bats covered with varnish, but chose to forget them, "the organs of touch seem sufficient to explain all the phenomena which bats exhibit." "To assent to the conclusions which Mr. de Jurine has drawn from his experiments," wrote a lesser hierarch a few years later, "that the ears of bats are more essential to their discovering objects than their eyes, requires more faith and less philosophic reasoning than can be expected of the zootomical philosopher, by whom it might fairly be asked, 'Since bats see with their ears, do they hear with their eyes?'" (All quotations cited by Griffin.) Thus the experiments were gradually lost to sight, and further investigation of the problem was postponed for a century, with incalculable effects not only upon biology but other branches of science. Every single successive contributor to the bat problem—Rollinat and Trouessart, Hahn, Maxim, Hartridge, up to Griffin himself—worked in partial or total ignorance of his predecessors' results. Griffin has discussed in detail how useful it would have been if bat echolocation had been investigated earlier; not only the blind might have benefited, but profound repercussions on the whole technology of active detection systems—radar, sonar, and so forth—might have been expected. As it is, many of the fruits of the investigation are still to be awaited. As for the possible effects on the development of science and technology as a whole, they would certainly not have been trivial. All this delay occurred through neglect of Sherlock Holmes' principle—if the probable is impossible, the improbable must be true.

We must be very careful not to make the same mistake over the much more general and important phenomena of telepathy, precognition, and psychokinesis. (For a convenient view of the state of the subject in the fifties, see Wolstenholme and Millar, ed., 1956. The theoretical sterility is depressing, but the symposium leaves one in no doubt of the facts.) Psychokinesis indeed is still little more than a possibility indicated by suggestive but inconclusive evidence. But the evidence for the mere existence of precognition is as copious as, that for telepathy far more copious than, the evidence for most other conclusions in any of the sciences; this is mainly because it has never occurred to anybody to pile up such huge masses of experimental evidence merely to prove the existence of, say, electrical activity in nerve. In such other contexts, scientists have proceeded to *examine* the activity. But where precognition and telepathy are concerned, little has been done to exploit the original discovery. Once their existence has been recognized, we should be looking for these processes in more important contexts than experiments with playing cards. A case in point is the activity of archeologists and paleontologists. With all allowance for inspired inference, their choice of spots on the vast surface of the earth is much too good to be true without paranormal activity. It is a great pity so few of these specialists write novels, for curiously enough it is to a novel that we owe the one authenticated instance of precognition in this field; by writing a novel, the Egyptologist Ebers made explicit imaginative processes which his colleagues must often use. Ebers wrote a novel, *An Egyptian Princess*, in which (to quote his preface to the fourth edition) "the reader will find an oculist from Sais among the characters . . ., who writes a work treating of diseases of the eye. The fate of this valuable work has an important bearing on the events of the story." In 1872-73, after the third edition of the novel was prepared, Ebers made one of his expeditions to Egypt, where he found "many new treasures, among them one of incomparable value, the great hieratic manuscript now preserved in the Leipsic Museum, and bearing my name. Ebers' papyrus, the second largest and the best preserved of all the documents of ancient Egypt still extant, was written in the sixteenth century B.C. . . . In this ancient scroll diagnoses are drawn up and remedies prescribed for the external and internal diseases affecting most parts of the human body. . . . The second line of the first page describes the document as coming from Sais. One long chapter is devoted to the optic nerve. The book on the eye . . . fills eight long pages. Till now we were obliged to refer to Greek and Latin authors for information regarding the oculistic knowledge of the Egyptians. The Papyrus Ebers is the sole Egyptian work from which we can learn anything regarding this branch of medicine among the ancients."

Clearly Ebers was not consciously using his remarkable insight to guide his search. Where scientists use telepathy or precognition, they must use it with just as little conscious control as they use the other processes of intelligence we have discussed. If there is one generalization we can make about these faculties, it is that they are almost universally dissociated in much the same way. They consequently operate in a largely instinctive way. Clearly precognitive dreams (in, e.g., Dunne, 1939; Sabine, 1951) "look" very much like other dreams. Freud (1933) took several apparently telepathic dreams and showed that the raw material obtained by telepathic processes was subjected to exactly the same dream-work as material obtained in more orthodox ways. The point appears rather strikingly when one compares the distortions of pictures which subjects are asked to draw when influenced by different verbal descriptions (in perfectly conventional conditions—Graham, 1951, Figure 30) with the distortions of pictures drawn by one subject when telepathically transmitted from another (Hardy, 1953, Figures 1–4).

This uncontrollable, dissociated, repressed quality of the paranormal extensions of intelligence, which exposes them to instinctive control, has led several biologists who take the subject seriously to a curious conclusion (e.g., Parkes in Wolstenholme and Millar, ed., 1953). They have supposed that the faculties are *vestiges* of instinctive faculties in animals, now disappearing because they have been replaced by the more efficient communication technique of speech. Considering that conventional speech is subject to all the limitations of classical mechanics, while telepathy and precognition are apparently not, this is a somewhat bizarre valuation. (It is rather like the man who refused a book-token with the words "Thank you, I already have a book.") We need not suppose the contrary—that speech is dispensable—for clearly the two modes of communication may be complementary. A more reasonable view would be that these faculties indeed evolved at a stage of purely instinctive control (though there is no decisive evidence for their presence outside man), and have not yet been brought under intelligent control. To achieve this should be a primary goal at this stage of human evolution. It is merely an extension of the goal implied in the last section—bringing all aspects of intelligence itself under full control by the conscious personality. One obviously important step in this direction would be the intensive scrutiny of dreams and other dissociated activities, in the hope of discovering criteria for distinguishing the two situations considered earlier—when an observation determining behavior is false and when it is true. Telepathy is indeed a natural extension of intelligent communication, precognition of intelligent prediction (cf. Von Bonin, 1950).

It would be foolish to entrust the study of these subjects, vitally relevant to every branch of science, to yet another class of specialists, such as "parapsychologists." They are very much the concern of all scientists, and should be approached with all the insights and enlightenments of cybernetics, behavioral science, and general systems theory. Present-day science, dominated by biology and the concept of information, should indeed be more receptive to such unconventional phenomena than that of the nineteenth century, dominated by physics and conservation principles. Biology stands firm on the rock of Darwinian theory; physics has never reached any sort of stability, and has always been notoriously more vulnerable to philosophy and superstition (cf. Pledge, 1939). The more recent discoveries about elementary particles seem to have left the science in a more labile state than ever, desperately seeking a new orientation. Serious study of the paranormal phenomena may be just what is needed. Perhaps the next Einstein (let us call him Zweistein) will be able to harmonize the concepts of energy and information, as Einstein did those of mass and energy, in a new and wider conservation or interconversion principle. Since time enters into all the formal definitions of information, such a theorem would at once embrace the paranormal processes and dispose of what Oppenheimer has called the "rich disorder of our new knowledge." (See editorial, *Nature*, 1956.) Oppenheimer has suggested that "the pioneer conceptions which led through Einstein to the splitting of the atom are now inadequate to yield an orderly description of the physical world. . . . The man or woman who can rescue us . . . [will probably be] someone able not merely to interpret the nuclear scientist to fellow natural scientists, but equally to set that new knowledge in the context of biological science and of the humanities." Zweistein will certainly have to tackle the paranormal, and perhaps when he has finished with mind and matter we shall no longer have to stumble in search of provisional definitions.

Meanwhile here is a tentative suggestion, which anyone who likes may regard as pure science fiction. Let us suppose that the only fundamental space is something we shall call *biological space*. Distances between points on this space are measured only by decrement of information transfer between them. (Cf., in this connection, Rapoport, 1956, and earlier, on the diffusion of information in various kinds of network.) This in turn may be partly determined by the amount of overlap between the internal message structure represented by each of the two points. The more they "resonate," as it were, the nearer they will come. Changes in a point's message structure may occur instantaneously, and two points far apart on this space may become neighbors in a moment. One way of bringing two such points together is literally to move them together in one of the more conventional geometric spaces; they now have more things in common—in particular, their coordinates in the conventional space. But this method of bringing the points together is time-consuming, and involves continuous movement in the classical sense. There may be other ways, as yet unknown to us, of bringing points together in biological space, by making their message structures more alike. Only when points are near together in biological space will they show causal interaction. Causality, in fact, reduces to the critical moments at which systems assume sufficient community of internal message structure to meet in biological space.

Such a view, clearly only the most impressionistic of sketches, would exorcise once and for all the nightmare of action at a distance, which neither Newton nor his modern successors seem ever really to have disposed of, and which obviously provides the main logical objection to the paranormal processes. Picturesquely, we might think of systems as pictorial patterns, intersecting at certain points representing causal interactions between them, and truly independent everywhere else. So far, we have only discovered some of the ways in which these interaction nodes appear and disappear. (The two formulations are obviously related, if we think of the intersection points in the second model as sharing coordinates in its framework, and hence part of their message structure.) Star systems, galaxies, elementary particles, and organisms may all be thought of as interacting in this manner, a limited interaction, but nothing like so limited as we still imagine. The paradoxes of nuclear physics might melt away in such a scheme. The notion of "resonance" is already dimly envisaged in paranormal contexts; thus Ebers could make his prediction only because he already had so much message structure in common with the system "remains of ancient Egypt," which he had studied and explored for decades. Finally, such a view, if developed, would go far to resolve such weird consequences of our present Weltanschauung as the concept of looking at a distant nebula as it was millions of years ago. Without some such reorientation, any serious interest in space travel would be preposterous. But enough of our science fiction, which here serves only to remind us how flexible must be our definition of mind, if we are to be ready for the developments of science in the next century.

Toward a Definition of Mind

We have now made a number of excursions in search of raw material, one of them pretty far afield. What we have gathered at least suggests some of the useful properties which a definition of mind should achieve. It should be concerned with message structure, and specifically with the availability of particular sets of messages at particular points in a system. It might well include some indication of evolutionary properties. If such a program led us into traps like imputing conscious states to a stochastic computing machine, or in a pantheistic way to the organic kingdoms as wholes, some correction might be necessary to restrict the definition to brains, possibly even to particular kinds of interaction within brains (e.g., those of neuropil or short-axon assemblies). Since our brains are beyond the experimental reach of the nuclear physicist, it would be hasty even to assume that matter is not in some unusual state in these conditions. But these are (at present) refinements of open-minded definition. It would be enough, to start with, if we could adumbrate a formal definition in terms of message structure. Such a definition would meet all the requirements we have encountered, and would be specially useful to the sociologist, who wishes to treat the mind of an individual as a unit in a larger network; evidently, in fact, he may have to think of several different kinds of unit in several different kinds of network, for the same human individual can take part in several different kinds of intelligent and instinctive interplays.

As a useful guiding model, we may consider how one of us tackled the much simpler, but in some ways analogous, problem of defining "drive" in lower animal behavior. After restricting the discussion to determination systems (see earlier), an attempt was made to choose output units, not too strictly defined. (Success in such an enterprise hinges on imprecise, and therefore modifiable, definition at the start, followed by a rigorous structure of analysis, which can then be shifted *en bloc* to meet new discovery—an endoskeleton rather than an exoskeleton.) The chosen unit was called an act. This regularly occurring, recognizably distinct output pattern was taken to imply a unit of coordination. Different kinds of measurement can be made upon acts, and these were classified into two groups, labeled as tendency and intensity. Either could be used for the next stages, which were actually developed in terms of act tendency. Operational methods were set up for deciding whether any given physical variable was effective in contributing to the variance of act tendency, and all the variables in the physical universe could then be classified as effective or ineffective for a given act. Having, in principle, determined a set of effective variables for a given act, we can use the ranges of variation and degrees of intercorrelation or independence of these variables to generate a further set, that of all possible combinations of their states. This set represents the set of all messages available to a unit of correlation associated with the act—the act-available message set. The specificity of control for a given act can be measured by comparing this with the set of messages available to the animal as a whole. (We were careful to indicate that, for instinctively controlled animals, this set is a purely theoretical construct, since there is in fact no integrative system like intelligence which can receive all these messages, some of which are in fact distributed to some correlation units, some to others. This point was unfortunately misunderstood by Thorpe, 1954, in his discussion of ethological concepts.) The relations between different correlation units could be clarified by developing various intersection sets of effective variables specific for one act or generic for several. Meanwhile all variables could be independently classified into those relayed immediately previously by exteroceptors and all others; further subsets could be developed along various lines, and these integrated with the original classification to produce such precisely defined concepts as internal act drive. Higher levels of interactions between units were examined, and their treatment sketched out. In particular, A. P. Mead developed a systematic classification of act assemblies on the basis of their specific and generic effective variables. The relative degrees of independence and interrelationship so specified could be usefully employed, in our present context, to clarify the status of two separate minds in telepathic contact.

Detailed examination of this analysis might supply many clues for a definition of mind, in terms of available message sets. Obviously we have to consider sets available for determining motor output somatic or visceral, available for attention, available for effects in various states of consciousness, for visualization, for verbalization. These sets, and the relations between them, would afford a language in which the various processes of dissociation could be precisely discussed. They would specify various kinds of unit in an interacting sociological network. They would make possible precise examination of the very urgent problem of increasing our powers of attention and conscious control over both instinctive and intelligent processes, over our bodily states of health and illness, our artistic and scientific inspirations, our paranormal faculties. We should have to consider the ways in which such sets contract or expand, on evolutionary principles, by specialization, regression, progress. One might recommend the case of dreams as an excellent test for such a theory; consideration of dreams in the early stages would make the classifications supple and powerful. It is unlikely that the very simple Boolian tools employed for the drive concept would suffice in this enterprise, which may well demand much more powerful mathematical instruments (perhaps especially those of machine theory—Ashby, 1956—or a development of the still embryonic graph theory—Harary, 1957, 1959). But the drive study supplies us with one hugely important general principle. We must not be hypnotized by the ultimate goal itself. Our first steps toward a definition of mind will take us away from it. We must begin by examining our output indicators—somatic and autonomic behavior, attention etc.—by choosing, not too strictly, units among these, and deciding how to measure them. It was not till near the end of the drive analysis that it became possible to develop highly elaborate concepts which at last began to "look like" the various usages of the term in common ethological practice. And it will only be at the end of an even longer journey that we begin to see familiar landmarks, and find we have arrived at definitions which really correspond to the current usages of the word "mind." "These concepts are the endproducts of processes of abstraction from simpler and more direct units which have not been explicitly discussed. Until we return to these simpler units, the misunderstandings will persist" (Russell, *et al.*, 1954). We end this article where we began it, for Craik said much the same thing in our opening quotation. But it is to be hoped we have gathered a little moss on the way, and provided tougher travelers with a primitive compass for their labyrinthine journey toward a definition of mind.

REFERENCES*

Adrian, Lord, Bremer, F., Jasper, H. H., and Delafresnaye, J. F. (ed.) (1954), *Brain Mechanisms and Consciousness*, Blackwell Sci. Publ., Oxford.
Ashby, W. Ross (1952), *Design for a Brain*, Chapman & Hall, London.
———— (1956), *An Introduction to Cybernetics*, Chapman & Hall, London.
Benton, R. F. (1950), unpublished lecture; personal communication.
Bertalanffy, L. von (1956), "General System Theory," *General Systems*, 1:1-10.
Beveridge, W. I. B. (1957), *The Art of Scientific Investigation*, 3rd ed., Heinemann, London.
Bonin, G. von (1950), *Essay on the Cerebral Cortex*, Charles C Thomas, Springfield, Ill.
Chance, M. R. A., and Russell, W. M. S. (1959), "Protean displays: a form of allaesthetic behaviour," *Proc. Zool. Soc. London*, 132:65-70.

* We have kept this list as short as possible. Much fuller documentation will be found in the publications of our own listed here.

Craik, K. J. W. (1943), *The Nature of Explanation*, Univ. Press, Cambridge.

Davis, J. M. (1958), "The transitivity of preferences," *Behav. Sci.*, 3:26-33.

Diebschlag, E. (1941), "Über den Lernvorgang bei der Haustaube," *Ztchr. vergl. Physiol.*, 28:67-104.

Dunne, J. W. (1939), *An Experiment with Time*, 5th ed., Faber & Faber, London.

Editorial (1956), "The balance of arts and sciences in education," *Nature*, 177:1095-1097.

Fisher, Sir Ronald (1954), "Retrospect of the criticisms of the theory of natural selection," in *Evolution as a Process*, ed. by Huxley, Hardy, and Ford, pp. 84-98, Allen & Unwin, London.

Freud, S. (1933), *New Introductory Lectures on Psycho-analysis* (transl. W. J. H. Sprott), Hogarth Press, London.

Gastaut, H. (1958), "Some aspects of the neurophysiological basis of conditioned reflexes and behaviour," in *Neurological Basis of Behaviour*, ed. by G. E. W. Wolstenholme and O'Connor, pp. 255-272, Churchill, London.

Graham, C. H. (1951), "Visual perception," in *Handbook of Experimental Psychology*, ed. Stevens, pp. 868-920, Chapman & Hall, London.

Granit, R. (1955), *Receptors and Sensory Perception*, Yale Univ. Press, New Haven.

Griffin, D. R. (1958), *Listening in the Dark*, Yale Univ. Press, New Haven.

Hagbarth, K. E. (1959), "Principles of neural control of receptors," *Proc. 15th Internat. Zool. Congr. London*, pp. 880-882.

Halstead, W. C. (1947), *Brain and Intelligence*, Univ. of Chicago Press, Chicago.

——— (1951), "Brain and intelligence," in *Cerebral Mechanisms in Behavior*, ed. Jeffress, pp. 244-272, Chapman & Hall, London.

Harary, F. (1957), "Structural duality," *Behav. Sci.*, 2:255-265.

——— (1959), "On the measurement of structural balance," *Behav. Sci.*, 4:316-323.

Hardy, Sir Alister (1953), "Biology and psychical research," *Proc. Soc. Psychical Research*, 50:96-134.

Hayes, J. S., Russell, W. M. S., Hayes, Claire, and Kohsen, Anita (1953), "The mechanism of an instinctive control system: A hypothesis," *Behaviour*, 6:85-119.

Holst, E. von (1950), "Quantitative Messung von Stimmungen im Verhalten der Fische," *Sympos. Soc. exper. Biol.*, 4:143-172.

Horn, G. (1960), "Electrical activity of the cerebral cortex of the unanaesthetized cat during attentive behaviour," *Brain*, 83:57-76.

———, and Blundell, J. (1959), "Evoked potentials in visual cortex of the unanaesthetized cat," *Nature*, 184:173-174.

Klüver, H. (1958), "Untitled contribution to discussion," in *Neurological Basis of Behaviour*, ed. by G. E. W. Wolstenholme and O'Connor, p. 182, Churchill, London.

Larrson, K. (1956), "Conditioning and sexual behaviour in the male albino rat," *Acta Psychol. Gothenburg.*, 1:1-269.

Leeper, R. (1951), "Cognitive processes," in *Handbook of Experimental Psychology*, ed. Stevens, pp. 730-757, Chapman & Hall, London.

Lotka, A. J. (1925), *The Elements of Physical Biology*, Baltimore.

McLardy, T. (1959), "Hippocampal formation of brain as detector-coder of temporal patterns of information," *Perspectives in Biology and Medicine*, 2, pp. 443-452.

Mead, A. P. (1953), "A study of the occurrence of conflict reactions in the behaviour of the albino rat," thesis for degree of Ph.D., Univ. of Birmingham, pp. 1-321.

Packard, V. (1957), *The Hidden Persuaders*, Longmans, London.

Penfield, W. G. (1958), "The role of the temporal cortex in recall of past experience and interpretation of the present," in *Neurological Basis of Behaviour,* ed. by G. E. W. Wolstenholme and O'Connor, pp. 149-174, Churchill, London.

——, and Rasmussen, T. (1952), *The Cerebral Cortex of Man,* Macmillan Co., New York.

Pledge, H. T. (1939), *Science since 1500,* H. M. Stationery Office, London.

Prechtl, H. F. R. (1956), "Neurophysiologische Mechanismen des formstarren Verhaltens," *Behaviour,* 9:243-319.

Pribram, K. H. (1959), "On the neurology of thinking," *Behav. Sci.,* 4:265-287.

Pringle, J. W. S. (1951), "On the parallel between learning and evolution," *Behaviour,* 3:174-215. (Reprinted, *General Systems,* 1956, 1:90-110.)

Rapoport, A. (1956), "The diffusion problem in mass behavior," *General Systems,* 1:48-55.

Russell, Claire, and Russell, W. M. S. (1957), "An approach to human ethology," *Behav. Sci.,* 2:169-200.

——, and Russell, W. M. S. (1958), "On manhandling animals," *Universities Federation for Animal Welfare Courier,* 14:1-13.

——, and Russell, W. M. S. (1959), "Human behaviour in an evolutionary setting," *Proc. 15th Internat. Zool. Congr. London,* pp. 862-865.

——, and Russell, W. M. S. (1961), *Human Behaviour: A New Approach,* Deutsch, London, Little, Brown, Boston.

Russell, J. R., and Reitan, R. M. (1955), "Psychological abnormalities in agenesis of the corpus callosum," *J. Nerv. Ment. Dis.,* 121:205-214.

Russell, W. M. S. (1952), "Quantitative studies of vertebrate instinctive behaviour, with special reference to the influence of hormones," dissert. for degree of Ph.D., Oxford Univ., pp. 1-363.

—— (1954), "Experimental studies of the reproductive behaviour of *Xenopus laevis.* I. The control mechanisms for clasping and unclasping, and the specificity of hormone action," *Behaviour,* 7:113-188.

—— (1956), "On misunderstanding animals," *Universities Federation for Animal Welfare Courier,* 12:19-35.

—— (1957), Supplementary note to a reprint of Russell *et al.* (1954), *General Systems,* 2:133-134.

—— (1958), "Evolutionary concepts in behavioural science. I. Cybernetics, Darwinian theory and behavioural science," *General Systems,* 3:18-28.

—— (1959a), "Evolutionary concepts in behavioural science. II. Organic evolution and the genetical theory of natural selection," *General Systems,* 4:45-73.

—— (1959b), "The evolution of animal experimentation," *Proc. 15th Internat. Zool. Congr. London,* pp. 99-101.

—— (1960), "Experimental studies of the reproductive behaviour of *Xenopus laevis.* II. The clasp positions and the mechanisms of orientation," *Behaviour,* 15:253-283.

——, and Burch, R. L. (1959), *The Principles of Humane Experimental Technique,* Methuen, London.

——, Mead, A. P., and Hayes, J. S. (1954), "A basis for the quantitative study of the structure of behaviour," *Behaviour,* 6:153-205. (Reprinted, *General Systems,* 1957, 2:108-133.)

Sabine, W. H. W. (1951), *Second Sight in Daily Life,* Allen & Unwin, London.

Schein, M. W., and Fohrman, M. H. (1955), "Social dominance relationships in a herd of dairy cattle," *Brit. J. Animal Behav.,* 3:45-55.

Shannon, C. E., and Weaver, W. (1949), *The Mathematical Theory of Communication*, Univ. of Illinois Press, Urbana.

Sheppard, P. M. (1954), "Evolution in bisexually reproducing organisms," in *Evolution as a Process*, ed. by Huxley, Hardy, and Ford, pp. 201-218, Allen & Unwin, London.

Simonson, E., and Brozek, J. (1952), "Flicker fusion frequency: Background and applications," *Physiol. Rev.*, 32:349-378.

Svaetichin, G. (1956), "Receptor mechanisms for flicker and fusion," *Acta physiol. Scand.*, Suppl. 134, 39:47-54.

Thorpe, W. H. (1954), "Some concepts of ethology," *Nature*, 174:101-104.

Tinbergen, N. (1942), "An objectivistic study of the innate behaviour of animals," *Bibliotheca Biotheoretica*, D, i, 2:39-98.

—————— (1948), "Social releasers and the experimental method required for their study," *Wilson Bull.*, 60:6-51.

—————— (1951), *The Study of Instinct*, Clarendon Press, Oxford.

——————, and Perdeck, A. C. (1950), "On the stimulus situation releasing the begging response in the newly hatched herring gull chick (*Larus Argentatus Argentatus* Pont.)," *Behaviour*, 3:1-39.

Whitfield, I. C. (1956), "Electrophysiology of the central auditory pathway," *Brit. Med. Bull.*, 12:105-109.

Wolstenholme, G. E. W., and Millar, Elaine C. P. (eds.) (1956). *CIBA Foundation Symposium on Extrasensory Perception*, Churchill, London.

H E R B E R T   F E I G L

Mind-Body, *Not* a Pseudo Problem

Any serious effort toward a consistent, coherent, and synoptic account of the place of mind in nature is fraught with embarrassing perplexities. Philosophical temperaments notoriously differ in how they react to these perplexities. Some thinkers apparently like to wallow in them and finally declare the mind-body problem unsolvable: *"Ignoramus et ignorabimus."* Perhaps this is an expression of intellectual masochism, or a rationalization of intellectual impotence. It may, of course, also be an expression of genuine humility. Others, imbued with greater confidence in the powers of philosophical insight or in the promises of scientific progress, offer dogmatic solutions of the old puzzle. And still, recognizing the speculative and precarious character of metaphysical solutions, and deeply irritated by the many bafflements, try to undercut the whole issue and declare it an imaginary problem. But the perplexities persist and provoke further efforts—often only minor variants of older ones—toward removing this perennial bone of contention from the disputes of philosophers and scientists. Wittgenstein, who tried to "dissolve" the problem, admitted candidly (*Philosophical Investigations,* Sec. 412): "The feeling of an unbridgeable gulf between consciousness and brain-process. . . . This idea of a difference in kind is accompanied by slight giddiness"; but he added quickly "which occurs when we are performing a piece of logical sleight of hand."

As I see it, Wittgenstein's casuistic treatment of the problem is merely one of the more recent in a long line of positivistic (ametaphysical, if

This essay is taken from *Dimensions of Mind,* edited by Sidney Hook (New York: New York University Press, 1960). Used by permission of New York University Press.

not anti-metaphysical) attempts to show that the mind-body problem arises out of conceptual confusions, and that proper attention to the way in which we use mental and physical terms in ordinary language will relieve us of the vexatious problem. Gilbert Ryle, B. F. Skinner, and— anticipating all of them—R. Carnap have tried to obviate the problem in a similar way: The use of mental or "subjective" terms is acquired by learning the language we all speak in everyday life. This language, serving as a medium of communication among human beings, is by its very nature *intersubjective*. It is on the basis of publicly accessible cues that, e.g., the mother tells the child "you feel tired," "now you are glad," "you have a headache," etc.—and that the child learns to use such phrases as "feeling tired," "being glad," "having a headache" as applied not only to others, but also to himself when he is in the sort of condition that originally manifested itself in the cues (symptoms, behavior situations and sequences, test conditions and results, etc.) observable by others. But here is the rub. Even if we *learn* the use of subjective terms in the way indicated, once we have them in our vocabulary we *apply* them to states or conditions to which we, as individual subjects, have a "priv- iledged access." If I report moods, feelings, emotions, sentiments, thoughts, images, dreams, etc., that I experience, I am *not referring* to my *behavior,* be it actually occurring or likely to occur under specified conditions. I am referring to those states or processes of my direct experience that I live through (enjoy or suffer), to the "raw feels" of my awareness. These "raw feels" are accessible to other persons only in- directly by inference—but it is *myself* who *has* them.

I do not wish to deny that ordinary language serves many purposes quite adequately. As I see it, ordinary language unhesitatingly combines mental (phenomenal) and physical (behavioral) terms in many descrip- tions and explanations of human and animal conduct or behavior. "Eager- ness was written all over his face"; "he was trembling with anxiety"; "no doubt his gastric ulcer is due to his suppressed hostility"; "an attack of the flu left him in a discouraged and depressed mood for several days"; "a resolute decision finally enabled him to overcome his addiction"; etc., etc. As these few illustrations indicate, ordinary langauge clearly reflects an interactionistic view of the relations of the mental and the physical. As long as we are not too particular about squaring our accounts with the facts established, or at least strongly suggested, by the advances of psychophysiology, we can manage to keep out of logical troubles. Some philosophers like Ryle, Strawson, Hampshire, and other practitioners of the ordinary language approach have most persuasively shown that we can talk about the mental life of *"persons,"* i.e., about episodes, dis- positions, actions, intentions, motives, purposes, skills and traits, without getting bogged down in the mind-body puzzles. But, notoriously, there is in this approach scarcely any reference to the facts and regularities of neurophysiology. Moreover, not all is well logically with these neobe-havioristic analyses. "Persons" remains a term insufficiently explicated; and what I could glean from Strawson's analysis[13] is that he defines "person" as a sort of synthetically glued-together unity of a living body and its mental states. Strawson accounts for introspection in terms of "self-ascription." While this is helpful, it cannot be the whole story about mental states: infants, idiots, and at least some of the higher animals undoubtedly have raw feelings, but are not "self-ascribers." If highly learned men nowadays express (philosophical) doubts about *other minds,* and debate seriously as to whether or not very complex robots have direct experiences, then obviously a better philosophical clarification of the relations of the mental to the physical is urgently needed.

The crucial and central puzzle of the mind-body problem, at least since Descartes, has consisted in the challenge to render an adequate account of the relation of the "raw feels," as well as of other mental facts (intentions, thoughts, volitions, desires, etc.) to the corresponding neurophysiological processes. The problems may fairly clearly be divided into scientific and philosophical components. The scientific task is pursued by psychophysiology, i.e., an exploration of the empirically ascertainable correlations of "raw feels," phenomenal patterns, etc., with the events and processes in the organism, especially in its central nervous system (if not in the cerebral cortex alone). The philosophical task consists in a logical and epistemological clarification of the concepts by means of which we may formulate and/or interpret those correlations.

Scientifically, the most plausible view to date is that of a one-one (or at least a one-many) correspondence of mental states to neurophysiological process patterns. The investigations of Wolfgang Köhler, E. D. Adrian, W. Penfield, D. O. Hebb, and W. S. McCulloch, *et al.,* strongly confirm such a correspondence in the form of an isomorphism of the patterns in the phenomenal fields with the simultaneous patterns of neural processes in various areas of the brain. The philosopher must of course regard this isomorphism as empirically establishable or refutable, and hence as *logically* contingent. It is conceivable that further empirical evidence may lead the psychophysiologists to abandon or to modify this view which, on the whole, has served so well at least as a fruitful working hypothesis. It is conceivable that some of the as yet more obscure psychosomatic phenomena or possibly the still extremely problematic and controversial "facts" of parapsychology will require emergentist or even interactionistic explanations. (As an empiricist I must at least go through the motions of an "open mind" in these regards!) But tentatively assuming isomorphism of some sort, a hypothesis which is favored by many "naturalistic" philosophers, are we then to interpret it philosophically along the line of traditional epiphenomenalism? Although

Professor Köhler[9] does not commit himself explicitly to this view, I am practically certain that this is the general outlook within which he operates. If the basic physical laws of the universe should be sufficient for the derivation of biological and neurophysiological regularities; if the occurrence of neural patterns (physical Gestalten) is not a case of genuine emergent novelty but a matter of composition of more elementary physical configurations; and if, finally, the experiential patterns correspond in some way isomorphically to neural process patterns—then this *is* epiphenomenalism in modern dress.

It will be best here not to use the somewhat ambiguous label "parallelism." Psychophysiological parallelism as held by some thinkers in an earlier period allowed for a "mental causality" to correspond to "physical (i.e., neurophysiological) causality." Sometimes it even connoted an all-pervasive correspondence of mental and physical attributes (à la Spinoza) and thus amounting to some form of panpsychism. But the favored outlook of modern psychophysiology amounts to postulating causal relations, i.e., dynamic functional dependencies only on the physical side, and then to connect the neural process patterns merely by laws of (simultaneous) coexistence or co-occurrence with the corresponding mental states. Only a small subset of neural processes is thus accompanied by mental processes.

Traditionally the most prominent objection to epiphenomenalism has been the argument from the "efficacy of consciousness." We seem to know from our direct experience that moods, pleasure, displeasure, pain, attention, vigilance, intention, deliberation, choice, etc., make a difference in the ensuing behavior. But, of course, this subjective impression of the casual relevance and efficacy of mental states can easily be explained by the epiphenomenalist: Since, *ex hypothesi,* some dynamically relevant physical conditions are invariably accompanied by mental states, there is then also a regular occurrence of certain types of behavior (or of intraorganismic events) consequent upon mental states. For empiricists holding an essentially Humean conception of causality, it is then quite permissible in this sense to speak of the causal efficacy of mental states. There are, it should be noted, countless highly "teleological" processes that occur in our organism evidently without the benefit of any mental influence, guidance, or instigation. For example, the kind of regenerations and restitutions that are involved in recoveries from many types of physical injury or disease appear as if they were most cleverly "designed"; but for many of these phenomena purely physiological (and perhaps ultimately physicochemical) explanations are available. Yet, according to the epiphenomenalistic doctrine such explanations are sufficient also for behavior which we ordinarily consider instigated, regulated, or modulated by mental factors. If an effort of concentration facilitates learning algebra, piano playing, or the like, then consciousness cannot be regarded as a causally irrelevant or superfluous "luxury." I don't think we need to apologize for arguments of this sort. It is true that radical materialists and behaviorists reject such arguments as "tender-minded." But then radical materialism or behaviorism typically *repress* or *evade* the mind-body problem. They do not offer a genuine solution. Epiphenomenalism, while not evading the problem, offers a very queer solution. It accepts two fundamentally different sorts of laws—the usual causal laws and laws of psychophysiological correspondence. The physical (causal) laws connect the events in the physical world in the manner of a complex network, while the correspondence laws involve relations of physical events with purely mental "danglers." These correspondence laws are peculiar, in that (crudely speaking) they postulate "effects" (mental states as dependent variables) which by themselves do not function, or in any case do not seem to be needed, as "causes" (independent variables) for any observable behavior.

Laws of concomitance in the physical world could usually be accounted for in terms of underlying *identical* structures. Thus, e.g., the correspondence of certain optical, electrical, and magnetic properties of various substance (as expressed in simple functional relations between the refraction index, the dielectric constant, and the magnetic permeability) is explainable on the basis of the atomic structure of those substances. Or, to take a slightly different example, it is in terms of a theory of *one* (unitary) electric current that we explain the thermal, chemical, magnetic, and optical effects which may severally or jointly be used in an "operational definition" of the intensity of the current. Similarly, it is at least a partially successful working program of psychophysiology to reduce certain correlated macrobehavioral features to underlying identical neurophysiological structures and processes. It should be emphasized, however, that a further step is needed if we are to overcome the dualism in the epiphenomenalist interpretation of the correlation of subjective mental states with brain states.

The classical attempts in the direction of such unification or of a monistic solution are well known: double aspect, double knowledge, twofold access, or double-language doctrines have been proposed in various forms. The trouble with most of these is that they rely on vague metaphors or analogies; and that it is extremely difficult to translate them into straightforward language. I can here only briefly indicate the lines along which I think the "world knot" (Schopenhauer's striking designation for the mind-body puzzles) may be disentangled. The indispensable step consists in a critical reflection upon the meanings of the terms "mental" and "physical"—and along with this a thorough clarification of such traditional philosophical terms as "private" and "public," "subjective" and "objective," "psychological space(s)," and "physical space," intentionality, purposiveness, etc. The solution that appears most plausible to me, and that is entirely consistent with a thoroughgoing naturalism, is an *identity theory* of the mental and the physical—in the following sense: certain neurophysiological terms denote (refer to) the very same events that are also denoted (referred to) by certain phenomenal terms. The identification of the objects of this twofold reference is of course logically contingent, although it constitutes a very fundamental feature of our world as we have come to conceive it in the modern scientific outlook. Utilizing Frege's distinction between *Sinn* (meaning, sense, intension) and *Bedeutung* (referent, denotatum, extension), we may say that neurophysiological terms and the corresponding phenomenal terms, though widely differing in *sense*, and hence in the modes of confirmation of statements containing them, do have identical *referents*. I take these referents to be the immediately experienced qualities, or their configurations, in the various phenomenal fields.

Well-intentioned critics have tried to tell me that this is essentially the metaphysics of panpsychism. To this I can only reply: (1) If this be metaphysics, make the least of it! (2) It is not panpsychism at all; either the "pan" or the "psyche" has to be deleted in the formulation. By way of very brief and unavoidably crude and sketchy comments, let me explain my view a little further. The transition from the logical positivism of the Vienna Circle to the currently prevalent form of logical empiricism, as I interpret it, involved a complete emancipation from radical phenomenalism, behaviorism, operationism, and their all-too-restrictive criteria of factual meaningfulness. Parallel with the critique of philosophical doubt by the Neo-Wittgensteinians, logical empiricists nowadays have no patience with skeptical questions regarding the existence of physical objects or of other minds. "Skeptical doubts" of these sorts are illegitimate not because the beliefs in question are incapable of confirmation or disconfirmation, but because doubts of this pervasive character would call into question the very principles of confirmation and disconfirmation that underlie all empirical inquiry—both on the level of common sense and that of science. There can be no question that assertions of the existence of stars and atoms, the occurrence of mental processes (conscious and unconscious), are subject to the normal procedures of inductive, analogical or hypothetico-deductive confirmation or disconfirmation. It is preposterous (if not philosophically "perverse" or "naughty") to deny that we have well-confirmed knowledge concerning imperceptible physical objects or concerning the mental states of other human beings. A mature epistemology can make explicit the principles of such, often highly indirect, confirmations or disconfirmations. And along with this a liberalized meaning-criterion can be formulated, broad enough to include whatever is needed by way of common sense or scientific hypotheses, and yet sufficiently restrictive to exclude transcendent metaphysical (pseudo) beliefs. Freed from the torments of philosophical doubt and from the associated reductive tendencies and fallacies of phenomenalism as well as of radical behaviorism, we can now with a good intellectual conscience embrace a genuinely critical and empirical realism.

Once this position is attained, a mind-body-identity theory of the kind sketched above appears as the most adequate interpretation of all the relevant facts and considerations. This is not panpsychism, since nothing in the least like a psyche is ascribed to lifeless matter, and certainly at most something very much less than a psyche is ascribed to plants or lower animals. The panpsychists claimed to reason by analogy, but this is precisely what they did not do in fact. The difference between the nervous system of, say, an earthworm and of a human being is so tremendous that we should in all consistency assume a correspondingly large difference in their respective mental states. And even on the human level there is no need whatever for the assumption of a psyche in the traditional sense of a soul that could act upon the brain, let alone being separable from it. One may, of course, doubt as to whether a purely Humean conception of the *self* (as a bundle and succession of direct data) will be sufficient for an adequate psychology. Nevertheless, no substantial entity is required. Events, processes, and their organization and integration properly defined, should be perfectly sufficient. Professor Stephen C. Pepper suggested to me (in conversation) that my view might be labeled "pan-quality-ism." While this locution is not pleasant to the ear, it does come much closer to a correct characterization than "panpsychism." But since Paul E. Meehl,[10] who understands my view at least as thoroughly as does Professor Pepper, has designated me a "materialist," perhaps one last word of elucidation may be in order.

I am indeed in agreement with one main line of traditional materialism in that I assume, as does Professor Köhler, that the basic *laws* of the universe are the *physical* ones. But (and this is so brief and crude a formulation that I fear I shall be misunderstood again) this does not commit me in the least as to the nature of the *reality* whose regularities are formulated in the physical laws. This reality is known to us by acquaintance only in the case of our direct experience which, according to my view, is the referent also of certain neurophysiological concepts. And if we are realists in regard to the physical world, we must assume that the concepts of theoretical physics, to the extent that they are instantialized in particulars, are not merely calculational devices for the prediction of observational data, but that they denote realities which are unknown by acquaintance, and which may in some way nevertheless be not entirely discontinuous with the qualities of direct experience. But—"whereof we cannot speak, thereof we must be silent." If this is metaphysics, it seems to me entirely innocuous. I have little sympathy with the mysticism of Eddington or the psychovitalism of Bergson. I reject the former because there is literally nothing that can be responsibly said in a phenomenal language about qualities that do not fall within the scope of acquaintance. Extrapolation will carry us at most to the concepts of unconscious wishes, urges, or conflicts as hypothesized by such "depth-psychologies" as psychoanalysis. And even here, future scientific developments may be expected to couch these concepts much more fruitfully in the language of neurophysiology and endocrinology. And I reject psychovitalism because it involves dualistic interaction. At the very best, "intuition" (empathetic imagination) may be heuristically helpful in that it can suggest scientific hypotheses in psychology (possibly even in biology), but these suggestions are extremely precarious, and hence must always be relentlessly scrutinized in the light of objective evidence.[7]

Does the identity theory simplify our conception of the world? I think it does. Instead of conceiving of two realms or two concomitant types of events, we have only one reality which is represented in two different conceptual systems—on the one hand, that of physics—and, on the other, where applicable (in my opinion only to an extremely small part of the world) that of phenomenological psychology. I realize fully that the simplification thus achieved is a matter of *philosophical* interpretation. For a synoptic coherent account of the relevant facts of perception, introspection, and psychosomatics, and of the logic of theory construction in the physical sciences, I think that the identity view is preferable to any other proposed solution of the mind-body problem. Call my view metaphysical if you must; I would rather call it *metascientific*—in the sense that it is the result of a comprehensive reflection on the *results* of science as well as on the logic and epistemology of scientific *method*. But I admit that for the ordinary purposes of psychology, psychophysiology, and psychiatry an epiphenomenalist position is entirely adequate, if only the traditional picturesque but highly misleading locutions (e.g., "substantial material reality and its shadowy mental accompaniments") are carefully avoided.

I conclude that the mind-body problem is not a pseudo problem. There are, first, a great many genuine but unanswered questions in psychophysiology. And, secondly, there is plenty of work left for philosophers in the logical analysis of the intricate relations between phenomenal and physical terms. Problems of this complexity cannot be relegated to the limbo of nonsensical questions. I doubt quite generally whether many issues in modern epistemology can be simply "dissolved" in the manner in which some artificially concocted pseudo problems can be disposed of by a minimum of reflection on the proper use of terms. Questions, such as: "How fast does time flow?"; "Do we really see physical objects?"; "Why is there anything at all rather than nothing?"; "Why is the world the way it is?"; etc.; can indeed be very quickly shown to rest on elementary conceptual confusions. But the issues of perception, reality, and of the mental and the physical require circumspect, perspicacious, and painstaking analyses.

NOTES AND REFERENCES

In a long essay[4] I attempted to do fuller justice to the complexities and the unresolved issues of the mind-body problem than I possibly could in the preceding brief comments. A very ample bibliography is appended to that essay. Since its publication I have found a welcome ally in J. J. C. Smart.[11] Carnap's early article, "'Psychologie in Physikalischer Sprache," which anticipated much of the neobehavioristic argument of Ryle, Skinner, and Wittgenstein, is at last available in English translation.[1] A brief but perhaps not sufficiently elaborate critical reply to the Wittgensteinian position on the problem of other minds is contained in my symposium article (response to Norman Malcolm) listed below.[5] An exposition and critical analysis of Carnap's physicalism is presented in[7]. For a forthright, but philosophically unsophisticated physicalistic solution of the mind-body problem, see Smith.[12] The brilliant psychologist and methodologist Paul E. Meehl has dealt with the mind-body problem and related issues in several chapters of a book[10] which, despite its primarily theological and religious intent, contains large parts of scientifically and logically important and incisive discussions.

1. Carnap, Rudolf, "Psychology in physical language," in A. J. Ayer (ed.), *Logical Positivism*, pp. 165-198, The Free Press of Glencoe, New York, 1959.
2. ———, "The methodological character of theoretical concepts," in *Minnesota Studies in the Philosophy of Science*, 1956, I:38-76, Univ. of Minnesota Press, Minneapolis.
3. ———, "The philosopher replies," in P. A. Schilpp, *The Philosophy of Rudolf Carnap*, Tudor Publishing Co. (forthcoming), New York.
4. Feigl, Herbert, "The 'mental' and the 'physical,'" in H. Feigl, M. Scriven, and G. Maxwell (eds.), *Concepts, Theories and the Mind-Body Problem: Minnesota Studies in the Philosophy of Science*, 1958, II:370-483, Univ. of Minnesota Press, Minneapolis; Notes and References (*ibid.*), pp. 483-497.
5. ———, "Other minds and the egocentric predicament," *Journal of Philosophy*, 1958, 50:978-987.
6. ———, "Philosophical embarrassments of psychology," *American Psychologist*, 1959, 14:115-128.
7. ———, "Critique of intuition from the point of view of scientific empiricism," *Philosophy East and West* (forthcoming).

8. ———, "Physicalism, unity of science and the foundations of psychology," in Schilpp, *op. cit.*
9. Köhler, Wolfgang, *The Place of Values in a World of Facts,* Liveright, New York, 1938.
10. Meehl, Paul E. (coauthor), *What, Then, Is Man?,* Graduate Study Number III, Concordia Publishing House, St. Louis, 1958.
11. Smart, J. J. C., "Sensations and brain processes," *Philosophical Review,* 1959, 68:141-156.
12. Smith, Kendon, "The naturalistic conception of life," *American Scientist,* 1958, 46:413-423.
13. Strawson, P. F., "Persons," in H. Feigl, M. Scriven, and G. Maxwell (eds.), *Concepts, Theories and the Mind-Body Problem: Minnesota Studies in the Philosophy of Science,* 1958, II:330-353, Univ. of Minnesota Press, Minneapolis. Reprinted (with some alterations) in Strawson, P. F., *Individuals, an Essay in Descriptive Metaphysics,* Methuen, London, 1959.

EDWARD W. BARANKIN

Concerning the Mind-Body Problem

I

The mind-body problem of psychology cannot be said to lack progress toward resolution for want of abundant or competent attention. From pre-Socratic times down to the present, deeply thoughtful men have given it direct consideration, scientific investigators have brought their specialized findings to bear on it, and commentators on the human scene have contributed their observations on it. Regarding the substantive content of the various attempts to achieve understanding of the empirical datum of a "material body" and a "nonmaterial mind" in mutually affective concomitance, we have seen the gamut run from the purest dualism of Plato to the profoundest monism of Spinoza, from the stark universal atomism of Democritus to the insightful integralism of the Gestalt school. Viewing this vast field of proposals, can we reasonably believe that a next significant step toward an answer must be utterly unlike any one of these proposals, that none of them points in some measure, in some way, toward truly deeper comprehension? We doubt if anyone will answer a bald "yes" to this question, although perhaps many will reserve the right to remain noncommittal. Those who, with the author, tend to believe that so much dedicated thought on the problem, based on so much observation and experi-

We are indebted to Dr. James B. MacQueen, who has read the manuscript and made valuable comments.

mentation, cannot but have produced some general ideas destined to be recognized as precursors of a new profundity of understanding—these people will, however, raise the probing questions: Why, if a significant idea is already at hand, can we not recognize it clearly? Or if some combination of these ideas is the key, why does it not now show forth convincingly?

The answer to these questions is embodied in the word *precision.* It is precision in the formulation of complexes of fundamental concepts that must carry us from the present state of affairs of a field of pregnant thought to an eventual deeper level of understanding. Let us be perfectly clear: we are not asserting that there exists a "method of precision," and that all that remains to be done is to apply this method to present conceptions; this is nonsense (the very nonsense that one encounters in certain quarters today). We are affirming that no substantial advance in the desired direction can come without a clear delineation of a collection of basic concepts accompanied by a precise set of relations between these concepts. There is no need to continue pressing our meaning in abstract terms; the history of human understanding abounds with examples. Every instance of a scientific discipline now well parted from its mother, philosophy, illustrates the point. Within psychology itself, the repeated appeals to the successful precision of biology and physics register the appreciation of the point in question. One of the finest, and best-known, illustrations of the triumph of conceptual precision is the Galileo-Newton dynamical formulation. And this example affords also an instructive view of the surpassing subtlety and individuality of broadly effective insights. It would have come to nothing to postulate a notion of mass in isolation or a notion of force in isolation. Only together and—in conjunction with the pertinent kinematical notions—woven into particular interrelation by the three precise laws of motion could they engender their immense explanatory power. There is here no simple juxtaposition or mere logical assembling of existing ideas. There is the achievement of a certain organization of concepts which, once at hand, reflects the correct general direction of thinking of various predecessors, but which has its own peculiar intuitional and nondeducible character, and which, above all, is fully precise.

If our example of Galileo-Newton has suggested that by "precision" we mean mathematics, then our next point is well anticipated. It is, indeed, this: that the precision of which we have been speaking, to its fullest extent, is mathematics, and mathematics is nothing beyond this. There are two assertions here, and it is essential to take careful account of both of them to understand that there is no whit of talking down involved here. The psychologist may react immediately by taking affront at our assertion that the ultimate precision he requires to resolve the mind-body problem is the business of mathematics. He will grant that the precision required by Galileo and Newton was naturally enough of a mathematical kind because they were concerned with purely physical processes; he will certainly point out the great extent to which mathematical deliberations are being applied now in certain areas of his own field, but he will perhaps want to draw the line at our implication that the very heart of his subject is a mathematical matter. If he is ready to agree that precision is of the first importance, must he also concede that that precision is mathematical in nature? It is our contention that it is. But the second of our assertions above softens the blow, so to speak. For it is to the effect that just this precision in regard to real phenomena is the part and parcel of mathematics. Mathematics is nothing other than the body of precise deliberations concerning reality. Thus, it is not as if the domain of investigation that we call mathematics were an other-than-real-world domain, which only coincidentally yields some considerations that happen to be applicable to real-world phenomena, and deigns to hand these to us from time to time. Far from this being the case, mathematics is—we claim— the evolving accumulation of more and more intimate, precise facts concerning real phenomena.

It is not disturbing to this position that large portions of today's mathematical knowledge are still without explicit application. Scientific history shows repeated instances of unexpected and surprising new "applications" of mathematics to real phenomena; for example, Einstein's particular employment of differential geometry in the general theory of relativity; or, in psychology itself, among other examples, there is Lewin's use of topological notions. This development will continue steadily and will, in itself, argue ever more convincingly toward the position we are affirming. It is no enigma, either, that mathematical constructs should continually come to our awareness without any immediately evident motivational ties to real happenings. Such "mathematical intuitioning" is not any different in nature from more usual, more mundane cases of the process of perception, deliberation, and insight. We meet a person and encounter him on several occasions; we are then led to think about him, perhaps to discuss him with others, in order to understand his personality and, possibly, to anticipate how he will behave in certain future circumstances. In the course of such deliberations about the person, our observations of him undergo repeated reviews and new integrations; some aspects of his behavior that we had at first deemed important are later seen to be perfunctory, others that had been considered trivial become very meaningful. We may even experience, during such deliberations, the kind of flash of realization that mathematicians are so famous for: we may suddenly hit on a correlation of certain particular actions of the person, which, in a single stroke, clarifies a large part of the pattern of his behavior. In this same way the mathematician deliberates on his structures and their relations, building new abstractions from accumulations of previous considerations, now considering one notion to be of principal importance, later wholly reorganizing his view on the basis of a deeper relational insight. But all of these deliberations did originally emerge from considerations of real situations, and they are from time to time further assisted by direct contact with particular real problems.

The objection may be raised that what we have just presented is a parallelism or an analogy, but not two cases of a unique kind of process. This objection may be elaborated as follows. In the case of our perception of a person, and subsequent deliberations about him, we are dealing with a special kind of real system, regarding the nature and behavior of which certain physical, physiological, and psychological laws pertain, and on which certain mathematical formulations can be brought to bear. Other kinds of real systems (a radio, an oil deposit, a gnu, a school full of children, etc.) are different in their fundamental nature, executing behavior according to altogether different kinds of laws, in connection with which very different areas of mathematics will be useful. Opposed to this, mathematics records the results of the pursuit of pure abstraction, aggregating a library of constructs and relations which we may draw on eclectically for possible use, but which possesses no thematic unity in conjunction with the empirical world. Thus two realms fundamentally apart from each other.

To answer this objection, let us begin by noting—what may not yet be very common knowledge—that mathematical fields with hard and fast separations between them no longer exist. The evidences of modern research are persistently in the direction of fruitful combinations of ideas and methods from nominally different mathematical areas. The emergence of a unitary sense in mathematics now looms clearly, and the meaning of this must go very deep. Indeed, this being so, the apparent unconnectedness of different, isolated mathematical treatments that we see over the domain of empirical science must necessarily be only apparent. The unity of mathematics must—through the many overt contacts of mathematics with evident reality—signal a corresponding unity in the empirical realm. That empirical unity, once put in evidence and understood, will reduce the above objection to nought on all counts. It will show that the distinct, special kinds of real systems alluded to in the objection are not at all conceptually distinct in regard to fundamental (really fundamental) description, but are simply different specific structures of the same general kind, made up of the same kind of basic building blocks. It will show that such compartmentalizing as "physical, physiological, and psychological" does not pertain to ultimate substantive differences, but only to classification according to particulars of structure. It will exhibit the different kinds of behavioral law, of the sort mentioned in the objection, as special cases, in special classes of specific structures, of a single dynamical law. In doing all of this, this empirical unity will draw on mathematics in a manner which of necessity must further elucidate the unity of organization of mathematics and simultaneously elucidate also the complete correspondence between the empirical and mathematical unities. More particularly, in this last regard, "pure mathematical" investigation will then appear as the pursuit of insight into the general structural forms (represented symbolically on the mathematician's writing pad) that constitute real systems. And so—to come back around to our assertion against which the objection was raised—the mathematician thinking and deliberating only about mathematics is, after all, thinking and deliberating about the structure of real systems. If, in our considerations about the person we met above, we make the statement that he would be a good committee chairman because he has the qualities of leadership, organizational ability, etc., we are affirming a relational fact regarding a real structure, an immensely complex structure—the person in question. Just so is the mathematician delving after relational facts in real structures, though indeed, in the present early stage of mathematical development, he is dealing with far more specialized items of structure than a full human being, items which, being of simpler form, will usually be found to be involved in a larger class of complex structures (as, for example, a carburetor structure is involved in certain airplanes, in automobiles, motorcycles, etc., while a full airplane structure is not involved in an automobile).

We have answered the objection in the only way it could be answered; namely, by countering its affirmation about the nature of mathematics vis-à-vis the nature of real systems with another, altogether different picture of this relationship. In painting this picture, we were led to develop at a little greater length, though still only in general terms, our thesis that mathematics is nothing other than the field of precise deliberations about real systems. Returning now to the main line of our argumentation, we find our protagonist confronting us as follows. If I can be convinced of what you suggest as the true state of affairs, then my sympathy and interest toward mathematics (I do not say mathematicians!) are newly awakened, for it and we (empirical scientists) are then altogether in the same boat. But if you are right, why are we sitting here talking about it? Put mathematics to work and bring up the resolution of the mind-body problem. There is no better way than that to convince me of all you say.

The fact of the matter is that we cannot meet this challenge in the sense of producing forthwith a complete solution. What is the significance of this circumstance? Are we, in this regard, in the same position as the mathematician who conjectures a theorem about a familiar mathematical construct, and who is at the moment unable to see how to prove it? In other words, are all the mathematical concepts needed for the solution actually already on hand, and the failure due simply to our inability thus far to see the line of argument? Mathematical proofs and lines of argument cannot be systematically hunted down; we have already remarked above that there is no general method of precision. The discovery of these is a matter of individual insight. Thus, it would be understandable if our failure before our protagonist were of this nature. But it is not of this nature. The trouble goes much deeper: it goes to the very heart of mathematics. Indeed, if it were not so, we should not here be elaborating a very consistent position. For, we have stressed a correspondence of the unities in mathematics and in the empirical realm. In view of this correspondence, it cannot be otherwise than that as profound an unresolved problem as that of mind-body must correspond to an equally profound difficulty in the mathematical realm. In fact, the difficulty to which we allude is customarily referred to as the problem of the foundations of mathematics. In a word, it is the problem of understanding correctly the concept of an infinite set. In mathematics, a set is, as in everyday usage, considered to be a collection of things, the things being called the points (members, elements) of the set. We deal freely with such infinite sets as the set of real numbers, the set of rotations of a sphere, etc., and we deal as well with infinite sets of sets. In the case of an infinite collection of sets, we consider, for example, that we may choose an element out of each set in the collection, thus obtaining a set of representative points of the sets in the collection. This gives an idea of how we idealize, to infinite collections, procedures that are physically feasible with empirical finite collections of objects. Are such idealizations sound, or is their reasonableness only an illusion? The too free application of the idealized procedure of collecting items into a set (that is, to form a set) can lead very readily to paradoxes (see, for example, the book[7] in the references at the end of this article). Attempts have been made to build systems of concepts that would render deliberations about sets free of these paradoxes, but nothing has come forth that is wholly convincing. Now, it is the case that all of analytical mathematics rests on operations with infinite sets. It will be granted, then, that there is truly a fundamental problem here for the mathematical realm. We suspect, from the wording of his challenge to us, that our empirical colleague was under the impression that all of mathematics was currently on firm, solid bedrock, with all basic concepts on hand and fully and clearly understood. This is not the case. Just as the field of psychology has been able to pursue its problems with some success while nevertheless the basic nature of its subject matter has remained a mystery, so in the field of mathematics have we been able to proceed to obtain results while the root concepts have persisted not satisfactorily clarified. We are, all of us, not only in the same boat, but as well mathematics' oars are not any longer than psychology's.

How do things stand, then? Will psychology and the other empirical sciences simply have to stand by and wait until mathematics resolves its foundational problems? We think not. Our view of the nature of things indicates very sharply that the mathematician will not solve his fundamental problem while sitting removed up in his ivory tower. He will have to discard the idealizations with which he has, to his own deception, "removed himself from reality," and, instead, frankly recognize that his work has none other than a basis in reality. The enigma of infinite sets will not be resolved without leaving the tower and scrutinizing the happenings going on all about. Therefore, it is interdisciplinary thinking that is called for. No specialized investigator will, confining himself to his own discipline, solve either his own or anyone else's fundamental problem. But all together will solve the single fundamental problem which is everybody's, in different guises and aspects.

II

We have said that the mind-body problem will yield along with, and only with, headway made against the fundamental problems regarding mathematics. We have pointed this up as a corollary of a complete unity of pertinence of mathematical and empirical scientific endeavors. It was with a less exact form of this corollary that we opened our discussion at the beginning of this article, stressing there the fact that the precision of mathematics will draw the answer out of the intuitive efforts of past thinkers. And we went on to evolve our thesis by way of responses to some of the questions and objections that are put by the standard mode of thinking about the nature and relative positions of the several scientific disciplines. Now, this complete unity of pertinence of mathematics and empirical science, which we are affirming, is argued in more particular terms than we have yet set forth above. There is a focal area of technical concepts which, when it is, as we believe, correctly viewed, reveals this unity—reveals it as a consequence of particular, specific, *precise* indications of the fundamental nature of real systems. The area of concepts we are referring to is that surrounding the notion of probability, and the view of these concepts that we have just spoken of is presented in our article.[1] We shall here briefly sketch some of the ideas we have put forward in that article.

The notion of probability stands today not yet satisfactorily clarified. This is the case even though there exists a large body of intricate mathematics called "probability theory." This body of mathematics should more correctly be designated as the "calculus of probabilities." Even among the purest mathematicians it is admitted that probability has something to do with down-to-earth reality; and here is where the question lies: What precisely is probability in the context of real systems? We apply so-called mathematical probability models to real phenomena to describe their behavior. What is there in the nature of real systems that calls for this? It is to this problem that the article[1] is addressed, and we have there proposed a form of answer that we believe will be ultimately substantiated. We have made certain crucial identifications of concepts, thereby fixing the form of answer, but it can by no means be said that we have given a complete answer. Indeed, the difficulties that still remain to be resolved are even more troublesome than we had suspected at the time of publication. These difficulties interfere seriously with our formulation of the dynamical law (pp. 35 *et seq.*),[1] and render that formulation not yet completely definitive. The mentioned difficulties go deep. They appear to point to the situation that we have not yet, in mathematics, put our finger on the properly general representation of a probability distribution, and that we shall not succeed in doing so until we correctly understand the nature of eventualities and their interrelations. In the mathematical formalism at present, eventualities are represented by sets; in view of what we have indicated in the preceding section concerning the mathematical notion of a set, there should be no surprise at the fact that our difficulties with the concept of probability lead us straightway to the problem of sets.

The term "eventuality" that we have just used signals our theory on the nature of probability and of real systems. It is usual, in discussing real phenomena, to speak of an "event"; for example, the event that individual M suffers an incidence of speech difficulty. The term event is, in fact, so employed that two different incidences of speech difficulty by M will be called two occurrences of the same event. But even disallowing this generic usage, the term event covers two distinct kinds of things which it is essential to distinguish; namely, *eventualities* and *acts*. An eventuality is, roughly speaking, a potential occurrence; it may or may not actualize. And an eventuality is unique: two eventualities may be classified as similar according to some criterion, but there is no such thing as two instances of the same eventuality. As an example: there may be an eventuality of M suffering an incidence of speech difficulty in his conversation with N yesterday. If there is this eventuality, M may or may not have actually had the difficulty. (If he did, the eventuality is definitely there.) There may be an eventuality of M suffering an incidence of speech difficulty tomorrow; if so, it may or may not actualize. These two eventualities are distinct things, not two instances of the same thing. An act is an occurrence taken place. An eventuality actualized results in an act. If M had a difficulty of speech yesterday, that is an act. As with eventualities, acts are distinct, unique things.

It is to eventualities, and not to acts, that probabilities attach. More precisely, there exist conditional probabilities of eventualities relative to other eventualities. For example, let A_1 denote the eventuality that M undergoes a stressful experience of a specified kind on a particular day, let B_1 denote the eventuality that M suffers an incidence of speech difficulty on that day, and let B_2 denote the eventuality that M does not suffer an incidence of speech difficulty on the day in question. Then, confined to the context of these eventualities, there exist conditional probabilities $P(B_1 \mid A_1)$ and $P(B_2 \mid A_2)$; and the sum of these two numbers is 1. [The symbol $P(B_1 \mid A_1)$ is read: "the conditional probability of the eventuality that B_1 relative to the eventuality A_1."] Likewise, if A_2 represents the eventuality that M experiences no stress of the specified kind on the particular day, there exist the conditional probabilities $P(B_1 \mid A_2)$ and $P(B_2 \mid A_2) = 1 - P(B_1 \mid A_2)$. There may be similar eventualities for all other days as well. Starting with some definite day, let us enumerate the succession of days into the indefinite future. Let $A_1^{(n)}$, $A_2^{(n)}$, $B_1^{(n)}$, $B_2^{(n)}$ be the eventualities, of the types described, for the nth day, $n = 1, 2, \ldots$. In the context of all these eventualities there exists a host of conditional probabilities; for example, $P(B_1^{(4)} \mid A_1^{(1)} \cap B_2^{(1)} \cap A_1^{(2)} \cap B_2^{(2)} \cap A_2^{(3)} \cap B_2^{(3)} \cap A_1^{(4)})$, which is the conditional probability that M suffers an incidence of speech difficulty on the fourth day relative to the eventuality that he has stressful experiences on the first, second, and fourth days and none on the third day, and has no speech difficulty on the first three days. (Notice that the symbol $\cap$ indicates the structure of an eventuality as a conjunction of other eventualities.) Although it is not indicated by the notation, these probabilities depend on M's history prior to the day we have numbered 1; that is, depending on M's actual prior history, they may have one or another set of values. Any such collection of eventualities and probabilities, together with the acts that result from actualization of these eventualities, is called a *stochastic process*. The eventualities and probabilities alone we call the *strain* of the process, and the acts that evolve in the process we call the *behavior* of the process.

The process we have just presented might be called the (specified) stress-speech-difficulty process of the individual M. There are evidently other processes that pertain to M. For example, for the several values of n and r, let $C_r^{(n)}$ denote the eventuality that M eats a diet of type r on the nth day. With these, there are conditional probabilities such as $P(C_r^{(n)} \mid C_{s_1}^{(1)} \cap C_{s_2}^{(2)} \cap \ldots \cap C_{s_{n-1}}^{(n-1)})$. One of these probabilities might be, for example, the conditional probability that M takes a low-starch diet on the tenth day relative to the eventuality that he takes a high-starch diet on each of the first nine days. Let us remark that from the probabilities that are of the form we have indicated, other probabilities of eventualities in the process can be calculated. (This is the business of the calculus of probabilities.) For example, in the stress-speech-difficulty process we may calculate the conditional probability of the eventuality that M suffers an incidence of speech difficulty on four particular successive days relative to the eventuality that there is no stress for the preceding two-week period. Or, we may calculate, in the nutrition process of M, the probability of the eventuality that M has a fish diet at least once a week.

We have illustrated two processes of M. Now, here is a crucial point: There is a single, comprehensive stochastic process––we may call it the nutrition-stress-speech-difficulty process of M—that contains the two separate processes in a perfectly precise sense. This observation is not merely crucial: It is utterly fundamental. It is, in our view, the key to the entire baffling question of the structural interrelatedness of the various aspects of an individual; it is, therefore—to recall our opening paragraph—the key to the mutually affective concomitance of a "material body" and a "nonmaterial mind." The nutrition-stress-speech-difficulty process (which we shall henceforth abbreviate to: n-s-s-d process) entails all of the eventualities $A_i^{(n)}$, $B_j^{(n)}$, $C_k^{(n)}$, all the probabilities pertaining to them, and all the acts which evolve by actualization of some of these eventualities. In this more comprehensive process there will be, for example, such probabilities as the conditional probability of the eventuality that M suffers an incidence of speech difficulty on a particular day relative to the eventuality that there is stress every day of the preceding week and a high-calorie diet is ingested every day of that week. This joint process is more of the individual M than the stress-speech-difficulty process and nutrition process separately side by side. If, for example, we are interested in the question of whether or not high-calorie intake counteracts the influence of stress toward precipitating speech difficulties in M, this can be discovered only by studying the n-s-s-d process; this information will not be forthcoming from putting together the studies of the two separate processes. As we have said, the two separate processes are contained in the joint, n-s-s-d process in a very precise sense. They are what we call (in the language of the calculus of probabilities) *marginal processes* of the joint process; their strains (that is, their eventualities and their probabilities) derive in a precise mathematical manner from the strain of that joint process, and their acts obtain from the acts of the joint process in the obvious way. Thus, the probabilities in the marginal processes are determined by the probabilities in the joint process. The reverse, however, is not in general true. This is the situation in precise terms that we have illustrated above by the question of the counterinfluence of diet against stress. It would seem, too, that this mathematical fact supplies the precise content of the statement often made regarding the aspects of an individual that the whole is more than the sum of the parts. There is a particular (mathematically precise) case in which the probabilities of marginal processes determine the probabilities in the joint process; this is the case of *stochastic independence* of the marginal processes. If the nutrition process and the stress-speech-difficulty process are independent, and only in this case, there is no influence one way or the other of diet on stress in producing speech difficulties. If the two processes are stochastically dependent, then diet either counteracts or abets (or perhaps sometimes one and sometimes the other) stress in its influence on speech. Let us remark that there are other marginal processes as well of the n-s-s-d process.

What of the work-exercise-play process of M, the heart and lungs functioning process of M, the family and community participation process of M, the creative process of M, etc., etc.? These are all stochastic processes, and they are, along with the n-s-s-d process, all marginal processes of a more comprehensive process. The picture now emerges: We contend that the individual M *is* a stochastic process, and the various aspects of him are the marginal processes of this comprehensive process. This would, at first glance, appear to conflict with the standard structural picture of the individual M, which finds him to be in the first place an ordered arrangement of physical particles. But there is, in fact, no conflict. For those physical particles as well are stochastic processes (marginal processes of M),[1] and the resolution of the apparent conflict comes out in the only way there is, namely, to recognize that physical particles are not ultimate structural constituents, that, rather, the ultimate real entities, the fundamental building blocks, are eventualities, probabilities, and acts. This assertion must not be taken as a mathematician's gaming in abstractions. We are earnestly proposing that the hard-core, objective elements of which an individual—and all reality

—is built up are these "impalpable" things: eventualities, probabilities, and acts. In this conception, they are to be thought of as "there," objectively existing—in the same way that we now think of a table as there, that we see across the room and can touch or sit at. To grasp this conception it is necessary only to relinquish the classical anthropocentric scientific attitude which holds that there are on the one hand human beings and on the other hand Nature. Thus, when I see the table across the room, the full objective fact is that I am seeing the table across the room—not simply that the table is there. Such an act is an element of both the process that is me and the process that is the table. The eventuality that I will dine at the table this evening is likewise an element of both the process that is the table and the process that is me. Yes, eventualities, probabilities, and acts are impalpable. But we must not remain tied to the incompetent notion that our being able to touch something is an impersonal criterion of reality; we must step up a level and see that our touching something is itself a full participation in reality.

The structural description we have outlined is not restricted to an individual. The individual M and the automobile he drives are a single process of which each is a marginal process. A group of individuals—a society—is a stochastic process. And so on. But concerning an individual M, and the problem of defining M's "mind," this, to begin with, may be said: If we can succeed in approximately satisfying our intuitive notion of mind with a precise definition, that definition will be the characterization of a certain marginal process of the process M. We may venture to say even more. There very likely are marginal processes of a human process that we will successively find it suitable to define as the mind (or, the psychical process); however, before we may consider ourselves close to the possibility of making a first selection of such a marginal process, we shall have to know much more concerning the various eventualities in a human process and their probabilities.

A few last words about the notions expounded here: the theory we have proposed must have in it a dynamical law which will assert, in the case of any particular process, what eventualities actualize. This we attempted to formulate;[1] in fact, we conceived four different forms of such a law, each one with such a strong intuitive claim that the challenge had to be taken up of demonstrating their equivalence. The unforseen difficulties thereupon encountered are, as we have already remarked above, indicative of fundamental problems yet to be cleared up regarding the nature and relations of eventualities. It is to be hoped that through the intermediation of this conjectured equivalence, which comes so strongly recommended by intuition, the path to resolving the fundamental problems may be sooner revealed. In connection with this dynamical formulation, one very interesting fact must be mentioned here. It has appeared indispensible to hypothesize that there is no such thing as an exhaustive collection of eventualities. For example, in the nutrition process, no list of diets for a particular day, however long (even infinite) and however reasonably presumed to cover all possibilities, will be such that one of these must turn out to be the diet actually ingested on that day. There is the eventuality that the man may fast on that day, the eventuality that an illness may cause him to lose the food before any appreciable digestion has taken place, the eventuality that he may die before that day, and so on. But this "and so on" is not merely to say that the unaccounted eventualities are too numerous to mention, or are infinitely many; it is to say that it is in the nature of things that there is no set of all of them. This notion is not unrelated to certain ideas that have arisen in attempts to resolve the difficulties in the mathematical notion of a set.

Let us reiterate, finally, that the theoretical efforts we have described here do not go forth from a full understanding of probability to define the structure of real systems—among them, human beings. These efforts are a simultaneous attack on both problems: What is the structure of a real system? And what is probability? And the import of this proposed theory is that probability is not to be defined in terms of other attributes of a real system, but that probability, along with eventualities and acts, is fundamental, undefined, and other attributes of a system are to be defined in terms of it.

III

Psychology is not unfamiliar with the formal mathematical notion of stochastic process. In recent years much investigation has been done on, for example, stochastic learning "models." But it is something far beyond such "construction of mathematical models" that is intended by the ideas we have set forth above. For us, a stochastic process is the real thing; what the mathematician currently calls a stochastic process is a formal depiction of the real thing. An individual's learning is a stochastic process, and in doing what is called "making a mathematical model" of this process we are guessing at basic eventualities and certain probabilities in the process and then deducing the probabilities of various combinations of these eventualities (which are likewise eventualities in the process). But not only is the individual's learning a stochastic process; every aspect of him is: physical, physiological, psychical, social, etc., etc. These aspects are to be understood by studying the characteristics of the pertinent marginal processes. Perhaps one of the most lucid ways to make this point is to indicate that the entire field of efforts represented by the book[2] is to be viewed as a well-rounded inquiry into the type of stochastic process which is a human being. If this is done—that is, if these efforts are translated into fundamental terms of eventualities, probabilities, and acts—then on some of the problems raised there a great deal can be said immediately. For example, in Chapter 13, entitled "Comparison of Psychological and Group Foci," by John P. Spiegel, there comes sharply to the fore the question of the interstructure of an individual's somatic, psychological, and social aspects. This is exactly the question that is answered in one fell swoop by the precise relation of marginal processes to more comprehensive processes. As another example, in Chapter 17, "Homeostasis Reconsidered," Anatol Rapoport refers to the recently exploited mathematical notion of information, and remarks that "the most hopeful sign of the possibility of relating this entity to ordinary physical observables" appears to be its relation to the mathematical notion of entropy. The fact is that information is a notion directly defined in stochastic processes, and, therefore, in the theory of structure of real systems that we have proposed, the relation of this notion to the fundamental real elements is immediate. Needless to say, most of the problems pointed up[2] are long-term tasks, calling for exact, detailed specifications of the particulars of structure of the stochastic processes in question, and for the stochastic formulation of various current concepts. For example, again in Chapter 17, Rapoport develops the radical behaviorist versus teleological antithesis. The reconciliation of these two views is an important problem; and we believe its solution is fairly within reach. The solution, of course, will be the stochastic characterization of *purpose*. Our optimism regarding the near achievement of this solution, and those of other problems of like nature, stems from an examination of the work of Tolman.[8] Indeed, we find the sense of Tolman's ideas to be entirely at one with our own ideas; in the notion of Sign-Gestalt there is to be seen the improvement of pure Gestaltist (as well as of behaviorist) notions toward precisely the stochastic process structure. Therefore, in particular, we judge that Tolman's analyses of the qualities of personality—as, for example, purpose—will greatly ease the work of characterizing these qualities stochastically.

It is perhaps hardly necessary to point out explicitly that with the increasing accumulation of knowledge of the particulars of the stochastic structure of the individual—some of the most recondite of which is supplied by the remarkable revelations of depth psychology—will come a *mathematical* understanding of psychotherapeutic processes, and therewith the capability of mathematical determination of therapeutic measures. This state of affairs is undoubtedly still many, many years off, but that it is implied is clear. It would be foolish to attempt to make very many statements of a more specific nature in this connection at this time, but we will venture just one; it is on the subject of symbolism. We shall preface our remarks with two quotations. In discussing Freud's ideas on the nature of symbols, and in particular his supposition that the symbolic relation is a genetic variant of a "former identity," Rieff (p. 208)[6] suggests an alternative hypothesis in the following words: "We can just as well suppose that the symbols testify to the presence of a general prerational, or unconscious, method of apprehending the peculiarity and connection of things—a method which each of us has at his command, though it is overlaid by the knowledge achieved by rational culture." Rieff then further quotes Groddeck as follows: "Symbols are not invented, they are there, and belong to the inalienable estate of man; indeed, one might say that all conscious thought and action are the unavoidable consequence of unconscious symbolization, that mankind is animated by the symbol." Now, the point we wish to make is that there seems to be a rather immediate explanation of the symbolic relation in terms of the concept of real structure that we have proposed, and this explanation is in agreement with the two authors just quoted as against the genetic hypothesis of Freud; in fact, Rieff's statement amounts to a fairly close qualitative description of it. The central fact is this: in our perception of things, those things come across to us in terms of their structure as stochastic processes. That is, whatever consciously reasoned structural conception we may have of a system (a table, a horse, an individual, . . .), it is in the nature of the perceptory process that, in our intercourse with the system, it impinges upon our awareness (conscious and/or unconscious) in terms of the actual elements of its structure, viz., eventualities, probabilities, and acts. It may be reasonably surmised, then, that the associations that occur in us, consequent upon our perceptions, are determined by mathematical isomorphism of marginal processes. An official successfully withdrawing a privilege from an individual is a marginal process of the official power; a foot bending and breaking the stalk of a plant beneath it is a marginal process of the foot. These two marginal processes are mathematically isomorphic. Hence, an association of foot with power, and in spite of the fact that the two comprehensive processes in question are far from isomorphic. This account of the symbolic relation allows us also to understand the variation of symbolic associations from occasion to occasion and from individual to individual.

In speaking, in the preceding section, of the mind as a marginal process of the individual M, we took pains not to leave the impression that we could one day arrive at a final, complete definition of such a marginal process. This is an ever-present fact concerning all processes, and is due to the curious situation we indicated of the nonexistence of exhaustive sets of eventualities. It may be illustrated by the simple example of the tossing of a coin. We might rest content that we had an adequate understanding of this tossing process, considering there to be the two eventualities of landing heads and landing tails on each occasion, as long as a head or a tail turned up in the tosses. But as soon as we encounter a toss wherein the result is that the coin comes to rest standing on its edge, then we have become aware of another kind of eventuality in the process, and we may want to deal henceforth with the more complete description, having three eventualities on each occasion. But neither could this description be considered ultimate; we might encounter a toss in which the outcome was of none of these three kinds. And so on, without possibility of ultimately complete description.

In bringing this exposition to a close, we might usefully make at least one reference to past ideas which are borne out by the theoretical formulation we have presented. Ernst Mach[4] was vigorous in his denunciation of the notion of a "thing-in-itself." His insight is fully engendered by the conception of eventualities and acts as primitive structural elements. It is clear from the description of a particular eventuality or act that it enters into the structure of many systems; for example, the individual M is constituted of many eventualities which are likewise structural constituents of *M*'s physical and social environment. The individual *M* is thus not a thing-in-itself, sharply differentiated from his environment. In the same way, there is no sharp dichotomy of body and mind.

REFERENCES

1. Barankin, Edward W., "Toward an objectivistic theory of probability," *Proceedings of the Third Berkeley Symposium on Mathematical Statistics and Probability*, Volume V, University of California Press, Berkeley, 1956.
2. Grinker, Roy R. (ed.), *Toward a Unified Theory of Human Behavior*, Basic Books, Inc., New York, 1956.
3. Lewin, Kurt, *Principles of Topological Psychology*, McGraw-Hill, New York, 1936.
4. Mach, Ernst, *The Analysis of Sensations*, Open Court, Chicago, 1914.
5. Murphy, Gardner, *Historical Introduction to Modern Psychology*, Harcourt, Brace, New York, 1949.
6. Rieff, Philip, *Freud, the Mind of the Moralist*, Viking Press, New York, 1959.
7. Russell, Bertrand, *My Philosophical Development*, Simon and Schuster, New York, 1959.
8. Tolman, Edward Chase, *Collected Papers in Psychology*, University of California Press, Berkeley, 1951.

J. B. C H A S S A N

Probability Processes
in Psychoanalytic Psychiatry

It seems to be a characteristic of maturity in human thought, whether it be concerned with the sciences or with everyday affairs, ultimately to recognize that everything is subject to variation and change. The realization finally dawns that conclusions are never final and predictions are never sure, however much they may be supported by contemporary evidence; and that often it is best to state them in a form which emphasizes—even quantifies—their uncertainty.[1]

The acceptance of uncertainty as ubiquitous in life seems difficult to achieve, or to accept fully on a conscious level of awareness. This appears to be true whether we are speaking of societies or of persons. Authoritarian attitudes, superstitious beliefs, and infantile desires for complete security and protection are among the forces which tend to undermine the realization of uncertainty as one of humanity's outstanding predicaments. The fact that probability theory itself had not begun to be developed until many centuries after the first die was tossed in some Roman version of the game of craps may attest to the existence of early psychological and cultural difficulties in coming to grips with the

1. "Elements of a theory of probability," J. H. Curtiss, Chap. 25 in *The Tree of Mathematics*, edited by Glenn James, The Digest Press, California, 1957.

acceptance of uncertainty as an object appropriate for systematic study and theoretic development.[2]

The theory of probability is considered to have begun in the sixteenth century, motivated by questions concerning betting odds in games of chance. In the centuries following this unworthy origin the theory has been successfully applied to many important branches of human knowledge, ranging from relatively early contributions in such areas as actuarial mathematics and mathematical astronomy, to quantum mechanics and cybernetics in the present era. For a long time, however, the use of probability among scientists was considered as a kind of temporary expedient, to be discarded the moment strict causal laws were established toward the complete exploration of a deterministic universe.

Such a philosophy of science may not only have been necessary for the contributions of Newton and his contemporaries, but was also of great social value in the early struggles against superstition and mass hysteria. The universe no longer had to be a complete and unpredictable mystery. It could be understood. Every effect had its cause, and eventually, through the application of scientific method, every cause could be found, and thus all phenomena could be explained. The early contributions in public health and medical science toward the elimination of epidemic scourges as well as the more recent discoveries and uses of the antibiotics have done much to strengthen a widespread adherence to and a feeling of security in the maintenance of a deterministic outlook.

But contemporary physical theory has struck a severe blow against determinism. In the spontaneous breakup of a radium atom, in which an alpha particle is given off and the atom becomes transformed, "it is not possible to foretell the instant when any particular radium atom will disintegrate; and, it was formerly supposed that this is because a radium atom contains hidden parameters—perhaps the positions and velocities of the neutrons and protons inside the nucleus—which are not known to us and which determine the time of the explosion. For reasons which belong to physics . . . it is now generally recognized that these hidden parameters do not exist. The disintegrations do not occur in a deterministic fashion, and the only knowledge which is even theoretically possible regarding the time of disintegration is the *probability* that it will happen within (say) the next year"[3]

We live in a universe in which our most advanced physical theories are probabilistic, and in which fundamental physical laws and relation-

2. This conjecture is made by M. G. Kendall, "Studies in the history of probability and statistics, II," *Biometrika*, 45:1-13, Parts 1 and 2, (June) 1956.

3. "Mathematics and logic," Sir Edmund Taylor Whittaker, in *What Is Science?* edited by James R. Newman, Simon and Schuster, New York, 1955.

ships are meaningful in terms of probabilities and averages alone. Although no one can be certain that this will always be the case, we are nevertheless faced with the conclusion that, as things now stand, the failure to accept the validity of probability and the statistical organization of data in scientific method and, one might add, in life itself, is simply not tenable, and either represents a deep-rooted prejudice or, in certain instances, may be symptomatic of psychic disturbance. Exaggerated strivings for security and certainty have often been recognized as disabling phenomena. Neurotic indecision, obsessional doubting, and even catatonic immobility may be rooted, to an extent, in an exaggerated fear of uncertainty and in a consequent inability to handle everyday necessary risks. The severe neurotic who is afraid that his hostile and apparently unworthy thoughts and fantasies may become transformed into infamous deeds cannot easily accept a refutation of this fear in the form of a statement of probability, however close to certainty such a probability may lie. The person who cannot offer love may not be capable of risking the possibility of rejection; i.e., he cannot act on a mere probability of being loved in return.

It is apparent that such personal difficulties can easily be reflected in the realm of scientific and professional thinking. An example is given by Arieti, of a patient, a mathematician who could not accept quantum theory because of its probability basis. This was also a patient who felt at a complete loss when he had to do something spontaneously, one for whom complete plans or complete knowledge was essential and whose feelings of security depended to a considerable extent on the performance of routine operations.[4]

It is interesting to note that while Arieti and other dynamically oriented psychiatrists consider such inability to accept uncertainty as symptomatic they have themselves given very little recognition to the importance of probability as a basic tool of scientific investigation in their own work.[5]

It is not too difficult to understand this lag in scientific philosophy if one takes into account Freud's mid-nineteenth-century orientation to causality and determination, a consequence of his emulation of the established physical science of his time. Determinism and causality still seemed as appropriate to nineteenth-century physics as the first law of thermodynamics, and it was natural for Freud to hold to determin-

4. Silvano Arieti, *Interpretation of Schizophrenia*, Robert Brunner, New York, 1955, p. 169.

5. Two noteworthy exceptions from somewhat divergent theoretical orientations are found among the contributions of Leopold Bellak, "An experimental exploration of the psychoanalytic process," *The Psychoanalytic Quarterly*, 1956, XXV:385-414, and Harry Stack Sullivan, *The Interpersonal Theory of Psychiatry*, edited by Helen Swick Perry and Mary Ladd Gawel, Norton, New York, 1953.

istic philosophy as he attempted to develop a first law for psychology from his acute clinical observations.

After three-quarters of a century of experience with psychoanalysis and psychoanalytic therapy it should certainly be evident that the fond hope of complete predictability is, at best, naive. It lays and has laid the foundation for an unending stream of theoretical modifications which by the sheer force of number can never be validated by continuing experience, and which, on the contrary, are most susceptible to demolition by the single case which doesn't fit, or by a single event within a single case. Yet, psychoanalysts sometimes write as though the abandonment of psychic determinism were equivalent to the acceptance of complete chaos in the realm of psychic phenomena, and as though the status of psychoanalysis as a science depended on the acceptance of determinism.[6]

The potential usefulness of a stochastic approach for psychoanalysis has been suggested some twenty years ago by Richard von Mises, the noted scientific philosopher. He writes:

Possibly, from a logical point of view, the objection could be raised that, instead of the concept of strict causality, a statistical relation should be applied to the interdependencies indicated by psychoanalysis—perhaps in the sense that persons under the influence of engrams are *more inclined* toward certain Freudian slips, nervous symptoms, and dream pictures than others who are free of them, just as a die that has been tampered with shows more sixes on the average than an unbiased one. The entire field of phenomena like dream images, slips, et cetera, seems much more similar to the type of recurrent events with which the calculus of probability is concerned, than to the type of physical events which led to the concept of causality. It is a reasonable conjecture that psychoanalytic theory would have received a more correct form, modified in this sense, if at the time of its creation the deterministic conception of all natural occurrences had not been so absolutely predominant in science. . . .

Psychoanalysis comprises the scientific theory of a specific area of psychological occurrences: on the grounds of uncontestable observations it constructs a causal connection between certain symptoms and the latent remainders of earlier experiences. Almost all objections raised against it so far are of an extralogical nature. But it seems justified to point out that the totality of the observations in this field seems to correspond more to the assumption of a statistical than of a strictly causal correlation.[7]

6. See, e. g., "Determinism, 'freedom' and psychotherapy," Robert P. Knight, in *Psychoanalytic Psychiatry and Psychology*, edited by Robert P. Knight and Cyrus A. Friedman, International Universities Press, Inc., New York, 1954, pp. 365-381.

7. Richard von Mises, *Positivism: A Study in Human Understanding*, Harvard University Press, Boston, 1950, p. 238, translation of von Mises' *Kleines Lehrbuch des Positivismus*, 1939.

These comments of von Mises apply as well to events associated with more recent theoretical developments in psychoanalysis such as are included in interpersonal theory and in ego psychology, as they do to data concerning the so-called primary processes. In fact, comparatively recent developments in psychoanalytic theory and in related psychoanalytically oriented psychotherapy add further strength to the justification for a fundamentally statistical view. In essence these represent the shift in emphasis from single traumatic events in childhood to the acceptance of steady day-to-day influences upon the developmental process, as providing a more useful framework for the understanding of neurosis, and the corresponding changes in psychoanalytic techniques and treatment expectations, in which long sequences of (presumably) corrective interchanges between therapist and patient are now regarded as essential to the therapeutic process, as opposed to the earlier emphasis on cathartic and anamnesic reactions. This change in approach is stated by Fromm-Reichmann as follows:

When Freud made his initial discovery of the therapeutic effect of forcing recall of "forgotten" inner and outward events, it was his belief that a single interpretation might do the curative job. But he and his disciples had to revise this concept in order to have it fall in line with their subsequent therapeutic experiences. At the present time classical psychoanalysts as well as other psychoanalytically oriented psychiatrists know that the experiences which are brought into awareness by the psychotherapeutic endeavor will be repeated and will express themselves time and again in patients' various and sundry communications. The dissociated and repressed material which reveals itself to patients under treatment in various connections—above all, in the realm of their relationship with the psychiatrist—must be tied together, and worked through repeatedly, until awareness and understanding are finally transformed into constructive and curative insight into the basic patterns of a patient's interpersonal experiences.[8]

The limitations of a psychoanalytic diagnostic system which fails to take into account the relative frequencies with which symptoms of one kind and another are demonstrated within the individual over time are discussed by Wolstein. He makes the point that diverse phenomena as are presumably described by such terms as phobia, anal-eroticism, compulsion, et cetera, should be studied as observable frequencies in their contingencies and individual differences instead of transforming them into fixed traits of the personality acquired as the consequence of a

8. Frieda Fromm-Reichmann, *Principles of Intensive Psychotherapy*, University of Chicago Press, Chicago, 1950, p. 81.

single significant traumatic event having occurred at some single point in the past, and therefore acquiring a deterministic status.[9]

Both, this question of the contingent relative frequencies with which an individual manifests his symptoms and the related matter of the repetition which is an essential part of working-through, provide a clear illustration of the relevance of statistical, or stochastic, processes to the process of intensive psychotherapy. Together, these may be viewed as a particular application of the statement of Barankin that "personality processes and stochastic processes are one and the same kind of thing."[10]

The difficulties in attempting to apply probability theory and statistics to the data of clinical psychiatry are well known to anyone who has even just thought of trying. The psychiatrist or clinical psychologist brings to the object of observation a degree of highly individualized past experience which influences the particular components of the multidimensional events which he observes, and which also influences his interpretation of them. The variability of past experiences, relevant to the observation and interpretation of psychiatric data—or more generally, data in the study of interpersonal processes—not only rules out the possibility (at least in the foreseeable future) of the achievement of a pure objectivity in this field of inquiry, but also makes it extremely difficult to achieve a substantial degree of intersubjective agreement or consensual validation.

These issues in psychiatry may be viewed in the light of recent contributions to the foundations of probability which have tended to stress the importance of personal judgment in the application of probability theory and statistics, in general. Until quite recently the trend appears almost entirely to have been toward greater emphasis on objectivity in the development of probability theory and its applications. There can be little question as to the great value of this emphasis in a wide range of applications and with respect to the development of probability theory itself. The concepts of randomness, the principles of experimental design, and industrial quality control are examples of statistical concepts developed in the framework of objectivistic probability. In recent years, however, mathematical statisticians and other scientists have also become involved in many areas of research requiring the application of inductive reasoning to situations in which controlled and objective data, to a certain extent, had to be supplanted by personal judgment and intui-

9. Benjamin Wolstein, *Transference: Its Meaning and Function in Psychoanalytic Therapy,* Grune and Stratton, New York, 1954, pp. 39-40.

10. E. W. Barankin, "Toward an objectivistic theory of probability," *Proceedings of the Third Berkeley Symposium on Mathematical Statistics and Probability,* edited by Jerzy Neyman, 1956, 5:21-52.

tion. It is probably as an outgrowth of this predicament that there has followed a reawakened interest in the subjective aspects of probability.

The point of view expressed by I. J. Good that the purpose of probability theory is the "valid extension of a body of beliefs," and that the "state of mind" is an important factor in the application of probability,[11] as well as L. J. Savage's "very tentative" definition of *statistics proper* as the "art of dealing with vagueness and with interpersonal difference in decision situations,"[12] provides a broad conceptual framework for the application of statistics to the generally subjective data of psychiatry and clinical psychology.

The idea of degrees of belief, or subjective probability as such, appears to have begun with the contribution of Bayes in the early eighteenth century. Bayes' view that one's subjective probability concerning the outcome of a single event could be determined on the basis of what betting action one is willing to take with respect to the event appears to have been the first in a series of contributions to the subjective foundations of probability theory culminating in recent contributions such as those of Good and Savage noted above. Of special interest in this line of development, from the point of view of this presentation, is the contribution of Ramsey.[13] In addition to his contribution to the axiomatic development of subjective probability, Ramsey offered some brief but insightful observations on the psychology of degrees of belief. In commenting on the limitations of the use of intensity of feeling accompanying a belief as a measure of the degree of the belief, Ramsey points out that very often the beliefs that one holds most strongly are accompanied by a minimum of observable feeling—"no one feels strongly about the things he takes for granted." Rather one tends to *act* according to one's beliefs, and "intensities of belief-feelings" are relevant from a practical point of view entirely in relation to their position as the "hypothetical causes of beliefs *qua* bases of action." Thus degrees of belief are to be measured in relation to relevant actions and decisions.

These conclusions are not only basic to the framework of contemporary subjective decision theory, but have also a relevance to the study of psychopathological and other interpersonal processes, when such processes are considered from the point of view of belief and distortion in belief. For instance, psychoanalytic concepts of transference and

11. I. J. Good, *Probability and the Weighing of Evidence*, Charles Griffin and Co., London, 1950, Chap. 1.

12. L. J. Savage, *Foundations of Statistics*, John Wiley and Sons, Inc., New York, 1954, p. 154.

13. Frank P. Ramsey, *Foundations of Mathematics*, 1928, reprinted, Humanities Press, New York, 1950.

countertransference or the concept of parataxic distortion within the interpersonal theory of psychiatry are used to describe certain kinds of errors in belief due to an overgeneralization of aspects of past experience. As an example, a person undergoing psychoanalysis may attribute to his analyst certain characteristics more appropriately descriptive of the person's father. With respect to these characteristics he believes the analyst is like his father. This belief, however, need not be strongly felt as such. The patient may never have had the distinct thought "the analyst is like my father." However, the belief may be implicit in the patient's productions during analysis—that is, his actions are consistent with such a belief.

In general the goal of psychoanalytic therapy may be considered as the transformation of a body of beliefs. The psychoanalyst's basis for judging the extent to which such a goal has been achieved with respect to a given patient is the degree to which the new and presumably healthier body of beliefs are supported by the action or behavior of the patient. That is, it is not sufficient that the patient gain *intellectual* insight. He must also be able to *work through* to the achievement of "true" or *emotional* insight, so that his feelings, insofar as they are capable of determining or guiding his actions are consistent with his intellectual acceptance of the new body of beliefs. The psychoanalyst's (or intensive psychotherapist's) criterion for the transformation of belief is thus entirely consistent with Ramsey's approach, and, in this connection, it is of particular interest to note that Ramsey referred to the use of "medical psychology" with regard to "hints for avoiding confusion" in a listing of factors to be considered under the content of logic.[14]

Beginning with Freud in the latest period of his contributions and more definitely since the contributions of Freud, the total personality in its day-to-day manifestations rather than the mere isolation of singular traumatic events of the past has become the focal area for the interpretation of psychopathology, and "habitual modes of adaptation (of the personality) are conceived and demonstrated as effects and developments

---

14. A semantic point must, however, be made with respect to the way in which the term, belief, or true belief, is sometimes used by the psychoanalyst, in contrast to his use of the term, emotional (or true) insight. As was stated above, the latter term is used by the analyst to describe a state of progress with respect to a body of beliefs (or a segment of a body of beliefs)—judged to be accurate or healthy—when a patient's actions and general behavior are consistent with it. The analyst, however, sometimes speaks of a patient's "true beliefs" when he is referring to the patient's potential for accepting at some future time the desirable body of beliefs supported by action. This use of "true belief" is not particularly based on the analyst's evaluation of the patient's having achieved intellectual insight, but rather upon what the analyst feels to be the pressure of biosocial forces building up against a neurotogenic or neurotic body of beliefs—sufficient to overcome repressive and other resistive forces maintaining such beliefs.

in an interpersonal field which is organized to cope with typical expectancies, real or distorted."[15] The "typical expectancies" of interpersonal events whether "real or distorted" may be viewed in a variety of situations, as probability estimates based on sequences of a great many events observed with corresponding relative frequencies of one kind or another.

In discussing such relative frequencies and functions of them it is recognized that complete (retrospective) data about them for use in an exact numerical sense will not be available in general. Nevertheless when it is said, for example, that a given person has been subject to a regular influence of one kind or another from both parents, this implies that the relative frequency of a certain class of past events related to the person's present expectation and belief is, on an average, greater than if the influence had just come from a single parent.

The postulation of the existence of such relative frequencies as an important influence on personality development and on degrees of expectation is hardly more than a consequence of the acceptance of environment (in its most general sense) as an essential factor in the development of personality and belief. The case of *extreme* psychopathology is often accompanied by various probability estimates (about interpersonal and related events) of unity or zero, reflecting complete expectancy or complete disbelief. Such estimates, at the extremes of the probability scale appear to be a reflection of those aspects of mental illness which are considered to be a product of a rigid background of constant repetition of classes of unfortunate events. If, for example, the idealized paranoid development, "pure paranoia," is viewed as one in which a person considers himself to be entirely blameless with regard to all disappointments and misfortunes, "real" or "imagined," which befall him, and places the blame for all such happenings on scapegoats, and on the world in general, then it is reasonable to assume that the background for such a development will contain much data consistent with such beliefs and expectations.

Based upon his clinical observations with respect to environmental factors in the paranoid process, Sullivan considers as a particular aspect of the data relevant to its development, that of an undiluted and fairly continuous stream of pertinent misinformation passing from parent to child, such misinformation being in the nature of explanations which always shift blame away from the child.[16] Thus, according to Sullivan, the "paranoid slant of a great many people" is determined by "the

15. B. Wolstein, *op. cit.*, p. 35.

16. Harry Stack Sullivan, *Clinical Studies in Psychiatry*, Norton, New York, 1956, pp. 342-344.

degree to which paranoid explanations, in the sense of explanations involving a transference of blame, have been *de rigueur* and satisfactory in the home environment." The paranoid process can be thwarted, "if one parent has on many occasions quite pointedly objected to the other parent's washing his or her hands of blame by moving it over to the neighbors, for instance, . . . the child who grows up in this home is, I believe, greatly impressed by the attitude of the person who opposes this blanket projection." Fortunate experiences with siblings, schoolmates, et cetera, may also provide data to arrest paranoid development. Thus, the subjective probabilities—subjective in the sense that they are derived from the experience of a particular person—attached to certain classes of propositions—such as, "the other person is to blame"—may be based upon long sequences of observations. As noted above, in the case of extreme forms of paranoid psychopathology such observations may be equivalent to a history of statements from, say, parent to child which did not discriminate between the truth or falsity of the proposition at each occasion, but which contained the message that it was always true (i.e., that the other person is to blame). Thus, however close the "true" observed relative frequency of the correctness of the proposition may have been to 0.5, or even to zero, the distortion provides a paranoid estimate close to unity, and this estimate is based on a relative frequency.[17]

In general, that is, not merely in relation to observed paranoid psychopathology, the relative frequency of statements asserting the truth of the proposition about blame consists of a number of component relative frequencies such as those corresponding to sequences of statements by the mother, father, and/or other significant figures, respectively, as well as components based on other qualitative considerations—for example, a mere statement about the truth or falsity of a proposition may have to be accompanied by a certain conviction for it to be accepted as true. The degree of belief concerning the truth of the "blame" proposition may then be regarded as some function of a corresponding set of relative frequencies, which is equal to unity in the special case of extreme paranoid development.

In theory, the severity of a paranoid tendency may then be measured by the extent to which more accurate data made "available" to the subject subsequent to the period during which most of the misinformation leading to the tendency was accumulated, can correct the earlier bias.

More generally, i.e., not only in specific instances of psychopathology,

17. Sequences of observations leading to paranoid probabilities need not be the result of observations which amount to an inaccurate account of past events, but obviously could also result from the experience of atypical events. Thus from purely logical empirical considerations a sequence of observations, in which the other fellow is really at fault, may lead to a certain belief, i.e., a belief with probability one, that the other fellow will again be at fault, despite other evidence to the contrary.

quantities of information or of misinformation passing from the parent to the child, either explicitly or implicitly, in the form of evaluations or of criticisms of the child contribute substantially to the determination of the child's body of beliefs about himself, and which may be held throughout adult as well as early life. In the terminology of Sullivan, the self (or the concept that one maintains about the self) is made up of "reflected appraisals" of significant others. In early life the child through lack of equipment and experience is hardly capable of genuine self-appraisal or evaluation, so that he cannot help but see himself in relation to the estimates of him as made by parents and other significant adults on a day-to-day basis. This is, of course, another way of asserting that once a sufficient accumulation of misinformation has been received, further corrective data—beyond the point in time by which such an accumulation may have taken place—may tend to lose its weight as evidence against the earlier distortions.

In extreme paranoid psychopathology, we may say that the inability of a patient to modify a paranoid probability or degree of belief of unity despite attempts to bring before him corrective data in the course of intensive psychotherapy or psychoanalysis (or, in general, in situations subsequent to the early disabling ones) may be regarded as consistent with the result from Bayes' theorem, which states that a prior probability of unity (or zero) foredooms the posterior probability to the same value, regardless of the quantity of data added. In such a case the scientific, or "normal," postulate, that the probability of an empirical proposition should never be zero or unity for the reason that no amount of additional evidence can then change its probability, is not or cannot be accepted by the patient. A less pessimistic view of the possible influence of corrective data is inferred when it is assumed that the prior paranoid probability is not quite unity (or zero). For then, the posterior probability on the new data represents an actual correction of the prior probability, and as the amount of corrective data grows indefinitely large, the posterior probability becomes independent of the prior probability. In practice, of course, it is not very likely that the psychotherapist ever reaches this goal or even comes very close to it. Not only are corrective data necessarily limited to a finite number in anyone's lifetime, but the rate at which corrective data are successfully transmitted, at least under present techniques, appears to be of the magnitude which requires considerable calendar time to effect a noticeable change in expectation.

The importance of prior data in relation to expectation in psychopathological states is, of course, not limited to the development of paranoid processes. As a second example, one can consider the development of neurosis in a person whose upbringing includes a steady inculcation of exaggerated goodness and self-sacrifice of one kind or another, to the denial of self-affirmation and the expense of considerable repression. In maintaining a set of expectations consistent with such an orientation such a person will expect, in one form or another, either consciously, or not entirely in awareness, a greater harvesting of rewards than the biosocial system (of which he is a member) may be capable of extending. A brief discussion of developmental factors (in a hypothetical case) leading to an acute neurosis based upon such expectations in relation to corresponding "irrational" symptoms of such a neurosis, and related problems of the psychoanalytic or psychotherapeutic process will provide a more complete picture of the problem of expectation in psychopathology and psychotherapy that could be given on a simple Bayesian or statistical level, and will indicate some of the more purely psychiatric aspects, as distinct from, and in relation to, the statistical components of expectation and psychopathology.

We may begin with the person who from early childhood has been subjected to intensive parental effort directed toward the development of their child into a model of goodness. Such a child may be "taught" that the expression of anger, and even thoughts of resentment are always bad, and that they invariably lead to punishment or suffering of one kind or another. Let us further assume that the subject's mother was extremely self-sacrificing, particularly in relation to her son, and that this was accompanied by the engendering, in well-known neurotogenic ways, of strong feelings of dependency upon her, to the neglect of the emotional growth of the son.

The child develops the expectation of reward for being dependently good, and punishment, or the withholding of reward, or a general feeling of anxiety when he is not. These expectations are reinforced by the actual data of the home environment. That is, the parents, particularly the mother, are in the position of providing the data to establish the validity of the beliefs which they seek to inculcate, and barring unusual mitigating circumstances they are generally successful. Thus the patient at an early age learns to be extremely good, considerate, nonassertive, dependent, etc., and considers such behavior as morally optimal, and ultimately rewarding. As time goes forward and contacts outside of the home are increased chances are that the subject may come into contact with an increasing number of persons whose attitudes and expectations differ to a considerable extent from his own. For example, the girl he falls in love with at college, who seems so much in many ways like his mother, somehow prefers to go with a classmate who is nowhere near as good, kind, and considerate (nonassertive and dependent) as he is.

Despite the information objectively contained in incidents of this kind, earlier relevant expectation may be so firmly entrenched as not to be easily modified by such negative experiences. On the other hand, after meeting with repeated frustrations of a kind, he may begin to obtain a more realistic picture of the pessimistic probability associated with a particular kind of situation. However, this does not imply that he will necessarily change his behavior or outlook, for its pattern was developed not simply for the expectation of a reward in a specific situation or in kinds of situations but also involves more ultimate considerations such as an implicit fear of punishment for being bad, or inconsiderate, or going against parental wishes, et cetera. Furthermore, it would not be unlikely for a kind of paranoic coloring to exist at least to the extent that there would be "something wrong" with the girl who wouldn't date the son, et cetera. This would of course tend to reinforce the basis of neurotic expectation and belief.

Although it is by no means certain that the person whose expectations we have been discussing thus far need have developed an acute neurosis, let us assume that whatever further combination of circumstances are sufficient to bring about an acute neurosis, as manifest by the particular symptomatology to be discussed in outline below, did actually prevail.

First, let us review the subject's view of himself in relation to the state of mind and expectancies which he holds prior to the onset of his symptoms. At the outset, he considers himself to be a person with a very high degree of morality about which he feels quite righteous; he is not aware of any deep feelings, latent or otherwise, of resentment, hostility or hatred, particularly against his mother whose standards and ideal, and their concomittant masochistic manifestations, he holds in high regard. He feels he is incapable of hurting anyone. Although things have not gone too well lately, he is still optimistic about "meeting the right girl" and his expectations for a good life, a happy marriage, and so on, run high. Although he may be a person endowed with other admirable qualities such as, for example, a high degree of intelligence, a good sense of humor, and so on, the essential factor in his estimate of a favorable or *worthy* future is his conception of his morality.

We may again summarize by stating that our subjects' state of mind:

1. Places a very great emphasis upon morality as taught and practiced by his mother and that

2. His belief that he conforms to these moral standards

3. Leads to his high degree of expectation of a favorable future.

Now, given a state of mind summarized by (1) and (2) and leading to the expectation (3), any strong or dramatic evidence repeatedly becoming manifest to the subject, which would *deny* (2) while leaving (1) unaltered could obviously have serious repercussions for the individual. When such evidence takes the form of a sudden onset of obsessional thoughts and "irrational" fears of inflicting bodily harm or of killing various members of his family, particularly his mother, and when such thoughts and fears persist, and anxiety about them increases, the subject is in need of treatment for an acute (obsessive-compulsive) neurosis. In such a neurosis, among other effects, a swift transition takes place in the state of mind which is accompanied by a sharp discontinuity in the degree of expectation along the time axis. That is, up until the incidence of the acute neurotic symptoms, the subjective probability of a "good life" might have been close to unity, while immediately thereafter it became approximately zero. The transition marked by such a discontinuity in degrees of belief or expectation obviously cannot be interpreted satisfactorily as a direct and simple matter of probability estimation as a function of slowly changing relative frequencies in accordance with Bayes' theorem (as, e.g., might be conceivable, at least conceptually in the example given up to the point of the occurrence of the discontinuity, or more generally in cases where the onset of distortion in expectation appears to be the result of a steady accumulation of misinformation). The basis for the explanation of such a shift in expectation as it occurs upon the incidence of acute neurosis obviously must be interpreted within the framework of clinical observation and psychoanalytic theory. Within such a framework the acute neurosis, the accompanying symptoms, and consequently the discontinuity in expectation are explained in terms of repression—in particular as a failure in repression.

In summary, we may say in a perhaps oversimplified form that the stream of neurotogenic data fed from the family, particularly the mother, to the son resulted in the development of a set of beliefs, expectations, feelings, and utilities which required extensive repression of other sets more suited to an optimal (i.e., mentally healthy) life. The *repressed set*, however, does not vanish entirely. Its components exist under the surface of awareness, in the unconscious, and remain as latent causes of anxiety and neurosis (as well as of milder forms of everyday psychopathology). But as long as repression is in effect—i.e., as long as the unconscious feelings are not acknowledged to the self, and as long as the effects of the strain of repression are not felt in the form of neurotic symptoms (or in milder form, in everyday psychopathology)— then Ramsey's criterion of action as determined by degrees of belief may be fulfilled, not by action based on repressed wishes or beliefs (however they may exist as a latent force), but on conscious ones, i.e., those which repressive forces allow and which therefore can be held in awareness.

When the mechanism of repression breaks down significantly as it may after a long series of frustrations and disappointments occurring contrary to neurotic expectations, various changes may take place in corresponding utilities and/or degrees of belief. In the example the break-through of repressed material occurred out of the context of a complex of beliefs and utilities whose validity was challenged, in part, by means of anxiety-producing obsessional symptoms. Certain of the subject's beliefs were changed—essentially his beliefs about himself— other beliefs remained apparently unaltered. That is, his conditional probability estimates about a good life have not changed, but the set of conditions which he feels applies to *himself* has changed, or he attributes a high probability to such change on the evidence of his hostile obsessional thoughts. Further symptomatic effects such as extreme fatigue, fear of being in certain situations (and their consequent avoidance), et cetera, may have the added effect of preventing the subject from functioning in accordance with his old body of beliefs. Thus, under various symptomatic pressures these beliefs or subjective probabilities are no longer, on the face of it, capable of determining his course of action as they "reasonably" should in accordance with the Bayes-Ramsey-Savage norm. However, if one considers that in the first place this body of beliefs *did* lead to difficulties in life even prior to the onset of the acute neurosis, then the inability to act in accordance with them may be considered as something other than simple irrationality. (Under optimal conditions following the onset of such a neurosis—as, for example, with the availability and subsequent success of psychoanalytic therapy—the old body of beliefs undergoes a transformation to a new set of beliefs and subjective probabilities, and is accompanied by actions consistent with them.)

The outbreak of the symptoms of an acute neurosis may thus be considered, in effect, as a challenge to a consciously held body of beliefs rather than as a simple inconsistency between belief and action. Apparently, however, the price paid for the early accumulation of intensive quantities of misinformation and repression of a neurotogenic nature in combination with the occurrence of day-to-day events sufficiently severe to produce an acute neurosis is such that the meaning of the obsessional symptoms experienced by the person undergoing the neurosis is obscure to him, and from his immediate point of view, they *are* painfully inconsistent. He does not see the sudden influx of obsessional and unwanted thoughts of murder as a symbolic explosion against past repression and the body of beliefs and actions developed in relation to them.

His inability to act in accordance with his old body of beliefs is matched by a complete disavowal of his obsessional symptoms of hostility as a basis for action. However, the disavowal pertains not only to the extremely hostile acts which are the subject of the most dramatic among his obsessional fantasies. It is also relevant to what would be considered (under a different body of beliefs) as a set of more objectively justifiable, and less devastating *thoughts* as well as acts of resentment. But this is simply a continuation of not acting (or accepting thoughts as a basis for action) contrary to the old set of beliefs. Thus, the onset of the symptoms of an acute neurosis, in general, tends to prevent action either in support of, or in direct opposition to, the old body of beliefs.

The prevention or inhibition of action in support of the old beliefs is, of course, only partial. Particularly as the acute intensity of the symptoms wears off (whether in the beginning course of psychotherapy, or under an alleviating environmental change, or through various defenses built up by the subject to handle the obsessional symptoms) there will still be a strong and dominating tendency to act in conformity with the old body of beliefs—although the ability to maintain such action (i.e., the old neurotogenic way of life) in general will vary inversely with the frequency with which the symptoms reappear and their intensity. That is, as long as there is comparatively little change in the old body of beliefs following the onset of the neurosis, one may expect a shifting back and forth from "neurotogenic" action (i.e., behavior principally consistent with the old body of beliefs) to manifest neurotic action or inaction, as a product of neurotic symptomatology, and not supportive of the old beliefs.

The goal of intensive psychotherapy or psychoanalysis, as has been noted, may be considered to be that of the transformation in the patient from one set or body of beliefs to another, and the corresponding change from both neurotogenic and neurotic (i.e., symptomatic, as used here) action and behavior to a more "normal" or healthy pattern consistent with the new body of beliefs. During the course of psychotherapy the patient, in general, *first* will see only the reasonableness of a new belief or body of beliefs without being able to act in accordance with it. To that extent, in psychoanalytic terms he is said only to have *intellectual* insight rather than *true* or *emotional* insight—the latter would mean that the patient is capable of acting in accordance with the new belief or body of beliefs as well as accepting it as valid in an intellectual sense. Thus, in this instance, the Ramsey criterion of degrees of belief as measured by action is also the criterion of true insight.

The procedures whereby the old beliefs are transformed into new ones in the course of psychoanalytic therapy are essentially techniques directed toward providing and uncovering data to counteract and correct the earlier accumulation of large quantities of misinformation absorbed within a concomitant framework of repression. Repression and related phenomena which contribute to the formation and development of character structure, in general, do not permit the correction of an engrained belief—particularly not to the criterion of action—by a simple corrective statement. Beliefs about one's self, one's observations about others, and one's way of relating to others are hardly distinguishable from "feelings," and depending on how deeply rooted a feeling may be, the mere presentation of a fact to contradict the validity of the feeling may have very little, if any, effect on changing it. It has a better chance of being changed, however, if evidence against it continues to accumulate, and if the evidence is likewise "felt" or effective. The first of these conditions may be regarded as essentially statistical, and a consequence of Bayes' theorem which transforms prior probabilities to posterior probabilities on the basis of the accumulation of new data. The second condition, that of making the new data effective, is the technical problem of psychoanalytic therapy.

In this regard the function of psychotherapeutic technique in relation to the statistical aspects of the process of psychotherapy is the presentation or representation of pertinent segments of data, such as had previously been kept out of awareness through the barriers of anxiety, repression, and related phenomena, and which therefore could not have altered the engrained body of beliefs and its associated probabilities. This applies whether technique is directed, e.g., toward the recollection of childhood memories and fantasies in the resolution of Oedipal conflicts (in which case the emphasis is upon the correction of data near the beginning of the development of the neurotogenic body of beliefs) or whether technique is focused upon ongoing interpersonal transactions, the emphasis then being upon the correction of inferences about current data, such inferences being rooted in the old body of beliefs. While psychotherapy is obviously more than a simple statistical matter, its statistical aspects may be considered as relevant to questions such as those dealing with the amount of therapeutic effort necessary to effect desired transformations of subjective probabilities. One can reasonably state that the question of calendar time, or the order of the number of items of data needed for such transformations will depend upon the extent to which the prior psychopathogenic body of beliefs are engrained. The amount of psychotherapeutic intervention required would thus vary directly with the disparity between relevant prior probabilities and the corresponding desired posterior probabilities which are sought in the transformation to a new body of beliefs.

The idea that personality processes and individual psychopathology have essential stochastic, or statistical properties has many important implications for the application of the principles of experimental design to research in clinical psychology and psychiatry. As these implications are discussed in some detail in other publications, a brief outline of some of the main points which are involved will be given here.[18]

18. For a detailed development of various aspects of these implications the reader is referred to the following publications:

First, it becomes apparent that mere end-point observations for the purpose of estimating change in the patient-state, after, say, the intervention of some form of treatment, places generally severe limitations on the precision of the estimation of change. For, random fluctuation in the patient-state can then easily be mistaken for systematic change. To overcome this difficulty, frequent repeated observations must be made of each patient in a study. The estimation of parameters and/or the testing of hypotheses must be performed *within* each patient over time in relation to changes in treatment, milieu, and so on. As each patient thus becomes his own control the statistical results which are obtained within a patient can be related to his specific set of background variables and other characteristics. That is, such data from a single patient can be regarded in theory as representative of a (possibly unique) population determined by all of the specific relevant characteristics of the patient.

It is suggested that only through systematic comparisons of results between such populations in relation to particular similarities and dissimilarities between them does it seem possible to use statistical methodology in pinning down those patient characteristics and parameters most relevant to patient change in relation to particular therapeutic interventions.

The alternative and conventional approach to research design, which is in general limited to end-point (or occasional) observation and in which hypotheses are tested only between patients cannot possibly approach such a goal. The failure of this model is a direct consequence of the relatively small number of patients available even in "large" clinical studies together with the general lack of homogeneity to be found in even quite small groups of patients. Further, related difficulties of such research pertain to the vagueness of the theoretical population from which the design sample was presumably drawn and to which operational consequences of the results can be applied.

The methodology of statistical design which utilizes intensive, or longitudinal observations on each patient further allows for the study of many kinds of phenomena which cannot be handled by what has been referred to here as conventional design. The study of symptom fluctuation and its contingencies within the individual over time, the statistical study

J. B. Chassan, "On probability theory and psychoanalytic research," *Psychiatry*, 1956, 19:55-61.

―――, "On the unreliability of reliability and some other consequences of the assumption of probabilistic patient-states," *Psychiatry*, 1957, 20:163-169.

―――, "The development of clinical statistical systems for psychiatry," *Biometrics*, 1959, 15:396-404.

―――, "A statistical description of a clinical trial of promazine," *Psychiatric Quarterly*, 33:700-714.

―――, "Statistical inference and the single case in clinical design," *Psychiatry*, 1960, 23:173-184.

of individual psychotherapy, the statistical analysis of interpersonal fields and their shifts over time are areas of investigation which can only be handled adequately in the framework of the frequent repetition of observations.[19]

In many applications of probability theory and statistics there is relatively little concern over the philosophical foundations of probability. A primary goal of statistical design in these areas is the achievement of a high degree of objectivity to the extent that the results of a study or experiment can be made to stand on its own, i.e., that its implications are specific and equally clear to all qualified investigators. Such a goal seems often at least approximated in many areas, e.g., in agricultural experimentation, in industrial quality control, in census work, etc.

Reference was made earlier in this paper to particular difficulties encountered in the application of statistics and probability to the data of psychiatry and clinical psychology. Many of the factors which contribute to this difficulty are well known. They include phenomena of participant-observation with their accompanying Heisenberg effects, so that many of the observations of clinical psychiatry must be made within the framework of interpersonal fields generated by both the observer and the subject (the conventionality of this dichotomy is well acknowledged). Observer A may differ from observer B in his evaluation of patient X, and such differences may be a function of differences of one kind or another between A and B.[20]

The concept of a body of beliefs discussed earlier in specific reference to neurotogenic processes obviously has a broader application. It may be extended more generally to an explication or interpretation of personality processes. This would be consistent with Good's use of *body of beliefs* and *state of mind* in his subjectivist axiomatization of probability theory, and with the earlier relevant observations of Ramsey as were noted above. It is clear in this connection that participant-observation as an essential aspect of the study of interpersonal and psychoanalytic processes inevitably involves the question of interpersonal differences in the interpretation and influencing of the data under study. Particular differences in the handling of such data resulting from differences in such factors as previous experience, personality, training, and theoretical orien-

19. The method of frequent observations on each patient over time is known as the *intensive* design, in contrast to the use of *extensive* for the design which is based on end-point observations alone. A distinction between this and the *longitudinal cross-sectional* dichotomy is that an intensive design can have cross-sectional aspects, as when, for example, daily observations are made on each of thirty patients on a ward, and the daily trend of ward movement (or of the movement of subgroups within a ward) are analyzed over specified periods—in addition to the statistical analysis of the data of each patient on the ward.

20. See, for example, Hans Strupp, *Psychotherapists in Action*, Grune and Stratton, New York, in press.

tation need not reflect the presence of gross distortion. The data—a priori with respect to a given interpersonal multidimensional event— that a given investigator may have up to the point of observing and interpreting an event may differ considerably from that of another investigator, and each could act reasonably, though differently, in the light of their respective samples of relevant past experience.[21]

The extent to which the quantity and quality of the investigator's deviate past experiences, including those manifest as personality differences, result in bias to the point of distortion is not always easy to determine, and may itself be a subject of disagreement in particular instances. However, the tools, techniques, and concepts which are used in the process of psychoanalysis and intensive psychotherapy for the correction of distortion and the transformation of belief in the treatment of neurosis and psychosis are also applied to the psychoanalyst in his own personal analysis and in his training, and, on an ongoing basis, by the analyst to himself as the part of participant observation in his practice of psychoanalytic therapy which involves the transformation of segments of his body of beliefs. The different ways in which countertransference, e.g., has been defined by different writers on psychoanalysis,[22] and various frameworks within which the concepts has been discussed are illustrative of the kinds of emotional response, bias, and distortion which the therapist may display, and which he attempts to correct during the course of his psychotherapeutic interventions.

While an understanding of the data which mark the ongoing situation in the process of psychotherapy more obviously demands an appreciation of predisposing influences which contribute to the filtering and selection as well as to the generation of data of this kind, it is noted that such influences may be present in relation to more formal and presumably objective statistical systems in clinical and behavioral studies (and to some extent even more generally). That is, even in carefully planned experimental designs there may exist, however vaguely, prior data which not only provide a necessary background for the determination of the design but which may be considered as biasing the selection of the particular data system implementing the design.

What seems clear is that a purely objectivistic framework for the application of probability theory and statistics (including universal agreement on the form and content of specific items of observation and their measurement) and one which would be acceptable to all research

---

21. It is noted that the question of what constitutes relevant past experience and differences in judgment concerning what is relevant to a given event may themselves reflect differences in corresponding aspects of experience.

22. See Mabel Blake Cohen, "Counter-transference and anxiety," *Psychiatry*, 1952, 15:231-243.

workers in clinical psychiatry is a long way off at best. Premature attempts to achieve such a pure objectivity seems doomed to frustration, as this cannot take place before a great deal more of systematic research effort is expended upon the exploration of interpersonal differences as an integral part of the understanding of the data of clinical psychiatry. This does not mean, however, that to be useful all research in the field of clinical psychiatry must deal with interpersonal differences between investigators. It is in the context of the development of stochastic models *within* a given theoretical structure or personality process that Good's contention that the purpose of probability theory is the valid extension of a body of beliefs becomes particularly meaningful. It seems to me that the failure to accept such a philosophy of probability, particularly within the subject matter that has been discussed, may be rooted in the same kind of insecurity which earlier found difficulty in accepting probability itself as the science of uncertainty.

PETER McKELLAR

The Method of Introspection

I do not see why the report of a person on his own mind should not be as intelligible and trustworthy as that of a traveller upon a new country whose landscapes and inhabitants are of a different type to any we ourselves have seen.—SIR FRANCIS GALTON

"Mind" is a word. It belongs to everyday speech rather than the vocabulary of science, and the most relevant branch of science—human psychology—has placed a peculiarly strong taboo upon its use. Contemporary psychologists are more alerted to investigating externally observed behavior than to the introspective study of human subjective experience. This chapter will discuss introspection as a method, survey salient features of its history, and illustrate its use in the investigation of human mental life.*

Warren (1934) defined *"introspectionism"* as "the doctrine that the introspective method is the fundamental method of investigation in psychology." It is not the purpose of this chapter to defend this doctrine. The various methods which involve the contemplation, reflection on, and reporting of subjective experiences are no longer the main tools of

---

I have to thank Professor Harry Kay and Mr. G. W. Pilkington of the Department of Psychology, University of Sheffield, and Mr. Frank Cioffi, who have contributed constructive advice and criticism of this paper.

* A comprehensive history of introspection has been compiled by Boring (1953), whose article is recommended to readers interested in fuller historical details.

the psychologist. There is no reason why they should be. Yet much of importance is lost, and avoidable mistakes can occur, if psychologists reject the methods, use them in a grudging or apologetic way, or adopt an attitude of mind not alerted to their use.

The low status of introspection has resulted partly from the doctrine of early behaviorism, its derivatives like behavior theory, and their effects on modern thinking. It was in 1913 that John B. Watson presented what might be called the manifesto of the behaviorist movement. He argued that psychology should be "a purely objective experimental branch of natural science"; it should concern itself with "the prediction and control of behavior"; the psychologist should no longer interest himself in "interpretation in terms of consciousness," and introspection should no longer play an essential part among his methods. (Watson, 1913, p. 158.)

Wanted babies have been known to disappear with unwanted bathwater! Failure to employ introspection where necessary can result in the loss of information of which it seems rational to take account. Even in the same year as Watson's manifesto, a distinguished psychologist much in sympathy with attempts to make psychology more "objective" sounded this note of caution: "It is a wise instinct which science has always followed to glean information *wherever* it can be found." (Angell, 1913, p. 269, italics mine.) The progress of human knowledge has, from time to time, been impeded by those who felt some inner urge to proscribe certain techniques, or to forbid others to investigate subject matter in which they, themselves, were not interested. Watson represented a tradition of this kind, a tradition whose strengths and weaknesses were assessed by a leading contemporary theorist when he said: "These men were narrow; they were wrong; and without them, without the simplification they achieved, modern psychology would not exist." (Hebb, 1953, p. 101.) Others of the same intellectual tradition now expound a more mellow doctrine. Thus, Spence (1948) points out that few psychologists would today label themselves "behaviorists"; he himself is even prepared—though without much apparent enthusiasm—to find a place for introspection among the methods of psychology in the guise of "verbal report": people's verbal reports are, after all, a form of behavior. Writing as a historian of psychology, Boring expresses the view that "introspection is still with us, doing its business under various aliases, of which *verbal report* is one." (Boring, 1953, p. 169, italics his.)

A more positive attitude toward introspection is to be found in some modern philosophers, for example, Carnap, who argues that the behaviorist's "total rejection of introspection was unwarranted." While severely critical of narrow introspectionism, Carnap regards the introspective method itself, though limited by its subjectivity, as "a legitimate source of knowledge." (Carnap, 1956, pp. 70-71.) This represents essentially the standpoint to be defended in the present chapter. One wonders why useful sources of information about human nature need to be disguised as "verbal reports" or, to use Boring's phrase, should have to appear under "various aliases." The word introspection does not denote a single method, but a family of methods. We shall be concerned with these methods, their history and their use, where necessary in undisguised form, Introspection will first be examined in terms of some salient aspects of its history.

Historical Outline

Introspective methods are closely associated with the beginnings of experimental psychology and its first laboratories. William James (1842-1910) was an "introspectionist" in that he had no doubt that psychology must rely on the introspection "first, and foremost, and always." For James the word "introspection" hardly needed definition: "It means, of course, looking into our minds and reporting what we there discover." (James, 1890, Vol. I, p. 185.)

Wilhelm Wundt (1832-1920), who has been called "the father of experimental psychology, was likewise an introspectionist. His standpoint *appears* to have resembled that of William James. For Wundt the subject matter of psychology was immediate experience: its method must, therefore, be immediate experiencing, that is, introspection. Despite their agreement that it was the primary method of psychology, William James and Wundt meant very different things when they spoke of "introspection." The *Principles of Psychology* and other writings testify to the importance which James placed upon relatively casual introspective activity, but Wundt had a rather different conception.

As practiced in Wundt's laboratory at Leipzig what came to be called "*classical introspection*" involved a highly systematic analysis of mental processes into elements. This analysis was in accord with prescribed conventions and by subjects trained for introspection in this way. Analysis was important to Wundt who conceived of psychology as a sort of mental chemistry, with states of consciousness as the compounds requiring skilled analysis into defined elements. The training required appears to have been thorough and exacting. Boring (1953) reports it as said that only after a student of Wundt's had performed 10,000 of these exercises were his introspections judged suitable material to be used in any published report from the Leipzig laboratory! It was the systematic introspective methods of Wundt that one of his most influential pupils, Titchener (1867-1927), brought to the American continent and practiced at Cornell between the years 1900 and 1920. When psychologists like Watson rebelled, they did so against this and certain related kinds of systematic introspection. Other revolts were in progress, or shortly to occur.

Some of the related kinds of systematic introspection themselves deviated considerably from the "classical" methods of Wundt. Another of Wundt's pupils, Külpe, and the group he gathered round him at Würzburg presented such a deviation. The *Würzburg School* was much concerned with the psychology of thinking: in approaching this subject matter Külpe and his colleagues found it necessary to modify the Wundtian methods. Thus, Watt, in studying the process of association developed his "*method of fractionation.*" In this the total period under introspective study would be divided into definite stages: repeated introspections would now be conducted, emphasis being placed on one or other of these stages at each repetition. Another leading Würzburg investigator, Ach, employed hypnotism in setting up certain processes which were then studied introspectively. Like Wundt at the Leipzig laboratory, the Würzburg investigators used subjects trained to introspect. Thus Bühler, in studying thinking, based his findings on the introspective reports of only two subjects: Külpe himself, and Dürr. The Würzburg investigators differed from Wundt in rejecting his kind of analysis into elements, in introducing additional techniques of their own, and in being concerned with somewhat different phenomena of mental life.

Interest in a different subject matter has, from time to time, resulted in modification of the methods of introspection employed. This is even more apparent in the *Gestalt school,* which became concerned with the psychology of perception. The emphasis of Wertheimer and his colleagues was on the necessity to adopt a naive attitude to the phenomena of ordinary experience rather than upon training in introspection. They were interested in how people in general perceive size, shape, color, movement, *etc.,* and not with introspections by trained observers who had learned Wundtian or other conventions of analysis. We shall be concerned with illustrations of the Gestalt type of introspection in a later section.

Introspection contributed much to the development of laboratory experimentation in psychology: it had other methods to contribute to what is now the repertoire of methods of the modern psychologist. Francis Galton (1822-1911) was not only the author of the questionnaire, but has been called the founder of *the method of mental testing.* Like laboratory experimentation, this second important method may be said to have emerged from introspective studies. Galton used the questionnaire as an instrument for studying differences between people. He employed it in eliciting differences of subjective experience that emerged from their recorded introspections, and along with this he developed statistical techniques for handling the resulting data. (Galton, 1880.) Galton studied mental imagery in this way and found wide individual differences. Since Galton's time it has become traditional to refer to imagery types: visiles, audiles, and motiles, according to the predominant form of mental imagery. The word "type" hardly does justice to the rich variety of differences which emerged from Galton's and subsequent studies.

People differ in the number of sense modalities in which they report imagery; in the predominance of one or other of these sense modalities; in ways in which such imagery is related to thinking, imagination and remembering; in vividness of imagery; in the extent to which their imagery is subject to voluntary control; in where they localise their images; in the stability and completeness of their imagery, and so on.

Galton found that over 10 per cent of a group of schoolboys reported an ability to form vivid and stable visual images which they were able to project. Imagery of this kind has since become known as *eidetic* imagery —mental imagery which in vividness, stability, and other ways possesses many of the qualities of percepts. The phenomenon was first noted in 1907 by V. Urbantschitsch and later gave rise to another important school of introspective investigation of Marburg (Jaensch, 1930). Galton's own work was concerned with the measurement of individual differences of a variety of kinds. Although he was concerned with differences of body structure and others that could be measured externally, his distinctive contribution was to draw attention to hidden, subjective differences between people. We shall return to imagery and other such phenomena in subsequent parts of this chapter.

Another kind of introspective approach to mental life is associated with Sigmund Freud and the various deviant movements which developed out of *psychoanalysis*. Bakan (1954) has suggested that the Würzburg school may have come to an end because the psychologists concerned, practicing intensive introspection on one another, encountered emotional problems of the kind Freud later explored. It is apparent that the type of introspection practiced by Freud on himself, in, for example, *The Interpretation of Dreams*, made exacting emotional demands upon him. Elsewhere (1954) the present writer once attempted a brief examination of the question: "Who analyzed Freud?" The answer is, "Freud himself," and the record of this analysis is to be found in his book *The Interpretation of Dreams*. To this it may be added that considerable emotional support seems to have been obtained by Freud from Wilhelm Fliess, who assisted Freud in his role of self-analyst. It is fortunate that the letters Freud wrote to Fliess during this period of his own introspective self-examination, important because it comprised the first psychoanalysis, have been preserved. (Bonaparte, M., Freud, A., and Kris, E., eds., 1954.)

Despite the emphasis which they placed upon "unconscious" mental life it is to be noted that Freud and his colleagues drew heavily upon introspective data. Rather too much seems to have been made of the argument that because psychoanalysis drew attention to unconscious aspects of motivation this gives some peculiar justification for abandoning the use of the introspective method. As O'Neill (1957) has wisely pointed out, even if some phenomena of mental life do not readily lend themselves for study by ordinary introspection, these are not grounds for giving up the study of those that do so lend themselves. Special techniques like hypnotism and free association may have been necessary to make available certain phenomena for introspective study, and it was precisely these techniques that Freud developed. Again, Freud's own work depends upon ordinary introspection to a greater extent than is often admitted; *The Interpretation of Dreams* itself consists largely of an introspective study conducted by Freud. A psychoanalysis involves a study of how the processes of association work in the patient, and an imparting to the patient of self-understanding on the basis of this study. In particular, in this situation, the patient is instructed in the ways in which resistances and self-deceptive strategies operate and impede his associative activity.

Despite obvious differences, there are certain similarities between the methods of Wundt and of Freud. If Wundt taught his students to introspect according to certain rules, Freud trained his patients and students to understand their own thinking, emotion, and motivation. A "strengthening of the ego"—a standing back from feelings and emotional involvements of a half-understood kind—was the goal of his training. Much of Freud's work was concerned with finding out new things about mental life, rather than with narrowly therapeutic aims; this is, for example, less obviously so in the work of Adler than in that of Freud. If the psychoanalysts sought to extend and adopt introspective methods for the study of complex problems of motivation and emotion, they brought a rather characteristic emphasis to the investigation of this subject matter. When, as often happens, an intelligent, sophisticated, and highly educated individual comes to be psychoanalyzed the analyst often needs to devote much time to discouraging such a person's tendencies to intellectualize. In this respect Freudian analysts actively seek to discourage intellectual activity of the very sort which Wundt and other earlier introspectionists seem to have fostered. Psychoanalysts have adopted the working principle that premature verbalizations can impede the subject's understanding of his own emotional and motivational life. In their understanding of this and in their concern to extend human awareness of some of the less introspectively obvious aspects of motivation, the psychoanalysts have materially broadened the perspective of modern thinking toward the possibilities of human self-knowledge. It has been noted that Boring holds that introspection remains a method of contemporary psychology, although under various aliases of which verbal report is one. Another "alias" of some importance is psychoanalysis.

In recent years the psychology of personality has made substantial use of introspection, or methods closely allied to it. McClelland (1955) has argued that psychoanalysis on the one hand and the projective technique movement on the other have contributed to a desirable reorientation: a greater readiness to collect reports of fantasies and subjective experiences. Projective techniques like the Rorschach and the Thematic Apperception Test were not available to the early introspectionists. Their appearance, which has provided new ways of studying the "content" of human consciousness, and not just processes—"thought sampling" as McClelland calls it—has opened up a new approach to the study of the human personality. In social as well as personality psychology use may be made of biographical information. A good example is to be found in the study which Allport and others (1941) made of biographical reports written by victims of the Nazis: these accounts included information on such subjects as thoughts and dreams. Others have drawn upon accounts, including introspective information, from former prisoners of war in attempts to understand methods of indoctrination and "brainwashing" (Schein, 1954). In dealing with material of this kind it becomes a little artificial to make sharp distinctions between observations and introspections. When asked to give such reports people may relate not only what they and other people did, but also their thoughts, dreams, and fantasies as well. Thus, Bettelheim (1943), as a prisoner in Nazi concentration camps who was also a psychologist, kept a diary of this period. His material is not confined to observations made on various of the prisoners; he also places much emphasis on his own introspections and on introspective data elicited by him.

From introspective and other biographical data recorded or elicited from others by psychologists may be distinguished similar data recorded or elicited by others. There will be differences of opinion as to the value of such information. Evidence suggests that, as an interviewer, the psychologist is not superior to the nonpsychologist, and that the clinical psychologist is not superior to his colleagues in this respect (Taft, 1955). The superiority of the professional psychologist as introspectionist has not, to the writer's knowledge, been scientifically demonstrated. In the absence of such evidence it seems reasonable to retain introspective reports by others when they provide data not elsewhere available. An illustration may be taken of this kind of introspection.

The Russian novelist Dostoevsky, whom incidentally Nietzsche assessed as "the only psychologist from whom I had anything to learn," was not a professional psychologist. His writings of life in a Siberian convict settlement provide biographical and introspective data of value to the understanding of desocialisation and regression (*The House of the Dead*). Elsewhere he records the subjective experiences which occur previous to an epileptic attack (*The Idiot*). As Dostoevsky was himself epileptic there is reason to believe he was drawing on his own introspections. Elsewhere (*The Gambler*) he takes the reader into the subjective experiences of an individual struggling with a vice from which he cannot free himself; biographical data again suggest sources in Dostoevsky's own life history. Yet elsewhere the novelist portrays the thoughts and feelings of a hardened criminal (*Letters from the Underworld*), and of an individual who experiences dissociation of personality (*The Brothers Karamazov*).

Psychologists may vary in their assessment of the value of data of these kinds. Many would probably accept the view that at least as a starting point, and so far as it assists in formulating hypotheses which can be tested in other ways, such information merits consideration.

The Problem of Empathy

Before summarizing these various methods of introspection and discussing data obtained from them, mention will be made of the possible value of introspection from the standpoint of empathy. The word "empathy" is here taken to denote imaginative identification with a person that permits fuller understanding of his mental life. As the writers of one psychological dictionary put it, empathy involves an implicit "I see how you feel." (English and English, 1958, p. 178.)

From time to time psychologists have sought ways of extending their knowledge of forms of mental life other than those with which they habitually live. Thus some investigators of blind people have themselves worn opaque glasses for periods of time, in order to be able to empathize with the problems of the blind. One investigator who attempted this reported that she had herself gained experience of what it *felt like* to be blind: this experience itself had value to her work over and above anything she could verbally communicate about it. One of the more difficult tasks of empathy is to achieve some understanding of what the subjective experiences of psychosis are like: as Kretschmer put it "the pane of glass is always there" to divide the psychotic from the normal person. Numerous investigators have suggested that a measure of empathic understanding of psychosis can be achieved from the nonpsychotic's introspective study of his own dreams and nightmares. There are drugs which have been used to produce phenomena of experience akin to those of psychosis; since 1895 mescaline, and since 1943 lysergic acid diethylamide, have been employed in this way. Hallucinations, particularly those of the visual kind, can be studied not only by using chemical agencies but also by the techniques of sensory deprivation that have developed at McGill University in recent years. In the training of psychiatrists, clinical psychologists, and others, experimental methods which enable normal people themselves to experience hallucinations, disturbances of perception and thinking, and changes of personality may well have an important place.

Some of these techniques may lead to a questioning of the view that the only value of introspection lies in what can be "verbally reported." The relation of verbal reporting and other forms of communication to introspection will be considered later. Apart from anything that is reported to the experimenter a secondary aim of introspection, in some cases at least, appears to have been an attempt by the investigator to extend his own ability to empathize in order to better understand the phenomenon under study.

The Methods of Introspection

It has been argued that "introspection" is not one, but a family of methods. We have seen from the previous historical outline that investigators who have been curious about human experience and behavior have, in fact, used a *variety of methods* of introspection. Some methodologists may wish to confine the word "introspection" to the study of subjective phenomena like mental images, fantasies, and hallucinations. Some may be prepared to include as introspective an individual's reports on his perceptual experiences, although similar reports can be obtained —in principle, and perhaps also in practice—from different observers. Others may be prepared to accept a still more catholic conception and to regard as introspection various techniques of a more biographical kind: therapists may, for example, glean useful information by comparisons of an individual's own autobiographical report with reports by other people on the events of his life. Rather than attempt formal definitions it is suggested that it is better to recognize a *family of introspective methods*, together with methods which shade into related techniques of a biographical kind. Important among the latter are some of the methods of personality and social psychology in which sharp distinctions between "observation" and "introspection" become difficult to maintain.

To refer back to our brief historical survey we may first contrast the systematic methods of "classical introspection" with those of a relatively unsystematic kind. Secondly, the use of trained introspectionists differs from the work of the Gestalt psychologists and others who sought, by introspection, to study the phenomena of naive human experience. Thirdly, introspections may be classified by the circumstances in which they are obtained: the laboratory, the clinic, the analytic situation, and daily life. Fourthly, some introspection is carried out mainly for communication to the experimenter, while in other cases it is carried out partly or largely to extend the investigator's own empathic understanding. Fifthly, introspection under normal circumstances may be contrasted with the use of the method in special, experimentally produced circumstances: those produced by drugs, sensory deprivation, hypnosis, etc. Sixthly, we may contrast introspections made or elicited by trained psychologists from those made or elicited by others.

From these variations of method we may turn to the use of introspection in a number of areas of psychology, to which they have contributed useful information. Such illustration must necessarily be representative rather than exhaustive.

The Phenomena of Human Experience

Human psychology has been defined as "the science of human experience and behavior." (Thouless 1951, p. 1.) Such a definition leads us to expect an interest by psychologists in such processes as thought, imagination, perception, emotion, and motivation. The psychologist is likely to be found applying his results in industrial, military, educational, or other ways. His methods of investigation will include mental measurement and experimentation. From this subject matter it will now be our task to illustrate the use of introspective methods in each of these areas.

Thinking and Imagination

Brief reference has been made to Galton's work on individual differences in thinking. We have noted their historical importance in relation to the development of questionnaire and mental testing methods. Galton's work has greatly enlarged our perspective toward the possibilities of mental life widely different from our own: he was himself surprised at some of the hidden differences between people which emerged, and records a parochial kind of tolerant incredulity on the part of many of his subjects. They have not been alone in exhibiting resistance to recognizing these differences. The full implications of this important investigation have not been appreciated even now by the scientific world: we shall consider the educational world later. As one psychologist, T. H. Pear, has remarked: "Some people write as if everybody is either a visile or ought to be!"

Another aspect of Galton's investigations involved establishing the existence and approximate incidence of a variety of phenomena of subjective experience. Some people report these, while others lack them. One of the rarest is number forms: the characteristic a few individuals have whenever they think about numbers to image them in some spatially arranged form. A related phenomenon is date forms: imagery of this kind for days of the week, months of the year, etc. Others again experience color associations: a regular tendency to associate specific colors with days, months, and numbers. Yet another experience is synesthesia: a tendency for a stimulus of one sense modality to evoke an image of another sense modality. The commonest-form of synesthesia involves having visual images of shapes and colors when listening to music. In a field of investigation of this kind it is necessary first to describe the experiences and sometimes to name them; then one can proceed to studies of their incidence and correlates. As a contribution to the task of establishing their incidence some reference will be made to the results of a study of 182 university students (McKellar, 1957).

The phenomenon of *déjà vu,* the experience of "I feel I have lived through this before though I know I haven't," was reported by 69% of these subjects. Vivid mental imagery, whether visual or of some other kind, experienced in the falling asleep state—hypnagogic imagery—was reported by 63%; similar experiences when waking up—hypnopompic imagery—occurred with 21% of the subjects. Synesthesia also had an incidence of 21%. Diagram forms—number forms, date forms, etc.,—were considerably less common: they occurred in only 7% of the subjects. A similar, but not identical student group, reported color associations in 20% of cases.

The naming of these and related phenomena of subjective imagination presents some interesting problems. Freud (1900) uses the word "hallucination" rather than "image" for the hypnagogic experiences. Particularly in the case of auditory hypnagogic images—reported by 45 per cent of our subjects—it becomes difficult to draw sharp distinctions between an image and an hallucination. Eidetic images (discussed above) present a similar problem: many of these phenomena shade into one another, and there are related atypical cases which also make naming difficult.

Two other subjective experiences are worthy of mention; both occur in the hypnagogic state and one of them, interestingly enough, though extremely common, lacks an accepted name. This is the experience of "falling" and waking with a start when dropping off to sleep; it was commoner even than *déjà vu* and occurred with 75 per cent of our subjects. The other phenomenon involves an impression of a change in the shape and/or size of one's body. This experience—"disturbances of the body image"—occurs in a variety of abnormal states but it also appears to occur quite frequently to normal individuals in the hypnagogic state. There are numerous ways in which a study of these phenomena may prove of importance to subsequent investigation and theory. Not least important is the light which a closer study of these normal phenomena may help to throw upon the understanding of the abnormal.

People are aware of their dreams by introspection, or retrospection on return to the state of wakefulness. The word "unconscious" should not mislead us: the Freudian use of this word is an explanatory concept, and bears no simple relation to ways in which one is "unconscious" while asleep. For this reason some investigators have preferred to speak of sleep as a "subconscious" rather than "unconscious" mental state. The introspections of individuals in other subconscious states, for example those of dissociation, have been employed by Morton Prince (1922). It is also, with some people, possible to obtain introspections from the sleeper. The writer has observed this on two occasions, and valuable data may emerge from studies of the introspections of sleeping persons who have answered affirmatively, while asleep, to the question: "Are you asleep?" Such introspective study may help to illuminate understanding of the functioning of neurological processes available to the sleeper. Dreaming itself has been regarded by various investigators, including Freud, as the thinking of the sleeping state: in such thinking mental imagery plays an obviously important part. Investigations have shown that imagery of the visual, auditory, tactile, motor, olfactory, and gustatory sense modalities can occur in dreams: the commonest form of dream involves both the visual and the auditory image. (Ramsey, 1953.)

Arguments as to whether people do or do not dream in color rank with generalizations about the relations of imagery to thinking. They are monuments to that attitude of mind which remains impervious to the fact that individuals differ. Some people report visual dreams and others do not, but most people do. Among those who do appear to dream visually the majority report that these dreams are achromatic, although colored dreams are not uncommon; there is some evidence of a sex difference in that women may dream in color more often than men. (Ramsey, 1953.) As is to be expected, the dreams of the congenitally blind are bereft of visual imagery, and those of the congenitally deaf lack auditory images. Kimmins (1937) reports evidence that individuals who become blind after the first five to six years of life experience visual dreams; if blindness occurs earlier visual dreams tend not to occur. The same investigator reports a dream by a fourteen-year-old blind boy.

In this the dreamer hears his mother cry out that the house is on fire. He dresses himself, feels himself grasped by his mother and forced down the stairs, and experiences the flames burning him just before he wakes. Visual imagery is quite absent from this dream, which illustrates how dreams can be composed of imagery of other kinds.

Some investigators have concerned themselves with the length of time it takes to dream, and Ramsey (1953) has gathered together evidence on this point. Despite the frequently quoted case of his instantaneous dream about the French Revolution reported by Maury, dreams have been found to last as long as ten minutes. Studies of hypnotically induced dreams show that they also can last for some minutes. There have been numerous differential studies of dreams in different categories of people, and of variations in the content of dreams at different ages: in general the content has regularly been found to derive from events in the dreamer's waking life. The view that stimulation of a sleeping person by touch, or in some other way, can affect the content of his dreams has found experimental support.

Dreams represent an instance in which introspective methods have provided data of a kind it seems necessary to obtain before adequate theorizing can proceed. It is more than difficult to think of techniques other than introspection which could have elicited this information.

Perception

Gibson (1959) describes introspection as "an excellent guide" to the study of perception. He adds:

A cultivated naiveté about what the world *does* look, sound, and feel like is almost necessary for determining what the problems of perception are. (Gibson, 1959, p. 461.)

Introspection has obviously been an important method in the study of perception: Boring (1953) refers to illusions as the "stock example" for introspection, and cites Gibson's work (1950) as a contemporary study of visual perception in terms of the phenomena of experience. Gestalt psychology has, as we have seen, placed emphasis on the necessity for such studies as this of the phenomena of perception. An illustration can be found in the work of a Gestalt psychologist like Katz:

Katz (1935) has been concerned with the different ways in which colours present themselves to perceptual experience. There are surface colours (e.g., the blue of the cover of the book beside my desk); film colours (e.g., the blue of the sky); and volume colours (e.g., the blue of a copper sulphate solution).

The Gestalists were not so invariably bereft of interest in individual differences as their critics have sometimes supposed. Katz deals with one case of a lesion of the occipital lobe, in which the patient was found to have lost his ability to perceive surface colors. Colored surfaces had, in general, the appearance of film colors: for example, when reaching out to touch a surface the patient would have the experience of *reaching into* the color.

The introspective method has contributed to the study of color blindness. It was in 1798 that John Dalton reported on the then unnamed oddities of his own color perception:

Woollen yarn dyed crimson or dark blue is the same to me . . . red and scarlet form a genus for me totally different from pink . . . the face of a laurel leaf is a good match for a stick of red sealing wax. (Dalton, 1798, pp. 104-105.)

It was with these first systematic introspections of Dalton that the study of color blindness began: we now have a specific name for Dalton's kind of color vision defect, namely "protanopia." While it is important to know that the protanope has a point of maximum sensitivity on the spectrum at 540 millimicrons, and that his spectrum is shortened at the red end in ways that can be quantitatively defined, this is not enough. We may still be curious about accompanying subjective experiences and problems of adjustment, and how these may differ from those in deuteranopia, tritanopia, and in the rather numerous subtypes of color blindness now known to exist. Such information can be ascertained by asking such people and by seeking their introspections when confronted with stimuli of various hues. The subjective experiences of the deuteranope differ from those of Dalton.

The popular name "green blindness" while an oversimplification is not wholly inappropriate for the deuteranope. One such individual, studied by the writer, confessed his inability to form any concept for green: it was evident that he thought in terms of brightness—blacks, greys and whites—when green was involved. He would, on occasion, quite argumentatively insist that a dark green object was "black" and a light green object "white." Like those of normal color vision he could distinguish blues and yellows from brightness. Yet he confessed himself unable to appreciate how *anybody* could regard green as "different" from brightness in any similar kind of way.

The totally color blind—the person with monochromatic vision—exhibits this characteristic more generally: he lacks the visual equipment with which to distinguish hue (or "color") from brightness. The writer has had the opportunity for studying two cases of this rare condition, one male and the other female. Both were, of course, given standard color vision tests but our immediate concern is with supplementary data about *what it is like* to have monochromatic vision. Useful information was yielded not only by the tests but also by asking for the subjects' introspections.

Neither was able to detect a red object against a black background, and it is of some interest to study the concepts and resulting thoughts of a person whose idea of "black" includes dark red! The male subject explained that he thought of colours "usually as dark, or light, or brilliant white." Color was wholly absent from his perceptual life. The female subject agreed that pink roses can look the same color as a blue sky, and described red and blue ink stains on a piece of paper as looking alike. She had numerous practical difficulties, not only in choosing clothes—when she always took a friend with her—but also in such an activity as picking blackberries: these she could only discriminate from the surrounding green foliage "by their feel."

There are several main types of color blindness, and a variety of individually varying forms ranging into normal color vision. The elementary nomenclature and study of abnormalities of color perception emerged from the introspections of Dalton. Much more work of an introspective kind remains to be done before we can fully understand the different problems of adjustment which confront those who exhibit the various types of color blindness.

Motivation and Emotion

In investigating deprivation and frustration, some investigators have been tempted by misguided "objectivity" into too behavioristic a formulation. An individual may be "frustrated" in the sense that he is observed to be thwarted in his pursuit of some goal, or he may be "frustrated" in the sense that he reports that he feels frustrated. There is not as simple a relation between the two as has sometimes been supposed. Generalizations which have assumed a connection between the ambiguous concept of "frustration" and the equally ambiguous concept of "aggression" (Dollard, *et al.*, 1944) have had to be abandoned. The aggression which seeks merely to brush aside some obstacle is psychologically different from the aggression of cold anger, and the malice of some forms of hatred: they seek different ends and appear to result from different circumstances. (McKellar, 1949, 1950.) Emotions like anger are provoked by circumstances. If one tries to study which circumstances provoke anger, or other emotions, it soon becomes evident that it is the individual's perception of the situation, and not the situation itself, which leads to the emotion. One may become angry if one believes oneself to be thwarted or threatened, and frightened if one apprehends the situation as dangerous. Provocation is a special case of perception and, not infrequently, of misperception, as when, for example, a person is mistaken in assessing the actions of other people as threatening or insulting. The writer has attempted a study of anger from this standpoint of provocation, and a similar investigation of fear is now in progress at this university. (Garwood, 1961.) A very profitable method in this field is to seek descriptions of *specific occasions* on which the emotion under study has been experienced, and to obtain relevant details about what happened, what the subject felt, and did. A further difficulty of procedures of too behavioristic a kind is apparent in the case of anger. Investigation shows that the commonest reaction to experienced anger, at least in the group investigated, was to suppress verbal reactions altogether—that is not to express the emotion in any way: objective methods are thus likely to result in substantial losses of data about an emotion. (McKellar, 1949.)

In the next section we shall be concerned with similar methods of investigation which have been developed independently, and employed extensively in the field of applied psychology, notably by Flanagan (1954), and will now be discussed.

Applied Psychology

Flanagan's "critical incident technique" has had both military and industrial applications. It has involved obtaining retrospective reports of a large number of specific incidents of relevance to aviation, or selection techniques.

Thus pilots returning from combat would be asked to report specific occasions on which they experienced acute disorientation or other such phenomena. Circumstances surrounding the incidents would then be investigated, and on the basis of analysis of many such incidents, recommendations would be made for the redesign of cockpits, instrument panels, etc. In the industrial situation, workmen or foremen would be asked to record specific occasions when they observed a foreman do something which they felt to be an example of good foremanship. Incidents of bad foremanship would be collected in the same way. Selection and training programmes would be set up, and validated, on the basis of principles which emerged from analysis of these critical incidents.

The critical incidents technique raises again the difficulty of making a sharp distinction between observation and introspection. Flanagan and his colleagues have made skillful use not only of biographical information of an observational kind. They also use introspections on thoughts, feelings, and judgments, obtained retrospectively from individuals who had worked beside or under others who had shown traits desirable, or undesirable, in a leader. It may be noted in passing that Flanagan makes explicit mention of the early work of Galton as the source of his method.

Applied psychology, when concerned with disorientation in a man operating a machine, might well take account of phenomena which appear to be related to the disturbances of the body schema of the hypnagogic state discussed above. Similar occurrences have been reported by motorists while driving in states of fatigue: for example, a persistent impression of the car having developed a lateral list or some other oddity, which has no basis in fact. Hypnagogic images, which are not infrequently experienced with open eyes, are also reported in the motoring situation, as in the case of the driver who "swerved to avoid an hallucinatory rabbit." (Anon., 1958.) Certain phenomena of the quasi-hallucinatory, or perceptual change kind, of distinct relevance to road safety, will not be elicited by investigators averse to the use of introspective methods.

Imagery differences may prove to be of distinct interest from the standpoint of educational and occupational psychology. Some ways in which imagery, or lack of it, can affect certain kinds of learning are illustrated in the following case.

The young woman in question is of superior intelligence and holds a University appointment: she is bereft of visual imagery. At school she found the map-reading parts of geography, together with geometry and zoology, extremely hard. Of her experiences in dissection when a medical student she reported: "I was all right with the simpler organisms but became a little baffled when we got to frogs and crayfish: I just couldn't remember what was inside them." She was unsuccessful at her medical studies for reasons which seemed to derive from her inability to image visually, and she found human anatomy beyond her learning capacity.

Writers of textbooks have not always fully appreciated differences in types of imagery among their student readers. An example may be taken. When a new editor took over preparation of a new edition of an anatomy textbook, he decided to exclude color from all the illustrations. He did this, he says in his Foreword, because it is just as easy to learn from black and white diagrams: color makes no difference. The writer sought the opinions of a group of forty medical students to whom he was teaching psychology and who were also studying anatomy. Only ten of these said that for them it would make no difference: the other thirty indicated that, in their case, an absence of color from the diagrams of their anatomy textbook would be a very serious disadvantage.

There appear to be several kinds of subject matter in the learning of which imagery differences may well be important. One can also think of occupations, for example, those of professional anatomist, surgeon, carpenter, metallurgist, in which absence of visual imagery might prove to be a serious disadvantage. Recent investigations have shown that important relations may exist between EEG records of electrical rhythms of the brain, mental imagery, and psychometric measures. (Stewart and Macfarlane Smith, 1959.) It is probable that subsequent research on imagery will involve a combined use of experimental, psychometric, and introspective methods.

The Methods of Psychology

When Darwin formulated his theory of evolution by natural selection it has been said of this time that "the storehouse of knowledge was fairly bursting for want of a generalization." No such statement can be made of psychology today. Solid advances have certainly been achieved in some areas: in others we are extremely deficient in basic, elementary observations. To some extent the ethologists like Tinbergen and Lorenz have reintroduced the methods of the naturalist into psychology. Yet in many areas of the subject there is a serious need for a generally large injection of the spirit of the naturalist. Much patient work of description, observation, and classification remains to be conducted before more ultimate tasks of theoretical explanation can be other than highly premature: the psychology of thinking and of emotion are two fairly obvious examples. Where evidence is scanty Angell's dictum has relevance: we should glean information wherever it can be found, and we should not neglect to use introspection where necessary.

Theories may be thought of as curves on graphed paper, and observations as the points through which such curves are drawn. If observations are few in number then a variety of quite different curves—numerous alternative theories—can be constructed: as observations increase in number the possibilities of curve drawing become more limited. It is in those fields of psychology where observations are most limited in number that introspective methods will have much to contribute. At very least they may help in a preliminary way to indicate how more "objective" information can be obtained by other methods. This does not, of course, imply that introspective methods are irrelevant to some of the *more* developed fields of psychology. In intelligence testing, for example, psychologists have become interested in the principles which determine "wrong" answers, not just in total tests scores. A readiness to draw on introspective evidence is throwing new light upon this, on the whole well-developed field.

It can be argued that when used along with other methods intro-spection may have important contributions to make. Psychometric measurement has become a major method in contemporary psychology: those who use such tests need to acquire some sophistication in under-standing the various ways in which the people tested may try to with-hold information. As Bakan (1954) puts it, if psychology is going to understand phenomena of emotional importance in the people it studies, it needs to extend its knowledge of the principles which underlie the revelation and retention of secrets. Using an introspective method Bakan conducted a "miniature investigation" of his own into this prob-lem; the relevance of such findings to research into methods of interro-gation, and the training of people to resist such interrogation, is obvious. Perhaps less obvious is its relevance to the use of mental tests themselves.

Some tests, like the Minnesota Multiphasic Personality Inventory (MMPI) have "lie scales." High scores on such scales are taken as evidence either of deception or of failure to take the testing seriously. Bakan points out that the MMPI lie scale is naive by contrast with what would emerge from a comprehensive investigation of the processes of keeping secrets. His own study revealed several different strategies available to those who want to keep a secret. The lie scale in question takes account of only one of these strategies.

The application of introspective methods to the design and refinement of psychometric tests merits emphasis. Experiences of the writer in teaching psychology also suggest the need to instruct students who are learning to administer such tests in the use of introspective methods. It is a desirable principle that no student should be permitted to admin-ister a test to anybody else until he has himself done it. This will enable him to gain some understanding of its uses and limitations from his own introspections.

The projective techniques represent an important method that was not available to the early introspectionists. Interesting issues arise in teaching students to use these techniques. Illustration may be taken from the Thematic Apperception test (TAT), in which the subject makes up stories about pictures in a standardized series. In the laboratory a stu-dent may ask various questions that imply chronic subterfuge by the person being tested. It may be necessary to reorient the questioner toward the task which will face him when he is using a technique like the TAT later on, outside the laboratory. He sometimes needs to be shown that a mental testing situation is often not a matter of open warfare in which a patient is determined to deceive a psychologist. In-stead it may well be a situation in which both patient and tester together are trying to elicit information which they both want, but which the patient is not able to provide from ordinary introspection. If the patient is cheating in some way it is often quite worth while to ask him, rather than resort to a more roundabout approach. A TAT story, whether told in the laboratory or clinic, may merely turn out to be an incident from a film, a play, or a novel; if this is the case, the person under study is often more ready to admit the fact than the trainee psychologist sometimes supposes.

What has been said of projective techniques and psychometric tests applies also to the method of experimentation. It may well be, as Reid (1960) has recently said, that "in psychology rats became a useful gimmick particularly since they were not able to make comments"! The moral of this is not that psychologists should give up doing animal experiments.* Perhaps it is that when they do use human subjects, they should not treat them as noncommunicating rats or pigeons, in the interests of a misguided sense of "objectivity." There have certainly been occasions when the subject—a human being, not a rat—has broken up the apparatus because the experimenter has given him an unreasonably severe electric shock! Safeguards will occur to some: it is both scientifically sound, and personally prudent, for the experimenter himself to undergo the experience as subject in his own apparatus before he uses it on somebody else. This allows him to note and eliminate discomforts and distractions, observable to the subject, which might otherwise ruin his main experiment. A second safeguard is to require introspections from all subjects, and to insist on them if they are not forthcoming; these will enable the experimenter further to refine his experimental procedure. They may also permit the experimenter to interpret fluctuations in his measurements, and often suggest profitable lines of future research.

In experiments in which electric shocks are given there arises a special case of difficulties resulting from the extreme variations which human beings exhibit. A shock barely noticeable to one such individual may be acutely painful to another. This is an illustration of the principle that when conditions, as externally observed, are identical, conditions experienced subjectively may vary enormously. Whatever else is done to deal with this type of difficulty it is prudent for the experimenter to himself undergo the experience first, and to elicit introspective reports from all human subjects.

Introspection has an important subsidiary function to play in psychology, even when it is not the main method employed. Illustration of this has been taken from psychometric testing, projective techniques, and laboratory experimentation.

---

* A doctrinaire opposition to animal experiments is, in its way, as tiresome as the determination to oppose the use of introspection.

The Problem of Communication

We have seen that William James defines introspection not merely as "looking into our own minds," but as in addition "reporting what we there discover." He adds: "If to *have* feelings or thoughts in their immediacy were enough, babies in the cradle would be psychologists, and infallible ones." (James, 1890, Vol. I, p. 189.) This point is developed in some detail by Mace (1950). Mace argues that investigators like Titchener failed to make clear, or even appreciate, that the difficulty of introspection is not so much one of observing the facts as of knowing how to describe them. It may not be very easy to say what one "sees" when "looking into one's mind." But, Mace adds, "This is not because it is difficult to see what is there. The difficulty is to say what you see— to say it in a clear, correct, and illuminating way." (*Ibid.*, p. 242.)

These problems of communication may derive from the nature of the experience under study. Dreams are not easy to communicate in words because dreams are typically visual in character. It is not easy to verbalize a complex visual image just as it is not easy to communicate a dream, or for that matter a complex visual perception. This is precisely because these things are visual and not verbal. As illustration we shall consider another complex visual experience; the imagery which occurs to a subject in an experiment with mescaline.

Such images may be of great complexity, rapidly changing, unusual in content, and unpredictable in their sequence; they may exhibit peculiarities of colour and illumination, and involve a content of familiar or strange objects from unusual angles. Some subjects resort to neologisms—invented words, or the giving of highly private meanings to familiar words. One of our subjects reported an image of a "quadrupus," which she defined as "a thing like an octopus but with four legs rather than eight." Thus the imagery involved may severely tax the vocabulary of the subject as is suggested by reports like: "they are scenes I wish I was able to paint"; "they are like pictures from the kind of travel book I don't read"; and "they seem strange and unlike the products of my own mental life."

Subjects in such experiments quite often give evidence of acute frustration at discrepancies between what they experience and what they can communicate about it. Those who take part as subjects in such experiments may become somewhat cautious in accepting the not infrequent identification of introspection with "verbal report."

On the first occasion when the writer, as subject, experienced mescaline imagery he was confronted with this problem of communication. His solution was to liken the imagery to another subjective experience he thought some of the experimenters might have had. This was the imagery of the falling asleep, or hypnagogic state. To draw such an analogy in words is not a verbal report of the ordinary kind, and it implied more than merely "read verbal reports of hypnagogic images." In addition, the subject, faced with a difficult task of communication, was trying to say: "Should any of you happen to have visual hypnagogic images think about these; my own imagery at the moment is very similar." It emerged subsequently, from a study of the journals, that others who had attempted the introspective study of mescaline imagery had, quite independently, resorted to the same analogy. One of these was Weir Mitchell (1896) whose introspections on mescaline imagery are, incidentally, superior to most of those that have been recorded. An important investigator of hypnagogic imagery, Leaning (1925) draws the opposite analogy. In her attempts to communicate in detail about the "liquid fire" and "strange luminosity" of some hypnagogic imagery, she quotes Weir Mitchell's descriptions of the color and lighting of mescaline images. The similarities which hold between the two types of phenomena have been discussed in fuller detail elsewhere. (Ardis and McKellar, 1956.)

Mace's emphasis on the place of communication in introspection is appropriate, but to identify such communication with "verbal report" seems less justified. How to communicate at all adequately can tax the ingenuity of the subject who may resort to various devices. Thus, one person in trying to explain the images or hallucinations she experienced when grazing into a crystal resorted to holding a photograph behind the sphere. She explained that here images in the crystal looked very similar to the photograph seen through the sphere in this way. Several of our subjects, both in the hypnagogic and mescaline studies, reported visual images they wished they had the talent to paint or draw; some attempted this. The Society for Psychical Research, London, possesses a collection of paintings made by Lady Berkeley of her own hypnagogic imagery; one of these is reproduced by Rawcliffe (1952, facing p. 14). Galton's subjects on occasion used drawings as well as verbal descriptions in attempts to communicate their number and date forms. Several attempts have been made to portray synesthesias by use of the movie film. Recently, following intensive study of monocular color blindness (Graham and Hsia, 1958), the colored film has been used to reproduce the visual world of the deuteranope so that others can understand what it is like.

Another source of difficulty in the accurate reporting of experience is the time factor. The events may occur with such rapidity that the subject's retrospections can be highly misleading. An example of this occurs with high-speed skills in which the operator may literally "not know" what he has done. Either he is unable to report on his performance, or his introspections bear little relation to his actual movements as recorded photographically. Bartlett discusses this problem in the case of bomb aiming:

Ask the operator how he has done his work, and different persons may invent, or at least describe, very differing techniques. (Bartlett, 1947, p. 13.)

Bartlett adds: "The plain fact is that many of them do not know." Such a limitation of the introspective method merits notice. There are, however, occasions on which discrepancies between actual performance and introspections about performance yields useful information. In occupational psychology, more generally, the process of job analysis merits consideration. The investigator seeks to find out the nature of the work from the operator, the supervisor, and perhaps from others. These different peoples' "perceptions" of the same activity may vary from one another, and all may differ from what photographic records reveal. It is on the basis of such comparisons that the occupational psychologist arrives at his conclusions.

Yet another source of difficulty results from limitations of vocabulary. Even in the case of visual perception such difficulties may arise, as when one seeks to explain in detail about a specific color. Munsell (1954) reproduces a letter in which Robert Louis Stevenson attempted to explain to a friend in England the color of a wallpaper he wished to be sent to him in Samoa. His communication was spectacularly unsuccessful both as regards the color required, and in his account of the other furnishings of his room. This type of difficulty led Munsell to develop his own well-known system of color notation. Attempts have been made to develop parallel systems in relation to other sense modes; Crocker (1946) represents such an attempt in the case of olfactory perception. Particularly in the case of the senses other than vision it becomes necessary to train people to use these specialized forms of communication; thus, trained taste and smell panels are used in various applied fields, and aspects of their work recall the "classical introspection" of the Wundtian period.

If we exclude trained experts, for most people communication about nonvisual sensory experiences presents difficulties. The sense of pain may be taken as an example. Some people resort to synesthetic ways of thinking about pain, and their communications may prove puzzling to their audience. One such individual explained of herself as a child:

I used to annoy my mother. She'd ask: "What sort of pain?" and I'd say "a yellow one." When interviewed as an adult she reported that her tendency to *think* in this way had persisted, though she had abandoned her attempts to *communicate* synaesthetically.

Some forms of synesthetic thinking have come into everyday usage; we speak of sounds as "penetrating," colors as "loud," and wines as "smooth," "round," and "velvety." Such communications shade into others which become more inefficient and private, as when a perfume chemist was quoted as saying:

Sometimes I found the scent was a little flat, a bit discordant: that it needed more body in the middle tones and less brass at the top! [*News Chronicle*, London, May 19, 1959.]

Such synesthetic metaphors, involving use of words appropriate to another sense modality, represent one interesting device—effective or otherwise—to which people resort in their attempts to communicate their own experiences. While it may be agreed that the kinds of introspection of interest to science involve communication, such communication may be difficult. It may assume a variety of forms, and can tax both the vocabulary and ingenuity of the subject in a variety of ways.

Toward a Definition of Mind

What then is mind? Insofar as this is not an issue for philosophy the question points—partly at least—to the subject matter of psychology. This includes the phenomena of human experience and their investigation by the methods of introspection. Illustration of such phenomena has included thoughts, percepts, mental images, dream life, hallucinations, and oddities of experience like *déjà vu*, number forms, and synesthesia. In the past, introspection has had a special value in the study of the least developed areas of the subject, and it may be predicted that this will apply to the future also. Yet it may also have something to contribute in the more advanced parts of psychology, and we have noted its place in various of the applied fields: educational, military, clinical, and industrial.

Psychology is concerned to describe, classify, and explain human experience and behavior. We are learning about "mind"—so far as the word refers to subject matter of scientific interest—as we progress toward this understanding. It has been argued that the methods of introspection have a legitimate contribution to make to this task, and that investigators should be alerted to their use.

REFERENCES

Allport, G. W., Bruner, J. S., and Jandorf, E. M. (1941), "Personality under social catastrophe: ninety life-histories of the Nazi Revolution, *Char. & Personal.*, 10:1-22.

Angell, J. R. (1913), "Behaviour as a category in psychology," *Psychol. Rev.*, 20:255-270.

Anon. (1958), "Motoring hallucinations," *The Motor*, Jan. 15, 1958, p. 917.

Ardis, J. A., and McKellar, P. (1956), "Hypnagogic imagery and mescaline," *J. Ment. Sci.*, 102:426, 2-29.

Bakan, D. (1954), "A reconsideration of the problem of introspection," *Psychol. Bull.*, 51:105-118.

Bartlett, F. C. (1947), "The measurement of human skill," *Brit. M. J.*, I:835-877.

Bettelheim, B. (1943), "Individual and mass behaviour in extreme situations," *J. Abn. Soc. Psychol.*, 38:417-452.

Bonaparte, M., Freud, A., and Kris, E. (eds.) (1954), *The Origins of Psycho-analysis: Letters to Wilhelm Fliess, Drafts and Notes 1887-1902*, Imago, New York.

Boring, E. G. (1953), "A history of introspection," *Psychol. Bull.* 50:169-189.

Carnap, R. (1956), "The methodological character of theoretical concepts," in Feigl, H., and Scriven, M. (eds.), *Minnesota Studies in the Philosophy of Science*, Vol. I, Univ. of Minnesota, Minneapolis.

Crocker, E. C. (1946), "Comprehensive method for the classification of odors," *Proc. Sci. Sect. Toilet Goods Association*, 6:Dec. 5, 1946.

Dalton, J. (1798), "Extraordinary facts relating to the vision of colours with observations," in W. Dennis (ed.), *Readings in the History of Psychology*, Appleton-Century, New York, 1948.

Dollard, J., Miller, N. E., Doob, L. W., Mowrer, O. H., and Sears, R. R. (1944), *Frustration and Aggression*, Kegan Paul, London.

English, H. B., and English, A. C. (1958), *A Comprehensive Dictionary of Psychological and Psychoanalytical Terms*, Longmans, New York.

Flanagan, J. C. (1954), "The critical incident technique," *Psychol. Bull.*, 51:327-358.

Freud, S. (1900), *The Interpretation of Dreams*, Hogarth, London, (edition 1953).

Galton, F. (1880), "Statistics of mental imagery," *Mind*, 5:301-318.

—— (1907), *Inquiries into Human Faculty*, Everyman, London, (edition 1919).

Garwood, K. (1961), "A psychological study of human fear," Unpub. Ph.D. thesis, Univ. of Sheffield.

Gibson, J. J. (1950), *The Perception of the Visual World*, Houghton Mifflin, Boston.

—— (1959), "Perception as a function of stimulation," in S. Koch (ed.), *Psychology: A Study of a Science*, Vol. I, McGraw-Hill, New York.

Graham, C. H., and Hsia, Y. (1958), "Colour defect and colour theory," *Science*, 127:3300, 675-682.

Hebb, D. O. (1953), "On human thought," *Canad. J. Psychol.*, 7:99-110.

Jaensch, E. R. (1930), *Eidetic Imagery*, Kegan Paul, London.

James, W. (1890), *The Principles of Psychology*, Vols. I & II, Macmillan, London.

Katz, D. (1935), *The World of Colour*, Kegan Paul, London.

Leaning, F. E. (1925), "An introductory study of hypnagogic phenomena," *Proc. Soc. Psychic. Res. London*, 35:289-409.

McClelland, D. C. (1955), "The psychology of mental content reconsidered," *Psychol. Rev.*, 62:297-302.

Mace, C. A. (1950), "Introspection and analysis," in Black, M. (ed.), *Philosophical Analysis*, Cornell Univ. Press, New York.

McKellar, P. (1949), "The emotion of anger in the expression of human aggressiveness," *Brit. J. Psychol.*, 39:148-155.

———— (1950), "Provocation to anger in the development of attitudes of hostility," *Brit. J. Psychol.*, 40:104-114.

———— (1954), "Freud's self-analysis," *Literary Guide*, 69:22-23.

———— (1957), *Imagination and Thinking: A Psychological Analysis*, Basic Books, New York.

————, and Simpson, L. (1954), "Between wakefulness and sleep: hypnagogic imagery," *Brit. J. Psychol.*, 45:266-276.

Mitchell, S. W. (1896), "Remarks on the effects of Anhalonium Lewinii (the mescal button)," *Brit. M. J.*, 2:1625.

Munsell, A. H. (1954), *A Colour Notation*, Munsell Colour Co., Baltimore.

O'Neill, W. (1957), *An Introduction to Method in Psychology*, Cambridge Univ. Press, New York.

Prince, M. (1922), "An experimental study of the mechanism of hallucinations," *Brit. J. M. Psychol.*, 2:3.

Ramsey, G. V. (1953), "Studies of dreaming," *Psychol. Bull.*, 50:432-455.

Rawcliffe, D. H. (1952), *The Psychology of the Occult*, Derricke Ridgway, London.

Reid, R. L. (1960), *Behaviour Theory and Ethology*, paper read to Annual Conference of the Brit. Psychol. Soc., 7th April, 1960.

Schein, E. H. (1956), "The Chinese indoctrination programme for prisoners of war: a study of attempted 'brainwashing,'" *Psychiatry*, 19:149-172.

Spence, K. W. (1948), "The postulates and methods of behaviourism," *Psychol. Rev.*, 55:67-78.

Stewart, C. A., and MacFarlane Smith, I. (1959), "The alpha rhythm, imagery, and spatial and verbal abilities," *Durham Res. Rev.*, 2:1-16.

Taft, R. (1955), "The ability to judge people," *Psychol. Bull.*, 52:1-23.

Thouless, R. H. (1951), *General and Social Psychology*, 3rd ed., Univ. Tutorial Press, London.

Warren, H. C. (1934), *Dictionary of Psychology*, Houghton Mifflin, Boston.

Watson, J. B. (1913), "Psychology as the behaviourist views it," *Psychol. Rev.*, 20:158-177.

I R V I N   R O C K

A Neglected Aspect

of the Problem of Recall:

The Höffding Function

For the experimental psychologist "mind" is a term rarely used, not only because of its possible philosophical connotations but because the study of "mind" is more or less synonymous with "psychology." Rather than dwell on the ontological question of what "mind" *is*, he prefers to investigate psychological processes, leaving it to the philosopher to draw implications from his work. It is in this spirit that the author proposes to discuss here a particular problem in the field of memory.

In the field of learning and memory the major concept is that of association (or translated into the language of the behavioristically inclined psychologist, habit; in this paper "association" may be taken to refer either to connecting up two stimulus items or to a stimulus and a response, as one's taste dictates). It is certainly true that many facts about learning and memory can be explained by the concept of association. Let us assume that two items (A and B)* become connected with one another at a Time 1 and further that this connection is preserved in

The preparation of this article was aided by Research Grant M-3435, National Institute of Mental Health, Public Health Service.

* Capital letters will be used to represent stimulus items, and the corresponding small letters to represent the memory traces of previous stimulus items.

some way over time by a trace. (The term "trace" is used as a construct to explain the preservation of the effects of the prior experience over time. It is used by many psychologists and is used by the present author in this limited sense and without any implications as to its particular neurophysiological basis.) Then failure of memory at Time 2 can be attributed either to some modification of the trace (such that it can no longer be said to preserve the association) or to some difficulty in passing from the *a* portion of the trace to the *b* portion. In this way successful remembering means that trace *a* arouses, activates, or redintegrates trace *b* and failure means it does not. For purposes of the present discussion it does not matter whether one believes that failure occurs because *a* is now more strongly connected to some other trace *c* (competition of response theory) or because it is no longer adequately connected to *b*, or for any other possible reason. All such considerations pertain to the concept of association.

The problem that is neglected here is how at Time 2 trace *a* is activated, since this must happen first. Of course, one may push the problem back by saying that trace *a* is connected to many other traces and that therefore we get to *a* from *x*, *y*, or *z* just as we get to *b* from *a*. But very frequently what happens is that A is presented or appears as a stimulus at Time 2. We see the man to whom we were previously introduced and must remember his name or the left-hand nonsense syllable reappears in the memory drum and we must remember the right-hand one that was paired with it. In these cases it would be gratuitous to assume we get to trace *a* via a chain of previously formed associations when it is clear that it is the reappearing stimulus that triggers the reaction. Thus, we must explain how we get from the stimulus A to the memory trace *a* of the previously encountered A. It is important to understand that *a* as a memory trace is not the same as the A that is encountered again at Time 2. This point was first made by Höffding[3] and has been elaborated by Köhler and others in recent years.[7] But for some reason the consequences which follow inescapably from this analysis have not been sufficiently appreciated. Höffding's statement of the issue was as follows: "In order that A may excite the ideas of B, C, D, with which it usually arises simultaneously in consciousness, it must first, so to speak, establish its identity. Thus, A must give rise to *a* and only then will it bring forth *b*, *c*, *d*" (p. 157).[3]

There are two important points here. One is *how* the appropriate trace *a* is aroused when stimulus A occurs. The other is the fact that the arousal of trace *b* depends upon the prior arousal of trace *a*, regardless of how the latter process occurs. As to the first point, the fact is that if A is a novel visual shape, its image may fall in almost any position on the retina (and correspondingly its pattern of excitation may fall anywhere on the visual cortex). When later A is seen again it may fall elsewhere on the retina (and cortex), but nevertheless trace a is apparently instantaneously aroused, as is evidenced by recognition of the shape. (The phenomenal experience of familiarity or recognition is here alleged to be mediated by the arousal of the trace appropriate to the present stimulus.) This fact suggests that access to the appropriate trace a cannot be a function of the stimulus A initiating excitation that traverses a particular pathway reserved for that trace. These considerations led Köhler to reason that it is the similarity of the perceptual process A to the earlier trace a that explains how the appropriate trace, from the almost infinite number of possible traces, is selectively aroused.

It is possible to argue that the trace is not located merely in the place where the original pattern of excitation fell in the visual cortex but rather is located elsewhere (and possibly even everywhere) in the cortex.* Hence, one might claim, in disagreement with Köhler, that stimulus A, wherever it falls, directly taps trace a and there is no need to speak of the role of similarity. In the opinion of the author, even if the trace is ubiquitous, it still does not obviate the need for postulating trace selection by similarity. If the trace of A is represented everywhere in the cortex, so too must be the traces of all other previously seen objects. Hence, in any one region an infinite number of traces would presumably be stored, so the problem would remain of why only the correct trace is aroused when stimulus A is given. If this question is answered by saying that only that trace is tapped which coincides perfectly with or is congruent with the stimulus, the further problem would remain of why recognition occurs readily when the figure is transposed in size. Here perfect coincidence could no longer be said to be a factor. It therefore seems logically necessary to conclude that the percept as an organized whole makes contact with the trace or traces of previously seen versions of itself by virtue of similarity—regardless of whether or not the trace is represented throughout the cortex.

An experiment by the author brings out the crucial role of similarity over and against anatomical locus in trace arousal.[13, 15] Subjects were first shown novel shapes. Subsequently the shapes were shown again in a test of recognition but they were viewed with the head tilted 90 degrees. Each original shape was shown twice, once in the position originally used in the training exposure and once tilted 90 degrees so

---

* The work of Lashley[9] and Sperry[17] supports this possibility. On the other hand, a recent experiment by Wallach and Austin[18] for the first time gives evidence for localization of the trace on the basis of a subtle difference in recognition depending on the retinal position of the stimulus.

as to be parallel to the observer's tilted head. Recognition proved to be significantly superior for the untilted figures, despite the fact that they fell in an orientation on the retina displaced by 90 degrees from the original position. The tilted figures were not easily recognized despite the fact that they fell in a retinal orientation identical with that of training. The reason for the superior recognition of the untilted figures is that by preserving their orientation in phenomenal space they apparently preserve their phenomenal shape. The tilted figures on the other hand are phenomenally different. (A fact that itself requires an explanation, but a discussion of which would carry us too far afield.) The result thus represents a victory of phenomenal similarity over identity of anatomical locus (orientation in this case) in trace arousal.

Of course, reference to similarity does not explain the mechanism, but it does point to some kind of process in which similarity is the selective factor. Duncker[1] compared trace arousal by similarity to resonance in physics whereby the sympathetic vibration of a body is brought about by sound waves which have a rate equal to the body's natural frequency of vibration. Others might prefer to think of a scanning mechanism. Since present knowledge of neurophysiology does not encompass any such mechanisms the similarity hypothesis has not met with much enthusiasm.

The second point can be considered more or less independently of the first, namely, that regardless of *how* trace *a* is activated, it is only through that trace that access to trace *b* is possible. Of course, it can be argued that there is no logical necessity for this step, that stimulus A can redintegrate any memory or response, including *b*. But this argument loses sight of the role that the association A–B is said to play. If A were directly to tap *b*, then since A has never occurred before, it would be a matter of pure chance. That is to say, it is the earlier A (now represented as a trace) that was connected with B. Hence, if the concept of association is to mean anything, it seems inescapable that *b* is aroused when A occurs because A activates *a*, which, in turn, by virtue of some functional connection between A and B left behind from learning, now redintegrates *b*. The notion of the arousal of *a* by A prior to the redintegration of *b* has come to be known as the "Höffding Function."

William James considered Höffding's argument and rejected it on the grounds that

The sensational process A and the ideational process *a* [trace *a*?] probably occupy essentially the same tracts. When the outer stimulus comes and those tracts vibrate with the sensation A, they discharge as directly into the paths which lead to B as when there is no other stimulus and they only vibrate with idea *a*. To say that the process *A* can only reach these paths by the help of the weaker process *a* is like saying that we need a candle to see the sun by (p. 592).[5]

It is obvious, however, that reference to common tracts and paths hardly does justice to the problems raised by facts of transposability of position and size. Also, James seems to have failed to grasp the point that it is *a* and not *A* that is connected to *b* unless he means to imply that the prior occurrence of *A* blazed a distinctive path that will now be followed by all future *A*'s. Otherwise path *A* can be traveled by any stimulus and why should it lead only to *B*? If he does mean it to be a distinctive path, then this path is his analogue of the trace *a* that is connected to *b*. But few today would accept such a theory.

To return to the argument, the major implication is that failure of recall may be due not only to some difficulty in the association, the A–B relation—which is the focus of all current theories of forgetting—but to some difficulty in the arousal of trace *a* by stimulus A, the A–*a* relation.

Köhler and von Restorff have demonstrated this point in their work on spontaneous recall.[8] In one variation the subject is given a series of nonsense figures that he is asked to look at attentively. The figures are all drawn in black. Of twelve figures shown, the sixth is later to be the critical one. Following this the subject is shown another series of objects, the tenth of which is the critical figure now drawn in green and smaller in size than the original version. He is told to interpret each of these objects and also to indicate whatever ideas may occur to him during the description. The crucial question is whether or not the critical figure will be spontaneously recognized when it reappears in the second series. If so, the subject will presumably indicate this fact in his comments when that figure is shown. The investigators showed that, whether or not the subject is reminded of the earlier figure (*a*), when it reappears (*A*) depends very much on the nature of the intervening events. If the first nine objects of the second series are also nonsense figures of about the same size as the critical tenth and of varying colors, spontaneous recognition of the critical figure is low (around 15 per cent). If, however, the first nine objects are entirely different in kind (for example, numbers, long nonsense words, or symbols), then recognition of the critical figure is quite high (around 75 per cent).*

If the subjects had been required to associate something with the critical figure in the first series, one might be inclined to interpret failure to give the association when the figure appeared in the second series as

---

* The design utilizes incidental learning and spontaneous rather than intentional recall, since otherwise a majority of subjects would recognize the figure and the differential effect between conditions would probably not obtain.

a failure in the A–B relation. (In fact, in other experiments by these investigators there *was* an associated content that was poorly recalled in the test when the intervening events were similar.) Since, however, it is clear from the absence of recognition that trace *a* is itself not aroused, it would seem that the locus of the disturbance is in the A–a relation. The experiment shows that the arousal of *a* by A depends upon the extent to which they are not merely similar but are distinctively similar. Köhler thus sees the A–a relation as a case of grouping by similarity, a grouping which involves a trace and a stimulus, instead of the usual case of grouping of *stimuli* by similarity. In the latter case it can also be shown that it is relative or distinctive similarity which is crucial.

The experiment illustrates another important point, namely, that *a* can be aroused by a similar stimulus; i.e., A need not be identical with *a* (see the discussion below of stimulus generalization). The claim that *a* is aroused by similar and not only identical A's brings Höffding's argument into line with Aristotle's "law" of similarity, at least according to the way the latter has generally been interpreted.

It is necessary to be specific about traces deposited at different times. One must avoid something analogous to Titchener's stimulus error. The tendency to represent objects as having a permanent and continuous existence operates to prevent us from conceptualizing each instance of encounter with it as depositing a different trace—different if for no other reason than that they occur at different times and are different events. This point can be illustrated by a problem which the author is currently exploring. Suppose a subject is presented with the same or a similar stimulus on two different occasions, each presumably leaving a trace, in such a way that the first is *not* brought to mind when the second is shown. If later the stimulus is exposed again, this time requesting recall, which of the two traces will be aroused if the subject is not geared to give both?

By way of illustrating this experimental design, a subject is shown a series of pictures of various fruits and vegetables in color, one of which is an apple and another an orange. The circular outline of these two figures is identical, the only difference being in coloration. The subjects have no trouble identifying these objects and, furthermore, when the second of them is shown (following several other intervening objects) they do not think of the first one in spite of the identical shapes. Thus the condition is met of depositing two independent similar traces each at a slightly different point in time. In the test situation a series of noncolored outline drawings of the fruits and vegetables is shown, and the subject is asked to identify those that had appeared in the first series and to name them. The question is, given the outline of the critical shape (A), which of the two previous traces of objects having the same shape is likely to be aroused, a_1 or a_2?

Is there a law governing such a situation, which forms a basis for prediction, as, for example, recency? In order to answer this question it is necessary to "tag" each trace by an associated content so that the one or the other associated response will indicate which of the two traces is now aroused. In the example, the associated content is the fruit represented by the shape. This problem is relevant to current theories of interference in forgetting where, for example, the subsequent learning of A–K is known to be quite disturbing to recall of previously learned A–B. The focus ordinarily is on the strength of A–B relative to A–K (in other words the A–B relation), but one can just as well focus on the question of which a trace is aroused when A is given in the test (in other words the A–a relation). By way of speculating a bit along this line: Supposing a law of recency to operate in the arousal of a by A, one might expect a recently formed association to A (K) to win out in recall over one formed earlier (B) even if the latter were a much stronger bond based on many repetitions. The reason for this prediction is that "strength" refers to the connection between a and b, whereas the selective factor here may be which a is tapped. Of course, there are many traces of a involved in the A–B association, and this complicates the situation. All these a traces are connected to b traces, whereas only one a trace is connected to k, and this statistical advantage may offset the factor of recency. It is even possible that the greater probability of eliciting a response in the case of a so-called "strong" association is this fact of multiple a traces (thus stressing the role of the A–a relation) rather than the strength of the A–B connection as is usually assumed to be the case.

Another experiment that clearly brings out the need for explanation in terms of specific traces rather than the objective thing they represent is by Wallach and Averbach on memory modalities.[19] These authors raise the question of whether the experience mediated by a particular sense modality leaves a memory trace specific to that modality. If so, the trace of a visually perceived word is quite a different entity from the trace of that same word when heard. In fact, the two traces are utterly dissimilar and incommensurate, the one being the aftereffect of a perceived shape, the other of a sound pattern. Were it not for their common meaning, therefore, there would be no basis in similarity for any functional relationship between them.

To test this thesis the authors presented their subjects with a list of nonsense words on a memory drum with instructions to read them alternately forward and backward. If NIVIK is read forward it may be presumed to leave a visual trace of NIVIK and an auditory trace which corresponds to the verbal pattern by saying NIVIK. If, however, LATUK is read backward, the sound pattern is given by KUTAL. In a subsequent recognition test the list is presented again, this time at a very fast rate, and the subject is to state whether each word had occurred before or was new. Presuming that the subject will not only see each word but now also say each word to himself, thus yielding a stimulus similar to the previously heard word, there are two bases for recognition of words read forward in the training exposure. Not so for words read backward in training, because the sound yielded by LATUK in the test is quite different than the sound of KUTAL from the training; only the visual stimulus remains the same for these words (see Diagram 1). Therefore, the authors predicted that words that had been read forward would yield a higher recognition score than those that had been read backward, and this was indeed the case. In another variation some words that had initially been read backward were presented in the test in reverse spelling

Training

VISUAL STIMULUS	AUDITORY STIMULUS
NIVIK	read forward: NIVIK
LATUK	read backward: KUTAL
BOSAP	read forward: BOSAP
	etc.

Test

NIVIK	all read silently forward: NIVIK
LATUK	LATUK
BOSAP	BOSAP
	etc.

DIAGRAM 1

—e.g., LATUK would now be written as KUTAL. Now only the auditory component remains the same for these words, but presumably there is no basis for recognition in the changed visual stimulus (see Diagram 2).

Training

VISUAL STIMULUS	AUDITORY STIMULUS
NIVIK	read forward: NIVIK
LATUK	read backward: KUTAL
BOSAP	read forward: BOSAP
	etc.

Test

NIVIK	all read silently forward: NIVIK
KUTAL (spelling reversed)	LATUK
BOSAP	BOSAP
	etc.

DIAGRAM 2

The results were commensurate with those where recognition was only possible via vision and, therefore, again inferior to the situation where recognition based on both modalities was possible. The results thus support the assumption of traces representing the unique sensory character of the stimuli which gave rise to them and the dependence of recognition on similarity to the appropriate trace.

Another area for which the A–a relation has relevance is that of stimulus generalization. Pavlov's finding that stimuli similar to that to which conditioning occurs will also elicit the conditioned response has led to countless experimental demonstrations but little theoretical clarification. In terms of the alleged role of similarity in the arousal of a by A, however, Köhler has argued it would follow as a matter of course that similar and not only identical stimuli would elicit the b associated with a. (In this case B is the conditioned response and A the conditioned stimulus.) Thus, stimulus generalization can be understood as a result of a tolerance of trace arousal by similarity—a kind of failure of precision—which is perhaps just what Lashley meant by his theory of "failure of association."[10] In this way, instances in daily life of faulty recognition can be understood.

From this point of view generalization would be expected to occur wherever similarity suffices to mediate arousal of a by A. Or rather wherever A is sufficiently similar to arouse trace a, there is as good a chance of b occurring as if A were identical to the earlier a. Of course, in both cases, a disturbance to the A–B relation may prevent the response from occurring. But where A is different, so that arousal of a is impaired, recall of b will suffer. To test this notion a student of the author, Alice Lasker, performed an experiment with adults in which they first learned a list of paired figures and nonsense syllables.[11] Subsequently different groups were tested for recall of the syllables when for one critical pair they were presented with either the identical figure or a somewhat changed figure. Directly after the test of recall for the critical pair the subjects were asked to say whether (1) they had recognized the form as identical to one seen in training, (2) had recognized it as only similar, or (3) thought it was different. Taking recognition as the phenomenological counterpart of arousal of trace a,* it was hypothesized that, where recognition to the changed stimulus did not decline, the probability of giving the associated syllable would be as good as when the identical stimulus was presented. Conversely, where recognition declined (col-

---

* On the human level, A–a will often lead to recognition as well as to the associated response b. But it is not necessary to assume that this step involving a phenomenal experience of familiarity always occurs when a stimulus A elicits the trace of that stimulus a which in turn elicits a previously associated response. On the animal level this experiential aspect might or might not occur.

lectively speaking), because the stimulus was quite different, it was expected that recall would decline.

Thus far in the research the results are in keeping with these predictions. Subjects who indicate that they are aware that the critical stimulus is similar but not identical nevertheless are just as likely to give the associated syllable as those who are shown the identical stimulus. Conversely there are no cases of successful response where the subject indicates nonrecognition. In other words, the crucial step is arousal of *a* by *A* whether or not this is accompanied by some awareness of a difference. It is, therefore, possible that as the stimulus becomes increasingly different, more and more subjects may fail to recognize it as "same" or "similar," and thus a decline in associated response will occur. This is precisely what happened in the case of certain changed stimuli.

Since the arousal of *a* by *A* would seem to be an all-or-none affair, it might be argued that there can be no gradient of generalization for any individual, only a discontinuous drop at the point where recognition fails. Collectively, however, a group of subjects may show a gradient. But other measures of generalization, as, for example, latency or amplitude, should show no gradient even using group data if the present interpretation is correct. Once trace *a* is aroused, whether by an identical *A* or a somewhat similar *A*, *b* should be forthcoming with undiminished magnitude and equivalent latency. Hence, if genuine gradients of generalization do exist using such measures, they would have to be explained as based upon cognitive uncertainty or halfheartedness—"Is this the stimulus to which I associated such and such response?" or "Am I supposed to respond to *this*?" In any case the Hullian notion that there are weaker connections or habits formed to the nonidentical stimuli is denied.

It is interesting to note that Pavlov's theory was directed at the A–*a* relation.[12] The conditioned stimulus excited a given point in the cortex representing a given point on the surface of the body. The excitation irradiated to neighboring cortical regions representing neighboring points on the surface of the body. When, therefore, the position of the stimulus was changed, it excited a cortical place, which place now also had some functional connection with the response. While such a theory is at least logically possible where the similarity dimension is one of *position*, it makes little sense for other dimensions of similarity, as, for example, shape, where on the basis of present knowledge it is not the case that every shape is registered in a unique locus in the nervous system reserved for just that shape, with similarity of shape paralleled by the proximity of their projections to one another. Hull and his followers, on the other hand, abandoned Pavlov's physiological theory and made no effort to substitute any other mechanism. Hull says that during learning "the reaction is conditioned not only to a tone but to a whole zone of tones of other pitches and intensities spreading in both directions along each dimension from the point conditioned" (p. 197).[4] Thus, he has retained the Pavlovian notion that the generalization occurs at the time of learning. It is difficult to understand how this is possible in the case of many continua which could hardly be said to have existential reality in the organism at the time of learning (e.g., circles of all different sizes). By contrast, the view presented here is that there is no generalization during learning and that something which seems to be generalization occurs at the time of the test for the reason stated above. This view is quite similar to Lashley's except that (1) the response need not imply failure of discrimination (cf. Alice Lasker's finding of generalization in spite of awareness of some dissimilarity[*]) and (2) an attempt is made to explain the mechanism in terms of the A–a relation.

The logical necessity of gaining access to trace b via trace a creates particular difficulties for the proposition that perception is determined by past experience. Let us assume that a given stimulus A, originally experienced as A, through learning comes to be experienced differently, as B. (As an example, a Street Figure which at first is seen as a mere array of spots, A, ultimately is seen as a familiar object, B.) When now A is presented, the influence of learning can only become manifest if A arouses b. But to do this it must first arouse a, presumably on the basis of similarity to A. In other words, even after the perceptual change has been acquired the stimulus must always be first "seen" (i.e., A must occur—in our example, the mere array of spots) exactly as it was initially, before becoming transformed into the new percept (the familiar object), although this fleeting stage of the process may not be present in conscious awareness. This sets up certain limitations on the possible influence of past experience in perception. The stimulus must be one which can be seen in different ways, one presumably being primary and itself not requiring past experience.

It seems reasonable to suppose that the similarity between A and a can be a conceptual one and not merely sensory. In other words, if A

---

[*] Scheerer[16] has pointed out that the term "stimulus generalization" is a misnomer if it is the case that it is based on failure to discriminate ("generalization by default"). The classical, or Aristotelian, definition of generalization is that it is the positive process of transferring a reaction to a whole class on the basis of experience with only some instances of the class by virtue of abstracting out the differences. To Scheerer's point we might add that it may be the case that an animal is aware of some differences in the stimulus but yet does not engage in "conceptual generalization." It may be struck by the similarity albeit non-identity, and respond somewhat automatically.

is a current *thought,* it would seem plausible in the light of the fore-going discussion that a trace of a similar thought would be aroused. Although in all the examples given in this paper A was a stimulus, it is probable that this would not be essential. The emergence of a particular thought on the basis of its similarity to an ongoing thought or experience thus becomes a major principle in accounting for the content within the stream of consciousness at any given moment. Association would be the other principle. It is instructive to note how often a particular idea apparently is brought to mind on the basis of similarity to the immediately preceding idea.

The examples cited here suggest that the critical locus in recall is often in the A–a relation rather than in the A–B relation. These cases have been emphasized because this aspect of recall has been neglected, but the question remains as to the relative contribution of the two relations to forgetting in daily life. In point of fact it would seem that the cause of forgetting is more frequently due to failure to get from a to b. This is evidenced by the fact that we generally succeed in recognizing the stimulus (for example, the face), which as noted above can be taken as proof that trace a has entered into the process. (In fact, it is difficult to demonstrate failure of recognition. It requires special conditions as in the technique used by Köhler and von Restorff described earlier.) On the other hand, we all too often are then unable to give the associated name. The same fact can be gleaned from the laboratory finding that where subsequent recognition for the *items* of a learned list remains excellent, recall of associations often fails.

At present we do not know why arousal of trace a by stimulus A occurs more readily or is more successful than arousal of trace b by associated trace a. One obvious explanation is that whereas the arousal of a by A is a one-stage process, the arousal of b, given A, is a two-stage process. Unfortunately, this simple explanation does not do justice to the facts. If recognition per se and recall of b following recognition were each about equally difficult, then of course, statistically speaking, recall of b given A (which we have argued presupposes recognition as the first step) would fail more often than would recognition alone. But the fact is that recognition is easier (more successful) than is the recall of an associated content *after* recognition has taken place.

It is, therefore, necessary to look more closely at the nature of the two relations. In the case of A–B, the association between trace a and b may no longer exist, whereas only the preservation of trace a is necessary, for it to be aroused by A. It is reasonable to suppose that correct associations may not remain indefinitely preserved (in the face of interference), whereas the component items may endure over much longer periods. But, in addition to this point, there is the difficulty in evoking an associated content even where it is known that the association exists. Experiments by the author and others employing a matching test of recognition consistently yield higher scores than the more traditional test of recall. Since a subject can pair A with the correct B (from among the many B items present on the test), only if the association is preserved, the greater difficulty in a test of recall (given A, to recall B) suggests that an additional process, that of evocation, is involved in the latter case. In matching, B is also given so that trace b is aroused by it. Hence, trace b does not have to be redintegrated by trace a.* The many cases in daily life of momentary or temporary forgetting—sometimes accompanied by a feeling that the forgotten item is on the "tip of one's tongue"—illustrate failure of evocation where it may be presumed the association is actually intact.

The problem of evoking an associated content in recall can be clarified by the following analysis. Since A is given by the stimulus, trace a does not have to yield up a conscious manifestation of itself for A to be experienced. A would be experienced even if there were no trace. The trace merely has to contribute an approval function ("this is familiar") or a veto function ("this is not anything familiar"). But B is not given by a present stimulus so that not only must b be tapped but the excitation must be such as to yield some conscious manifestation (for example, hearing the name in the "mind's ear" or visualizing a face in the "mind's eye"). An unpublished thesis by Karp[6] illustrates this point. Subjects were required to learn paired nonsense figures under conditions where either the left-hand member was easy (a fairly simple pattern) and the right-hand one difficult (a more elaborate pattern) or vice versa. The former condition proved the more difficult, although in a control experiment, testing by matching, there was no difference. Presumably the greater difficulty in evoking a memory of a more complex pattern in recall accounted for the results, since the equivalence in the control experiment suggests that the association was no more difficult to form in either direction. The well-known superiority of recognition over reproduction in work on memory for form also points up the distinction between the preservation of a trace and the evocation of it without the aid of the stimulus.[2, 14]

What general implications for the study of "mind" can be drawn from the above discussion of memory phenomena? One is that it would seem

---

* It is possible that matching is superior to recall for some reason other than the one here suggested so that this problem warrants experimental investigation. But at this writing the additional step of evocation seems the most plausible explanation.

possible to develop an explanatory science of mental events in terms of the characteristics of certain hypothetical constructs (e.g., memory trace) which need not be stated in neurophysiological terms. Ultimately it may be supposed that a translation can be made, but in the meanwhile it is quite possible to explain a good deal about memory (to stick to this topic) by making certain assumptions about the trace and how it behaves. Thus, for example, we can explain a fact such as recognition by assuming it to be the phenomenological counterpart of the reactivation of an appropriate trace when the corresponding stimulus is given. Or we can explain failure of recall in some cases by assuming failure of the stimulus to arouse its previously established trace or in other cases by assuming failure of that trace to redintegrate its associated content. It need hardly be added that beyond merely accounting for certain known facts of memory, the assumptions made about the trace lead to specific predictions.

The notion that a science of psychology can be developed in nonphysiological terms is not new, since S–R theorists such as Hull and Spence have attempted quite explicitly to do precisely this during the last twenty-five years. But S–R theories do not attempt to develop constructs which are meant to correspond to the unobservable but nevertheless existentially real processes presumed to underlie observable experience and behavior. Thus, for example, Hull's concept of habit is not meant to point to anything which exists in the organism. It merely refers to the fact that after such and such conditions for learning have been met it is now safe to predict that certain consequences will follow. A trace-linkage as the carrier of a learned habit, on the other hand, *is* something presumed to exist in the organism. (For this type of theory, therefore, the possibility of translation into neurophysiological terms is always implicit, since this is the only realm in which such constructs can be thought to exist. But that does not contradict the point made above that explanation is often possible without such translation.)

A further implication of tailoring constructs to correspond to what presumably is actually taking place in the organism is this: One has to face up to certain specific problems which otherwise can be ignored. The problem discussed earlier of how the appropriate trace can be activated when the stimulus is given is an example. The problem of stimulus generalization is another example. As noted above, it does not seem plausible to say that stimuli which are similar to the training stimulus become connected to the response as a result of training if such stimuli could not be thought to be represented in the organism during learning. Rather, it seems plausible to assume that only a trace of the stimulus actually employed is connected with the response. If this is true, then stimulus generalization must be some function of the activation of that trace by similar stimuli at the time of the test. In other words, once certain initial assumptions are made (such as the highly plausible one that given experiences or behaviors are represented in memory by corresponding memory traces), certain problems logically follow which seem to require a particular direction for their solution.

REFERENCES

1. Duncker, K., "On problem-solving," *Psychol. Monog.*, 1945, 58: No. 5.
2. Hanawalt, N. G., "Memory trace for figures in recall and recognition," *Arch. Psychol.*, 1937, 31 (No. 216).
3. Höffding, H., *Outlines of Psychology*, Macmillan, London and New York, 1891.
4. Hull, C. L., *Principles of Behavior*, Appleton-Century-Crofts, New York, 1943, p. 197.
5. James, W., *Principles of Psychology*, Dover Publications, 1950.
6. Karp, S., *On Methods of Testing Association*, M.A. thesis, New School for Social Research, New York, 1952.
7. Köhler, W., *Dynamics in Psychology*, Liveright, New York, 1940.
8. ———, and von Restorff, H., "Analyse von Vorgängen im Spurenfeld. II, Zur Theorie der Reproduktion," *Psychol. Forsch.*, 1935, 21:56-112.
9. Lashley, K. S., *Brain Mechanisms and Intelligence*, Univ. of Chicago Press, Chicago, 1929.
10. Lashley, K., and Wade, M., "The Pavlovian theory of generalization," *Pyschol. Rev.*, 1946, 53:72-87.
11. Lasker, A., *The Problem of Recognition in Stimulus Generalization*, Ph.D. thesis, New School for Social Research, New York, 1959.
12. Pavlov, I. P., *Conditioned Reflexes*, trans. G. V. Anrep, Oxford Univ. Press, New York, 1927.
13. Rock, I., "The orientation of forms on the retina and in the environment," *Am. J. Psychol.*, 1956, 69:513-528.
14. ———, and Engelstein, P., "A study of memory for visual form," *Am. J. Psychol.*, 1959, 72:221-229.
15. ———, and Heimer, W., "The effect of retinal and phenomenal orientation on the perception of form," *Am. J. Psychol.*, 1957, 70:493-511.
16. Scheerer, M., "Cognitive theory," Chap. 3 in *Handbook of Social Psychology*, ed. by G. Lindzey, Addison-Wesley, Reading, Mass., 1954.
17. Sperry, R. W., "Cerebral organization and behavior," *Science*, 1961, 133:1749-1757.
18. Wallach, H., and Austin, P. A., "Recognition and the localization of visual traces," *Am. J. Psychol.*, 1954, 67:338-340.
19. ———, and Averbach, E., "On memory modalities," *Am. J. Psychol.*, 1955, 68:249-257.

MILTON V. KLINE

Mind: A Descriptive Operational Definition

Philosophers, psychologists, physiologists, and physicists, representing the major reaches of science both in antiquity and modern times, have in a variety of ways searched for a definition of mind. Such attempts have, for the greater part, either been descriptive and designed to construct a model for further conceptualization and eventual pragmatic exploration or have represented observations necessary for the development of constructs in connection with the phenomenological structuring of mind.

The purpose of this paper shall not be to attempt a unified concept of mind, but to conceive of an operational descriptive definition of mind which can permit its extensions into areas available for empirical, mechanistic, as well as dynamic and experiential examination and experimentation.

William James[1] in one of his many profound and meaningful observations, comments that: "We conceive of a world spread out in a perfectly fixed and orderly fashion, and we believe in its existence. The question is: How does this conception and this belief arise? How is the the chaos smoothed and straightened out?"

As Carl Rogers[9] and the nondirective school of psychotherapy have dramatically pointed out in recent times, we can very often only answer certain questions by posing, in turn, other questions. This is not of necessity evasion, and the avoidance of a direct encounter with a problem or situation for which a definitive explanation or response is not available but constitutes a means of manipulating a complex percept into a more delimited and perhaps more accessible frame of reference so as to permit its careful evaluation and consideration.

James, in his very pointed question, emphasizes the very core of what to many of us is the essence of mind.

If we are to extend the concept developed by Sullivan,* the architect, namely, that form follows function, then it is not inconceivable that the form of mind can best be understood by its function. The psychic apparatus of man being essentially a learning modality and involving the flexibility and plasticity which permits stimulus transformation, displacement, and conservation seems endowed with the necessary and highly versatile capacity for transforming its structure into a variety of forms in order to meet those functions with which it is beset either in terms of external arousal or internal stimulation. In essence, our minds are concerned with the structuring of reality both in the outer space around us and in the inner space of our own existence. It is here that the sensory input-output mechanisms of behavior upon which we are eternally dependent become interdependently mixed with the dynamisms and abstracts of philosophic considerations and at times create ideational chaos and confusion as one dimension seems unable to be congruent or even tangential to the other dimension.

John Mill,† reviewing various opinions about belief as it relates to the perception of reality made the following observation:

What is the difference to *our minds* between thinking of a reality and representing to ourselves an imaginary picture? I confess I can see no escape from the opinion that the distinction is ultimate and primordial. There is no more difficulty in holding it to be so, than in holding the difference between a sensation and an idea to be primordial. It seems almost another aspect of the same difference—I cannot help thinking, therefore, that there is in the rememberance of a real fact, as distinguished from that of a thought, an element which does not exist—in the difference between the mere ideas which are present to the mind in the two cases. This element, howsoever we define it, constitutes belief, and is the difference between Memory and Imagination. From whatever direction we approach, this difference seems to close our path. When we arrive at it, we seem to have reached, as it were, the central point of our intellectual nature, presupposed and built upon in every attempt we make to explain the more recondite phenomena of our mental being.

Thus, in considering mind and the preception of reality, we must also come face-to-face with the ultimate nature of what constitutes belief. For herein lie the operational levers wherein we effect awareness in its sensory element, which leads to some structuring or operant behavior with its ultimate shaping determined by innate experiences and capacities and yielding in a construction of logic coincidental with the

* Louis H. Sullivan (1856-1924).
† In W. James, *Principles of Psychology*, Vol. II, p. 285.[1]

evolvement of tangential feeling or affect. The process itself is that of mind, the experience is that of *being* which we term the perception of reality.

James,[1] again points out in perhaps one of his most meaningful and penetrating observations that the true opposites of belief, psychologically considered, are doubt and inquiry, not disbelief. In both these states, he feels, the inner state of our mind is one of unrest, and the emotion that is engendered is precisely like the emotion of belief itself, perfectly clear and distinct, but completely indescribable in words. It is his feeling that both types of affect may be pathologically endowed. One of the fascinations of being drunk or the use of drugs which obliterate certain aspects of ego defenses relating to vigilance unquestioningly lies, as James points out, in the deepening of the sense of reality and truth which is gained therein. Thus, he says;[1] "In whatever light things may then appear to us, they seem more utterly what they are, more 'utterly utter' than when we are sober. This goes to a fully unutterable extreme in the nitrous oxide intoxication in which a man's very soul will sweat with conviction and he be all the while unable to tell what it is he is convinced of at all."

The brain which can be approached anatomically has, as we know, many functions physiologically. One of the major functions being that of the creation of the mind. The mind is both creative and a function of the brain. This does not necessitate a philosophic dualism between brain and mind or mind and body but a distinctiveness and an understanding of the point at which distinctiveness is necessary between structure and activity, form and function. Mind is a function evolving from brain structure. The form of mind itself must, of necessity, be examined through its functional properties.

Thus, the parallel approach to the anatomy of the brain is the psychology of the mind. Traditionally, we have gleaned men's minds through their productivity. Through their ideas, thoughts, works, actions, efforts, and their beliefs. Unfortunately, these productions very often are determined by more than the mind or, despite our wishes to the contrary, sometimes determined even by the brain. At any rate, these end results, like other forms of cognitive behavior, are not alone the results of mind but are the results of the totality of behavior.

Therefore, we must delimit our own examination and delimit our own end products in order to carefully examine mind function and mind form. In dreaming and in the structuring of secondary sensory constructs which we term perceptual we come very close to having the inner elements which describe the essence of mind.

Through dreams, hallucinations, imagery functions, and their emotional expressions, we have an opportunity in a delimited operational sense to conceive of the mind both in definition and form. Of the many avenues and modalities for conceiving and studying this aspect of human existence, hypnosis is one that has traditionally afforded great accessibility to the human mind and, in itself, has appeared to be one of the properties of the mind as it becomes elucidated through interpersonal relationships.

In this brief paper, we shall devote our attention to considering some of the characteristics of hypnosis, hypnotic behavior, and observations gained through hypnotic interaction, which shed some light on the nature of reality, its development and evolvement under these restricted and delimited conditions, with a view toward their examination and incorporation into an operational definition of mind.

Contemporary advances in the understanding of hypnosis, as well as its incorporation into psychological and medical therapeutics, have removed it from its historically archaic identification with the coercive influences of submissiveness or its hierarchal role of passive dependency. As we investigate hypnosis as a reality structuring procedure, not only do we gain further insight into the nature of hypnosis but also acquire some direct access to the conceptualization of mind which is the awareness determined by perceptual reality. Of the many phenomenological experiences that can be produced through hypnosis, one of the more striking, for purposes of our consideration, is that of hypnotically induced age regression. In recent years clinical and experimental investigations of hypnotically induced age regression have reported some of the following conclusions:

1. Evocation of patterns of intellectual functioning, including spatial, motor, and sensory components consist with earlier phylogenetic aspects of intelligence and adaptative capacities, the simulation of which on a statistical level would be extremely unlikely.[2]

2. The loss of ejaculatory, though not erection, capacity in some male subjects in age regressions.[4]

3. The duplication of symptoms of some physical illnesses in some subjects when regressed to the time of the actual time occurrence of these illnesses.[3]

4. Epileptic EEG patterns changing to normal EEG patterns when patents have been regressed to an age prior to the onset of epilepsy.[6]

5. The appearance, in some instances, of a Babinski or infantile plantar reflex during regression to infancy.[4]

It is in connection with our interest in the nature of mental functioning as it relates to the mind that we might use some of these observations. For example, if we take the last point, the appearance of a Babinski response, its occurrence cannot easily be accounted for without a review of the response itself as well as the procedure which elucidates it. Babinski originally held that there need be no anatomical or histological lesion of the pyramidal tract to account for the response. Although, for the greater part, it is held to be a pathological response usually related to anatomical or histological pathology. It has, however, been observed in strychnine poisoning and when the poison has worn off, the abnormal response became normal. There is little question but that the Babinski response in healthy normal adults does not occur, and its appearance is generally assumed to be a sign of abnormality.

Actually, the Babinski reflex is to be found in two conditions: in one of which the pyramidal tracts are abnormal and the other in which they are normal. Thus, while the appearance of the Babinski reflex can genuinely be described as a pathological response, it can only be taken that it is an indicator that there is an abnormality of *function* in the central nervous system. It must be pointed out, however, that there never has been a correlation between the anatomical or histological state of a corticospinal tract and the plantar response, performed on an acceptable statistical level. It is well known that the Babinski response occurs during hypoglycemia, general anesthesia, and the injection of hyoscine—it can occur in epileptics during or after a seizure and it can occur in the normal during sleep.

Thus, while it is not an absolute indicator of central nervous system disease, it does appear to be a genuine indicator of some abnormality of function of the central nervous system which may arise out of varying conditions, some of which are reversible, some of which are not. In an attempt to appraise the present evidence regarding this response, it would seem that the Babinski response can occur in a state of altered consciousness, and that this state of consciousness may permit perceptual reorganization leading to stimulation via previously blocked or inactive, older and simpler neural pathways. Consciousness can be altered by activity as well as by disease; activity constituting elements of emotional excitation, inhibition, and their perceptual correlates becomes a dual function of disease and adaptation, degeneration, and regression, perceptual disorganization and perceptual transformation, all of which constitute the creation of reality.

It would thus appear that, of necessity, the psychopathological elements in the functioning of the psychic apparatus need not be related to psychological components in the physiological apparatus, but may be autonomously related structures maintained and reinforced within the structure and function of the psychic apparatus itself. Thus, the mind apart from the brain is capable of its own organized levels of normality and abnormality which are independent in many instances of correlated or even associated activities in connection with cortical abnormality. That disorders of the function of the mind may derive from disorders of

the brain and other parts of the physiological apparatus is beyond question, but in terms of our development of the concept of the mind, we
must bear in mind the fact that mind as a perceptually organizing
modality has incorporated within it, like other psychic functions, the
ability to reproduce parallelisms to be found in the older biological
systems with its counterparts in terms of functional abnormality, functional reversibility, and many of the mechanisms of biologic activity
which in the psychic apparatus becomes less mechanistic and more
dynamic, or in a sense assumes the quality which in older terminology
has been viewed as being more like those which occur on a hysterical
rather than an organic basis. Bearing in mind that both, as a subjective
response, constitute a degree of reality beyond experiential disbelief
and, as such, are the realities of the mind and constitute an important
ingredient in existence and the sense of being.

One of the primary characteristics of hypnosis appears to be the
elucidation of a transference relationship which assumes great importance
to the subject and which permits a degree of freedom and spontaneity
most characteristic of the preadolescent period. In this respect, it is
more open because it lacks the criticalness which is more typical of later
psychological development. The lack of critical capacity is, of course,
accompanied by a reduction of ego defenses and reality testing. When
reinforced through the use of strong supportive and ego-recognizing
devices, this breach in the defenses of the individual does not pose any
more of a problem than it would in any other adaptive situation.

Through the use of relationship experience rather than suggestiveness
alone, there develops within the regression a reconstruction of the many
attitudes and values which go into the creation of the world of reality
as we know it. In this rather primitive interaction, the subject makes
available aspects of his own self concept and body image which may
now be influenced and directed through the regressive experience, and,
while repetitive of earlier developmental experiences, has within it the
uniqueness of the therapeutic relationship which was previously lacking.

It would seem that at this level, therapist and patient interact at a
point where, with such uncritical ego functioning as exists in regression,
it is possible to strengthen and initiate drives, affects, and values. As they
become more intense, they assume greater reality in the nonhypnotic
state and become synthesized into workable and acceptable ideas, feelings, wishes, and desires. These are the cornerstones of human behavior
and personality which apparently only in regressive states do we have
the opportunity to encounter openly and without the long-developed
defenses characteristic of neuroses.

The results point not to the use of regression as a technique in
therapy but as an intense dynamic experience within which the patient's

world of reality may for the first time since his own childhood be touched and influenced in perhaps a more constructive and productive manner.

Apart from its value as a component of psychotherapy, a major result of this type of investigation has been to focus our attention upon the nature of hypnotic regression as phenomena of behavior which has proven to be provocative in connection with the very nature of reality itself. It is now in this direction that we should like to channel our attention and take the results of these experiences to the task of describing the nature of mind and its development.

In hypnosis, reality appraisal as it exists in the waking state is temporarily disrupted. Associative links with temporal, sensory, and motor cues are either dissociated or so effectively blocked or masked as to permit the emergence of reality appraisal on a newly structured hypnotic basis.

Subjects in hypnosis believe in the essential nature of the hypnotically induced reality not through suggestion but through the natural utilization of more primitive mechanisms of reality appraisal. These are essentially the regressive structures of cognition and the internalized process of perception which may be described under a variety of headings ranging from dissociation and subliminal, to infantile and dependent.

The interpretation of such a process must await a more thorough measuring of this process and its appropriate role in the hierarchy of behavioral organizing process. Although there still remains a considerable amount of work in dealing with the data obtained in the investigation of age regression through both therapeutic and experimental approaches, it is possible on the basis of data thus far available to conceptualize some of the results.

Previous studies of hypnotic age regression have indicated that the designated or selected age in the regression is highly variable and very selective and that within any regression there will be found elements of behavior which are either at or below the chronological point of regression and others which are obviously considerably higher. To some extent this has led certain investigators to question the validity of age regression and to view it as a role-playing phenomenon. This latter interpretation fails to take into account the major operational function in age regression which is a reversibility of reality appraisal from an operational structure, weighted, if not in dynamic equilibrium, with the use of cognitive and perceptual mechanisms which we identify as ego functions.

With regression, as in any psychological process, the internalization of perception cannot exist in isolation but must be converted to a structured whole which of necessity, is characterized by laws of individuality that apply to the system of personality as a whole. In this manner, the operation of regression can be combined spontaneously into the operation of

dissociation. The action of perceptual or operational reversibility starting as a mechanism envelopes the whole characterological system of self.

Thus, as in architecture, the form of regression takes on the form of
its function and not just the isolated characteristics of the stimulus for
the reversibility.

Just as an externalized stimulus may initiate dreaming, the nature
of the personality and the serial reality links to the initiating stimulus
will formalize or conceptualize the dream. From the point of view of
psychological activity, the criterion for the appearance of age regression
in hypnosis is the construction of invariants or concepts of the self
through conservation.*

Conservation may be equated on a behavioral level with the activating
element behind reality appraisal, structuring body image, and awareness
of self in relation to externalized symbols. In this respect, conservation
is the process of logical organization even though it may deal with
illogical components. It may well be that much of what happens within
the reconstructing-conservation process in hypnosis is very similar to
what goes on in the condensation and reconstruction process in dreaming. The process of conservation must, therefore, be considered as the
result of operational reversibility. Operational reversibility in this sense
is based upon Piaget's[7] genetic model of the development of logical
structures in the mental development of children and relates to the
capacity in manipulate observations through the logical associations of
externalized connections as compared with the capacity to deal with
observations through internalized associations. Response mechanisms
relate to modality functions of tension, awareness, and the gradations of
consciousness as they may be viewed in terms of criticalness and vigilance. Operational reversibility in this sense is the structural process
within which cognitive and perceptual mechanisms develop and emerge.

From this theoretical model, hypnotic age regression and its various
dimensions of behavior cannot be restricted to a criterion of "chronology,"
either with respect to validity or genuiness. Age, time, space, and other
externalized loci for the orientation of self can only be viewed as the
initiating stimuli of operational structures within which reversibility and
conservation compose the major mechanisms in the evolution of symbols
and the development of expressive behavior.

Hypnosis and its phenomena, like age regression, can in this sense
only be understood in relation to a classificatory system of cognition and
perception which, of necessity, presupposes an existence and an understanding of the serial relations set off by operational reversibility. From

* Conservation as a cognitive, perceptual process is here used in the way Piaget
utilized it in his concept of the development of logical structures.

this it follows that such emergent behavior will be greatly influenced by: (1) the degree of operational reversibility that is available, i.e., the depth of hypnosis, the degree of dissociation, the detachment from reality appraisal, the weakening of ego defenses, or the plasticity of prelogical operations in the development of symbolic behavior; and (2) the nature of the construction of conservation, i.e., the elimination of invariants necessary for reality appraisal and their replacement by equally effective ones for the logical perception and reinforcement of the emergent operational reversibility. At this juncture, the process of hypnosis and its dissociative mechanism are greatly influenced by the dynamics of the hypnotic relationship both at its inception and during its management.

The separation of the mechanistic from the dynamic components in hypnotically induced age regression can be inferred and perhaps examined, but together form the pathway through which the subject reconstructs his perceptual and cognitive functions.

In the framework of this concept of age regression, it becomes increasingly evident that one cannot really characterize age regression produced through hypnosis as fundamentally different from any other state of being or alteration of self-concept, produced through hypnosis. For in all states of hypnosis, we find the same process present.

The operational reversibility of reality percepts and their replacement through symbolic conservation may constitute the major mechanism in the psychological development of hypnotic behavior. Simultaneous or serially synchronized functions of regression and of the construction of a system of symbolic logical structures consistent with the regressed state lead to the development of hypnotic behavior still structured as a whole but with respect to waking reality levels much more internalized and much less subject to external stimulation.

In this respect it is our observed opinion that the process which leads to increasingly greater reliance upon the internalized process for reality appraisal and behavior-organizing operations in itself constitutes a gradient of perceptual masking or dissociation. The masking of external stimulation in itself would appear to constitute an archaic and regressive phenomenon which, in varying degrees, is to be found in all aspects of behavior but which assumes paramount importance in hypnosis.

The introduction of activating stimuli, such as elements of age, time, space, and other symbols of serial relations in thinking and emotion, represents only the diverting of operational reversibility and its actual construction, which, of necessity, must still incorporate thought on the part of the subject without interference from externalized sources of stimulation which he is constantly being bombarded with.

All states of hypnosis by this criterion become regressive, varying only in degree, and the alterations in behavior which emerge are a reflection of the degree of regressive involvement. Depth of hypnosis in itself becomes a measure of the depth or the degree of regression.

Internalization as a process of logical structuring is a developmental process which becomes increasingly restricted by maturation and learning and the use of reality symbols which we identify with our own concept of consciousness. For us, consciousness and personality become interdependent in many respects, an absolute norm being nonexistent.

Externalization as a mode of operation activity is both psychologically and biologically identified with the gradual development of thinking, reasoning, reality appraisal, and critical judgment from birth to maturity. The activity process may be classified as one moving from internalization as a perceptual-cognitive operation to externalization as a perceptual-cognitive operation.

The equilibrium between the use of externalized and internalized structures for reality appraisal would appear to be strongly identified as characteristics which lead to those factors we identify as adjustment and maladjustment, consciousness and unconsciousness, reality and unreality, being and nothingness.

This balance in the operation activity of man is dynamic and not static. It may be influenced by a wide range of psychophysiological processes like sleep, dreaming, illness, emotion, and thought.

The nature of operational reversibility, as described in this paper, is pertinent not only to our understanding of hypnosis but also the factors which determine the broader variants of consciousness within which hypnosis emerges as a regressive phenomenal fundamental in the development of logical operations and reality structures in the general development of mental functioning.

The observations derived from a study of age regression in hypnosis and their theoretical interpretations would appear to hold for the nature of hypnosis itself rather than for any one of the behaviorisms found within or elucidated through hypnosis.

Developmentally, motor activity in children represents intelligence without thought activity. Spontaneous sensorimotor reactions tend to increase during hypnotic age regression and to represent via conservation much affect and ideation which, in the dissociated state of hypnosis, cannot be discharged with its usual verbal or affective characteristics.

Schneck[10] has reported and evaluated the meaning of spontaneous sensorimotor phenomena during the induction of hypnosis and during the course of psychotherapy which supports the observation that subjects in hypnosis have increased need for sensorimotor behavior. The relation of this regressive mechanism of emergent intelligence to somatization reactions and the organ system language of neuroses and psychoses is of interest.

Since the sensorimotor period ranges roughly from zero to two years, the relative degree of such patterns of reactions attest to the level of regression and the importance that such a primitive or basic need for expression may have for the individual.

Spontaneous Babinski responses are not found in a high percentage of age regression, but it has been our experience that it occurs in individuals whose operational reversibility is so complete as to constitute the greatest possible dissociation or masking of externalized associative activity. As such, we have found either spontaneous or elucidated Babinski or infantile plantar responses in many forms of hypnosis apart from age regression, and particularly in complete or deep levels of hypnosis where no alteration in age was either suggested or indicated but in which there were major reversibility patterns of perception and of sensation.*

The age of two to seven finds the emergence of prelogical modes of perception and thinking which include the construction of imagery. Thus the field of intelligence becomes enlarged in the normal development of mental functioning. Now, to actions occurring in the child's immediate externalized environment, are added actions that have occurred in the past. This involves the use of magical thinking and the need to utilize psychological operations as a solution for problems.

Piaget writes[8] that in this stage there is the equating of percepts without recourse to critical judgment, which is only now beginning to emerge. For example, a child during this phase of development may pour liquid from one glass jar into another of a vastly different shape and will believe that the actual quantity in the second bottle is increased or decreased in the process.

When equal parts are taken away from the two equal whole figures, the child refuses to believe that the remainders are equal if the perceptual configurations are different.

Thus the child, at this level of psychological development, has operationally moved past the level of sensorimotor adaptation and seeks conceptual solutions. Concept formation at this level is essentially prelogical; that which we might call magical in nature and restricted with respect to critical judgment. Internalized actions and experiences are tied in with externalized perceptions to a very great extent. Behavioral responses weighted in part by externalized influences are the criteria of maturation in this stage of growth.

In hypnosis and age regression we find that subjects are very quick to accept or to develop magical explanations for their own experiences. Rationalizations for apparently paradoxical experiences such as induced

---

* In induced states of weightlessness as well as hypnotically induced alterations of bodily image.

hallucinations and other altered percepts are essentially expressed as having derived through previous though illogical experience.

Thus, when a subject is shown two identical fountain pens in hypnosis and is told that one weighs a few ounces and the other several hundred pounds, he accepts this explanation with little question, although he may express some surprise when he finds he cannot lift the "heavier" pen though the "light" one is lifted easily at once.

After repeated trials during which the subject fails to lift the "heavier" pen, he is told that he should think of the heavy pen as if it were *exactly* like the other one. After some deliberation and preoccupation he usually succeeds slowly in lifting the "hallucinated heavy" pen. At this point, if he is asked to count backward from twenty-five to zero while again lifting the "heavy" pen, he will be unable to lift it.

The use of associated ideas is easily acceptable in such a state of regressive mental functioning and subject to much plasticity and manipulation.

Most typical of regressed subjects in this connection is a lack of logical congruity with perceptual configuration. Illogical associations can be formed readily and accepted readily. This is true both of those induced hypnotically and those derived from spontaneous experience during hypnosis and particularly through age regression.

Responses to the Thematic Apperception Test[5] and similar projective psychological tests reveal a marked incorporation of prelogical thinking and ideas which are accepted as explanations for percepts. In the waking state, while the themes which the subjects develop may not lose their original character, the logical development of explanations is more congruent with reality testing even though they may be more evasive and less revealing of self-concept at a fundamental level.

By way of note, it should be kept in mind that the state of hypnosis while, showing beginning signs of operational reversibility, does not usually lead to a more complete level of regression except through the use of long periods of time within hypnosis or directly induced alterations of reality.

The study and observation of hypnotic age regression over a long period of time, both within psychotherapy and experimental investigation, continue to emphasize the meaningfulness of this aspect of behavior. The criterion of genuine age regression has little to do with chronological age but has much to do with the decline of reality testing based on externalization as a cognitive-perceptual process and the emergence of internalization as the major modality for experiential, perceptual, and behavioral organization.

The concept of operational reversibility and the conservation of symbolic and motor stimuli originally advanced by Piaget in connection with the development of logical thinking in genetic psychology appears with modification to apply to hypnotic behavior.

The temporal factor of age is no different than any other external focal point around which hypnotic behavior may be directed, and, therefore, the description of the psychological process described here in connection with age regression through hypnosis is thought to be applicable to hypnosis itself as well as to any of the phenomena elucidated through hypnosis.

To this degree hypnosis is apparently a completely regressive phenomenon initiated through mechanisms of dissociation or perceptual masking of eternalized stimulation and having a gradient of completeness which correlates with the clinical symptom-like classification of depth as it is usually used in connection with hypnotic evaluation.

Emergent behavior is determined largely by the degree of completeness of operational reversibility and the role of hypnotic transference in this constructive process. Regression of a hypnotic nature gives rise to greater utilization of sensorimotor systems of response formation and prelogical forms of thinking.

Mind is a creative function of consciousness, emerging from a physiological origin of brain activity and developing a parallel though autonomous direction. The ultimate manner in which we may become acquainted with complex experiences need not in the least resemble the manner in which our consciousness evolved. As a creative function of man, mind is free to assume whatever form the functional process of living demands of it.

REFERENCES

1. James, W., *Principles of Psychology*, Dover Publications, New York, 1950.
2. Kline, M. V. (ed.), *Hypnodynamic Psychology*, Julian Press, New York, 1953.
3. ———, "Stimulus transformation and learning theory in the production and treatment of an acute attack of benign paroxysmal peritonitis," *J. Clin. Exp. Hypnosis*, 1954, 1:93-98.
4. ———, "Soviet and western trends in hypnosis research," *Internat. J. Parapsychol.* 1959, 1:89-105.
5. ———, *Freud and Hypnosis*, Julian Press, New York, 1958.
6. Kupper, H. I., "Psychic concomitants in wartime injuries," *Psychosomatic Med.*, 1945, 4:15-21.
7. Piaget, J., *The Construction of Reality in the Child*, Basic Books, New York, 1954.
8. ———, *Logic and Psychology*, Basic Books, New York, 1957.
9. Rogers, R. C., *Client-Centered Therapy*, Houghton Mifflin, Boston, 1951.
10. Schneck, J. M., *Studies in Scientific Hypnosis*, Williams and Wilkins, Baltimore, 1954.

G U S T A V   B E R G M A N N

The Contribution of John B. Watson

Second only to Freud, though at a rather great distance, John B. Watson is, in my judgment, the most important figure in the history of psychological thought during the first half of the century. Nor is his impact limited to the science of psychology. Understood or misunderstood, quoted or misquoted, his name and his work are a symbol around which debate has swirled for quite some time, not only among psychologists but also generally among intellectuals of our civilization, although the attention he receives now, in the fifties, is perhaps not as great as it was in the twenties and thirties. There are two reasons for this eclipse, which I believe is temporary. Among psychologists the sound core of Watson's contribution has been widely accepted; his errors and mistakes have been forgotten. Naturally, then, psychologists have less reason to discuss either. In our civilization at large, the center of the debate has, during the last ten or fifteen years, shifted so far toward the antiscientific —and often quite irrational—right that Watson's bitterest enemies, who have always quoted him most eagerly, feel that they need no longer bother to refute him. They only use his name occasionally to scare little children in the existentialist dark. For both these reasons Watson, though

Reprinted from *Psychol. Rev.*, 1956, 63:265-276, by permission of the author and the American Psychological Association.

This is, with very minor alterations, the text of an address delivered before the Psychology Club of the University of Chicago and at Northwestern University. I have tried to preserve as much of the livelier and less formal tone of the spoken word as was possible and seemed proper; and I have, in the same vein, dispensed with the apparatus of references and footnotes.

happily alive, is by now a historical figure. So it is perhaps not too rash if one tries to look at both the man and his work historically.

Most of what I shall say will be about the work. Let us then first briefly glance at the man. There is a French saying that the style is the man. If it is right, as I believe it is, then one of the best ways to get the flavor of Watson's intellectual personality is to turn to his writings. Doing that, one receives above all the impression of simplicity, lucidity, vigor, and intellectual courage. Reading on, one is soon struck by the vices which in this case go with these virtues. The simple at times shades into the *simpliste;* the intellectual strength is often without subtlety; even the courage becomes less attractive when blended with the recklessness of the extremist. These are strong words, both for better and for worse. If they are justified, then there is much light as well as much shadow. Such men make a certain kind of contribution. So I shall inquire whether the analysis of the contribution agrees with the thumbnail sketch of the man. I believe that it does.

Watson is not only an experimental *psychologist,* fairly distinguished no doubt but without transcendent distinction; he is also a systematic thinker, that is, a philosopher of psychology, or, as one says, a *methodologist.* In this latter area he made his major contribution. But he is not only a methodologist, he is also a *social philosopher*—I am almost tempted to call him a social prophet—and he is, finally, a *metaphysician.* Since he is, vigorously and unsubtly as usual, a man of one piece, these four sides of him—the psychologist, the methodologist, the prophet, and the metaphysician—have often interfered with each other, very much to the *logical* detriment of each.

Let me set the tone of this talk by anticipating some of the judgments at which I shall eventually arrive. I shall be quite blunt—as blunt, perhaps, as Watson himself would be. His social philosophy is, in my opinion, deplorable. His metaphysics is silly. (Philosophers use this word, silly, without malice; e.g., a realist might say that phenomenalism is a silly philosophy and yet recognize that some of the arguments made in its favor are ingenious or even, as he thinks, irrefutable.) But then, again, things are not that simple; they are, Watson to the contrary notwithstanding, neither all white nor all black. Thus I hasten to add that the rationale behind his social gospel was a very high-minded, though naive and, alas, misguided type of idealism fairly widespread in this country at the beginning of the century. His metaphysics, quite similarly, has a core both true and important. The trouble there was that Watson, unsubtle and, I fear, also very ignorant in philosophical matters, did not know how to state the true and commonsensical core without at the same time asserting a lot of patent nonsense. ("Nonsense" is another word philosophers use without malice.) But, again, it is only fair to add that in this he was no worse, though he certainly was no better, than most of his fellow metaphysicians—technical philosophers and philosophical scientists alike.

Leaving the social philosophy to the end, I begin with an examination of the metaphysics. It should help if I anticipate the result of this examination. The thesis Watson was above all eager to establish and, man of action that he was, to inculcate, is that *there are no interacting minds*. This thesis is true beyond reasonable doubt. It is in fact sheer scientific common sense. Thus it is metaphysical only in the peculiar sense that, as experience has taught us, not only in the case of Watson, the philosophical analyst's professional skill is required to state it correctly, that is to say, without at the same time asserting a lot of patent nonsense. Watson's particular mistake was that in order to establish that there are no interacting minds, which is true, he thought it necessary to assert that *there are no minds,* which is not only false but silly. This, then, is the pattern. Watson's conclusion, that there are no interacting minds, is true and, certainly by now, sheer common sense. His premise, that there are no minds, is false and sheer nonsense. But I notice that at this point some explanations are in order.

First, with respect to minds—or, rather, the word "mind"—I do not use it for that ancient notion which is traditionally called a substantial mind. Nor would it make sense historically had Watson tried to lay once more this particular ghost; substantial minds had been banned effectively from psychology by Wundt a generation earlier. What I mean, therefore, when for brevity's sake I speak of minds, are so-called mental contents, or awarenesses, or phenomenal givenesses, such as percepts, volitions, memories, thoughts, and so on. That there are such things and that they are not, literally, physical things, either inside or outside the human body, is obvious. It is not the task of logical analysis either to prove or to refute the obvious. The task is, rather, to keep us out of trouble when talking about it. So I turn next to an explanation of the word "interaction" and of the phrase "interacting minds." I shall make use of what philosophers of science call a thought experiment.

Imagine a world with space and time like ours but otherwise so impoverished that it contains only Newtonian mass points which are colored, each of them being either red or green or blue. The mass points obey Newton's law; that's why I call them Newtonian. This law is a process law, which means that, given the masses, the positions, and the velocities of a (closed) configuration at a moment, one can, by means of this law, compute (predict) their positions and velocities at an earlier or later moment. In this respect my imaginary world is thus like ours. With respect to color it is very different. The whole of its space is divided into three regions, call them R, G, and B, respectively, such that whenever a mass point is in R it is red, whenever it is in G it is green, and so on. This world thus has two fundamental laws; one is Newton's law, which is of the process type; the other is the color law I just stated, of the type called cross-sectional. The point of the story is, of course, that it permits me to explain the relevant meanings of "interaction" and of the related phrase "causally closed." Using them correctly in speaking about this world of my fancy, one would say that there are colors in it but that these are noninteracting colors. Or one might say that this world minus its colors is causally closed under the Newtonian process law. But, I repeat, to say this is not to say either that there are in this world no colors or that in it there does not hold a law, of the cross-sectional variety, which coordinates to each position a color. The moral of the fable is obvious. To say that there are no interacting minds is to say, first, that men's bodies with all their stuffings, including of course their central nervous systems, are part of the physical universe, and, second, that the physical universe is causally closed under laws none of which ever mentions anything mental. But, to repeat once more, to say this is not to say that there are no minds.

Anyone with some knowledge of the intertwined histories of psychology and philosophy may at this point wonder why I have bothered to elaborate the obvious. For you may remember, from the history of philosophy, that the thesis I have just explained so meticulously was, at Watson's time and before, well known and widely accepted under the name of epiphenomenalism. I shall counter the question with another. Why, I ask, did Watson himself bother? Why didn't he simply accept some version of epiphenomenalism, particularly since it was, at least latently, also the philosophy of the Functionalists, and let it go at that? Nor shall I stop there but go on to point out that, as you may remember from the history of psychology, Watson, as he saw himself, rebelled not only against Wundtianism, or, as it was called in this country, Structuralism, but also and at least as vigorously against the Functionalism of his teachers at the University of Chicago. This is prima-facie evidence for something more than meets the eye at a first glance. It is also my cue to say what needs to be said about the intellectual background from which Watson arose and against which his contribution must be understood and appraised.

Among the relatively few men who had an appreciable impact on the development of ideas, even fewer, probably only a minority, were also able to see their own role in this development correctly. Watson does not belong to that doubly distinguished minority. Moreover, it would seem that those who up to now have written about him and about the recent history of psychology in this respect share his illusions. As Watson sees himself and, following him, as these writers see him, he is above all a radical innovator. Functionalism, accordingly, is merely the last gasp of classical psychology. Watson made the break; with him modern psychology began. As I see him, Watson is above all a completer and a consummator—the greatest, though not chronologically the last, of the Functionalists. The break, accordingly, occurred between Structuralism and Functionalism. With the latter, modern psychology had begun before Watson appeared on the scene. The one methodological contribution of Watson which is specifically his own is merely a footnote—though, I insist, a most important one—to the methodological ideas of the Functionalists. These are somewhat unconventional assertions. Starting with them, I have once more, for clarity's sake, reversed the order of thesis and argument. So I hurry to supply the latter.

Experimentally, work of the kind the Functionalists emphasized had of course been done, a least incidentally, before their time. Systematically, though, they were, under the impact of Darwinism, the first to introduce certain ideas into the very groundwork—to introduce them, as it were, on the very ground floor of their conception of psychology. The most important of these ideas is that of process. According to the Functionalists, the psychologist must, like any other scientist, search for process laws. Specifically, this means that he must search for laws which permit him to predict, from sufficient information about the present state of a man, or any number of men, and their environment, the future course of events concerning both the man or men and the environment. To us this is a truism, except that, as we have since realized, we may have to supplement the information about the present with some about the past. Or, at least, we must be prepared to do that at certain stages of our knowledge. In the broad pattern which I am trying to trace, this qualification, though I think not unimportant, is merely a detail. Details apart, the emphasis on in principle comprehensive process is by now a truism. Let me say, then, as a simple matter of historical justice, that in psychology those who made it a truism are the Functionalists and Watson. The unconventional part of my thesis lies of course in the last two words: "and Watson." You will not on this occasion expect a full documentation for either its conventional or its unconventional part. But I shall adduce some facts which should at least lend some credence to both.

If I were allowed a choice of only three documents from which to teach the history of Functionalism I would choose, first, Dewey's "The Reflex Arc Concept in Psychology," of 1896, which is the opening shot of the movement; second, J. R. Angell's presidential address, "The Province of Functional Psychology," of 1907, which marks its first peak; and, third, Carr's text, *Psychology*, of 1925. There is, of course, a difference between these documents. The first two are what historians call primary sources; the third, being a text, is merely a secondary source; however, it was for its time a very good text; it was, I take it, very successful; and it represents very adequately the maturity of the movement. Now in Carr's text our great truism is not only stated precisely, without any flaw whatsoever, but it permeates the whole book. In Dewey's paper you will look for it in vain. (This is easily understood from Dewey's intellectual background, to which I could not possibly attend on this occasion.) In Angell's address you will find it, but only if you know how to look for it. If you do, then you will discover it here and there, but always, or virtually always, with a certain metaphysical blur. The blur stems, both logically and historically, from the metaphysical purposivism of the philosophical Darwinians. If you reflect on this temporal sequence extending through about three decades, from Dewey over Angell to Carr, you will, I hope, at least find plausible what I believe to be a historical fact, namely, that within this development the first incisive statement of our great truism, made by a psychologist for psychologists, lucidly and without any teleological blur, occurs in Watson's classical "Psychology as the Behaviorist Views It," of 1913. This is what I had in mind when I called him the great consummator of Functionalism. With Carr, if I may so put it without disrespect, the insight had reached textbook level.

We are ready to see how all this squares with epiphenomenalism or, rather, with Watson's failure to adopt it and, as I said, let it go at that. In the paper just mentioned he accused the Functionalists of being interactionists who merely pose as epiphenomenalists when they want to give themselves the air of scientific righteousness. In the calm light of a later day the accusation seems grossly unfair. The Functionalists were not really interactionists. They were much too sane for that (always excepting Dewey, who is a case by himself). On the other hand, though, while the substance and structure of their thought was epiphenomenalist, they did not at first come right out and say so. Angell, in his politically very astute presidential address, even derided what he calls the pale ghost of epiphenomenalism. This helps to explain why Watson made those accusations. To understand fully one must, I think, recall the larger scheme of things, academic as well as nonacademic, intellectual as well as ideological, which the Functionalists found when, about half a generation before Watson, they opened their campaign. The then regnant philosophy was either dualistic or idealistic and, therefore, not at all favorable to a science of man.

Cleverly taking advantage of some favorable circumstances that were also present, e.g., the American enthusiasm for "applied science," the Functionalists tried to make in this scheme of things a place for psychology as we know it. Their success is a matter of record. Naturally, it required statesmanship and, perhaps, a modicum of diplomatic equivocation. (There are always some who sincerely believe what is also expedient.) This is how I would account for those occasional purple patches in their earlier writings, such as Angell's derision of epiphenomenalism or his quaintly Victorian hymn, in the same piece, to the "stellar role" mind plays in the "cosmic sweep" of evolution. Young Watson, alas, was neither statesman nor diplomat. I can easily imagine that he grew quite angry at all that rhetoric. Among the cruder ideological dynamisms, such indignation was, perhaps, the major cause for his rejection of even epiphenomenalism as not sufficiently radical. There were contributory causes, to be sure, such as the ideas of Loeb and Watson's own commitment to animal work. I shall pass these over and, finally, turn to his specific contribution, the one which for the sake of emphasis I called a footnote, though, I repeat, a very important one.

The contribution was not, as probably Watson thought, his materialism or *metaphysical behaviorism*—i.e., the thesis, which is merely silly, that there are no minds—but, rather, his *methodological behaviorism*. Let me then for a moment disregard history and present what I take to be a correct and defensible statement of this thesis. Consider three kinds of variables; call them behavioral, physiological, and environmental, respectively. Behavior and, therefore, the behavioral variables are physical. Smiling, frowning, talking, and so on, whatever else they may be or betoken, are certainly also physical events. The nature of the psysiological variables I shall take for granted. They describe, for the most part though not exclusively, the stuffings of the organism. The environment in which we move is to a very large extent social. This, however, means merely that it contains, in addition to other kinds of physical objects, other people. Thus the environment could in principle be described in terms of physical, physiological, and behavioral variables. Notice, incidentally, that I just used "physical" in a narrower sense which is quite customary. Notice, furthermore, that I did not claim that these three kinds of variables are independent of each other. Combine, next, Watson's good thesis, that there are no interacting minds, with the great Functionalist truism about process. What follows is the thesis of methodological behaviorism. It must *in principle* be possible to predict future behavior, including verbal behavior, from a sufficiency of information about present (and past) behavioral, physiological, and environmental variables. This is the thesis. Let me also state one of its corollaries. Speaking commonsensically or, for that matter, clinically, we often attribute to a person a certain state of mind. We say that he or she perceives something, remembers something, plans something, is sad or gay, and so on. Nor is there any doubt, commonsensically, that we know what we mean when we assert such things, or, for that matter, that sometimes we are even right. It follows that it must *in principle* be possible to coordinate to any such statement another one, however complex, which mentions only behaviorial, physiological, and environmental items, such that they are either both true or both false. Otherwise one would have to maintain that we can, literally and not metaphorically speaking, directly observe other people's state of mind. Few nowadays are either bold or foolish enough to assert that.

As I have just cautiously formulated it, methodological behaviorism, like Functionalism, has conquered itself to death. It, too, has become a truism. Virtually every American psychologist, whether he knows it or not, is nowadays a methodological behaviorist. That goes for those who glorify John B. Watson as well as for those who belittle him. He himself has at several places stated the thesis very clearly. But then he also said so much else that could be, and has been, misunderstood. Some comments are therefore in order.

Notice, first, in my formulation, the important qualification "in principle." The phrase is ambiguous. One thing we may mean when accepting something with this qualification is that it is not anything to be acted upon but, as one says, merely a frame of reference, logical or philosophical. The other thing we may mean is that we accept something as a program to be acted on and which, therefore, after a reasonable time may be judged by its fruits. Methodological behaviorism is a matter of principle in both senses; and it has, as I see it, in both senses so far stood the test of time. Philosophically, it is certainly not the whole of the best contemporary analysis of the traditional tangle known as the mind-body problem. But it fits into this analysis and is, in fact, an important part of it. This analysis as a whole avoids the many perplexities of traditional epiphenomenalism as well as those of Watsonian materialism. These, however, are matters better left to the epistemological seminar. So I shall say no more about them on this occasion. As a program, methodological behaviorism, as I just cautiously formulated it, has done well, too. To be overly modest is, to my mind, as unwise as it is to claim too much. Scientifically, psychologists do not know very much about human behavior, certainly not as much as they would like; but they by now do know quite a bit. And, whatever they thus know they state, wittingly or unwittingly, in behavioristic terms. At least, they try to do that; they usually succeed to a considerable extent; and they are the better pleased the more nearly they succeed. Nor is it, I think, unreasonable to claim that this tendency has had a salutary and sobering effect and has thus helped us, at least indirectly, to acquire whatever little knowledge we have. This is the bright side of the picture. Let me now turn to another.

During the late thirties and early forties Watsonianism was ardently embraced by a group of then very vociferous philosophers, the so-called physicalists. The offspring of the embrace was *physicalistic behaviorism,* which is not at all the same thing as methodological behaviorism. A physicalist insists not only, as a methological behaviorist does, that in the science of psychology we can and in principle must speak about such things as, say, smiling and frowning as physical events. He also insists that we can and in principle must avoid these very words, smiling and frowning. That is to say, he insists that in the science of psychology we can and in principle must describe a smiling or a frowning face without using any other words than those used in describing, literally and not metaphorically, inanimate objects such as a machine or a landscape. The difference is clearest where it is also most important, namely, in the case of language. Assume that we hear somebody say that he is sad or, for that matter, that he is cold. The methodological behaviorist assumes and, particularly in the area of personality, often must assume, not necessarily that the speaker is sad or cold, for he may of course be lying or attitudinizing, but, rather, that the noises "mean something" and, also, that the speaker "knows what they mean." Not so the physicalist. He merely hears noises. Thus he cannot, as a scientist, use the two phrases within quotation marks without first providing for them equivalents which contain only words belonging to his very limited vocabulary. This is what physicalistic behaviorism means. What shall we think of it?

Philosophically I think it is both sound and important. The reason for its being sound is that philosophical analysis is, to a very large extent and in a subtle way which I cannot take time to explain, a matter of principle only, in the sense in which this phrase does not signify a program to be acted upon. As a scientific program physicalistic behaviorism always was, still is, and for all I know may forever remain fantastically unrealistic. Methodological behaviorism is sound both as a frame of reference and as a program. The difference is worth pointing out. For, had it always been clearly understood, we might have saved ourselves much commotion; needless apprehensions and often quite irrational aversions by the clinical and social psychologists on the one hand, much shallow talk and a good deal of silly doctrinairism by the physicalists on the other. Under the circumstances it is natural to ask what stand Watson himself took on this issue or, perhaps better, pseudo issue. The difficulty one encounters in trying to answer the question is that, when the issue came to the fore, Watson had already withdrawn from public participation in such debates. Thus the best one can do is to look for hints in his earlier writings. In the animal field, from which he came, the difference makes, of course, no difference. In his writings on personality he started, with eminent common sense and without any compunction whatsoever, from the variables of the clinical psychologist. Logically, in a footnote to his very first methodological paper, the one mentioned before, he refers to what he there calls the "language method" as merely an expedient short cut. In some cases that is, indeed, all it is. In some others, the gap which the so-called short cut bridges is, logically speaking, very wide. One may well wonder whether Watson ever appreciated how wide it really is.

This brings me to my next point, no longer about the contribution as such and its later vicissitudes but, rather, about the historical Watson. The point once needed emphasis very badly in order to counteract one of the most widely spread and most shallow clichés. Even now such emphasis is not wholly lost. In order to provide it, I shall avail myself of a phrase that was dear to the very propagators of those clichés. Watson's psychology was not, at any stage of his thought, one of "muscle twitches." To say the same thing more academically, Watson was never and, I venture to guess, would not be today a doctrinaire advocate of physiological reduction. He was, quite to the contrary a vigorous and, if anything, over-optimistic advocate of behavioral research, clinically as well as in the laboratory.

I have just touched on a contemporary issue. Such issues are tender to the touch. In order to reduce the sensitivity, I shall avail myself of one of the precautions I built into the formulation of methodological behaviorism. Remember that I listed three kinds of variables: behavioral, environmental, and physiological. If there are no interacting minds, as of course there are not, and if the world is completely and comprehensively lawful, as of course it is (in spite of the *apparent* exception of quantum mechanics, which is so frequently misunderstood but to which I cannot possibly attend on this occasion), then it follows that there are complete and comprehensive process laws covering human behavior, which contain, though of course not independently, at most our three kinds of variables. It does not follow that there are also such laws containing only two of the three kinds, namely, the behavioral and environmental ones. In other words, it may well be and it is, in fact, quite plausible that if we pursue purely behavioral research long enough, we shall *in the long run* come upon a barrier. That is to say, we may eventually reach a point where, though the laws we shall then have will not be complete and comprehensive process laws, we shall yet not be able to advance further as long as we limit ourselves to these two kinds of variables while, on the other hand, we could do better if we introduced the third kind, i.e., the physiological variables. This long-run possibility or, if you prefer, plausibility, is the sound core of what is in all other respects the purely ideological clamor of the contemporary enthusiasts for physiological reduction. I call the clamor ideological because, as I see it, its real purpose, whether conscious or unconscious, is not to make the very theoretical and quite uncontroversial point on which I have just insisted but, rather, to talk up the *short-run* prospects of research in physiological psychology by talking down the short-run prospects of behavioral work. Such talk judges itself. Behavioral research has produced at least some knowledge, however incomplete and imperfect in many respects it may be, in areas to which physiological research has as yet contributed nothing. In his own time Watson vigorously took the side of behavioral work. So, I venture to guess, he would today. He even was, as I also mentioned, overoptimistic about both the short-run and the long-run prospects of purely behavioral work. The overoptimism fits well into the picture I have formed for myself of the man. Watson, as I see him, was above all a man of action, primarily a doer and only incidentally, as it were, a thinker. Doer that he was, he was eager to start building the house of psychology. In this task, which he gravely underestimated, he knew that he could expect no help from the physiological psychologists of his day, just as behavioral research today can as yet expect but little help from these quarters. This, I believe, is one major reason why Watson was not in his day and probably would not be today what I call an ideological reductionist. (Nonideologically, there is no issue.) But there was still another such reason. Watson had an amazingly naive and almost superstitious distrust of any appeal to the action of the central nervous system. Reading him, one cannot help feeling that that evil thing, that darling of priests and kings, the enemy of all human happiness and progress, the interacting mind, begins one-half inch beneath the skin of the skull. How queer! How amusing in one sense and how pathetic in another! But, then, we had better accept our great men as they are. Let me connect this comment with another.

Contemporary behaviorism, if there still is such a thing in addition to a group of important truisms, is certainly not another "school" of psychology. Early behaviorism or Watsonianism was the last of the schools; certainly it was more of a school than Functionalism in its maturity. (This neglects psychoanalysis, which is a historical phenomenon of different magnitude, as well as Gestalt, which, though chronologically later, belongs structurally to the German nineteenth century.) A school, as I use the term, is a group of men who propound a doctrine that is a mixture of three quite heterogeneous ingredients. (Also, a school is typically associated with the advocacy of, or, at least emphasis on a special research interest.) The three heterogeneous ingredients of the classical mixture are, first, a more or less articulate philosophical position; second, some methodological insights *about* psychology; and, third, a group of beliefs concerning matters of fact and law *within* psychology. Such matters of fact and law are, of course, philosophically and methodologically quite neutral. The members of the school nonetheless fuse and confuse them with their philosophical and methodological tenets, as if they were a logically inseparable part of them. In Watson's case the first ingredient is his materialism or metaphysical behaviorism, the thesis that there are no minds. The second ingredient is his specific contribution, methodological behaviorism. The associated research interest was animal work. The third ingredient is his trio of pseudo-methodological tenets, as I like to call them. There is, first, his peripheralism. There is, second, his inclination to favor pure contiguity over so-called reinforcement theories of learning. There is, third, his denial of individual differences. The first two are related to his metaphysics. The third is very intimately connected with his social philosophy. I shall take them up in this order and, in conclusion, say a few words about his social philosophy.

Watson propounded, dogmatically and on ideological grounds, a peripheral theory of thought and a glandular theory of emotion. My emphasis is on the adverbial clause, "dogmatically and on ideological grounds"; for the facts, whatever they may be, are philosophically and methodologically neutral. This commitment was probably among the circumstances that saved Watson from ideological reductionism. The intellectual motive behind it appears clearest in his second fundamental paper, "Image and Affection in Behavior," of 1913, which he read before the Columbia seminar. A phrase of Külpe's provides the cue. Külpe, as you may remember, distinguished between peripherally and centrally aroused sensations. What he meant is perfectly clear. An image I now have of my mother's face is not immediately preceded by the sort of peripheral stimulation I used to have when I still could look at her. Such an image is, according to Külpe, centrally aroused. That does not mean that it is outside the causal nexus of our three kinds of variables. Watson, however, confused "centrally aroused" with "uncaused." Images, he concluded, are children of the devil, or, more precisely, of an interacting mind. Thus he decreed that there are none, except perhaps a sporadic few which do not matter. Strangely, he did not see that even a single one would suffice to destroy his case. If any one wonders whether the mistake is really that obvious, I suggest that he examine the text. Watson's peripheralism is beyond all doubt tied up with his antimentalism. Motivations, though, are complex. His activism probably had its part in this preference. For, surely, he realized that in the eventual development of physiological psychology, detailed knowledge and control of the central nervous system would in all probability come last.

The glands that, according to this early paper, are the peripheral seat of the emotions are the sex glands. Nor does Watson miss the opportunity to endorse some of the basic ideas of psychoanalysis. Naturally, he objected and in his later writings continued to object vigorously to its mentalistic bias. Yet he recognized its significance as early as 1913. What appealed to him above all was the insight, which he himself elaborated in his later writings, that man's behavior, however complex, can and must be causally explained in terms of his primary needs. The first to build an elaborate structure on this ground was Freud. As far as I know, the first experimental psychologist who understood him and had the courage to speak up for him was Watson. In this respect his record is admirable indeed. Freud's remarks about behaviorism in his *Autobiography* of 1925 leave no doubt that he, for all his towering greatness, did not understand Watson.

The emphasis on learning, important and influential as it was, merely continued what the Functionalists had auspiciously begun. The distrust of reinforcement theories which I attributed to Watson was his own. Notice, though, that I was cautious, speaking merely of an inclination to favor what we now call contiguity theories. The reason for my caution is that, when Watson was active, theorizing in this area was as yet most rudimentary. So it does not seem fair to interpret anything he then said as a firm commitment to any of the more elaborate theoretical structures of today. The ideological root of whatever preference for contiguity he had is not hard to discover. In an understandable—though, again, not very subtle—reaction to speculative Darwinism, he probably saw reinforcement theories as an entering wedge for metaphysical purposivism. By now it is understood that there is no logical connection between the two. Foremost among the psychologists who in the twenties and early thirties clarified this point is probably Tolman. The philosopher from whom he received support is R. B. Perry.

The third pseudo-methodological tenet is an extreme environmentalism. I shall first consider it logically, then as the expression of a social gospel. According to Watson, a child is at birth equipped with nothing but the structure of its body and a few elementary unlearned responses. All the rest is learning. What that means depends on what is meant by "structure." If structure includes fine structure, including all the as yet unknown characteristics of the central nervous system, then the thesis is certainly true but, alas, only because it says virtually nothing. Certainly it is broad enough to allow for the inheritance of very specific talents, and even personality traits. If, on the other hand, "structure" merely means gross structure, or relatively gross structure, which is what Watson meant, then his pronouncement was and, for all I know, still is most dogmatic. To me, it is not even plausible. So I shall look at the gospel behind the dogma.

The best way and, if one must be brief, the only way to describe a man's social philosophy is to describe his Utopia, i.e., the society he considers ideal. Watson's Utopia has been very accurately described in two novels, Aldous Huxley's *Brave New World* and Skinner's *Walden Two*. They leave no doubt that he stands in the succession of Plato. The one major difference is that while Plato wants us to be ruled by philosopher-kings, Watson's chosen ruler is the scientist and, in particular, the psychologist. His Utopia is thus a totalitarian technocracy. I use the word technocracy deliberately. It indicates, at least succinctly, how Watson fits into the temper of his time. The other great intellectual technocrat of his day, though by far not as totalitarian, was Thorstein Veblen. His chosen rulers were the engineers. The bridge of wishful thinking which, in Watson's case, leads from his Utopia to his environmentalism is rather obvious. Man is infinitely plastic and thus *can* be molded because he *ought* to be molded.

This is not the place to review those features of the American scene during the first quarter of the century which make it plausible that such men as Watson and Veblen held these views. Nor do I wish to make any dogmatic pronouncements of my own on such difficult questions as the role of the expert in a technological society, or on how democratic ideals can be reconciled with a sober appraisal of human nature. In his admirable piece on the Moses of Michelangelo, Freud described the emotion —a mixture of compassion, anger, and indignation—which sometimes overcomes an outstanding man when he reflects on the misery of the human condition. Watson, I like to think, was overwhelmed by this mixed emotion when he wrote, as unhappily he did, particularly in the last chapter of his *Behaviorism,* of 1925, as if he were the sworn enemy of freedom and the inner life. So I shall limit myself to a few words about the intellectual confusions which were among the causes of these unfortunate statements.

Social arrangements differ significantly in the number and kind of choices they provide. Some choices, such as that of a profession or a mate, are "important"; some others are less so. The consequences, including all sorts and degrees of "penalties," which by social arrangement attend a choice, are of course part of the "choice situation." Along such lines a notion of human freedom can be elaborated. Perhaps it is vague. It may even be irremediably vague. That does not mean that it is either "metaphysical" or incompatible with the idea of comprehensive process. Watson did not grasp the distinction. For him, freedom, in any sense, was an illusion spawned by that arch-evil, the illusion of interacting minds. So he wrote almost as if he had set out to provide ammunition for those who now try to convince us that if we want to preserve human freedom, we must abandon the idea of a science of man, and, instead, adopt their creeds. What goes for freedom goes equally for what I called the inner life. For what I mean by this phrase, the inner life, is nothing "metaphysical," but rather the availability, the complexity, the originality, and the adequacy of the implicit verbal response. Or, at least, that is what it amounts to in psychological terms. Watson, once more, failed to grasp the distinction.

I do not feel like ending on this sour note. Some painters over-emphasize both the lights and the shadows, particularly when they are asked to do a portrait in a very limited time. Perhaps I have done the same in trying to sketch an intellectual portrait of John B. Watson. Yet I have not the slightest doubt that, with all the light and all the shadow, he is a very major figure. Psychology owes him much. His place in the history of our civilization is not inconsiderable and it is secure. Such men are exceedingly rare. We ought to accept them and appreciate them for what they are.

HAROLD GARFINKEL

Common-Sense Knowledge

of Social Structures:

The Documentary Method of Interpretation

Sociologically speaking, "common culture" refers to the socially sanctioned grounds of inference and action that people use in their everyday affairs[1] and which they assume that other members of the group use in the same way. Socially-sanctioned-facts-of-life-in-society-that-any-bona-fide-member-of-the-society-knows depict such matters as conduct of family life; market organization; distributions of honor, competence, responsibility, goodwill, income, motives among members; frequency, causes of, and remedies for trouble; and the presence of good and evil purposes behind the apparent workings of things. Such socially sanc-

This investigation was supported by a Senior Research Fellowship SF-81 from the U.S. Public Health Service. The materials for this paper are taken from a book in preparation by the author, *Common-Sense Actions as Topic and Features of Sociological Inquiry.* I wish to thank my colleagues Egon Bittner, Aaron V. Cicourel, and Eleanor Bernert Sheldon for many conversations about these materials. Thanks are due to Peter McHugh for his help with the experiment and for many useful ideas in his report.

1. The concept "everyday affairs" is intended in strict accord with Alfred Schutz' usage in his articles, "On multiple realities," *Philosophy and Phenomenological Research,* 1945, 4:533-575; "Common sense and scientific interpretation of human action," *Philosophy and Phenomenological Research,* 1953, 14:1-37.

tioned facts of social life consist of descriptions from the point of view of the collectivity member's[2] interests in the management of his practical affairs. Basing our usage upon the work of Alfred Schutz,[3] we shall call such knowledge of socially organized environments of concerted actions "common sense knowledge of social structures."

The discovery of common culture consists of the discovery *from within* the society by social scientists of the existence of common-sense knowledge of social structures, and the treatment by social scientists of knowledge, and of the procedures that societal members use for its assembly, test, management, and transmission as objects of mere theoretical sociological interest.

This paper is concerned with common-sense knowledge of social structures as an object of theoretical sociological interest. It is concerned with descriptions of a society that its members, *sociologists included,* as a condition of their enforceable rights to manage and communicate decisions of meaning, fact, method, and causal texture without interference, use and treat as known in common with other members, and with other members take for granted.

As an object of theoretical sociological interest, such knowledge is both a topic as well as a feature of sociological inquiry. One facet of this assertion will be treated in this paper. Its interests are directed to a description of the work whereby decisions of meaning and fact are managed, and a body of factual knowledge of social structures is assembled in common-sense situations of choice.

The Documentary Method of Interpretation

There are innumerable situations of sociological inquiry in which the investigator—whether he be a professional sociologist or a person

2. The concept of "collectivity membership" is intended in strict accord with Talcott Parsons' usage in *The Social System,* The Free Press of Glencoe, New York, 1951, and in *Theories of Society,* Vol. I, Part Two, The Free Press of Glencoe, New York, 1961, pp. 239-240.

3. Alfred Schutz, *Der sinnhafte Aufbau der sozialen Welt,* Verlag von Julius Springer, Wien, 1932; "The problem of rationality in the social world," *Economica,* 1943, 10:130-149; "Some leading concepts in phenomenology," *Social Research,* 1945, 12:77-97; "On multiple realities," *Philosophy and Phenomenological Research,* 1945, 4:533-575; "Choosing among projects of action," *Philosophy and Phenomenological Research,* 1951, 12:161-184; "Common sense and scientific interpretation of human action," *Philosophy and Phenomenological Research,* 1953, 14:1-37; "Concept and theory formation in the social sciences," *American Journal of Philosophy,* 1954, 51:257-274; "Symbol, reality, and society," *Symbols and Society,* Fourteenth Symposium of the Conference of Science, Philosophy, and Religion, edited by Lyman Bryson and others, Harper and Brothers, New York, 1955, pp. 135-202.

undertaking an inquiry about social structures in the interests of managing his practical everyday affairs—can assign witnessed actual appearances to the status of an event of conduct only by imputing biography and prospects to the appearances, which he does by embedding the appearances in presupposed knowledge of social structures. Thus it frequently happens that in order for the investigator to decide what he is now looking at he must wait for future developments, only to find that these futures in turn are informed by *their* history and future. By waiting to see what will have happened he learns what it was that he previously saw. Either that, or he takes imputed history and prospects for granted. Motivated actions, for example, have exactly these troublesome properties.

It, therefore, occurs that the investigator frequently must elect among alternative courses of interpretation and inquiry to the end of deciding matters of fact, hypothesis, conjecture, fancy, and the rest despite the fact that in the calculable sense of the term "know," he does not and even cannot "know" what he is doing *prior to or while he is doing it.* Field workers, most particularly those doing ethnographic and linguistic studies in settings where they cannot presuppose a knowledge of social structures, are perhaps best acquainted with such situations, but other types of professional sociological inquiry are not exempt.

Nevertheless, a body of knowledge of social structures is somehow assembled. Somehow decisions of meaning, facts, method, and causal texture are made. How, in the course of the inquiry during which such decisions must be made, does this occur?

In his concern for the sociologist's problem of achieving an adequate description of cultural events, an important case of which would be Weber's familiar "behaviors with a subjective meaning attached and governed thereby in their course," Karl Mannheim[4] furnished an approximate description of one process. Mannheim called it "the documentary method of interpretation." It contracts with the methods of literal observation, yet it has a recognizable fit with what many sociological researchers, lay and professional, actually do.

According to Mannheim, the documentary method involves the search for ". . . an identical, homologous pattern underlying a vast variety of totally different realizations of meaning."[5]

The method consists of treating an actual appearance as "the document of," as "pointing to," as "standing on behalf of" a presupposed underlying pattern. Not only is the underlying pattern derived from its

4. Karl Mannheim, "On the interpretation of weltanschauung," *Essays on the Sociology of Knowledge,* translated and edited by Paul Kecskemeti, Oxford University Press, New York, 1952, pp. 53-63.
    5. *Ibid.,* p. 57.

individual documentary evidences, but the individual documentary evidences, in their turn, are interpreted on the basis of "what is known" about the underlying pattern. Each is used to elaborate the other.

The method is recognizable for the everyday necessities of recognizing what a person is "talking about" given that he doesn't say exactly what he means, or in recognizing such common occurrences as mailmen, friendly gestures, and promises. It is recognizable as well in deciding the sociologically analyzed occurrence of events like Goffman's strategies for the management of impressions, Erickson's identity crises, Riesman's types of conformity, Florence Kluckhohn's value premises, Malinowski's magical practices, Bales' interaction counts, Merton's type of deviance, Lazarsfeld's latent structure of attitudes, and the U.S. Census' occupational categories.

How is it done by the investigator that from replies to a questionnaire he finds the respondent's "attitude"; that via interviews with office personnel he reports their "bureaucratically organized activities"; that by consulting crimes known to the police, estimates are made of the parameters of "real crime"? More literally, what is the work whereby the investigator sets the observed occurrence and the intended occurrence into a correspondence of meaning such that the investigator finds it reasonable to treat witnessed actual appearances as evidences of the event he means to be studying?

To answer these questions it is necessary to detail the work of the documentary method. To this end a demonstration of the documentary method was designed to exaggerate the features of this method in use and to catch the work of "fact production" in flight.

An Experiment

Ten undergraduates were solicited by telling them that research was being done in the Department of Psychiatry to explore alternative means to psychotherapy "as a way of giving persons advice about their personal problems" [sic]. Each subject was seen individually by an experimenter who was falsely represented as a student counselor in training. The subject was asked to first discuss the background to some serious problem on which he would like advice, and then to address to the "counselor" a series of questions each of which would permit a "yes" or "no" answer. The subject was promised that the "counselor" would attempt to answer to the best of his ability. The experimenter-counselor heard the questions and gave his answers from an adjoining room, via an intercommunication system. After describing his problem and furnishing some background to it, the subject asked his first question. After a standard pause, the experimenter announced his answer, "yes" or "no." According to instructions, the subject then removed a wall plug connecting him with the counselor so that the "counselor will not hear your remarks" and tape-recorded his comments on the exchange. After these were completed, the subject plugged the microphone in and asked his next question. After he received the answer, he again recorded his comments, and thus proceeded through at least ten questions and answers. The subject had been told, "Most people want to ask at least ten questions."

The sequence of answers, evenly divided between yes's and no's, was predecided with a table of random numbers. All subjects asking the same number of questions were administered the same series of yes and no answers. Following the exchange of questions and answers the subject was aksed to summarize his impressions of the entire exchange. An interview followed.

The following are illustrative unedited protocols.

Case 1

SUBJECT: Ok, this is the situation that I am presented with. I happen to be of the Jewish faith and I have been dating a Gentile girl now for about two months. My dad is not directly opposed to this situation, but I feel at the same time that he is not exactly pleased with it. Mother feels that as long as dad is not directly opposed to this situation that I should go ahead and continue dating until he makes some direct statement to the contrary. My reason for feeling why he is not too pleased with this is that he has never said don't date her, but at the same time he will come up with digs and sayings that make me feel very ill at ease about dating the girl. My question is, do you feel under the present circumstances that I should continue or stop dating this girl? Let me put that in a positive way. Do you feel that I should continue dating this girl?

EXPERIMENTER: My answer is no.

SUBJECT: No. Well, that is kind of interesting. I kinda feel that there is really no great animosity between Dad and I but well perhaps he feels that greater dislike will grow out of this. I suppose or maybe it is easier for an outsider to see certain things that I am blind to at this moment.

I would like to ask my second question now.

EXPERIMENTER: Okay.

SUBJECT: Do you feel that I should have a further discussion with Dad about this situation or not? Should I have further discussion with Dad over this subject about dating the Gentile girl?

EXPERIMENTER: My answer is yes.

SUBJECT: Well I feel that is reasonable but I really don't know what to say to him. I mean he seems to be not really too understanding. In other words he seems to be afraid really to discuss the situation. I mean at least it appears that way to me so far. But I guess if it is worthwhile to me, if I really want to continue to date her that I will go on and have this discussion with Dad. I really don't know what to say because I mean I am dating her. I am not in love with her or anything but I really never know what is going to come out. I guess we should have a discussion based on what the future possibilities might be and how he would feel about that. He may not be too strongly opposed now because we are only dating but perhaps he sees future complications that he would really like to get off his chest at the moment. I am ready for my third question now.

If after having my conversation with Dad and he says to continue dating her but at the same time he gives me an impression that he is really not, he really does not want me to date her, but he is only doing it because he wants to be a good dad, should under these conditions, should I still date the girl?

EXPERIMENTER: My answer is yes.

SUBJECT: Well I am actually surprised at the answer. I expected a no answer on that. Perhaps this is because you are not quite aware of my dad and his reactions and he seems to be the type of person that is sensitive and therefore he is very careful in the way that he will handle things. Even though he might have said go ahead and date her I perhaps would feel guilty in knowing that he really did not want me to continue to date her. Though I don't know that it would actually help the situation any. So, well, perhaps we will look into this further and that is another question. I am ready for the fourth question now.

If after having this discussion with Dad and getting a positive answer from him but at the same time felt that this was not his honest opinion do you think that it would be proper for me to have my mother have a serious talk with him and therefore try and get a truer reaction to Dad's opinion on the situation?

EXPERIMENTER: My answer is yes.

SUBJECT: Well this seems fair to me. I feel perhaps that he would be honester with Mother about the situation. Of course that might present a problem. Would Mother come back and be completely honest with me? She seems to be more liberal than Dad, not to say that Mother would lie about it, but she would be a little more liberal about things like this and perhaps in her course of conversation with Dad she would try and present my side to him and therefore once again I get two answers. If I look at it that way I don't think that I am going to get to first base anyway, but at least I feel that we are moving along some way. I am ready for my fifth question now.

Do you think that I should tell this Gentile girl who I am dating the problem that I am having with my folks at home or should I wait until, well that is another question. Do you feel that I should tell the girl that I am dating the problems that I am having at home over her religion?

EXPERIMENTER: My answer is no.

SUBJECT: Well once again I am surprised. Of course, that might depend on how much you care for the girl and how much longer I feel that I am going to be dating her. But I personally feel that it is only right to tell her for if she is perhaps thinking more serious than I am, she might, it might be best for us to understand the full situation and if she feels that this will be a block then I feel perhaps that would end the situation right there without telling her. I feel that perhaps I am going to show this in different ways and she will be unaware of what the real situation is and perhaps react back to me in a certain way spoiling our dating and everything else like that. I am ready for my sixth question.

If I was to fall in love with this girl and want to make plans for marriage do you feel that it is fair that I should ask her to change her religion over to my belief?

EXPERIMENTER: My answer is no.

SUBJECT: Well, no. Well, this has me stymied. No. Well, I honestly feel that I have been brought up in a certain way and I believe that she has too, and I feel pretty strong about the way that I believe. Not that I am completely orthodox or anything, but of course there is always family pressure and things like that. And I am quite sure that she feels, unfortunately I have never seen a family with a split in religion that really has been able to make a success out of it. So I don't know. I think that perhaps I would be tempted to ask her to change. I don't think that I would be able to really. I am ready for number seven.

Do you feel that it would be a better situation if we were to get married and neither one of us were willing to talk about the religious difference or to give in on either one side, that we bring our children up in a neutral religion other than the two that we believe in?

EXPERIMENTER: My answer is yes.

SUBJECT: Well perhaps this would be a solution. If we could find a religion that would incorporate our two beliefs to a certain extent. I realize that perhaps this might be literally impossible to do. Perhaps in a sense this neutral religion might be something almost made up by ourselves because I honestly feel that religious training no matter which belief it is if not carried to extremes is good, for everyone should have a certain amount of religious training along these lines. Perhaps this might be a solution to the problem. I guess I should follow this along a little bit further and see exactly what happens. I am ready for number eight.

If we were to get married would it be best for us to live in a new community where we will not be in contact with our parents if we were getting a lot of family pressure over religious differences?

EXPERIMENTER: My answer is no.

SUBJECT: Well, I kinda tend to agree with this answer. I feel that you wouldn't be accomplishing too much by running away from the issue and that perhaps it would be one of those things in life that eventually you would just be willing to accept it and that the families and we would get along harmoniously together. At least I hope it would work out if that situation comes about. I think it would be best for both families together that we are not going to work it out if we run away from our problem. So we best remain there and try and work it out. I am ready for number nine.

If we did get married and were to raise our children do you think that we should explain and tell our children that we once had this religious difference or would we just bring them up in this new religion, that is their religion, that we talked about, and let them believe that that is what we originally believed in?

EXPERIMENTER: My answer is no.

SUBJECT: Once again I kinda agree with this. I think they should be told because undoubtedly they will find out. And if they did find out that there was this difference that we once had they would feel that we were sneaking or trying to hide something from them and this would not be the best situation either. So I believe this would be the best situation. I am ready for number ten.

Do you feel that our children, if there were any, would have any religious problems themselves because of us the parents and our difficulties?

EXPERIMENTER: My answer is no.

SUBJECT: Well I really don't know if I agree with that or not. Perhaps they would have trouble if confusion set in and they were to feel that they did not know which is right and which is wrong or what side to pick if they did not want to stick with their religion. But I kinda feel that if their religion was a wholesome one which supplied the needs of a religion and that which a religion does supply that there would not be any problems with them. But I suppose that only time will tell if such problems would come about. I am finished with my comments now.

EXPERIMENTER: Okay, I will be right in.

The experimenter appeared in the room with the subject, handed him a list of points that he might comment on, and left the room. The subject commented as follows.

SUBJECT: Well the conversation seemed to be one-sided because I was doing it all. But, I feel that it was extremely difficult for Mr. McHugh to answer these questions fully without having a complete understanding of the personalities of the different people involved and exactly how involved the situation was itself. The answers I received I must say that the majority of them were answered perhaps in the same way that I would answer them to myself knowing the differences in types of people. One or two of them did come as a surprise to me and I felt that the reason perhaps he answered these questions the way he did is for the reason that he is not aware of the personalities involved and how they are reacting or would react to a certain situation. The answers that I received were most of them I felt that he was for the most part aware of the situation as we moved along in that I was interpreting his answers even though they were yes or no answers as fully meditating over these situations that I presented to him and they had a lot of meaning to me. I felt that his answers as a whole were helpful and that he was looking out for the benefit to the situation for the most part and not to curtail it or cut it short in any means. I heard what I wanted to hear in most of the situations presented at time. Perhaps I did not hear what I really wanted to hear but perhaps from an objective standpoint they were the best answers because someone involved in a situation is blinded to a certain degree and cannot take this objective viewpoint. And therefore these answers may differ from the person who is involved in the situation and the person who is outside and can take an objective viewpoint. I honestly believe that the answer that he gave me, that he was completely aware of the situation at hand. Perhaps I guess that should be qualified. Perhaps when I said should I talk to Dad for instance he was not positive. When I said should I talk to Dad for instance he was not positive what I was going to talk to Dad about. In a full capacity. He knew the general topic but he is not aware how close I am to Dad or how involved the conversation might get. And if his saying "do talk" in knowing that Dad will not listen, well this perhaps isn't best, or if Dad is very willing to listen he says it may not help. Or don't talk. Well this once again is bringing in personalities which he is not aware of. The conversation and the answers given I believe had a lot of meaning to me. I mean it was perhaps what I would have expected for someone who fully understood the situation. And I feel that it had a lot of sense to me and made a lot of sense. Well I felt that the questions that I asked were very pertinent and did help in understanding the situation on both sides, that is myself and the answerer and my reaction to the answers like I have stated before were mostly in agreement. At times I was surprised but understood that because he is not fully aware of the situation and the personalities involved.

Here is another protocol.

Case 2

SUBJECT: I would like to know whether or not I should change my major at the present time. I have a physics major with quite a deficit in grade points to bring up to get my C average in physics. I would like to switch over to mathematics. I have a little difficulty in it but I think maybe I could handle it. I have failed several math courses here at U.C.L.A. but I have always repeated them and had C's. I have come close to getting a B in math in one specific course because I studied a little more than in others but my question is still should I change my major?

EXPERIMENTER: My answer is no.

SUBJECT: Well he says no. And if I don't then I will have to make up my deficit in grade points which will be awfully difficult because I am not doing too well this semester. If I pull through this semester with seven units of A then I can count on possibly going on to get my degree in physics in February but then I have this stigma of nuclear physics facing me. I thoroughly dislike the study of nuclear physics. Nuclear Physics 124 will be one of my required courses to get a degree in physics.

Do you think I could get a degree in physics on the basis of this knowledge that I must take Physics 124?

EXPERIMENTER: My answer is yes.

SUBJECT: He says yes. I don't see how I can. I am not that good of a theorist. My study habits are horrible. My reading speed is bad, and I don't spend enough time in studying.

Do you think that I could successfully improve my study habits?

EXPERIMENTER: My answer is yes.

SUBJECT: He says that I can successfully improve my study habits. I have been preached to all along on how to study properly but I don't study properly. I don't have sufficient incentive to go through physics or do I?

Do you think I have sufficient incentive to get a degree in physics?

EXPERIMENTER: My answer is yes.

SUBJECT: He says my answer is yes. I think possibly so if I didn't have a bad scholastic record behind me to follow me up. It would be awfully difficult to get that degree.

Do you think I could successfully do my studying while trying to keep happy relations at home with my wife and still get my work done? I don't do my studying well at school and I don't have much incentive to study when I am at home. But when my wife comes home, I like to study. Yet this keeps us from doing things, and whenever she doesn't do things, it gets on my nerves because there is all this work piling up. Do you think I could successfully do my studying at home?

EXPERIMENTER: My answer is no.

SUBJECT: He says no. I don't think so either.

Should I come to school every night after supper and do my studying?

EXPERIMENTER: My answer is no.

SUBJECT: He says I shouldn't come to school and study. Where should I go? Should I go to the library on campus to do my studying?

EXPERIMENTER: My answer is yes.

SUBJECT: He says I should go to the library to do my studying. Which library? They may not have all the references there that I may need but that is not always necessary. I need at least three more questions. Do you think I can develop sufficiently good study habits and incentive to actually achieve developing those habits such that I wouldn't have to stay up late at night and not get the work done in the first place?

EXPERIMENTER: My answer is no.

SUBJECT: He says no. I can't develop the study habits properly to be able to pull myself through. If you don't think that I can develop the proper study habits and carry them through to reach my goal do you on the basis of this still believe that I can get a degree in physics?

EXPERIMENTER: My answer is no.

SUBJECT: According to that I won't get a degree. What should I do? Are you still there?

EXPERIMENTER: Yes, I am.

SUBJECT: If you don't think I will make the—achieve the necessary goal of improving my study habits and getting a degree in physics do you recommend that I quit school?

EXPERIMENTER: My answer is yes.

SUBJECT: He says I should quit school. Are you still there?

EXPERIMENTER: Yes.

SUBJECT: I have one more question. I would like to get a commission in the Air Force. I have completed the Air Force R.O.T.C. training program but to get a commission I need a degree. If I don't get the degree the chances are very strong that I may not get the commission although there are in's and out's that there is still some possibility that I may still get a commission without a degree, although this is not desirable. The question is, will I get a commission in the Air Force?

EXPERIMENTER: My answer is yes.

SUBJECT: He says I will get a commission in the Air Force and that is what I am looking forward to, but will I ever get a degree? If I get a commission without a degree will I ever get a degree in anything?

EXPERIMENTER: My answer is no.

SUBJECT: This leaves me somewhat unhappy although I don't really need a degree in the type of work that I desire to do. Are you there? Come back in.

The subject commented as follows.

Well, as far as what I got from the conversation, it is rather foolish for me to pursue my work any further as far as getting a degree in anything. Actually I have felt all along that the type of work I am interested in which is inventing is not something that requires a degree necessarily. It requires a certain knowledge of math and physics but it doesn't require a degree to do inventing. From the conversation I gather that I should just quit school and go ahead and get my commission but how I don't know. But it would be awfully nice to have a degree. That degree would be able to get me into other schools. Otherwise I will have the statement that I went through college but I never got out. I also get the impression that my study habits will never improve as much as I would like them to anyway. I will not get a degree. I will get a commission and it is fruitless for me to study either at home or at school. Especially in the evening. I wonder if I should do any studying at all, or if I should learn to do all my studying at school. What to do? I have the feeling that my parents would be very unhappy and also my wife's parents would be very unhappy if I never did get a degree or at least especially right now. I have the feeling that this past conversation is based on what one should have learned to do years ago, that is, as a growing child. To ask themselves questions and give himself an answer of some type, yes or no, and to think out reason why either yes or no holds or might hold and upon the validity or the anticipation of the validity of that answer what one should do accomplish his goal or just exist. I personally think I can do better in math than I can in physics. But I won't know until the end of the summer.

Findings

An examination of the protocols revealed the following:

A. *Getting through the exchange.*

None of the subjects had difficulty in accomplishing the series of ten questions, and in summarizing and evaluating the advice.

B. *Answers were perceived as "answers-to-questions."*

1. Typically the subjects heard the experimenter's answers as answers-to-the-question. Perceptually, the experimenter's answers were motivated by the question.
2. Subjects saw directly "what the adviser had in mind." They heard "in a glance" what he was talking about, i.e., what he meant, and not what he had uttered.
3. The typical subject assumed over the course of the exchange, and during the post-experimental interview, that the answers were advice to the problem, and that this advice as a solution to the problem was to be found via the answers.
4. All reported the "advice that they had been given" and addressed their appreciation and criticism to that "advice."

C. *There were no pre-programed questions; the next question was motivated by the retrospective-prospective possibilities of the present situation that were altered by each actual exchange.*

1. No subject administered a pre-programed set of questions.
2. Present answers altered the sense of previous exchanges.
3. Over the course of the exchange the assumption seemed to operate that there was an answer to be obtained, and that if the answer was not obvious, that its meaning could be determined by active search, one part of which involved asking another question so as to find out what the adviser "had in mind."
4. Much effort was devoted to looking for meanings that were intended but were not evident from the immediate answer to the question.
5. The present answer-to-the-questions motivated the succeeding set of possibilities from among which the next question was selected. The next question emerged as a product of reflections upon the previous course of the conversation and the presupposed underlying problem as the topic whose features each actual exchange documented and extended. The underlying "problem" was elaborated in its features as a function of the exchange. The sense of the problem was progressively accommodated to each present answer, while the answer motivated fresh aspects of the underlying problem.
6. The underlying pattern was elaborated and compounded over the series of exchanges and was accommodated to each present "answer" so as to maintain the "course of advice," to elaborate what had "really been advised" previously, and to motivate the new possibilities as emerging features of the problem.

D. *Answers in search of questions.*

1. Over the course of the exchange, subjects sometimes started with the reply as an answer and altered the previous sense of their question to accommodate this to the reply as the answer to the retrospectively revised question.

2. The identical utterance was capable of answering several different questions simultaneously, and of constituting an answer to a compound question that in terms of the strict logic of propositions did not permit either a yes or no or a single yes or no.

3. The same utterance was used to answer several different questions separated in time. Subjects refered to this as "shedding new light" on the past.

4. Present answers provided answers to further questions that were never asked.

E. *Handling incomplete, inappropriate, and contradictory answers.*

1. Where answers were unsatisfying or incomplete, the questioners were willing to wait for later answers in order to decide the sense of the previous ones.

2. Incomplete answers were treated by subjects as incomplete because of the "deficiencies" of this method of giving advice.

3. Answers that were inappropriate were inappropriate for "a reason." If the reason was found, the sense of the answer was thereupon decided. If an answer made "good sense" this was likely to be what the answerer had "advised."

4. When answers were incongruous or contradictory, subjects were able to continue by finding that the "adviser" had learned more in the meantime, or that he had decided to change his mind, or that perhaps he was not sufficiently acquainted with the intricacies of the problem, or the fault was in the question so that another phrasing was required.

5. Incongruous answers were resolved by imputing knowledge and intent to the adviser.

6. Contradictories faced the subject with electing the real question that the answer answered which they did by furnishing the question with additional meanings that fit with the meanings "behind" what the adviser was advising.

7. In the case of contradictory answers much effort was devoted to reviewing the possible intent of the answer so as to rid the answer of contradiction or meaninglessness, and to rid the answerer of untrustworthiness.

8. More subjects entertained the possibility of a trick than tested this possibility. All suspicious subjects were reluctant to act under the belief that there was a trick involved. Suspicions were

quieted if the adviser's answers made "good sense." Suspicions were most unlikely to continue if the answers accorded with the subject's previous thought about the matter and with his preferred decisions.

9. Suspicions transformed the answer into an event of "mere speech" having the appearance of coincidental occurrence with the occasion of the questioner's question. Subjects found this structure difficult to maintain and manage. Many subjects saw the sense of the answer "anyway."

10. Those who became suspicious simultaneously, though temporarily, withdrew their willingness to continue.

F. *"Search" for and perception of pattern.*
   1. Throughout, there was a concern and search for pattern. Pattern, however, was perceived from the very beginning. Pattern was likely to be seen in the first evidence of the "advice."
   2. Subjects found it very difficult to grasp the implications of randomness in the utterances. A predetermined utterance was treated as deceit in the answers instead of as an utterance that was decided beforehand and that occurred independently of the subject's questions and interests.
   3. When the possibility of deception occurred to the subjects, the adviser's utterance documented the pattern of the deceit instead of the pattern of advice. Thus the relationship of the utterance to the underlying pattern as its document remained unchanged.

G. *Answers were assigned a scenic source.*
   1. Subjects assigned to the adviser as his advice the thought formulated in the subject's questions. For example, when a subject asked, "Should I come to school every night after supper to do my studying," and the experimenter said, "My answer is no," the subject in his comments said, "He said I shouldn't come to school and study." This was very common.
   2. All subjects were surprised to find that they contributed so actively and so heavily to the "advice that they had received from the adviser."
   3. Upon being told about the deception the subjects were intensely chagrined. In most cases they revised their opinions about the procedure to emphasize its inadequacies for the experimenter's purposes (which they understood still to be an exploration of means of giving advice).

H. *The vagueness of every present situation of further possibilities remained invariant to the clarification furnished by the exchanges of questions and answers.*

1. There was vagueness (a) in the status of the utterance as an answer, (b) in its status as an answer-to-the-question, (c) in its status as a document of advice with respect to the underlying pattern, and (d) in the underlying problem. While, after the course of an exchange, the utterances furnished "advice about the problem," their function of advice also elaborated the entire scheme of problematic possibilities so that the over-all effect was that of a transformation of the subject's situation in which the vagueness of its horizons remained unchanged and "problems still remained unanswered."

I. *In their capacity as members, subjects consulted institutionalized features of the collectivity as a scheme of interpretation.*

1. Subjects made specific reference to the social structures in deciding the sensible and warranted character of the adviser's advice. Such references, however, were not made to any social structures whatever. In the eyes of the subject, if the adviser was to know and demonstrate to the subject that he knew what he was talking about, and if the subject was to consider seriously the adviser's descriptions of his circumstances as grounds of the subject's further thoughts and management of these circumstances, the subject did not permit the adviser, nor was the subject willing to entertain, *any* model of the social structures. References that the subject supplied were to social structures which he treated as actually or potentially known in common with the adviser. And then, not to *any* social structures known in common, but to normatively valued social structures which the subject as a collectivity member accepted as *conditions* that his decisions, with respect to his own sensible and realistic grasp of his circumstances and the "good" character of the adviser's advice, had to satisfy. These social structures consisted of normative features of the social system *seen from within* which, for the subject, were definitive of his memberships in the various collectivities that were referred to.

2. Subjects gave little indication, prior to the occasions of use of the rules for deciding fact and nonfact, what the definitive normative structures were to which their interpretations would make reference. The rules for documenting these definitive normative orders seemed to come into play only after a set of normative features had been motivated in their relevance to his interpretive tasks, and then as a function of the fact that the activities of interpretation were underway.

3. Subjects presupposed known-in-common features of the collec-

tivity as a body of common-sense knowledge subscribed to by both. They drew upon these presupposed patterns in assigning to what they heard the adviser talking about, its status of documentary evidence of the definitive normative features of the collectivity settings of the experiment, family, school, home, occupation, to which the subject's interests were directed. These evidences and the collectivity features were referred back and forth to each other, with each elaborating and being thereby elaborated in its possibilities.

J. *Deciding warrant was identical with assigning the advice its perceivedly normal sense.*

Through a retrospective-prospective review, subjects justified the "reasonable" sense and sanctionable status of the advice as grounds for managing their affairs. Its "reasonable" character consisted of its compatability with normative orders of social structures presumed to be subscribed to and known between subject and adviser. The subject's task of deciding the warrented character of what was being advised was identical with the task of assigning to what the adviser proposed (1) its status as an instance of a class of events; (2) its likelihood of occurrence; (3) its comparability with past and future events; (4) the conditions of its occurrence; (5) its place in a set of means-ends relationships; and (6) its necessity according to a natural (i.e., moral) order. The subjects assigned these values of typicality, likelihood, comparability, causal texture, technical efficacy, and moral requiredness while using the institutionalized features of the collectivity as a scheme of interpretation. Thus, the subject's task of deciding whether or not what the adviser advised was "true" was identical with the task of assigning to what the adviser proposed its perceivedly normal values.

K. *Perceivedly normal values were not so much "assigned" as managed.*

Through the work of documenting—i.e., by searching for and determining pattern, by treating the adviser's answers as motivated by the intended sense of the question, by waiting for later answers to clarify the sense of previous ones, by finding answers to unasked questions—the perceivedly normal values of what was being advised were established, tested, reviewed, retained, restored; in a word, managed. It is misleading, therefore, to think of the documentary method as a procedure whereby the advice was admitted to membership in a common-sense corpus in the same way that the rule of observation is a procedure whereby propositions are accorded membership in an ideal scientific corpus. Rather the documentary method developed the advice so as to be continually "membershipping" it.

Examples in Sociological Inquiry

Examples of the use of the documentary method can be cited from every area of sociological investigation.[6] Its obvious application occurs in community studies where warrant is assigned to statements by the criteria of "comprehensive description" and "ring of truth." Its use is found also on the many occasions of survey research when the researcher, in reviewing his interview notes or in editing the answers to a questionnaire, has to decide "what the respondent had in mind." When a researcher is addressed to the "motivated character" of an action, or a theory, or a person's compliance to a legitimate order and the like, he will use what he has actually observed to "document" an "underlying pattern." The documentary method is used whenever selected features of an object are used to epitomize the object. For example, just as the lay person may say of something that "Harry" says, "Isn't that just like Harry?" the investigator may use some observed feature of the thing he is referring to as a characterizing indicator of the intended matter. Complex scenes like industrial establishments, communities, or social movements are frequently described with the aid of "excerpts" from protocols and numerical tables which are used to epitomize the intended events. The documentary method is used whenever the investigator constructs a life history or a "natural history." The task of historicizing the person's biography consists of using the documentary method to select and order past occurrences so as to furnish the present state of affairs its relevant past and prospects.

The use of the documentary method is not confined to cases of "soft" procedures and "partial descriptions." It occurs as well in cases of rigorous procedures where descriptions are intended to exhaust a definite field of possible observables. In reading a journal account for the purpose of literal replication, researchers who attempt to reconstruct the relationship between the reported procedures and the results frequently encounter a gap of insufficient information. The gap occurs when the reader asks how the investigator decided the correspondence between what was actually observed and the intended event for which the actual

---

6. In his article, "On the interpretation of weltanschauung," Mannheim argued that the documentary method is peculiar to the social sciences. There exist in the social sciences many terminological ways of referring to it, viz., "the method of understanding," "sympathetic introspection," "method of insight," "method of intuition," "interpretive method," "clinical method," "emphatic understanding," and so on. Attempts by sociologists to identify something called "interpretive sociology" involve the reference to the documentary method as the basis for encountering and warranting its findings.

observation is treated as its evidence. The reader's problem consists of having to decide that the reported observation is a literal instance of the intended occurrence, i.e., that the actual observation and the intended occurrence are identical *in sense*. Since the relationship between the two is a sign relationship, the reader must consult some set of grammatical rules to decide this correspondence. This grammar consists of some theory of the intended events on the basis of which the decisions to code the actual observations as findings are recommended. It is at this point that the reader must furnish the account an investment of interpretive work and an assumption of "underlying" matters "just known in common" about the society in terms of which, what the respondent said, is treated as synonymous with what the observer meant. Correct correspondence is apt to be meant and read on reasonable grounds. Correct correspondence is the product of the work of investigator and reader as members of a community of cobelievers. Thus, even in the case of rigorous methods, if a researcher is to recommend, and the reader is to appreciate, published findings as members of the corpus of sociological fact, the work of the documentary method is employed.

Sociological Situations of Inquiry
as Common-Sense Situations of Choice

It is not unusual for professional sociologists to speak of their "fact production" procedures as processes of "seeing through" appearances to an underlying reality; of brushing past actual appearances to "grasp the invariant." Where our subjects are concerned, their processes are not appropriately imagined as "seeing through," but consist instead of coming to terms with a situation in which factual knowledge of social structures—factual in the sense of warranted grounds of further inferences and actions—must be assembled and made available for potential use despite the fact that the situations it purports to describe are, in any calculable sense, unknown; in their actual and intended logical structures are essentially vague; and are modified, elaborated, extended, if not indeed created, by the fact and manner of being addressed.

If many of the features of our subject's documentary work are recognizable in the work of professional sociological fact production, similarly many situations of professional sociological inquiry have precisely the features that our subjects' situations had. Such features of situations of professional sociological inquiry may be more exactly specified as follows.

1. In the course of an interview an investigator is likely to find himself addressing a series of present situations whose *future states that a contemplated course of treatment will produce* are characteristically

vague or even unknown. With overwhelming frequency these as of here-and-now possible future states are only sketchily specifiable prior to undertaking the action that is intended to realize them. There is a necessary distinction between a "possible future state of affairs" and a "how-to-bring-it-about-future-from-a-present-state-of-affairs-as-an-actual-point-of-departure." The "possible future state of affairs" may be very clear indeed. But such a future is not the matter of interest. Instead we are concerned with the "how to bring it about from a here-and-now future." It is this state—for convenience, call it an "operational future"—that is characteristically vague or unknown.

An illustration. A trained survey researcher can describe with remarkable clarity and definiteness what questions he wishes answers to in a questionnaire. How actual replies of actual subjects are to be evaluated as "replies to the questions" are incorporated in a set of procedural decisions known as "coding rules." Any distribution of replies to the questions that is possible under the coding rules is a "possible future state of affairs." After suitable exploratory work such distributions are clearly and definitely imaginable to trained field workers. But with overwhelming frequency it occurs that even late in the *actual* course of the inquiry the questions and answers that will *in effect* have been asked and answered under the various ways of evaluating actual subjects' responses as "replies to the question," given the practical exigencies that must be accommodated in accomplishing the actual work of the inquiry, remain sketchy and open to "reasonable decision" even up to the point of composing the results of the inquiry for publication.

2. Given *a* future, any future, that is known in a definite way, the alternative paths to actualize the future state as a set of stepwise operations upon some beginning present state are characteristically sketchy, incoherent, and unelaborated. Again it is necessary to stress the difference between an inventory of available procedures—investigators can talk about these quite definitely and clearly—and the deliberately pre-programed stepwise procedures, a set of predecided "what-to-do-in-case-of" strategies for the manipulation of a succession of actual present states of affairs *in their course*. In actual practices such a program is characteristically an unelaborated one.

For example, one of the tasks involved in "managing rapport" consists of managing the stepwise course of the conversation in such a way as to permit the investigator to commit his questions in profitable sequence while retaining some control over the unknown and undesirable directions in which affairs, as a function of the course of the actual exchange, may actually move.[7] Characteristically the researcher substitutes for a

7. Cf. Robert K. Merton and Patricia L. Kendall, "The focused interview," *American Journal of Sociology*, 1946, 51:541-557.

pre-programed stepwise solution, a set of *ad hoc* tactics for adjusting to present opportunity, with these tactics only generally governed by what the investigator would hope to have finally found out by the end of the conversation. Under these circumstances, it is more accurate to talk of investigators acting in fulfillment of their hopes, or in avoidance of their fears, than of acting in the deliberate and calculated realization of a plan.

3. It frequently occurs that the investigator takes an action, and only upon the actual occurrence of some product of that action do we find him reviewing the accomplished sequences in a retrospective search therein for their decided character. Insofar as the *decision that was taken* is assigned by the work of the retrospective search, the outcome of such situations can be said to occur *before* the decision. Such situations occur with dramatic frequency at the time the journal article is being written.

4. Prior to his actually having to choose among alternative courses of action on the basis of anticipated consequences, the investigator, for various reasons, is frequently unable to anticipate the consequences of his alternative courses of action and may have to rely upon his actual involvement in order to learn what they might be.

5. Frequently, after encountering some actual state of affairs, the investigator may count it as desirable, and thereupon treat it as the goal toward which his previously taken actions, as he reads them retrospectively, were directed "all along" or "after all."

6. It frequently occurs that only in the course of actually manipulating a present situation, and as a function of his actual manipulation, does the nature of an investigator's future state of affairs become clarified. Thus, the goal of the investigation may be progressively defined as the consequence of the investigator's actually taking action toward a goal whose features as of any present state of his investigative action he does not see clearly.

7. Characteristically such situations are ones of imperfect information. The result is that the investigator is unable to assess, let alone calculate, the difference that his ignorance in the situation makes upon the accomplishment of his activities. Nor, prior to having to take action, is he able either to evaluate their consequences or to assess the value of alternative courses of action.

8. The information that he possesses, that serves him as the basis for the election of strategies, is rarely codified. Hence, his estimates of the likelihood of success or failure characteristically have little in common with the rational mathematical concept of probability.

In their investigative activities, investigators characteristically must manage situations with the above features, given the following additional conditions: that some action must be taken; that the action must be taken by a time and in pace, duration, and phasing that is coordinate with the actions of others; that the risks of unfavorable outcomes must somehow be managed; that the actions taken and their products will be subject to review by others and must be justified to them; that the elections of courses of action and the resultant outcome must be justified within the procedures of "reasonable" review; and that the entire process must occur within the conditions of, and with his motivated compliance to, corporately organized social activity. In their "shop talk" investigators refer to these features of their actual situations of inquiry and to the necessity for managing them as their "practical circumstances."

Because their features are so easily recognized in the activities of daily life, situations with such features may appropriately be called "common-sense situations of choice." The suggestion is recommended that when researchers call upon "reasonableness" in assigning the status of "findings" to their research results, they are inviting the use of such features as these as a context of interpretation for deciding sensibility and warrant. Findings as outcomes of documentary work, decided under circumstances of common-sense situations of choice, define the term "reasonable findings."

The Problem

Much of "core sociology" consists of "reasonable findings." Many, if not most, situations of sociological inquiry are common-sense situations of choice. Nevertheless, textbook and journal discussions of sociological methods rarely give recognition to the fact that sociological inquiries are carried out under common-sense auspices *at the points where decisions about the correspondence between observed appearances and intended events are being made.* Instead, available descriptions and conceptions of investigative decision-making and problem-solving assign to the decision-maker's situation contrasting features[8] as follows.

1. From the decision-maker's point of view there exists as a feature of each of his here-and-now states of affairs a recognizable goal with specifiable features. Where sociological inquiry is concerned, this goal consists of the investigator's present problem for the solution to which

8. I wish to thank Drs. Robert Boguslaw and Myron A. Robinson of the System Development Corporation, Santa Monica, California, for the many hours of discussion that we had about calculable and noncalculable situations of choice when we were trying together to work through the problem of how consistently successful play in chess is possible.

the investigation will have been undertaken. The goal's specifiable features consist of the criteria whereby, as of any present state of affairs, he decides the adequacy with which his problem has been formulated. In their terms, too, the event, "adequate solution," is defined as one of a set of possible occurrences.

2. The decision-maker is conceived to have set for himself the task of devising a program of manipulations upon each successive present state of affairs that will alter each present state so that over their succession they are brought into conformity with an anticipated state, i.e., the goal, the solved problem.[9]

These features may be restated in terms of the rules of evidence. As a calculable state of affairs, an investigator's problem may be regarded as a proposition whose "application" for membership, i.e., whose warranted status, is under review. The rules of procedure whereby its warranted status is decided thereby operationally define what is meant by "adequate solution." In ideal scientific activities an investigator is required to decide the steps that define an adequate solution prior to his taking the decided steps. He is required to make this decision before he carries out the operations whereby the possibilities that the proposition proposes will be decided as to their having actually occured or not. The task of deciding an adequate solution thereby has logical precedence over the actual observation. The observation is said thereby to be "programed," or, alternatively, the intended event is given an "operational definition," or, alternatively, the conditions for the occurrence of an intended event are furnished, or, alternatively, a "prediction" is made.

A prominent argument on behalf of this emphasis is that the documentary method is a scientifically erroneous procedure; that its use distorts the objective world in a mirror of subjective prejudice; and that where common-sense situations of choice exist they do so as historical nuisances. Protagonists for methods such as those used in survey research and laboratory experimentation, for example, assert their increasing exemption from situations with common-sense characteristics and documentary dealings with them. After World War II a flood of textbooks on methods was written to provide remedies for such situations. These methods are intended to depict the ways of transforming common-sense situations into calculable ones. Most particularly, the use of mathematical models and statistical schemes of inference are invoked as calculable solutions to the problems of deciding sensibility, objectivity, and warrant in

9. In some cases, students of decision-making have been interested in those programs that represent fully calculated solutions to the decision-maker's problems. In other cases studies have addressed the fact that the decision-maker may invoke probabilistic rules to decide the differential likelihood that alternative courses of action would alter a present state of affairs in the desired direction.

a rigorous way. Immense sums of foundation money, criteria defining adequate research designs, and may careers rest on the conviction that this is so.

Yet is it common knowledge that in the overwhelming number of researches that are methodologically acceptable, and, paradoxically, precisely to the extent that rigorous methods are used, dramatic discrepancies are visible between the theoretical properties of the intended *sociological* findings of inquirers and the mathematical assumptions that must be satisfied if the statistical measures are to be used for the literal description of the intended events. The result is that statistical measurements are most frequently used as indicators, as signs of, as representing or standing on behalf of the intended findings rather than as literal descriptions of them. Thus, at the point where sociological findings must be decided from statistical results,[10] rigorous methods are being asserted as solutions to the tasks of literal description on the grounds of "reasonable" considerations.

Even if it is demonstrable that these features are present, let alone prominent, in sociological inquiries, is it not nevertheless true that a situation of inquiry might receive documentary treatment and still the factual status of its products would be decided differently? For example, is it not the case that there are strictures against ex post facto analysis? And is it not so that a field worker who learned after he consulted his notes what problems he had "in the final analysis" obtained answers to, might reapply for a grant to perform a "confirmatory study" of the "hypotheses" that his reflections had yielded? Is there, therefore, any *necessary* connection between the features of common-sense situations of choice, the use of documentary method, and the *corpus of sociological fact?* Must the documentary method necessarily be used by the professional sociologist to decide sensibility, objectivity, and warrant? Is there a necessary connection between the theoretical subject matter of sociology, as this is constituted by the attitude and procedures for "seeing sociologically" on the one hand, and the canons of adequate description, i.e., evidence, on the other?

Between the methods of literal observation and the work of documentary interpretation the investigator can choose the former and achieve rigorous literal description of physical and biological properties of soci-

10. The term "results" is used to refer to the set of *mathematical* events that are possible when the procedures of a statistical test, like chi square, for example, are treated as grammatical rules for conceiving, comparing, producing, etc., events in the mathematical domain. The term "findings" is used to refer to the set of *sociological* events that are possible when, under the assumption that the sociological and mathematical domains correspond in their logical structures, sociological events are interpreted in terms of the rules of statistical inference.

ological events. This has been demonstrated on many occasions. Thus far the choice has been made at the cost of either neglecting the properties that make events sociological ones, or by using documentary work to deal with the "soft" parts.

The choice has to do with the question of the conditions under which literal observation and documentary work necessarily occur. This involves the formulation of, and solution to, the problem of sociological evidence in terms that permit a descriptive solution. Undoubtedly, scientific sociology is a "fact," but in Felix Kaufmann's sense of fact, i.e., in terms of a set of procedural rules that *actually* govern the use of sociologists' recommended methods and asserted findings as grounds of further inference and inquiries. The problem of evidence consists of the tasks of making this fact intelligible.

CLIFFORD GEERTZ

The Growth of Culture

and the Evolution of Mind

The statement "the mind is its own place," as theorists might con-
strue it, is not true, for the mind is not even a metaphorical "place."
On the contrary, the chessboard, the platform, the scholar's desk,
the judge's bench, the lorry-driver's seat, the studio and the football
field are among its places. These are where people work and
play stupidly or intelligently. "Mind" is not the name of another
person, working or frolicking behind an impenetrable screen; it is not
the name of another place where work is done or games are played;
and it is not the name of another tool with which work is done, or
another appliance with which games are played.—GILBERT RYLE

1

In the intellectual history of the behavioral sciences the concept of
"mind" has played a curious double role. Those who have regarded the
development of such sciences as involving a rectilinear extension of the
methods of physical science into the realm of the organic have used it as
a devil word, the referent of which was all those methods and theories
which failed to measure up to a rather heroic ideal of "objectivism."

I am indebted to Lloyd A. Fallers, Dell Hymes, David Schneider, and Sherwood
L. Washburn for valuable critical comments on earlier drafts of this paper.

713

Terms such as insight, understanding, conceptual thinking, image, idea, feeling, reflection, fantasy, etc., have been stigmatized as mentalistic, "i.e., contaminated with the subjectivity of consciousness" (Scheerer, 1959), and the appeal to them castigated as a lamentable failure of scientific nerve. But those who have, on the contrary, regarded the move from a physical to an organic, and most especially to a human, subject matter as implying far-reaching revisions in theoretical approach and research procedure have tended to use "mind" as a cautionary concept, one intended more to point to defects in understanding than to repair them, more to stress the limits of positive science than to extend them. For such thinkers its main function has been to give a vaguely defined but intuitively valid expression to their settled conviction that human experience has important dimensions of order which physical theory (and, *pari passu,* psychological and social theories modeled on physical theory) omits to consider. Sherrington's (1953, p. 161) image of "naked mind"—"all that counts in life. Desire, zest, truth, love, knowledge, values"—going "in our spatial world more ghostly than a ghost," serves as an epitome of this position; as Pavlov's reported (Kubie, 1954) practice of levying fines on any of his students who so much as uttered mentalistic words in his laboratory does of the opposite.

In fact, with some exceptions, the term "mind" has not functioned as a scientific concept at all but as a rhetorical device, even when its use has been forbidden. More exactly, it has acted to communicate—and sometimes exploit—a fear rather than to define a process, a fear of subjectivism on the one hand and of mechanism on the other. "Even when fully aware of the nature of anthropomorphic subjectivism and its dangers," Clark Hull warns us solemnly (1943), "the most careful and experienced thinker is likely to find himself a victim to its seductions," and urges as a "prophylaxis" the strategy of viewing all behavior as if it were produced by a dog, an albino rat, or safest of all, a robot. While, for the opposition, Gordon Allport (1947) professes to see a threat to human dignity in such an approach, complaining that "the models we have been following lack the long-range orientation which is the essence of morality . . . an addiction to machines, rats, or infants leads us to overplay those features of human behavior that are peripheral, signal-oriented, or genetic [and] to underplay those features that are central, future-oriented, or symbolic." In the face of such contradictory descriptions of the specter that is haunting the study of man, it is small wonder that a recent group of psychologists, torn between their wish to present a convincing analysis of the directional aspects of human behavior and to meet scientific canons of objectivity, found themselves tempted by the rather desperate strategem of referring to themselves as "subjective behaviorists" (Miller, *et al.,* 1960).

So far as the concept of mind is concerned, this state of affairs is extremely unfortunate because an extraordinarily useful notion and one for which there is no precise equivalent, save perhaps the archaism "psyche," is turned into a shibboleth. It is even more unfortunate because the fears which have so crippled the term are largely baseless, the dying echoes of the great mock civil war between materialism and dualism generated by the Newtonian revolution. Mechanism, as Ryle (1949) has said, is a bogey, because the fear of it rests on the assumption that it is somehow contradictory to say that one and the same occurrence is governed by mechanical laws and moral principles, as though a golfer cannot at once conform to the laws of ballistics, obey the rules of golf, and play with elegance. But subjectivism is a bogey too, for the fear of it rests on the equally peculiar assumption that because I cannot know what you dreamed of last night, thought of while memorizing a string of nonsense syllables, or feel about the doctrine of infant damnation unless you choose to tell me, that any theorizing I may do about the role such mental facts play in your behavior must be based on a false "anthropomorphic" analogy from what I know, or think I know, about the role they play in mine. Lashley's (1958) tart comment that "metaphysicians and theologians have spent so many years weaving fairy tales about [mind] that they have come to believe one another's phantasies," is inaccurate only in that it neglects to note that a great many behavioral scientists have been engaged in the same sort of collective autism.

One of the most frequently suggested methods for rehabilitating mind as a useful scientific concept is to transform it into a verb or participle, "Mind is minding, the reaction of an organism as a whole as a coherent unit . . . [a view which] releases us from the verbal bondage of a sterile and paralyzing metaphysics, and sets us free to sow and reap in a field what will bear fruit" (White, 1949, pp. 52, 54). But this "cure" involves falling in with the school bench story that "a noun is a word that names a person, place, or thing," which was not true in the first place. The use of nouns as dispositional terms—i.e., words denoting capacities and propensities rather than entities or activities (Ryle, 1949)—is actually a standard and indispensable practice in English, both natural and scientific. If "mind" is to go, "faith," "hope," and "charity" will have to go with it, as well as "cause," "force," and "gravitation" and "motive," "role," and "culture." "Mind is minding" may be all right, "science is sciencing" (White, 1949) at least bearable, but "superego is superegoing" is a little awkward. But, even more important, although it is true that part of the fog of confusion which has arisen around the concept of mind is a result of a false analogy with nouns which do name persons, places, or things, it mainly springs from much deeper sources than the merely linguistic. Consequently, making it into a verb is no real protection at all against "a sterile and paralyzing metaphysics." Like mechanists, subjectivists are men of infinite resource, and an occult activity may simply be substituted for an occult entity, as in the case, for example, of "introspecting."

From the scientific point of view, to identify mind with behavior, "the reaction of the organism as a whole," is to render it as uselessly redundant as to identify it with an entity "more ghostly than a ghost." The notion that it is more defensible to transform a reality into another reality than to transform it into an unreality is not correct: a rabbit disappears just as completely when he is magically changed into a horse as he does when he is changed into a centaur. "Mind" is a term denoting a class of skills, propensities, capacities, tendencies, habits; it refers in Dewey's phrase (1934) to an "active and eager background which lies in wait and engages whatever comes its way." And, as such, it is neither an action nor a thing, but an organized system of dispositions which finds its manifestation in some actions and some things. As Ryle has pointed out, if a clumsy man trips accidentally, we do not regard it proper to his actions or the workings of his mind, but if a clown trips on purpose we do feel it proper to say this:

> The cleverness of the clown may be exhibited in his tripping and tumbling. He trips and tumbles just as clumsy people do, except that he trips and tumbles on purpose and after much rehearsal and at the golden moment and where the children can see him and so as not to hurt himself. The spectators applaud his skill at seeming clumsy, but what they applaud is not some extra hidden performance executed "in his head." It is his visible performance that they admire, but they admire it not for being an effect of any hidden internal causes but for being an exercise of skill. Now a skill is not an act. It is therefore neither a witnessable nor an unwitnessable act. To recognize that a performance is an exercise of a skill is indeed to appreciate it in the light of a factor which could not be separately recorded by a camera. But the reason why the skill exercised in a performance cannot be separately recorded by a camera is not that it is an occult or ghostly happening, but that it is not a happening at all. It is a disposition, or complex of dispositions, and a disposition is a factor of the wrong logical type to be seen or unseen, recorded or unrecorded. Just as the habit of talking loudly is not itself loud or quiet, since it is not the sort of term of which "loud" or "quiet" can be predicated, or just as a susceptibility to headaches is for the same reason not itself unendurable or endurable, so the skills, tastes, and bents which are exercised in overt or internal operations are not themselves overt or internal, witnessable or unwitnessable. (Ryle, 1949, p. 33.)

A similar argument applies to objects; we would not refer, save in a metaphorical way, to the legendary burned pig the Chinese produced by accidentally setting fire to his house as "cooked," even though he ate it, because it did not result from the exercise of a mental capability called "knowledge of cooking." But we would so refer to the second such pig the now educated Chinese produced by deliberately burning down his house again, because it did result from such a capability, no matter how crude. Such judgments, being empirical, may be wrong; a man may have really tripped when we thought he was only clowning, or a pig really been cooked when we thought it merely burned. But the point is that when we attribute mind to an organism we are talking about neither the organism's actions nor its products per se, but about its capacity and its proneness, its disposition, to perform certain kinds of actions and produce certain kinds of products, a capacity and a proneness we of course infer from the fact that he does sometimes perform such actions and produce such products. There is nothing extramundane about this; it merely indicates that a language lacking dispositional terms would make the scientific description and analysis of human behavior extraordinarily difficult, and severely cripple its conceptual development, in the same way that a language, such as the Arapesh (Mead, n.d.), in which you must enumerate by saying "one, two, two and one, one dog (i.e., 'four'), one dog and one, one dog and two, one dog and two and one, two dogs, . . . etc.," cripples mathematical development by making counting so troublesome that people find it such an effort to go beyond two dogs and two dogs and two dogs (i.e., "twenty-four") that they refer to all larger quantities as "a lot."

Further, within such a general conceptual framework it is possible to discuss the biological, psychological, sociological, and cultural determinants of man's mental life concurrently without making any reductionist hypotheses at all. This is because a capacity for something, or a proneness to do something, not being an entity or a performance, is simply not susceptible to reduction. In the case of Ryle's clown, I could say, no doubt incorrectly, that his tumbling was reducible to a chain of conditioned reflexes, but I could not say that his skill was so reducible, because by his skill I only mean to say that he can tumble. For "the clown can tumble," it is possible, if simplistic, to write "(this organism) can (produce the described reflex series)," but it is possible to get the "can" out of the sentence only by replacing it with "is able to," "has the capacity to," etc., which is not a reduction but merely an immaterial shift from a verbal to an adjectival or nounal form. All one can do in the the analysis of skills is to show the way in which they are (or are not) dependent upon various factors such as nervous system complexity, repressed desires to exhibit, the existence of social institutions such as circuses, or the presence of a cultural tradition of mimicking clumsiness for the purposes of satire. Once dispositional predicates are admitted into scientific description they are not eliminated by shifts in the "level" of description employed. And, with the recognition of this fact, a whole range of pseudo problems, false issues, and unrealistic fears can simply be set aside.

In perhaps no area of inquiry is such an avoidance of manufactured paradoxes more useful than that of the study of mental evolution. Burdened in the past by almost all the classic anthropological fallacies— ethnocentrism, an overconcern with human uniqueness, imaginatively reconstructed history, a superorganic concept of culture, a priori stages of evolutionary change—the whole search for the origins of human mentality has tended to fall into disrepute, or at any rate to be neglected. But legitimate questions—and how man came to have his mind is a legitimate question—are not invalidated by misconceived answers. So far as anthropology is concerned, at least, one of the most important advantages of a dispositional answer to the question, "What is mind?" is that it permits us to reopen a classic issue without reviving classic controversies.

2

Over the past half century, two views of the evolution of the human mind, both inadequate, have been current. The first is the thesis that the sort of human thought processes Freud (1900, 1911) called "primary"—substitution, reversal, condensation, etc.—are phylogenetically prior to those he called "secondary"—directed, logically ordered, reasoning, etc. Within the confines of anthropology, this thesis has been based on the assumption that it is possible simply to identify patterns of culture and modes of thought (Lévy-Brühl, 1923). On such an assumption, groups of people lacking the cultural resources of modern science which have been, at least in certain contexts, so effectively employed in directive reasoning in the West are considered *ipso facto* to lack the very capacity for intellection these resources serve; as though the confinement of the Arapesh to combinations of "one," "two," and "dog" were a result rather than a cause of their lack of mathematical facility. If one then adds to this argument the invalid empirical generalization that tribal peoples employ whatever meager culture resources they do have for intellection less frequently, less persistently, and less circumspectly than do Western peoples, the proposition that primary process thinking proceeds secondary process thinking phylogenetically needs only the final mistake of viewing tribal peoples as primitive forms of humanity, "living fossils," to complete it (e.g., Arieti, 1959).[1]

1. In addition, this proposition has been supported, as Hallowell (1939) has pointed out, by an uncritical application of Haeckel's now rejected "law of recapitu-

It was in reaction to this tissue of errors that the second view of human mental evolution arose, namely, that not only is the existence of the human mind in essentially its modern form a prerequisite for the acquisition of culture, but the growth of culture in itself has been without any significance for mental evolution:

The bird gave up a pair of walking limbs to acquire wings. It added a new faculty by transforming part of an old one. . . . The airplane, on the contrary, gave men a new faculty without diminishing or even impairing any of those they had previously possessed. It led to no visible bodily changes, no alterations of mental capacity. (Kroeber, 1948, p. 5.)

But, in turn, this argument implies two corollaries, one of which, the doctrine of the psychic unity of mankind, has found increasing empirical substantiation as anthropological research has proceeded, but the other of which, the "critical point" theory of the appearance of culture, has become increasingly tenuous. The doctrine of the psychic unity of mankind (*ibid.*, p. 573), which so far as I am aware, is today not seriously questioned by any reputable anthropologist, is but the direct contradictory of the primitive mentality argument; it asserts that there are no essential differences in the fundamental nature of the thought process among the various living races of man. If the existence of a modern type of mind is held to be prerequisite to the acquisition of culture, the universal possession of culture by all contemporary human groups, of course, makes of the psychic unity doctrine a simple tautology; but whether genuinely tautological or not, it is a proposition for whose empirical validity the ethnographic and psychological evidence is altogether overwhelming (Kluckhohn, 1953).

As for the critical point theory of the appearance of culture, it postulates that the development of the capacity for acquiring culture was a sudden, all-or-none type of occurrence in the phylogeny of the primates (Kroeber, 1948, pp. 71-72). At some specific moment in the new unrecoverable history of hominidization a portentous, but in genic or anatomical terms probably quite minor, organic alteration took place—presumably in cortical structure—in which an animal whose parents had not been disposed "to communicate, to learn and to teach, to generalize from the endless chain of discrete feelings and attitudes" was so disposed and "therewith he began to be able to act as a receiver and transmitter and begin the accumulation that is culture" (*ibid.*). With him culture was born, and, once born, set on its own course so as to grow

---

lation," in which presumed parallels in the thought of children, psychotics, and savages were used as evidence of the phylogenetic priority of autism. For suggestions that primary processes are not even ontogenetically prior to secondary ones, see Hartmann, 1939, and Hartmann, Kris, and Lowenstein, 1946.

wholly independently of the further organic evolution of man. The whole process of the creation of modern man's capacity for producing and using culture, his most distinctive mental attribute, is conceptualized as one of a marginal quantitative change giving rise to a radical qualitative difference, as when water, reduced degree by degree without any loss of fluidity suddenly freezes at 0° C. (*ibid.*) or when a taxiing plane gains sufficient speed to launch itself into flight (White, 1949, p. 33).

But we are talking of neither water nor airplanes, and the question is can the sharp line between enculturated man and non-enculturated non-man that this view implies in fact to be drawn, or, if we must have analogies, would not a more historical one, such as the unbroken gradual rise of modern out of medieval England, be more apt. Within the physical branch of anthropology, the doubt that one can talk about the appearance of man "as if he had suddenly been promoted from colonel to brigadier general, and had a date of rank" (Howells, 1950) has grown with increasing rapidity as the Australopithecene fossils of South Africa have come to be placed more and more in the hominid line. These fossils (Dart, 1957), which date from the lower Pleistocene period of more than a half-million years ago, show a striking mosaic of primitive and advanced morphological characteristics, in which the most outstanding features are a pelvis and leg formation strikingly similar to that of modern man and a cranial capacity hardly larger than that of living apes. Although the initial tendency was to regard this conjunction of a "man-like" bipedal locomotive system and an "ape-like" brain as indicating that the Australopithecenes represented an aberrant and ill-fated line of development separate from both hominids and pongids (Hooton, 1949, pp. 281-88), the contemporary consensus follows Howells' (1950) conclusion that "the first hominids were small-brained, newly bipedal, proto-australopith hominoids, and that what we have always meant by 'man' represents later forms of this group with secondary adaptations in the direction of large brains and modified skeletons of the same form."[2]

Now, these more or less erect, small-brained hominids, their hands freed from locomotion, manufactured tools (Oakley, 1957; Leakey, 1960) and probably hunted small animals (Washburn and Howell, 1960). But that they could have had a developed culture comparable to that of, say, the Australian aborigine or possessed language in the modern sense of the term with 500 cubic centimeters of brain is unlikely (Hallowell, 1960). In the Australopithecenes we seem to have, therefore, an odd sort

2. By "hominoid" is meant the superfamily of animals, living and extinct, to which both man and the pongid apes (gorilla, orang, chimpanzee, and gibbon), belong, and by "hominid," the family of animals, living and extinct, to which man belongs, but not the apes.

of "man" who evidently was capable of acquiring some elements of culture—simple toolmaking, sporadic "hunting," and perhaps some system of communication more advanced than that of contemporary apes and less advanced than that of true speech—but not others, a state of affairs which casts fairly serious doubt on the viability of the "critical point" theory. In fact, as the Homo sapiens brain is about three times as large as that of the Australopithecenes, the greater part of human cortical expansion has followed, not preceded the "beginning" of culture (Washburn, 1959), a rather inexplicable circumstance if the capacity for culture is considered to have been the unitary outcome of a quantitatively slight but qualitatively metastatic change of the freezing of water sort. Not only has it now become misleading to employ the appointment to rank image for the appearance of man, but "it is equally doubtful whether we should any longer talk in terms of the 'appearance of culture,' as if culture, too, along with 'man,' had suddenly leaped into existence" (Hallowell, 1959; cf. Hallowell, 1960).

As paradox is a sign of antecedent error; the fact that one of its corollaries seems to be valid while the other does not suggest that the thesis which holds mental evolution and cultural accumulation to be two wholly separate processes, the first having been essentially completed before the second began, is itself incorrect. And if this is the case, it becomes necessary to find some way in which we can rid ourselves of such a thesis without at the same time undermining the doctrine of psychic unity, in whose absence "we should have to consign most of history, anthropology and sociology to the scrap heap and begin over again with a psychosomatic genetic interpretation of man and his varieties" (Kroeber, 1948, p. 573). We need to be able both to deny any significant relationship between (group) cultural achievement and innate mental capacity in the present, and to affirm such a relationship in the past.

The means by which to accomplish this oddly two-headed task lies in what may appear to be a simple technical trick, but is actually an important methodological reorientation; the choice of a more finely graduated time scale in terms of which to discriminate the stages of evolutionary change which have produced Homo sapiens out of an Eocene proto-hominoid. Whether one sees the appearance of the capacity for culture as a more or less abrupt, instantaneous occurrence, or a slowly moving, continuous development obviously depends, at least in part, on the size of the elementary units in one's time scale; for a geologist, measuring by eons, the whole evolution of the primates may look like an undifferentiated qualitative burst. In fact, the argument against the critical point theory might be more precisely phrased in terms of a complaint that it derives from an inappropriate choice of time scale, a time scale whose basal intervals are too large for a refined analysis of recent evolutionary history, in the same way as a biologist foolish enough to study human maturation with decades as his interval would see adulthood as a sudden transformation of childhood and miss adolescence altogether.

A good example of such a cavalier approach to temporal considerations is implicit in what is probably the most frequent kind of scientific data invoked in support of the "difference in kind rather than difference in degree" view of human culture; the comparison of man with his closest living relatives, the pongids, and particularly the chimpanzee. Man can talk, can symbolize, can acquire culture, this argument goes, but the chimpanzee (and, by extension, all less endowed animals) cannot. Therefore, man is unique in this regard, and insofar as mentality is concerned "we are confronted by a series of leaps, not an ascending continuum" (White, 1960; but the argument is very common). But this overlooks the fact that, although the pongids may be man's closest relatives, "close" is an elastic term and, given a realistic time scale from the evolutionary point of view, they are really not so close at all, the last common ancestor being at the very least an upper Pliocene (and at the very most an upper Oligocene) ape and phyletic differentiation having proceeded with ever-increasing rapidity since that time (Spuhler, 1959). The fact that chimpanzees do not talk is both interesting and important, but to draw from that fact the conclusion that speech is an all-or-nothing-at-all phenomenon is to collapse anywhere from one to forty million years into a single instant of time and lose the whole pre-sapiens hominid line as surely as our biologist lost adolescence. Interspecific comparison of living animals is, if handled with care, a legitimate and, in fact, indispensable device for deducing general evolutionary trends; but in the same way that the wave length of light limits the degree of refinement in quantum level physical measurements, so the fact that the closest living relatives of man are at best pretty far-removed cousins (*not* ancestors) limits the degree of refinement in the measure of evolutionary change in the hominoid line when one confines oneself entirely to contrasts between extant forms.[3]

If, on the contrary, we spread hominid phylogeny out along a more appropriate time scale, training our attention on what seems to have happened in the "human" line since the radiation of the hominoids, and in particular since the emergence of *Australopithecus* in the lower Pleistocene, a subtler analysis of the evolutionary growth of mind is made possible. Most crucially, it then becomes apparent that not only was cultural accumulation under way well before organic development

3. For a general discussion of the dangers involved in an uncritical use of comparisons among contemporaneous forms to generate historical hypotheses, see Simpson, 1950.

ceased, but that such accumulation very likely played an active role in shaping the final stages of that development. Though it is apparently true enough that the invention of the airplane led to no visible bodily changes, no alterations of (innate) mental capacity, this was not necessarily the case for the pebble tool or the crude chopper, in whose wake seems to have come not only more erect stature, reduced dentition, and a more thumb-dominated hand, but the expansion of the human brain to its present size (Washburn, 1959). Because tool manufacture puts a premium on manual skill and foresight, its introduction must have acted to shift selection pressures so as to favor the rapid growth of the forebrain as, in all likelihood, did the advances in social organization (Bartholomew and Birdsell, 1953), communication (Hayes and Hayes, 1955), and moral regulation (Hallowell, 1959), which there is reason to believe also occurred during this period of overlap between cultural and biological change. Nor were such nervous system changes merely quantitative; alterations in the interconnections among neurons and their manner of functioning may have been of even greater importance than the simple increase in their number (Spuhler, 1959; Bullock, 1958). Details aside, however—and the bulk of them remain to be determined—the point is that the innate, generic constitution of modern man (what used, in a simpler day, to be called "human nature") now appears to be both a cultural and a biological product in that "it is probably more correct to think of much of our structure as a result of culture rather than to think of men anatomically like ourselves slowly discovering culture" (Washburn, 1959).

The Pleistocene period, with its rapid and radical variations in climate, land formations, and vegetation, has long been recognized to be a period in which conditions were ideal for the speedy and efficient evolutionary development of man (Emiliani, 1960); now it seems also to have been a period in which a cultural environment increasingly supplemented the natural environment in the selection process so as to further accelerate the rate of hominid evolution to an unprecedented speed (Spuhler, 1959; Leakey, 1960). The Ice Age appears not to have been merely a time of receding brow ridges and shrinking jaws, but a time in which were forged nearly all those characteristics of man's existence which are most graphically human: his thoroughly encephelated nervous system, his incest taboo-based social structure, and his capacity to create and use symbols. The fact that these distinctive features of humanity emerged together in complex interaction with one another rather than serially as for so long supposed is, if it is a fact, of exceptional importance in the interpretation of human mentality, because it suggests that man's nervous system does not merely enable him to acquire culture, it positively demands that he do so if it is going to function at all. Rather than culture acting only to supplement, develop, and extend organically based capacities logically and genetically prior to it (Bidney, 1953, Chap. 3), it would seem to be ingredient to those capacities themselves. A cultureless human being would probably turn out to be not an intrinsically talented though unfulfilled ape, but a wholly mindless and consequently unworkable monstrosity. Like the cabbage it so much resembles, the Homo sapiens brain, having arisen within the framework of human culture, would not be viable outside of it.[4]

In fact, this type of reciprocally creative relationship between somatic and extrasomatic phenomena seems to have been of crucial significance during the whole of the primate advance. That any (living or extinct) infra-hominid primates can be said to possess true culture—in the narrowed sense of "an ordered system of meaning and symbols . . . in terms of which individuals define their world, express their feelings and make their judgments" (Geertz, 1957)—is, of course, extremely doubtful. But that apes and monkeys are such through-and-through social creatures as to be unable to achieve emotional maturity in isolation (Harlow, 1959), to acquire a great many of their most important performance capacities through imitative learning (ibid.; Nissen, 1955), and to develop distinctive, intraspecifically variable collective social traditions which are transmitted as a nonbiological heritage from generation to generation (DeVore, n.d.) is now well established. As DeVore (ibid.) remarks in summary of the available material, "Primates literally have a 'social brain.'" Thus, well before it was influenced by cultural forces as such, the evolution of what eventually developed into the human nervous system was positively shaped by social ones.[5]

On the other hand, however, a denial of a simple independence of sociocultural and biological processes in pre-homo sapiens man does not imply a rejection of the doctrine of psychic unity, because phyletic differentiation within the hominid line effectively ceased with the terminal Pleistocene spread of Homo sapiens over nearly the whole world and the extinction of whatever other Homo species may have been in existence at that time. Thus, although some minor evolutionary changes have no doubt occurred since the rise of modern man, all living peoples form part of a single polytypical species and, as such, vary anatomically and physiologically within a very narrow range (Montague, 1950). The combination of weakened mechanisms of reproductive isolation, an

4. As for "wolf-children" and other feral fantasies, see Lorenz, n.d.

5. Some subprimate mammals also follow a definitely social mode of life (Thompson, 1958), so that this whole process probably predates primates altogether. The social behavior of some birds (Lorenz, 1952) and insects (Emerson, 1958) is of less immediate relevance, however, because these orders are tangential to the human developmental line.

extended period of individual sexual immaturity, and the accumulation of culture to the point where its importance as an adaptive factor almost wholly dominated its role as a selective one produced such an extreme deceleration of the hominid rate of evolution that the development of any significant variation in innate mental capacity among human subgroups seems to have been precluded. With the unequivocal triumph of Homo sapiens and the cessation of the glaciations, the link between organic and cultural change was, if not severed, at least greatly weakened. Since that time organic evolution in the human line has slowed to a walk (Carter, 1953), while the growth of culture has continued to proceed with ever-increasing rapidity. It is, therefore, unnecessary to postulate either a discontinuous, "difference-in-kind" pattern of human evolution or a non-selective role for culture during all phases of hominid development in order to preserve the empirically established generalization that "as far as their [inborn] capacity to learn, maintain, transmit, and transform culture is concerned, different groups of Homo sapiens must be regarded as equally competent" (Mead, 1958). Psychic unity may no longer be a tautology, but it is still a fact.

3

One of the more encouraging—if strangely delayed—developments in the behavioral sciences is the current attempt of physiological psychology to arouse itself from its long enthrallment with the wonders of the reflex arc (Pribram, 1960). The conventional picture of a sensory impulse making its way through a maze of synapses to a motor nerve culmination is coming to be revised, a quarter century after its most illustrious proponent pointed out that it was inadequate to explain the integrative aspects of the behavior of a sparrow or a sheep dog, much less that of a man (Sherrington, 1953, p. 170). Sherrington's solution was a spectral mind to pull things together (as Hull's [1943] was a no less mysterious automatic switchboard), but today the stress is upon a more verifiable construct; the concept of rhythmic, spontaneous, centrally proceeding pattern of nervous activity upon which peripheral stimulus configurations are superimposed and out of which authoritative effector commands emerge. Advancing under the banner of "an active organism," and supported by the closed circuit anatomizing of Cayal and de Nó (1943), this new persuasion emphasizes the way in which the ongoing processes both of the brain and subordinate neuronal aggregates select precepts (Bruner, 1958), fix experiences (Gerard, 1960), and order responses (Lashley, 1951) so as to produce a delicately modulated pattern of behavior:

. . . the working of the central nervous system is a hierarchic affair in which functions at the higher levels do not deal directly with the ultimate structural units, such as neurons or motor units, but operate by activating lower patterns that have their own relatively autonomous structural unity. The same is true for the sensory input, which does not project itself down to the last final path of motor neurons, but operates by affecting, distorting, and somehow modifying the pre-existing, preformed patterns of central coordination, which, in turn, then confer their distortions upon the lower patterns of effection and so on. The final output is then the outcome of this hierarchical passing down of distortions and modifications of intrinsically performed patterns of excitation which are in no way replicas of the input. The structure of the input does not produce the structure of the output, but merely modifies intrinsic nervous activities that have a structural organization of their own. (Weiss, 1951.)

Further development of this theory of an autonomously excited, hierarchically organized central nervous system not only promises to make the brisk competence of Sherrington's sheep dog as it collects its scattered flock from the hillside less of a physiological mystery, but it should also prove valuable in providing a credible neurological underpinning for the complex of skills and propensities which constitute the human mind; the ability to follow a logic proof or a tendency to become flustered when called upon to speak demand more than a reflex arc, conditioned or otherwise, to support them biologically. And, as Hebb has pointed out, the very notion of "higher" and "lower" evolutionary levels of mentality seems in itself to imply a comparable gradation in degree of central nervous system autonomy:

I hope I do not shock biological scientist by saying that one feature of the phylogenetic development is an increasing evidence of what is known in some circles as free will; in my student days also referred to as the Harvard Law, which asserts that any well-trained experimental animal, on controlled stimulation, will do as he damn well pleases. A more scholarly formulation is that the higher animal is less stimulus-bound. Brain action is less fully controlled by afferent input, behavior therefore less fully predictable from the situation in which the animal is put. A greater role of ideational activity is recognizable in the animal's ability to "hold" a variety of stimulations for some time before acting on them and in the phenomenon of purposive behavior. There is more autonomous activity in the higher brain, and more selectivity as to *which* afferent activity will be integrated with the "stream of thought," the dominant, ongoing activity in control of behavior. Traditionally, we say that the subject is "interested" in this part of the environment, not interested in that; in these terms, the higher animal has a wider variety of interests and the interest of the moment plays a greater part in behavior, which means a greater unpredictability as to what stimulus will be responded to and as to the form of the response. (1954, references omitted.)

These over-all evolutionary trends—increasing ability to focus attention, delay response, vary interest, sustain purpose, and, in general, deal positively with the complexities of present stimulation—culminate in man to make of him the most active of active organisms, as well as the most unpredictable. The extreme intricacy, flexibility, and comprehensiveness of what Kluckhohn and Murray (1948) have aptly called regnant processes in the human brain—the processes which make these abilities physically possible—are but the outcome of a definable phylogenetic development which is traceable back at least to the coelenterates (Bullock, 1958). Though they lack a central nervous concentration—a brain—and therefore the various parts of the animal operate in relative independence, each possessing its own set of sensory, neural, and motor elements, these humble jellyfish, sea anemones, and the like nevertheless show a surprising degree of intrinsic modulation of nervous activity: a strong stimulus received in the daytime may be followed by locomotion during the following night; certain corals experimentally subjected to excessive stimulation luminesce for several minutes afterward with a spontaneous frenzy which suggests "beserking"; and regularized stimulation may lead, through some still obscure form of "memory," to a coordination of activity in different muscles and to a patterned recurrence of activity over time (*ibid.*). In the higher invertebrates (crustaceans, etc.) multiple pathways, graded synaptic potentials, and triggered responses all appear permitting precise pacemaker control of internal functions as in the lobster heart (*ibid.*), while with the arrival of the lower vertebrates both peripheral sensory and effector elements and neuronal conduction between them—i.e., the celebrated reflex arc—are essentially perfected (Gerard, 1960). And, finally, the bulk of the fundamental innovations in the design of nervous circuits—i.e., closed loops, the superposition of higher level loops on lower ones, etc.—probably were accomplished with the arrival of the mammals (*ibid.*), at which time at least the basic differentiations of the forebrain were also achieved (Pribram, 1958). In functional terms, the whole process seems to be one of a relatively steady expansion and diversification of endogenous nervous activity and the consequent increasing centralization of what were previously more isolated, independently acting part-processes.

What sort of neural evolution has taken place during the phyletic differentiation of the mammals—i.e., in particular, during the advance of the primates and hominids,—is, evidently rather less clear and more controversial, however. On the one hand, Gerard has argued that the changes have been almost entirely quantitative, a growth in the sheer number of neurons, as reflected in the rapid expansion of the brain size:

The further gains in capacity, seen most strikingly in the primate line and culminating in man are due to simple increase in numbers rather than to improvement in units or patterns. The increasing brain size parallels richer performance, even for particular regions and functions (e.g., tongue motor area and speech), is a commonplace (see Spuhler, 1959); how this operates is less clear. Sheer increase in number, without secondary specification (which does also occur), might seem unable to generate new capacities but only to intensify old ones, but this is not the case. . . . In the brain, an increase in the anatomical neurone population raises the limit on the physiological neurone reserve and so allows greater variety of selection and greater richness of analysis and combination expressed in modifiable and insightful behavior. (1960; see also, 1959.)

But Bullock, though agreeing that the nervous systems of the higher animals and man show no important differences in terms of known neurophysiological mechanisms or architecture, sharply questions this point of view, and argues that there is a pressing need to search for yet undiscovered parameters of nervous functioning, "emergent levels of physiological relations between neurons in masses," to account for the subtleties of behavior in advanced organisms:

Though we cannot point to fundamentally new elements in the neuronal mechanisms of the higher centers, still it is difficult to assume that their greatly enlarged accomplishments are solely attributable to the great increase in numbers and interconnections between them, unless this in itself brings on new properties and mechanisms. Many apparently assume as a first approximation that the main factor in increasing behavioral complexity in evolution is the number of neurons—even invoking a kind of critical mass which permits new levels of behavior . . . [but] it seems clear that the number of neurones correlates with behavioral complexity so poorly as to explain little unless we add as the really essential part that certain kinds of neurons, not now definable, or—what is the same thing—certain kinds of newer properties of consequences or neuronal architecture, are the important substratum of advance. . . . I do not believe that our present physiology of neurons, extrapolated, can account for behavior. The main factor in evolutionary advance is not just numbers of cells and connections. . . . Our hope lies in the discovery of new parameters of neuronal systems. (1960.)

To an outsider, perhaps the most striking aspect of this controversy is the degree to which both parties seem somewhat uneasy and vaguely dissatisfied with the unalloyed versions of their own argument, the degree to which it seems not to be entirely plausible even to themselves. On the one side there is an admission that the precise nature of the relation between brain size and behavioral complexity is indeed unclear and some *sotto voce* reservations about "secondary specification"; on the other, a frank puzzlement concerning the apparent absence of novel mechanisms in advanced nervous systems and a hopeful murmuring about "emergent properties." There is actually something of an agreement that the attribution of the secular increase in mammalian mental capacity solely and simply to a gross increase in neuron population taxes credulity. The difference is that in one case doubts are quieted by a stress on the fact that a parallelism between increasing brain size and richer performance does, anyhow, obtain; while, on the other, doubts are accentuated by a stress on the fact that something seems to be missing to make this parallelism satisfactorily explicable.

This issue may eventually be clarified as Gerard (1959) suggests, by advances in work with computer circuits where performance does improve with a simple multiplication of identical units; or, as Bullock (1960) suggests, by further refinements in the analysis of chemical differences between nerve cells. But it is even more likely that the main avenue to its resolution lies in the abandonment of the wholly nativistic conceptualization of nervous functioning in the higher mammals which seems to be implicit in both these approaches. The synchronic emergence in primates of an expanded forebrain, developed forms of social organization, and, at least after Australopithecenes got their hands on tools, institutionalized patterns of culture indicates that the standard procedure of treating biological, social, and cultural parameters serially—the first being taken as primary to the second, and the second to the third—is ill-advised. On the contrary, these so-called "levels" should be seen as reciprocally interrelated and considered conjointly (Parsons, 1959). And if this is done, the sort of novel properties we will search for within the central nervous system to serve as a physical basis for the striking development of autonomous fields of recurrent neural excitation in primates generally, and in man particularly, will differ radically from the sort of properties we would seek were we to regard those fields as "logically and genetically prior" to society and culture, and therefore requiring a full determination in terms of intrinsic physiological parameters alone. Perhaps we have been asking too much of neurons; or, if not too much, at least the wrong things.

In fact, so far as man is concerned, one of the most striking characteristics of his central nervous system is the relative incompleteness with which, acting within the confines of autogenous parameters alone, it is able to specify behavior. By and large, the lower an animal, the more it tends to respond to a "threatening" stimulus with an intrinsically connected series of performed activities which taken together comprise a comparatively stereotyped—which is *not* to say unlearned—"flight" or "fight" response (Lorenz, 1952). Man's intrinsic response to such a stimulus tends to consist, however, of a diffuse, variably intense, "fear" or "rage" excitability accompanied by few, if any automatically preset, well-defined behavioral sequences (Hebb and Thompson, 1954).[6] Like a frightened animal, a frightened man may run, hide, bluster, dissemble, placate, or, desperate with panic, attack; but in his case the precise patterning of such overt acts is guided predominantly by cultural rather than genetic templates. In the always diagnostic area of sex, where control of behavior proceeds phylogenetically from gonadal, to pituitary, to central nervous system prepotency, a similar evolutionary trend away from fixed activity sequences toward generalized arousal and "increasing flexibility and modifiability of sexual patterns" is apparent (Beach, 1958; cf., 1947); a trend of which the justly famous cultural variation in the sexual practices of man (Ford and Beach, 1951) would seem to represent a logical extension.[7] Thus, in apparent paradox, an increasing autonomy, hierarchical complexity, and regnancy of ongoing central nervous system activity seem to go hand in hand with a less fully detailed determination of such activity by the structure of the central nervous system in and of itself; i.e., intrinsically. All of which suggests that some of the more important developments in neural evolution which occurred during the period of overlap between biological and sociocultural change may turn out to consist of the appearance of properties which improve the performance capacity of the central nervous system but reduce its functional self-sufficiency.

From this standpoint, the accepted view that mental functioning is essentially an intracerebral process, which can only be secondarily assisted or amplified by the various artificial devices which that process has enabled man to invent, appears to be quite wrong. On the contrary,

6. The uncritical use of the term "instinct" so as to confuse three separate (but not unrelated) contrasts—that between behavior patterns which rest on learning and those which do not; that between behavior patterns which are innate (i.e., an outcome of genetically programed physical processes) and those which are not (i.e., an outcome of extragenetically programed physical processes); and that between behavior patterns which are inflexible (stereotyped) and those which are flexible (variable)—has led to an incorrect assumption that to say a behavior pattern is innate is to say that no learning is necessary for its performance and that it is inflexible in its expression (Beach, 1955; Pribram, 1958). Here, the term "intrinsic," as against "extrinsic," is used to characterize behavior which, on comparative grounds, seems to rest largely, or at least preponderantly, on innate dispositions, independently of questions of learning or flexibility as such.

7. But, again, this general trend appears already well established in the subhuman primates: "Some [male] chimpanzees have to learn to copulate. It has been noted that sexually mature but inexperienced males placed with the receptive female show signs of marked sexual excitement, but the resulting attempts to accomplish copulation are usually unsuccessful. The naive male appears incapable of carrying out his part of the mating act, and it has been suggested that a great deal of practice and learning is essential to biologically effective coition in this species. Adult male rodents which have been reared in isolation copulate normally the first time they are offered an estrous female" (Beach, 1947). For some vivid descriptions of generalized fear and rage in chimpanzees, see Hebb and Thompson, 1954.

a fully specified, adaptively sufficient definition of regnant neural processes in terms of intrinsic parameters being impossible, the human brain
is thoroughly dependent upon cultural resources for its very operation;
and those resources are, consequently, not adjuncts to but constituents
of mental activity. In fact, thinking as an overt, public act, involving the
purposeful manipulation of objective materials, is probably fundamental
to human beings; and thinking as a covert, private act, and without resource to such materials, a derived, though not unuseful, capability. As
the observation of how school children learn to calculate shows, adding
numbers in your head is actually a more sophisticated mental accomplishment than adding them with a paper and pencil, through an arrangement of tally sticks, or by counting, piggy-fashion, one's fingers and toes.
Reading aloud is a more elementary achievement than reading to oneself, the latter ability having only arisen, as a matter of fact, in the
Middle Ages (Ryle, 1949, p. 27). And a similar point about speech has
often been made; except in our less naive moments, we are all like
Forester's little old lady—we don't know what we think until we see what
we say.

It has sometimes been argued against this last point that "the comparative evidence, as well as the literature on aphasia, clearly makes
thought prior to speech, not conditional on it" (Hebb, 1954). But, though
true enough in itself, this does not undermine the general position taken
here—namely, that human culture is an ingredient not supplementary to
human thought—for several reasons. First, the fact that subhuman animals
learn to reason with sometimes startling effectiveness, without learning
to speak (Harlow, 1958), does not prove that men can do so, any more
than the fact that a rat can copulate without the mediation of imitative
learning or practice proves that a chimpanzee can do so. Second, as-
phasics are people who have learned to speak and to interiorize speech,
and then lost (or, more usually, partially lost) the former capacity, not
people who have never learned to speak at all (Goldstein, 1959). Third,
and most important, speech in the specific sense of vocalized talk is far
from being the sole public instrumentality available to individuals projected into a pre-existing cultural milieu. Such phenomena as Helen
Keller (1931) learning to think through a combination of the manipulation of such cultural objects as mugs and water taps and the purposeful
patterning (by Miss Sullivan) of tactile sensations on her hand, or a
pre-speech child developing the concept of ordinal number through
the setting up of two parallel lines of matched blocks (Lashley, 1949),
demonstrate that what is essential is the existence of an overt symbol
system of any sort.[8] For man, in particular, to conceive of thinking as

8. It is perhaps advisable also to point out explicitly that the view that humans
normally learn to talk intelligently aloud and with others before they learn to "talk"

essentially a private process is to overlook almost completely what people actually do when they go about reasoning.

Imaginal thinking is neither more nor less than constructing an image of the environment, running the model faster than the environment, and predicting that the environment will behave as the model does. . . . The first step in the solution of a problem consists in the contruction of a model or image of the "relevant features" of the [environment]. These models can be constructed from many things, including parts of the organic tissue of the body and, by man, paper and pencil or actual artifacts. Once a model has been constructed it can be manipulated under various hypothetical conditions and constraints. The organism is then able to "observe" the outcome of these manipulations, and to project them onto the environment so that prediction is possible. According to this view, an aeronautical engineer is thinking when he manipulates a model of a new airplane in a wind tunnel. The motorist is thinking when he runs his finger over a line on a map, the finger serving as a model of the relevant aspects of the automobile, the map as a model of the road. External models of this kind are often used in thinking about complex [environments]. Images used in covert thinking depend upon the availability of the physico-chemical events of the organism which must be used to form models. (Galenter and Gerstenhaber, 1956.)

It is a further implication of this view of reflective thought as consisting not of happenings in the head but of a matching of the states and processes of symbolic models against the states and processes of the wider world, that it is stimulus deficit which initiates mental activity and stimulus "discovery" which terminates it (Deutsch, 1953). The motorist running his finger over a road map is doing so because he lacks information about how to get where he is going and he will cease doing so when he has acquired that information. The engineer performs his experiments in the wind tunnel in order to find out how his model airplane behaves under various artificially produced aerodynamic conditions, and he will quit performing it if and when he indeed finds out. A man searching for a coin in his pocket does so because he lacks a coin in hand, and he stops searching when he gets hold of one (ibid.)—or, of course, when he comes to the conclusion that the whole project is bootless, because it happens that there is no coin in his pocket, or that it is uneconomical, because the effort involved is such that the search "costs more than it comes to." Motivational problems (which involve another sense of "because") aside, directive reasoning begins in puzzlement and ends in either the abandonment of inquiry or the resolution of puzzlement: "The function of reflective thought is . . . to transform a

---

to themselves, in silence, does not involve either a motor theory of thought or an argument that all covert mentation takes place in terms of imagined words (see Whorf, 1956, pp. 66 ff.).

situation in which there is experienced obscurity . . . of some sort, into a situation that is clear, coherent, settled, harmonious" (Dewey, 1939, p. 851).

In sum, human intellection, in the specific sense of directive reasoning, depends upon the manipulation of certain kinds of cultural resources in such a manner as to produce (discover, select) environmental stimuli needed—for whatever purpose—by the organism; it is a search for information. And this search is the more pressing because of the high degree of generality of the information intrinsically available to the organism from genetic sources. The lower an animal, the less it needs to find out in detail from the environment prior to behavioral performance; birds need not build wind tunnels to test aerodynamic principles before learning to fly—those they already "know." The "uniqueness" of man has often been expressed in terms of how much and how many different sorts of things he is capable of learning. Although monkeys, pigeons, and even octopuses may now and then disconcert us with the rather "human" things they prove capable of learning to do (Pribram, 1958), in a general way this is true enough. But it is of perhaps even more fundamental theoretical importance to stress how much and how many things man *has* to learn. That, "fetalized," "domesticated," and generally unhardy as he is, man would be a physically unviable animal independently of culture has often been pointed out (e.g., La Barre, 1954); that he would be mentally unviable as well has been rather less frequently noted (but see Dewey, 1917; Hallowell, 1953).

All this is no less true for the affective side of human thought than it is for the intellective. In a series of books and papers (Hebb, 1946, 1949, 1954; Hebb and Thompson, 1954) has developed the intriguing theory that the human nervous system (and to a correspondingly lesser extent, that of lower animals) demands a relatively continuous stream of optimally existing environmental stimuli as a precondition to competent performance. On the one hand, man's brain is "not like a calculating machine operated by an electric motor, which can lie idle, without input, for indefinite periods; instead it must be kept warmed up and working by a constantly varied input during the waking period at least, if it is to function effectively" (1954). On the other hand, given the tremendous intrinsic emotional susceptibility of man, such input cannot be too intense, too varied, too disturbing, because then emotional collapse and a complete breakdown of the thought process ensue. Both boredom and hysteria are enemies of reason (Solomon, *et al.*, 1957; Chapman, *et al.*, 1958).

Thus, as "man is the most emotional as well as the most rational animal" (Hebb and Thompson, 1954), a very careful cultural control of frightening, enraging, suggestive, etc., stimuli—through taboos, homogenization of behavior, rapid "rationalization" of strange stimuli in terms of familiar concepts, etc.—is necessary to prevent continual affective instability, a constant oscillation between the extremes of passion. But, as man cannot perform efficiently in the absence of a fairly high degree of reasonably persistent emotional activation, cultural mechanisms assuring the ready availability of the continually varying sort of sensory experience which can sustain such activities are equally essential. Institutionalized regulations against the open display of corpses outside of well-defined contexts (funerals, etc.) protect a peculiarly high-strung animal against the fears aroused by death and bodily destruction; watching or participating in automobile races (not all of which take place at tracks) deliciously stimulates the same fears. Prize fighting arouses hostile feelings; a firmly institutionalized interpersonal affability moderates them. Erotic impulses are titilated by a series of devious artifices of which there is, evidently, no end; but they are kept from running riot by an insistence on the private performance of explicitly sexual activities.

But, contrary to what these rather simplistic examples suggest, the achievement of a workable, well-ordered, clearly articulated emotional life in man is not a simple matter of ingenious instrumental control, a kind of clever hydraulic engineering of affect. Rather, it is a matter of giving specific, explicit, determinate form to the general, diffuse, ongoing flow of bodily sensation; of imposing upon the continual shifts in sentence to which we are inherently subject a recognizable, meaningful order, so that we may not only feel but know what we feel and act accordingly:

[It is] mental activity . . . [that] chiefly determines the way a person meets his surrounding world. Pure sensation—now pain, now pleasure—would have no unity, and would change the receptivity of the body for future pains and pleasures only in rudimentary ways. It is sensation remembered and anticipated, feared or sought, or even imagined and eschewed that is important in human life. It is perception molded by imagination that gives us the outward world that we know. And it is the continuity of thought that systematizes our emotional reactions into attitudes with distinct feeling tones, and sets a certain scope for the individual's passions. In other words: by virtue of our thought and imagination we have not only feelings, but a *life of feeling*. (Langer, 1953, p. 372; italics original.)

In this context our mental task shifts from a gathering of information about the pattern of events in the external world per se toward a determining of the affective significance, the emotional import of that pattern of events. We are concerned not with solving problems, but with clarifying feelings. Nevertheless, the existence of cultural resources, of an adequate system of public symbols, is just as essential to this sort of process as it is to that of directive reasoning. And therefore the development, maintenance, and dissolution of "moods," "attitudes," "sentiments," etc.—which are "feelings" in the sense of states or conditions, not sensations or motives (Ryle, 1949, Chap. IV)—constitute no more a basically private activity in human beings than does directive "thinking." The use of a road map enables us to make our way from San Francisco to New York with precision; the reading of Kafka's novels enables us to form a distinct and well-defined attitude toward modern bureaucracy. We acquire the ability to design flying planes in wind tunnels; we develop the capacity to feel true awe in church. A child counts on his fingers before he counts "in his head"; he feels love on his skin before he feels it "in his heart." Not only ideas, but emotions too are cultural artifacts in man.[9]

Given the lack of specificity of intrinsic affect in man, the attainment of an optimal flow of stimulation to his nervous system is a much more complicated operation than a prudent steering between the extremes of "too much" and "too little." Rather, it involves a very delicate qualitative regulation of what comes in through the sensory apparatus; a matter, here again, more of an active seeking for required stimuli than a mere watchful waiting for them. Neurologically, this regulation is achieved by efferent impulses from the central nervous system which modify receptor activity (Granit, 1955). Psychologically, the sense process may be phrased in terms of the attitudinal control of perception (Bruner and Postman, 1947). But the point is that in man neither regnant fields nor mental sets can be formed with sufficient precision in the absence of guidance from symbolic models of emotion. In order to make up our minds we must know how we feel about things; and to know how we feel about things we need the public images of sentiment which only ritual, myth, and art can provide.

4

The term "mind" refers to a certain set of dispositions of an organism. The ability to count is a mental characteristic; so is chronic cheerfulness; so also—though it has not been possible to discuss the problem of motivation here—is greed. The problem of the evolution of mind is,

9. The kind of cultural symbols which serve the intellective and affective sides of human mentality tend to differ (Langer, 1949, Chap. 4)—discursive language, experimental routines, mathematics, etc., on the one hand; myth, ritual, and art on the other. But this contrast should not be drawn too sharply: mathematics has its affective uses, poetry its intellectual; and the difference in any case is only functional, not substantial.

therefore, neither a false issue generated by a misconceived metaphysic, nor one of discovering at which point in the history of life an invisible anima was superadded to organic material. It is a matter of tracing the development of certain sorts of abilities, capacities, tendencies, and propensities in organisms and delineating the factors or types of factors, upon which the existence of such characteristics depends.

Recent research in anthropology suggests that the prevailing view that the mental dispositions of man are genetically prior to culture and that his actual capabilities represent the amplification or extension of these pre-existent dispositions by cultural means is incorrect.[10] The apparent fact that the final stages of the biological evolution of man occurred after the initial stages of the growth of culture implies that "basic," "pure," or "unconditioned," human nature, in the sense of the innate constitution of man, is so functionally incomplete as to be unworkable. Tools, hunting, family organization, and, later, art, religion, and "science" molded man somatically; and they are, therefore, necessary not merely to his survival but to his existential realization. It is true that without men there would be no cultural forms; but it is also true that without cultural forms there would be no men.

The application of this revised view of human evolution leads to the hypothesis that cultural resources are ingredient, not accessory, to human thought. As one moves from lower to higher animals phylogenetically, behavior is characterized by increasing active unpredictability with reference to present stimuli, a trend apparently supported physiologically by an increasing complexity and regnancy of centrally proceeding patterns of nervous activity. Up to the level of the lower mammals, at least the major part of this growth of autonomous central fields can be accounted for in terms of the development of novel neural mechanisms. But in the higher mammals such novel mechanisms have as yet not been found. Although, conceivably, mere increase in numbers of neurons may in itself prove able fully to account for the florescence of mental capacity in man, the fact that the large human brain and human culture emerged synchronically, not serially, indicates that the most recent developments in the evolution of nervous structure con-

10. In using such variably employed terms as "mind" and "culture," the decision of how far down the phylogenetic ladder to extend them—i.e., how broadly to define them—is in great part but a matter of custom, policy, and taste. Here, perhaps somewhat inconsistently, but in line with what seems to be common usage, opposite choices have been made for mind and culture: mind has been defined broadly to include the learned capacities of monkeys to communicate or rats to solve T-mazes; culture has been defined narrowly to include only post-toolmaking symbolic patterns. For an argument that culture should be defined as "a learned pattern of the meaning of signals and signs" and extended through the whole world of living organisms, see Parsons (1959).

sist in the appearance of mechanisms which both permit the maintenance of more complex regnant fields and make the full determination of these fields in terms of intrinsic (innate) parameters increasingly
impossible. The human nervous system relies, inescapably, on the accessibility of public symbolic structures to build up its own autonomous,
ongoing pattern of activity.

This, in turn, implies that human thinking is primarily an overt act
conducted in terms of the objective materials of the common culture,
and only secondarily a private matter. In the sense both of directive
reasoning and the formulation of sentiment, as well as the integration
of these into motives, man's mental processes indeed take place at the
scholar's desk or the football field, in the studio or lorry-driver's seat,
on the platform, the chessboard, or the judge's bench. Isolationist
claims for the closed-system substantiality of culture (White, 1949),
social organization (Radcliffe-Brown, 1957), individual behavior (Skinner, 1938), or nervous physiology (Lashley, 1958) to the contrary notwithstanding, progress in the scientific analysis of the human mind
demands a joint attack from virtually all of the behavioral sciences,
in which the findings of each will force continual theoretical reassess-
ments upon all of the others.

REFERENCES

Allport, G. W., 1947. "Scientific models and human morals," *Psychol. Rev.*, 54:182-
192.
Arieti, S., 1959, "Schizophrenia: The manifest symptomatology, the psychodynamics
and formal mechanisms," in *American Handbook of Psychiatry*, ed. by S. Arieti,
Basic Books, New York, Vol. 1, pp. 455-484.
Bartholomew, G. A., and Birdsell, J. B., 1953, "Ecology and the proto-hominids,"
Am. Anthropologist, 55:481-498.
Beach, F. A., 1947, "Evolutionary changes in the physiological control of mating
behavior in mammals," *Psychol. Rev.*, 54:293-315.
———, 1955, "The de-scent of instinct," *Psychol. Rev.*, 62:401-410.
———, 1958, "Evolutionary aspects of psycho-endocrinology," in *Culture and Be-
havior*, ed. by A. Roe and G. Simpson, Yale University Press, New Haven, pp.
81-102.
Bidney, D., 1953, *Theoretical Anthropology*, Columbia University Press, New York.
Bruner, J. S., 1958, "Neural mechanisms in perception," in *The Brain and Human
Behavior*, ed. by H. Solomon, *et al.*, Williams and Wilkins, Baltimore, pp. 118-
143.
———, and Postman, L., 1947, "Emotional selectivity in perception and reaction,"
J. Personality, 16:69-77.
Bullock, T. H., 1958, "Evolution of neurophysiological mechanisms," in *Behavior and
Evolution*, ed. by A. Roe and G. Simpson, Yale University Press, New Haven,
pp. 165-177.

Carter, G. S., 1953, "The theory of evolution and the evolution of man," in *Anthropology Today*, ed. by A. L. Kroeber, University of Chicago Press, Chicago, pp. 327-342.

Chapman, L. F., 1958, "Highest integrative functions of man during stress," in *The Brain and Human Behavior*, ed. by H. Solomon, *et al.*, Williams and Wilkins, Baltimore, pp. 491-534.

Clark, W. E. LeGros, 1950, *History of the Primates*, British Museum, London.

Dart, R. A., 1959, *Adventures with the Missing Link*, Harpers, New York.

Deutsch, J. A., 1953, "A new type of behavior theory," *Brit. J. Psychol.*, 44:304-317.

DeVore, B. I., n.d., *Primate Behavior and Social Evolution*, unpublished MS.

Dewey, J., 1917, "The need for a social psychology," *Psychol. Rev.*, 24:266-277.

————, 1934, *Art as Experience*, Minton, Balch and Co., New York.

————, 1939, *Intelligence and the Modern World*, ed. by J. Ratner, Modern Library, New York.

Emerson, A. E., 1952, "The evolution of behavior among social insects," in *The Evolution of Behavior*, ed. by A. Roe and G. Simpson, Yale University Press, New Haven, pp. 311-355.

Emiliani, C., 1960, "Dating human evolution," in *The Evolution of Man*, ed. by S. Tax, University of Chicago Press, Chicago, pp. 57-66.

Ford, C. S., and Beach, F. A., 1951, *Patterns of Sexual Behavior*, Harpers, New York.

Freud, S., 1900, "The interpretation of dreams," translated in *The Basic Writings of Sigmund Freud*, ed. by A. A. Brill, Modern Library, New York, 1938, pp. 179-548.

————, 1911, "Formulations regarding two principles in mental functioning," in *Collected Papers of Sigmund Freud*, Hogarth Press, London, 1946, Vol. IV, pp. 13-27.

Galenter, E., and Gerstenhaber, M., 1956, "On thought: the extrinsic theory," *Psychol. Rev.*, 63:218-227.

Geertz, C., 1957, "Ritual and social change: a Javanese example," *Am. Anthropologist*, 59:32-54.

Gerard, R. W., 1959, "Brains and behavior," in *The Evolution of Man's Capacity for Culture*, ed. by J. Spuhler, Wayne State University Press, Detroit, pp. 14-20.

————, 1960, "Becoming: the residue of change," in *The Evolution of Man*, ed. by S. Tax, University of Chicago Press, Chicago, pp. 255-268.

Goldstein, K., 1959, "Functional disturbances in brain damage," in *American Handbook of Psychiatry*, ed. by S. Arieti, Basic Books, New York, Vol. 2, pp. 770-794.

Granit, R., 1955, *Receptors and Sensory Perception*, Yale University Press, New Haven.

Hallowell, A. I., 1939, "The recapitulation theory and culture," reprinted in *Culture and Experience*, by A. I. Hallowell, University of Pennsylvania, Philadelphia pp. 14-31.

————, 1953, "Culture, personality and society," in *Anthropology Today*, ed. A. L. Kroeber, University of Chicago Press, Chicago, pp. 597-620.

————, 1959, "Behavioral evolution and the emergence of the self," in *Evolution and Anthropology: A Centennial Appraisal*, ed. by B. J. Meggers, Anthropological Society of Washington, D.C., pp. 36-60.

————, 1960, "Self, society and culture in phylogenetic perspective," in *The Evolution of Man*, ed. by S. Tax, University of Chicago Press, Chicago, pp. 309-372.

Harlow, H., 1958, "The evolution of learning," in *The Evolution of Behavior*, ed. by A. Roe and G. Simpson, Yale University Press, New Haven, pp. 269-290.

————, 1959, "Basic social capacity of primates," in *The Evolution of Man's Capacity for Culture*, ed. by J. Spuhler, Wayne State University Press, Detroit, pp. 40-52.

Hartmann, H., 1939, "Ego psychology and the problem of adaptation," translated and abridged in *Organization and Pathology of Thought*, ed. by D. Rappaport, Columbia University Press, New York, 1951, pp. 362-396.

——, Kris, E., and Lowenstein, R., 1946, "Comments on the formation of psychic structure," in *The Psychoanalytic Study of the Child*, Vol. II, pp. 11-38, International Universities Press, New York.

Hayes, K. J., and Hayes, C., 1955, "The cultural capacity of the chimpanzee," in *The Non-Human Primates and Human Evolution*, ed. by J. Gavan, Wayne State University Press, Detroit, pp. 110-126.

Hebb, D. O., 1946, "Emotion in man and animal: An analysis of the intuitive process of recognition," *Psychol. Rev.*, 53:88-106.

——, 1949, *The Organization of Behavior*, John Wiley, New York.

——, 1954, "The problem of consciousness and introspection," in *Brain Mechanics and Consciousness*, ed. by E. Adrian, *et al.*, Blackwell's, Oxford, pp. 402-417.

——, and Thompson, W. R., 1954, "The social significance of animal studies," in *Handbook of Psychology*, Addison-Wesley Press, Reading, Mass., pp. 532-561.

Hooton, E., 1949, *Up from the Ape*, revised edition, Macmillan Co., New York.

Howells, W. W., 1950, "Concluding remarks of the chairman," in *Cold Spring Harbor Symposia on Quantitative Biology*, 15:79-86.

Hull, C. L., 1943, *Principles of Behavior*, D. Appleton-Century, New York.

Keller, H., 1931, *The Story of My Life*, Doubleday, Doran, New York.

Kluckhohn, C., 1953, "Universal categories of culture," in *Anthropology Today*, ed. by A. L. Kroeber, University of Chicago Press, Chicago, pp. 507-523.

——, and Murray, H., (eds.), 1948, *Personality in Nature, Society and Culture*, Knopf, New York.

Kroeber, A. L., 1948, *Anthropology*, Harcourt Brace, New York.

Kubie, L. S., 1954, "Psychiatric and psychoanalytic considerations of the problem of consciousness," in *Brain Mechanisms and Consciousness*, ed. by E. Adrian, *et al.*, Blackwell's, Oxford, pp. 444-467.

La Barre, W., 1954, *The Human Animal*, University of Chicago, Chicago.

Langer, S., 1949, *Philosophy in a New Key*, New American Library (Mentor), New York.

——, 1953, *Feeling and Form*, Scribners, New York.

Lashley, K. S., 1949, "Persistent problems in the evolution of mind," *Quart. Rev.*, 24:28-42.

——, 1951, "The problem of serial order in behavior," in *Cerebral Mechanisms and Behavior*, ed. by L. Jeffress, John Wiley, New York, pp. 112-136.

——, 1958, "Cerebral organization and behavior," in *The Brain and Human Behavior*, ed. by H. Solomon, *et al.*, Williams and Wilkins, Baltimore.

Leakey, L. S. B., 1960, "The origin of the genus homo," in *The Evolution of Man*, ed. by S. Tax, University of Chicago Press, Chicago, pp. 17-32.

Lévy-Bruhl, L., 1923, *Primitive Mentality*, Allen and Unwin, London.

Lorenz, K., 1952, *King Solomon's Ring*, Methuen and Co., London.

——, n.d., Comment, in *Discussions on Child Development*, 1:95-96, ed. by J. Tanner and B. Inhelder, International Universities Press, New York.

Mead, M., 1958, "Cultural determinants of behavior," in *Culture and Behavior*, ed. by A. Roe and G. Simpson, Yale University Press, New Haven.

——, n.d., Comment, in *Discussions on Child Development*, 1:480-503, ed. by J. Tanner and B. Inhelder, International Universities Press, New York.

Miller, G. A., Galanter, E. H., and Pribram, K. H., 1960, *Plans and the Structure of Behavior*, New York.

Montagu, M. F. A., 1950, "A consideration of the concept of race," in *Cold Spring Harbor Symposia on Quantitative Biology,* 15:315-334.

Nissen, H. W., 1955, "Problems of mental evolution in the primates," in *The Non-Human Primates and Human Evolution,* ed. by J. Gavan, Wayne State University Press, Detroit, pp. 99-109.

Nó, L. de, 1943, "Cerebral cortex architecture," in *The Physiology of the Nervous System,* ed. by J. F. Fulton, Oxford, New York.

Oakley, K., 1957, "Tools makyth man," *Antiquity,* 31:199-209.

Parsons, T., "An approach to psychological theory in terms of the theory of action," in *Psychology: A Study of a Science,* ed. by S. Koch, McGraw-Hill, New York, 3:612-711.

Pribram, K. H., 1958, "Comparative neurology and the evolution of behavior," in *Behavior and Evolution,* ed. by A. Roe and G. Simpson, Yale University Press, New Haven, pp. 140-164.

———, 1960, "A review of theory in physiological psychology," *Ann. Rev. Psychol.*

Radcliffe-Brown, A. R., 1957, *A Natural Science of Society,* The Free Press of Glencoe, New York.

Ryle, G., 1949, *The Concept of Mind,* Barnes and Noble, New York.

Scheerer, M., 1954, "Cognitive theory," in *Handbook of Social Psychology,* Addison-Wesley Press, Reading, Mass.

Sherrington, C., 1953, *Man on His Nature,* 2nd edition, Doubleday (Anchor), New York.

Simpson, G., 1950, "Some principles of historical biology bearing on human organisms," in *Cold Spring Harbor Symposia on Quantitative Biology,* 15:55-66.

Skinner, B. F., 1938, *The Behavior of Organisms,* Appleton-Century, New York.

Solomon, P., *et al.,* 1957, "Sensory deprivation: a review," *Am. J. Psychiat.,* 114:357-363.

Spuhler, J. M., 1959, "Somatic paths to culture," in *The Evolution of Man's Capacity for Culture,* ed. by J. M. Spuhler, Wayne State University, Detroit, pp. 1-13.

Thompson, W. R., 1958, "Social behavior," in *Behavior and Evolution,* ed. by A. Roe and G. Simpson, Yale University Press, New Haven, pp. 291-309.

Washburn, S. L., 1959, "Speculations on the interrelations of tools and biological evolution," in *The Evolution of Man's Capacity for Culture,* ed. by J. M. Spuhler, Wayne State University, Detroit, pp. 21-31.

———, and Howell, F. C., 1960, "Human evolution and culture," in *The Evolution of Man,* ed. by S. Tax, University of Chicago Press, Chicago, pp. 33-56.

Weiss, P., 1951, "Comment on Dr. Lashley's paper," in *Cerebral Mechanisms in Behavior,* ed. by L. A. Jeffress, John Wiley, New York, pp. 140-142.

White, L. A., 1949, *The Science of Culture,* Grove Press (Evergreen), New York.

———, 1960, "Four stages in the evolution of minding," in *The Evolution of Man,* ed. by S. Tax, University of Chicago Press, Chicago, pp. 239-253.

Whorf, B. L., 1956, *Language, Thought and Behavior,* ed. by J. B. Carroll, John Wiley, New York.

SUBJECT INDEX

NAME INDEX